ANGLO-NORMAN MEDICINE

VOLUME I

ROGER FRUGARD'S *CHIRURGIA*
THE *PRACTICA BREVIS* OF PLATEARIUS

ANGLO-NORMAN MEDICINE

BY

Tony Hunt

Fellow of St Peter's College, Oxford

VOLUME I

ROGER FRUGARD'S *CHIRURGIA*
THE *PRACTICA BREVIS* OF PLATEARIUS

D. S. BREWER

First published 1994
D. S. Brewer, Cambridge

ISBN 0 85991 401 1

D. S. Brewer is an imprint of Boydell & Brewer Ltd
PO Box 9, Woodbridge, Suffolk IP12 3DF, UK
and of Boydell & Brewer Inc.
PO Box 41026, Rochester, NY 14604-4126, USA

British Library Cataloguing-in-Publication Data
Anglo-Norman Medicine. – Vol.1:Roger
Frugard's "Chirurgia";"Practica Brevis"
of Platearius
I. Hunt, Tony
610.942
ISBN 0–85991–401–1

Library of Congress Cataloging-in-Publication Data
Anglo-Norman medicine / edited by Tony Hunt.
    p.   cm.
Includes bibliographical references and index.
Contents: v. 1. Roger Frugard's Chirurgia, The Practica brevis of Platearius.
ISBN 0–85991–401–1 (hardback : alk. paper)
1. Medicine, Medieval – England. 2. Anglo-Saxons – Medicine.
I. Ruggero, Frugardo, 12th cent. Chirurgia. English.
II. Platearius, Joannes, fl. 1090–1120. Practica brevis. English.
III. Hunt, Tony.
[DNLM: 1. History of Medicine, Medieval.   WZ 294 A589 1994a]
R128.A44   1994
610'.942'0902 – dc20
DNLM/DLC
for Library of Congress   94–14486

The paper used in this publication meets the minimum requirements
of American National Standard for Information Sciences –
Permanence of Paper for Printed Library Materials, ANSI Z39.48–1984

Printed in Great Britain by
St Edmundsbury Press Ltd, Bury St Edmunds, Suffolk

CONTENTS

PREFACE

As a sequel and complement to *Popular Medicine in Thirteenth-Century England* (Cambridge, D.S. Brewer: 1990) the present volume, the first of two, concentrates attention on the surviving corpus of Anglo-Norman medical treatises which may fairly be described as 'learned', in the sense that they are translations of Latin works which are concerned not merely with therapy but with aetiology and symptomatology and hence display a theoretical content completely absent from the 'receipts' already published. This first volume presents two major medical texts which, like all the other material in *Anglo-Norman Medicine*, have never been published. Roger Frugard's *Chirurgia* (c.1180) is the first original treatise on surgery to have been written in the medieval West, and the Anglo-Norman translation, as if coming from nowhere, is a remarkable achievement, further enhanced by the beautiful illustrations which formed the subject of *The Medieval Surgery* (Woodbridge, The Boydell Press: 1992). There is no modern edition of the *Practica brevis*, though this Salernitan compendium was one of the major products of the twelfth-century 'renaissance', copied and excerpted by many other writers associated with the school of Salerno. The Anglo-Norman translation is noteworthy for its fullness and accuracy and, like that of Frugard's treatise, exhibits a fascinating vernacular medical terminology almost wholly unrecorded in the dictionaries. The texts offered in *Anglo-Norman Medicine* provide intriguing evidence of the transmission of medical knowledge in thirteenth-century England. But a paradox remains. These vernacular texts were certainly copied in England, but it is by no means certain that they originated in this country. In MS Cambridge, Trinity College 0.1.20 a second, fragmentary translation of the *Chirurgia* is unmistakably northern French in origin, and there is little linguistic evidence to deny the same possibility in the case of the translation of the *Practica brevis*. Another paradox: whatever their origins, these two texts antedate anything that survives in France and thus confirm in a new area what has become known as 'la précocité de l'anglo-normand'.

The second volume of *Anglo-Norman Medicine* will contain a series of shorter treatises, with a general introduction, bibliographies and index.

For a grant towards the costs of publication I am grateful to the Curators of the Taylor Institution who made a contribution from the Zaharoff Fund.

ROGER FRUGARD'S
CHIRURGIA

INTRODUCTION

1. Early Writing on Surgery

Surgery is as old as humanity itself.[1] Three areas of operative surgery – circumcision, trephination of the skull, and cutting for bladder stone – are attested by the earliest prehistoric records.[2] The evidence for minor operative procedures such as incision of boils, extraction of foreign bodies, and for manipulative surgery e.g. the reduction of fractures and dislocations, is naturally more precarious, but not to be rejected. Curiously, cutting with the knife is absent from the one medical papyrus from ancient Egypt which transmits a surgical text, namely the Edwin Smith papyrus in New York.[3] The surgical sections of the *Corpus Hippocraticum* (5th – 3rd C. BC) are amongst the most successful of the writings inspired by 'the Father of modern medicine', however conservative they may be, and provide interesting accounts of trephination and thoracocentesis.[4] In the particular attention given to the traumatology of headwounds and the belief in suppuration as an essential process in the healing of wounds there are obvious similarities to the contents of early medieval treatises. The considerable advances marked by Celsus's *De medicina* were unfortunately veiled to the Middle Ages until its first printing in 1478.[5] In addition to traumatology (Bk 5), lithotomy (Bk 7) and fractures and dislocations (Bk 8), the importance of factors such as the patient's age, constitution, way of life and the time of the year is seriously considered for the treatment

---

[1] The most useful general histories of surgery are K. Sudhoff, *Beiträge zur Geschichte der Chirurgie im Mittelalter* 1–2, Studien zur Geschichte der Medizin 10, 11–12 (Leipzig, 1914/1918); E. Gurlt, *Geschichte der Chirurgie und ihre Ausübung* I–III (Berlin, 1898); R.A. Leonardo, *History of Surgery* (New York, 1943); A. Pazzini, *Bio-Bibliografia di storia della chirurgia* (Roma, 1948); W.J. Bishop, *The Early History of Surgery* (London, 1960); P. Huard and M.D. Grmek, *Mille ans de chirurgie en occident: v – xve siècles* (Paris, 1966); C. d'Allaines, *Histoire de la chirurgie* 2e éd. (Paris, 1967); R.H. Meade, *An Introduction to the History of General Surgery* (Philadelphia etc., 1968); O.H. & S.D. Wangensteen, *The Rise of Surgery: from empiric craft to scientific discipline* (Minneapolis / Folkestone, 1978); H. Schwabe, *Der lange Weg der Chirurgie: vom Wundarzt und Bader zur Chirurgie* (Zürich, 1986); D. De Moulin, *A History of Surgery with emphasis on the Netherlands* (Dordrecht, 1988); M.-C. Pouchelle, *The Body and Surgery in the Middle Ages* tr. by Rosemary Morris (Cambridge, 1990).

[2] See especially the early pages of Bishop, *op. cit.* which provide a fascinating conspectus of the variety of treatments amongst primitive peoples throughout the world. See also S.L. Rogers, *Primitive Surgery* (Springfield, Illinois, 1985).

[3] See H. Ranke, "Medicine and Surgery in Ancient Egypt", *Bull. Hist. Med.* 7 (1933), 237–57.

[4] See D. Ruster, *Alte Chirurgie: Legende und Wirklichkeit* (Berlin, 1984) and M. Michler, *Das Spezialisierungsproblem und die antike Chirurgie* (Wien, 1969).

[5] For bibliographical information on ancient medical texts see G. Sabbah *et al.*, *Bibliographie des textes médicaux latins: antiquité et haut moyen âge* (Saint-Etienne, 1987). On Celsus see pp. 53 and 172.

of wounds and there is an impressively detailed account of herniotomy. How much of Celsus was known to the medieval West is a question which needs to be carefully explored. What it certainly did know, of course, was the humoral pathology propounded by Galen. Emanating from four organs – the heart, liver, spleen and brain – the four humours were held to correspond to the four elements with which they each shared two principal qualities: air/blood (warm and moist); fire/yellow bile (warm and dry); earth/black bile (cold and dry); water/phlegm (cold and moist). The dependence of health on the proper blending ('crasis') of the humours and their qualities naturally led to the prescription of a variety of expellents – emetics, laxatives, sudorifics – and to the use of bleeding (cupping or the application of a *setaceum* or vesicatory). For healing wounds Galen preferred desiccative medicines, his anatomical knowledge was superior to that of Hippocrates, and he made use of the vascular ligature. It is difficult, however, to be sure just how much of the surgical matter in Hippocrates, Celsus and Galen was absorbed by the early medieval West. Certainly there circulated a number of excerpts from Galen's commentaries on the Aphorisms of Hippocrates, there was an elementary treatise on terminology known as the *Cirurgia Eliodori* and an abbreviation of Book 3 of Alexander of Tralles (525–605) dealing with diseases of the ear. This can hardly be regarded as an impressive base for the evolution of sophisticated surgical practice.

A more striking account of the achievements of ancient surgery before the fall of Alexandria in 643 AD will be found in the *Compendium of Medicine* or *Epitome* written in Greek by Paul of Aegina and translated into Arabic in the ninth century and into Latin c.900.[6] Paul's work was unfortunately little known in the West but happily became the starting point for the development of an Arabic surgery which, like Arabic pharmacology, consolidated the knowledge of Antiquity and transcended it with remarkable speed. Book 6 of the *Epitome* has 122 chapters on surgical therapy, while Book 4 deals with the general treatment of wounds, headwounds receiving particular prominence. Paul's work rapidly found favour with Arab doctors. Hunain ibn Ishaq (809–77), known in the West as Johannitius, translated, *inter alia*, both Paul's *Epitome* and the On *materia medica* of Dioscorides. Some surgical material was incorporated by Rhazes (c.850–923) in his *al-Hawi*, translated as *Liber continens* in 1279, and included in an abbreviated version translated in the twelfth century by Gerard of Cremona, who also translated the *Canon medicinae* of Avicenna (980–1037). Largely based on Paul of Aegina is Book 9 of the *Practica* which forms part of Constantine the African's translation of the *al-Malaki* of Haly Abbas (930–994) which was known as the *Pantegni*.[7] The most influential achievement of Arabic surgery, however, was the thirtieth treatise of a great compendium by al-Zahrawi (936–1013), known as

---

6   M. Tabanelli, *Studi sulla chirurgia bizantina: Paolo di Egina* (Firenze, 1964). See also V. Nutton, "Byzantine Surgery", in J. Scarborough (ed.), *Symposium on Byzantine Medicine*, Dumbarton Oaks Papers 38 (1984).
7   See M.T. Malato and L. Loria (eds.), *Constantino l'Africano: Chirurgia* (Roma, 1960) who edit the 117 chapters of the translation from MS Montecassino 200 (s.xi).

Abulcasis / Albucasis,[8] which Gerard of Cremona translated as *Liber Alzaharavi de cirurgia*, the MSS of which are celebrated for their illustrations of surgical instruments. Yet, despite the progress indicated by Arabic writers' treatment of surgery,[9] the renewal of surgical writing in the West is marked by a work which shows almost no knowledge of Arabic developments other than the more traditional elements transmitted in the *Pantegni*.

2. Roger and the *Chirurgia*

Roger Frugard, often misleadingly referred to as Roger of Salerno or, with greater justification, Roger of Parma, is an important figure in the revival of surgical writing in the West,[10] which originates not in Salerno, as was for so long assumed, but in northern Italy, notably in Parma and Bologna. There Roger belongs in the company of Hugo Borgognoni (b. Lucca, 1155), his son Theodoric (?1205–98)[11] and Bruno da Longoburgo,[12] whose treatise on surgery appeared in 1252. Roger lectured at Parma but did not himself produce a treatise. This was done by Guido of Arezzo the Younger, who had earlier completed his *Liber Mitis*.[13] In the 1170s Guido, 'logicae professionis minister', with the assistance of a number of Roger's pupils, gathered together a set of lecture notes and revised and edited them. This involved the systematic ordering of the material in four books under distinctive chapter headings, a task which seems to have been congenial to a man of Guido's theoretical interests who had already in his compendium *Liber Mitis* displayed skill in symmetrical arrangement. Guido prefixed to his redaction of the *Chirurgia* a long preface which has been misprinted, mispunctuated and, consequently, misunderstood by generations of scholars and which shares with the prefaces to the other books a sophisticated artistry.[14] There is no adequate inventory of the surviving MSS, but those which have been recorded and examined have yielded the dates 1170, 1180, and 1230 as the time of composition. There now seems to be general agreement that 1180 is the most likely of these.[15]

The *Chirurgia* is almost untouched by Arabic influence, except for the

---

[8] See M. Tabanelli, *Albucasi: un chirurgo arabo dell'alto medioevo* (Firenze, 1961); M.S. Spink and G.L. Lewis, *Albucasis: On Surgery and Instruments* (London, 1973).

[9] A.A. Azmi, "Contribution of Muslim Physicians to the Development of Surgery during the Middle Ages", *Stud. Hist. Med.* 8 (1984), 49–59, repr. in *Hamdard Medicus* 29, 1–2 (1986), 126–37.

[10] The principal monograph on Roger is A. Pazzini, *Ruggero di Giovanni Frugardo maestro di chirurgia a Parma e l'opera sua* (Roma, 1966).

[11] See E. Campbell and J. Colton, *The Surgery of Theodoric c. A.D. 1267*, 2 vols. (New York, 1955/60) and J.L. Valverde & T.B. Mendez, *El codice de 'Cyrurgia' de Teodorico de la Biblioteca Universitaria de Granada* (Granada, 1984).

[12] M. Tabanelli, *Un chirurgo italiano del 1200: Bruno da Longoburgo* (Firenze, 1970).

[13] See K. Goehl, *Guido d'Arezzo der Jüngere und sein 'Liber Mitis'*, 2 vols. (Pattensen/Hannover, 1984).

[14] For a corrected version of Sudhoff's text and a translation see Goehl, *supra* 1, pp.145–47.

[15] See Pazzini, *op. cit.*, pp. 23–24.

inevitable ripples from Constantine the African's *Pantegni* translation. Roger, a teacher of independent and pragmatic stamp, was able to correct the deficiencies of his predecessors through his own intelligence and operative skill. Indeed, he cites few authorities of any sort, ancient or modern, Byzantine or Arabic. It is this fact, perhaps, which has led to his quite unjustified neglect by historians of surgery.[16] The surviving MSS number at least twenty and the two favoured by Sudhoff in his edition[17] – clm 376 (written in S. Italy) and Florence, Bibl. Naz. cod. Magliabecchianus J.10.16 (possibly from Salerno) – date from the end of the twelfth century and from the early thirteenth century respectively. Yet there is surprisingly little evidence of Roger's influence on other surgical writers and few signs that his fame continued beyond a century after he wrote. He is not included in incunabula and the Juntine print of 1546 paradoxically marks the end of his fortunes. These fortunes are reflected in a complex pattern of transmission involving Salerno, Montpellier, northern Italy and Germany and following the sequence primitive text – new edition – commentaries and glosses – vernacular versions – translation back into Latin.[18] After the production of a text under the direction of Guido of Arezzo the Younger the work was well received at Salerno where it was glossed and commented upon, a continuous, supplementary gloss being produced by c.1200.[19] This 'First Salernitan Gloss' quickly incited one of Roger's disciples at Parma, Roland, to revise the text of the *Chirurgia* and provide a new set of marginal *additiones*. Later, perhaps c.1230, after his move to Bologna, where he was a rival of Hugo Borgognoni, Roland again revised the text of Roger together with his own *additiones*, merging two originally distinct texts in a new edition which retained the anatomical / topographical structuring principle, but combined commentary and text. This edition promptly achieved a preeminent position. Again in Salerno, the new 'Rolandina' became the recipient of further glosses which coalesced in the form of the 'Four Masters Gloss', a collective enterprise which attracted a legendary ascription to Archimathaeus, Petroncellus, Platearius and Ferrarius, but possibly connected with Johannes Jamatus.[20] The text was considerably rearranged according to a new structural principle governed by

---

16 There is not, for example, a single reference to him in Bishop, *op. cit.*

17 K. Sudhoff, *Beiträge zur Geschichte der Chirurgie im Mittelalter* 2 (Leipzig, 1918), pp.156–236 (= text).The Juntine edition of Roger, together with variants from MS Paris, B.N.7035, is reprinted in S. de Renzi, *Collectio Salernitana* 2 (Napoli, 1853), pp. 425–93. There is a translation and commentary in M. Tabanelli, *La chirurgia italiana nell'alto medioevo: Ruggero – Rolando – Teodorico* 1 (Firenze, 1965), pp.1–107. On the MSS see Sudhoff, *supra*, pp.149ff and Pazzini, *op. cit.*, pp.14–16. There is a text in MS London, Royal College of Physicians 227 (s.xiv in) ff. 8–89, see N.R. Ker, *Medieval Manuscripts in British Libraries* 1 (London, 1969).

18 See Sudhoff, *Beiträge* 2, pp. 238f and Keil [below n. 23] 212.

19 See S. de Renzi, *Collectio Salernitana* 2 (Napoli, 1853), pp. 425–96 [the Juntine text with var. from MS Paris B.N. lat. 7035]; Pazzini, *op. cit.*, pp.15f, 27, 64ff.

20 See Ch. Daremberg, *Glossulae quatuor magistrorum super chirurgiam Rogerii et Rolandi* (Neapoli / Parisiis, 1854) [the introd. is republ. in Italian in Renzi, *Coll. Sal.* 3 (Napoli, 1854), pp. 205–54]; Renzi, *Coll. Sal.* 2, pp. 497–724; A. Lodispoto, *Brevi glosse dei quattro maestri sulla chirurgia di Ruggero e Rolando* (Roma, 1961); A. Nalesso, "Una singolare 'aggiunta' nel codice Ambrosiano della 'Chirurgia' di Ruggero e Rolando", *Coll. Pag. Storia Med. Misc.* 21 (Roma, 1968), pp.143–54 and *id.*, "Il codice Ambrosiana della 'Chirurgia' di Ruggero e Rolando (cod. Ambr. I,18 sup.)", *Pag. Storia Med.* 11(6) (Roma, 1967), 49–55.

pathological / traumatological factors. Instead of the old anatomical ordering *a capite ad calcem* there is a new sequence on a humoral-pathological basis. Although there is a clear separation between text and commentary, the 'Four Masters Gloss' includes several layers of commentary since it comments on the commentary sections of the 'Rolandina'. In Montpellier several contributions were made to the expansion of Roger's *Chirurgia*. The materia medica was augmented in a set of therapeutic glosses c.1200[21] and William de Congenis used the *Chirurgia* as the basis of his own teaching which was set down by a pupil soon after his death c.1250[22] and later translated into Hebrew. Further glosses and translations were produced in Germany.[23] Pazzini summed up the character and content of Roger's *Chirurgia* as follows:

> La Chirurgia di Ruggero (da non confondersi con la Rogerina di Ruggero di Montpellier) si distingue nettamente dalla chirurgia salernitana, sia per ispirazione, per suddivisione della materia, per criteri curativi prettamente chirurgici, esponenti di una scuola nettamente differente da quello di Salerno, arabistica, quest'ultima, medica e quasi per nulla chirurgica, di mentalità coordinatrice prossima a quella degli Arabi. (p. 83)

In this connection a word must be said about Salernitan surgery.[24] However obscure the origins of the medical school at Salerno, it is certain that by the twelfth century it enjoyed wide esteem for its empirical approach to therapeutic medicine. In the field of surgery, however, there is almost no documentary evidence and what has survived is curiously inconclusive. In MS 174 of the Bibliothèque Municipale at Montpellier Henry Sigerist discovered what he described as a Salernitan student's surgical notebook.[25] More importantly, Karl Sudhoff had discovered in the Bamberg Royal Library two MSS which contained a surgical text associated with Salerno.[26] The so-called 'Bamberg Surgery' was subsequently found to exist in two further MSS.[27] None of them, however, is demonstrably earlier than Roger and the work is much less impressive, having something of the

---

[21] See Sudhoff, *Beiträge* 2, pp. 265–96

[22] See Sudhoff, *ibid.*, pp. 297–384.

[23] See G. Keil, "Gestaltwandel und Zersetzung: Roger-Urtext und Roger-Glosse vom 12. bis ins 16. Jahrhundert" in A. Buck & O. Herding (eds.), *Der Kommentar in der Renaissance* (Bonn / Boppard, 1975), pp. 209–24 repr. in G. Baader and G. Keil (eds.), *Medizin im mittelalterlichen Abendland* (Darmstadt, 1982). See also A. Hirschmann, *Die Leipziger Rogerglosse. Ein chirurgischer Text aus dem Meissnisch-nordschlesischen Raum* 1 (Pattensen / Hannover, 1984).

[24] The most authoritative study of Salerno is P.O. Kristeller, *Studi sulla scuola medica salernitana* (Napoli, 1980). Still of value are S. de Renzi, *Collectio Salernitana* 1–5 (Napoli, 1852–59); id., *Storia documentata della scuola medica di Salerno* (Napoli, 1857; repr. Milano, 1967); P. Giacosa, *Magistri salernitani nondum editi* (Torino, 1901); P. Capparoni, '*Magistri salernitani nondum cognoti*'. *A Contribution to the History of the Medical School of Salerno* (London, 1923). See most recently P. Morpurgo, "The Salernitan School between Hippocrates, Aristotle and Magic", *Quaderni Catanesi* 6 (1984), 197–218 who suggests that the idea of a 'unitary' School of Salerno is a misleading oversimplification.

[25] H.E. Sigerist, "A Salernitan Student's Surgical Notebook", *Bull. Hist. Med.* 14 (1943), 505–16.

[26] See Sudhoff, *Beiträge* 2, pp.103–47.

[27] See G.W. Corner, "On early Salernitan surgery and especially the 'Bamberg Surgery'", *Bull. Hist. Med.* 5 (1937), 1–32.

character of a commonplace book made up of excerpts from a variety of writers, the most important of which is certainly Constantine the African and his surgical treatise which constitutes Bk 9 of the *Practica* section of the *Pantegni*. Other sources of the 'Bamberg Surgery' include Vindician (Second Epitome),[28] Oribasius (*Euporistes*), Johannitius or Hunain ibn Ishaq (*Isagoge*) and almost the whole of the *Flebotomia Ypocratis*. The famous anaesthetic 'spongia somnifera' makes its appearance[29] and there are many prescriptions drawn from *antidotaria* and *receptaria*. If we leave aside a few original touches – the method of suturing a wound over a cannula, the use of trephination in the treatment of epilepsy, the employment of ashes of seaweed and sea sponge in the cure of goitre – we are forced to conclude that the school of Salerno had not at this time produced a methodical surgery which might stand comparison with the work of Roger. Roger remains, therefore, the first 'modern' western writer on surgery[30] and something of his influence may now be seen by examining the vernacular versions made of his *Chirurgia*.

3. Vernacular Versions of Roger's *Chirurgia*

(a) The Occitan version of Raimon of Avignon[31]

MS Bologna Bibl. Univ. 2836 contains 23 folios measuring approx. 180 x 119 mm, written in a small gothic bookhand of the second half of the thirteenth century. It transmits a single text, a rendering into Occitan verse of Books 1–3 of Roger's *Chirurgia*. The adaptation seems to have been made by Raimon of Avignon by 1209 and was subsequently copied by a Catalan scribe. Throughout, the author assumes a Salernitan origin for the *Chirurgia*; as we have seen, the work had certainly been well received in Salerno and, indeed, glossed there, by 1200. The Bologna MS alternates red and blue initials and rubrics, the first rubric being *Incipit cirurgia magistri Rogerii Salernitanensis translata in lingua romana a magistro Raimundo Avinionense*. In a statement to his sponsor, who seems to have been Raimon d'Uzès, called Rascas, Lord of Uzès from 1168–1209, the translator Raimon reveals his own familiarity with Salerno: 'Si vols obrar segons l'escrit salernitan, / Eu que la fuy lo te faray entendre plan' (ll. 25–26). Later he makes further references to Salernitan practices: 'le mandamens es de Salern, so mi soven' (l.

28 On Vindician see G. Sabbah *et al.*, *op. cit.*, pp.154–57.
29 See M. Pantaleoni, "La spongia somnifera al vaglio della critica moderna", *Atti del XXI Congresso Nazionale di Storia della Medicina, Perugia 11–12 settembre 1965* 2 (Perugia, 1965), pp. 485–90.
30 For the later period see V. Nutton, "Humanist Surgery" in A. Wear, R.K. French and I.M. Lonie (eds.), *The Medical Renaissance of the Sixteenth Century* (Cambridge, 1985), pp. 75–99.
31 See A. Thomas, "La Chirurgie de Roger de Parme en vers provençaux", *Romania* 10 (1881), 63–74 and *ibid.* 11 (1882), 203–12; U. Cianciolo, "Il compendio provenzale verseggiato della Chirurgia di Ruggero da Salerno", *Archivum Romanicum* 25 (1941), 1–85; L.M. Paterson, "Military Surgery: Knights, Sergeants, and Raimon of Avignon's Version of the Chirurgia of Roger of Salerno (1180–1209)", in C. Harper-Bill and R. Harvey (eds.), *The Ideals and Practice of Medieval Knighthood II. Papers from the third Strawberry Hill Conference 1986* (Woodbridge, 1988), pp.117–46 (Paterson has invented a Gui of Arles in error for Guido of Arezzo).

941); 'Que .l sens et l'us sai de Salern e .l saber ai' (l.1511). References in the text suggest that it might be both heard and read and there is no doubt that Raimon sacrifices technical detail to lively presentation, despite the opening remarks which seem destined for the schoolroom:

> Plas vos ausir qu'eu vos diga m'entension?
> Per que .l letin qu'eu ay apres, eu vos despon,
> Per enseynar los nescis com fes Salamon
> E Precian lor enseynet e puys Caton. (ll. 7–10)

The versification is unusual, comprising, initially, monorhyme stanzas of dodeca-syllables, but in l. 55 the author anounces his intention to abandon 'tan gran rima' and thereafter he writes monorhyme quatrains. It would be interesting to compare the metrical version with the entirely unstudied prose adaptation from the four-teenth century which is found in MS Basel, Universitätsbibl. D.II.11.

Raimon's style is lively and personal. Thus the three parts of the treatise are presented through the image of the boar:

> (end of Book 1)
> Lo porc cenglar, la merce Dieu, ai consegut,
> Et ay lo cap tant ai sudat e corregut;
> Ar pausaray tant que recobre ma vertut,
> Que tot soy las tant ai maltrach, si Dieus m'aiut. (763–66)

> (opening of Book 2)
> Ar ay pausat et recobrat mon esperit,
> E ai gran gaug quar lo primier libr' es complit,
> Mas lo segon aprin et non t'oblit
> Queu que te voyl dir... (767–70)

> (end of Book 2)
> Del porc avia sol lo cap, ar ai so col,
> Si mala lenga de nemic non lo mi tol.
> Et que no.m trobe paoros et de cor mol;
> Ben me.n poiria d'autramentz tener per fol. (923–26)

> (end of Book 3)
> Del porc senglar, amics, te fis present fort bon
> Que .l cap e .l col sai que a girat ab lo menton;
> Aras t'aport trastot lo cau entro.l crepon:
> Dins et de foras potz legir la garizon! (1554–57)

Raimon's engaging personality is everywhere evident and the tone is often collo-quial rather than formal, entertaining rather than didactic. Raimon attempts to offer practical, if sometimes rather sketchy, instruction to surgeons in the field as to who is likely to suffer particular types of wound and why. He has read Roger attentively but makes no attempt to render him exhaustively. The following two passages will give some idea of the more thorough adaptations of Roger's material:

> (I,XXVI) De cauteriis que fiunt contra maniam vel melancoliam:
> Ad maniam vel melancoliam in summitate capitis incidatur cutis in

modum crucis et craneum perforetur ut materia exhalet ad exteriora. Patiens autem in vinculis teneatur et vulnus curetur, sicut in curis vulnerum superius diximus.

Si vol[s] valer a malenconi desennat
Per son aver et per ta plana volentat,
Enans que.l fassas autre, ben l'aias liat,
Que.l pusques ben tener et raire mal son grat,

E travellar ardidamentz ses tot esglay.
Ben o faras con as apres, que ben o sai;
Que totz soi las dir tan soven: 'enaisi fay';
Per que d'aquest no.t desespers tot t'o dirai.　(ll. 523–30)

(I,XXVIII)　De pilis qui preter naturam in palpebris oriuntur: Si pili in palpebris preter naturam continentur et fuerit in palpebris multa carnositas, ut pili superflui videri non possint, primo fricentur palpebre interius foliis paritarie et cum sanguis exierit et carne minuta pili conparuerint, con picicariolis retortis pili radicitus evellantur. Postea superponatur albugo ovi in estate et si fuerit in hyeme aliquantulum de croco in albumine resolvatur et, quotiens pili ibidem renati fuerint, idem fiat.

De pilis contra naturam in palpebre nascentibus

Contra natura naisson pels prims et agutz
Sus sas parpelas de sos ols grans et cregutz,
Per que vermel son et ploros et confundutz,
De qu'eu ti don conseyl triat et elegutz.

Ab pinsadoiras fort gent fay ton afar
E aias cura d'aquels pels ad arabar.
Si vana cams fa destorbier a ton afar,
Ab qualque causa la poiras aspereiar.

Fuella d'espargula si l'as mit sus ton det
E mena la sus la parpella suavet.
E, quant veiras que si demostren li pelet,
Foras los tray si tot lur er un pauc aigret,

Et en estiu sus la parpela solament
Mit clara d'ou per tost venir a gariment;
En temps d'ivern prin de safran et mesclament
Pausa lo sus et complit rasolnament.　(ll. 531–46)

Raimon's translation is an important witness to the flourishing activity of medical writers in southern France before 1250.[32]

---

32 For medical writing in the south of France see L.M. Paterson, "La Médecine en Occitanie avant 1250", in P.T. Ricketts (ed.), *Actes du 1er Congrès de l'Association Internationale d'Etudes Occitanes* (London, 1987), pp. 383–99.

(b) Continental Versions in Old French

MSS London, B.L. Sloane 1977 and 3525 present similar texts of an Old French translation of Roger's *Chirurgia* which, although investigated by Paul Meyer,[33] has not been edited. MS Sloane 3525 is an important medical compendium containing texts of Aldebrandino of Siena's *Régime du corps* (ff. 24ra–81ra), Old French translations of the celebrated Salernitan herbal *Circa instans* (ff.108rb–178vb) and of the equally influential pharmacological guide, the *Antidotarium Nicolai* (ff. 222vb–244va). There is also an Old French version of the *Trotula* on ff. 246vb–253rb. The MS contains 259 folios, approx. 235 x 165 mm, written two columns per page, 36 lines to a column, in a hand of the early fourteenth century. Meyer, who printed a number of illustrative extracts, observed that 'La langue est bien celle de Paris ou des environs' whilst noting that two receipts written in an English hand are found on ff.178vb and 179ra and that the well known verses beginning 'Urbanus pro se nescit numerum scabiose' on f. 259r have been added by an English hand of the fifteenth century. The text of the translation of Roger's *Chirurgia* occupies ff.180ra–208rb and begins with the following prologue:

> Aprés ce que Deus out criez le munde et il [l']out enbeli de sustance terriene, si vout former home et mit en lui espirit de vie. Et li pluit que home fut formé de vil matere et de froisable [et] que l'espirit fut de glorieuse sustance et de espirituel et pardurable. Et mist en home et l'enbeli gloriosement de forme et de sapience et li dona entendement de faire bien ou mal et enseignement et comandement de fere le bien et de lessier le mal. Et a ceus qui trepassent son comandement il a appareillé divers tormenz selun les divers maus. Et por l'escience que il lor a doné il avront ignorance et iront du regne a e(n)sil et de lumere en tenebres, de delices en chativetez, et de soveraine joie seront il envoié en grant tri[s]tesce, si com il ont deservi. Et cil qui ont laissé le mal et ont fait le bien iront en joie pardurable, laquel Dex nos otroit a deservir.
>
> Ci[s]t soverain[s] mires qui fi[s]t le munde vout a soi retenir la cure de la partie pardurable [c'est de l'ame, Sl.1977], et nos deguerpi et laissa la cure de la chativeté terriene [c'est du cors, Sl.1977] a curer, si cumme il sunt des plaies et des autres enfermetez, de[s]queles theorique [f.180rb] est nostre mestresse, et practique si en est ministre [ministresse, Sl.1977] de laquele practique le office est a curer les accidens et les maladies que avenent en cors humane dedenz et dehors. Et por ce que en ce livre sont contenues [MS continues] les cures des maladies que avenent en divers cors par dehors, si comme par plaies qui sunt apelees en fisique solucion de continu[i]té por ce que par plaies est departie la continu[i]té des membres, ce est la joincture de l'une char a l'autre, cist livre reçoit la digneté et le non de cyrurgie, lequel livre nos avons translaté et mis en escrit a la priere et a la requeste de nos compaignons nobles et sages, en tel maniere et en tel entente que il le puissent retinir et entendre et en puissent profitier. Et que Dex otroit et nos en doint deservir parfete gloire et loenge pardurable. Nos avons porveu a deviser ce livre en quatre parties, si que nos puissons assener [afiner, Sl.1977] les cures de diverses parties de cors et que nos

---

[33] See "Manuscrits médicaux en Français", *Romania* 44 (1915–17), [161–214] 163–72 (Sloane 1977) and 182–214 (Sloane 3525).

puissons metre en ce livre fin loable. Et por ce que le chief est la plus digne partie, nos comencerons al chief. Et puis dirons les chapitres l'un aprés l'autre par ordre. Primes dirons en queles manieres le chief est plaié et les signes de la bleceure de[s] taies et aprés de la bleceure del test aperte a grant plaie que est [f.180va] fete ou d'espee ou de autre chose [om. Sl.1977]. Aprés de la mauvese char que croist sur la dure mere et de la superflu[i]té de la char que nest sur la jointe du test et des autres cures par ordre [om. Sl.1977].

The following passages will serve as illustrations of the translator's technique:

[f.186ra][I,XXVI] De [MS Se] *la maladie du chief qui est apelee manie et melancolie.*
De [MS Se] la maladie du chief qui est apelee manie et melancolie, ce est une maladie que les [MS ces] genz apelent desverie: trenche le cuir [l'os, Sl.1977] et la char du chief en croiz et fore le test, que la matere de la maladie s'en isse fors. Et fai bien lier le malade tant que la plaie soit garie. Et fai issi comme nos avons enseignié es autres cures.

[f.186ra][I,XXVIII] Se li poil sunt creu es paupieres [outre nature et les paupieres, Sl.1977] sunt [MS lunt] chernues issi que tu ne puisses mie voir les peus, frote les paupieres des euz o le paritarie et comme li sanc s'en istra et la char sera amenuisé, tu porras adonc necar [vooir, Sl.1977] les peus. E [a]rasche les o les piceroles. Aprés met sus l'aubun d'uef [ce feras tu en esté, Sl.1977] et se il est iver, mele [met, Sl.1977] sus l'aubun d'ues un pou de safran; issi feras tu quant /f.186rb/ li poil serunt revenu et lie la paupiere, si qu'elle tende amont. Et se il covient que les paupieres ne soient mie charnues, esrache les peus. Aprés frote les paupieres o les fueilles de la paritaire, si que li sanc en isse et fai issi comme je ai dit devant en ceste meisme cure. A ceste meismes chose vaut le jus des tendruns des ronces [et] de l'aluine et mesle ovec aubun d'uef et avuec eue rose et met sus en maniere d'emplastre.

As in the complete Anglo-Norman translation, there is a final section on 'mormal' which is not found in the text of Sudhoff's edition:

[f.208ra]*Mal* [MS mil] *mors:* Mal [MS mil] mors est une maladie qui vient de melancolie et nest es jambes et es cuisses [illiers, Sl.1977] et es braz et si le conoistras par ces signes: li malades doit avoir un malans lais et durs et ses et sans manjue et c'est la differance entre sause flamme et mal mort: sause flame fait grater le malade et mal mort non. La cure est tele: done au malade oximel squillitique ou [s]cabiose et rue [quant eles] serunt cuites. Quant li malades aura usé oximel .xv. jors, purge le de beneoite meslee ovec geralogodion aguisé d'allebore noir et d'armodactelles. .iii. jors aprés la poison fai estuver le malade les jambes chaudes d'erbes cuites en fort vin ou loissive. Aprés oing le malade de l'oingnement fusse et de l'oingnement blanc et de l'oingnement a sause flame ensemble aguisié d'ellebore blanc et noir. De cest oingnement oindras tu le malade .ii. foiz le jor jusc'a .vii. jorz. A ce meismes pren limaces et si les trible et cuis en fort vin ou en /f.208rb/ loissive. Aprés coil la cresse qui vendra pardesus et si en oing les jambes. Explicit Cyrugie.

Extremely close to the translation of the *Chirurgia* in MS Sloane 3525 is that found on ff.10ra–46ra ('Explicit la cyrurgie mestre Rogier de Salerne') of MS Sloane 1977, much more celebrated on account of a set of coloured illustrations to the text, 144 in all (ff. 2–9). This MS was written in France c.1300 and also contains a vernacular version of the *Circa instans* (ff. 48ra–135va 'Explicit circa instans estrait de latin en françois'). The folios measure approx. 234 x 161 mm and the text of the *Chirurgia* is written in two columns, 29 lines to a column. It is preceded on f.1r–v by a list of contents and chapters of the MS in which the *Chirurgia* is announced in a red rubric *Cist livres est apelez 'Post mundi fabricam' en françois selonc le latin entierement . . . Ceste cyrurgie est li cyrurgie mestre Rogier de Salerne.*

Totally unstudied are the Old French versions in MSS Paris B.N. f.f.14827 (s.xv) ff.1r–54v and f.f.1288 ff. 207r–231v.

(c) The Translation into Middle English

MS London, B.L. Sloane 240 (s.xv¹) contains two important adaptations of medical works into Middle English, namely Roger's *Chirurgia* (ff.1r–47v) and, in the same hand, a receipt-book in five parts (ff. 48r–137r), not a surgery proper, but a complement to Roger's treatise. The preface to this *receptarium* runs (f. 48r):

> Though that heretofor writen hath sufficiently betreatede of surgery, from the hiest part of man unto the lowest, towching cutting with other grete curese, 3et for as moche as I fynde many other medicyns and remedese writen in many and sondrey oder queris whech ar right necessary to be known and this saide boke of surgery to be made the more perfecte, I purpose by godis grace as here aftir schal folowe so to ordre them that the redar may the souner fynde the remedy sought for, devidyng them into .iiii. partis thuse proceding.

The Middle English text of Roger's *Chirurgia* is written on pages measuring approx. 265 x 190 mm. On f.1r is a short preface (see below) followed by a 'kalendre' i.e. a list of contents (f.1v *Explicit tabula primi libri* – such a table occurs at the beginning of each book) in which the lists of chapters and the rubric are splashed in yellow and accompanied by a red paragraph mark. The preface to each book begins with a large red initial. There are some marginal headwords with red paragraph marks and yellow splashes. The verso of each page has the letter L at the top and the recto bears the number of the book (from I to IIII). The preface to the adaptation differs from the Latin preface and runs as follows (f.1r):

> Here begynneth a breve treatese of surgery, which treatese is devidede in to .iiii. partis consernyng the remedise which by mysfortune, casualite, or chaunce myght happe to man or any other superfluous humour to growe in any part of his body what so ever it be. And for as moche as the hede is the most wurthy part of man, therfor in the furst boke of this saide treatese shal be shewid of the partis of the same with the curys longyng therto and aftirwarde in other bokis of other partis and of every boke the kalendre shal make mencion befor of the maters folowing.

The first chapter of Book One then commences on f. 2r. A conspectus of the chapters retained in the Middle English adaptation may be obtained from the synoptic table of chapter headings printed below. The text as transmitted in MS Sloane 240 shows both omissions and additions. The latter may range from modest explanatory phrases like 'al docturs acorden of our science that lynett is a great dryer and a grete clenser' (I,XVI f. 7r) to wholesale substitutions like that in I,LI (Of akyng of teth, f.14v) which is quite different from the Latin and ends 'And knowe this for a good rule that ther is no medicyn so good for a roten toth as is pulling out þer of, for þat is most sekerest medicyn'. Many chapters are omitted (e.g. Book IV lacks chapters 5–7 & 16–20) and frequently the receipts themselves are abbreviated. Surgical instruments are very rarely given their technical names.

The excerpts which follow will afford some idea of the adaptor's care and accuracy.

In I,XX the operation for removing the shaft of an arrow is particularly detailed and careful:

> [f. 7v] And if it so be that the schaft stike fast in the hede, then owght the wounde to be made more large besyde the schaft and put in a tent so that it may towche the yren. And strewe powdre of coperose upon the tente anoyntyde befor with a litil hony. And when the place is somewhat made large within, than tak hede if the schaft stycke fast in the hede and if it so do, than mewe the schaft with thi handys hidderwarde and thiddirwarde and with the mewing of the schaft the hede shal mewe and wex lose and so schalt thou bring it out lightly. And if it so be that the hede be therin and the schaft broken away, [f. 8r] than shalt thou aske the pacient howe he stode whan he was hurt and than shalt thou take a serchowre and serche therwith the wounde and if it so be that the serchour may not cum therto, then shalt thou strewe therin powdre of coperose to large the hole within untyl thou may towch the hede. Þan shalt thou have an instrumente in the maner of a paire of litill tongys and drawe out the hede therwith. And if it so be that the hede may not be drawn oute but with great hevynesse, than it is better to late the hede abyde still therin then the pacient to be in dispair of his lyve, for I knowe diverse persons that have lyvide many 3eres that have hade arwes hedis and dart hedys left within hem . . . And beware that thou heale it not to sone unto the tyme the rust of the hede and the corruption be put owt ther fro. Wherfor it is bettir to anoynte the tent with larde of bakune than with fresch swynys grece. And when thou seist that the wounde is faire and clene and sendeth not owt gore but begynnyth to dry up, than withdrawe thi tent and put no moo þerin.

> I,XXI [f. 8v] Of a wounde made with a brode hokyde arwe: . . . First we must have tonges made therfor and thrist the berdis of the hede togiddre with the tonges and than afturward first holde be these .ii. berdys and drawe it out warly. And if it sticke so that it may not be done soo, then shalt thou tak .ii. hole pypes of iren or of brasse and sett hem upon þe hokys of the arwe and then fest thi tonges upon the mydde party of the hede and drawe it out wislye and the same werking may thou doo with .ii. pennyse of a gosys wyng and when it is out, hele it as I have spoken in the last chapitur.

I,XXV [f. 9v] *Of scropules* [sic] *that ben in the hede*: Also ther spryngeth certayn rownde knobbys in the hede like kirnelles and some are gretter than some and we call hem in englisch tong 'wennes' and some of these knobbys ar harde and some nessch and some of hem are meuable and some onmewable . . .

I,XXXIX [f.12r] *Of polippus and his tokyns*: . . . the grettir that it waxith it fallith downwarde more and more both by cause of his own peyse and of the wynde that passeth throwgh the nose thirles dryving it outwarde befor him, and it semyth as it were a gobett of flesch hanging in the nose thirle . . .

I,XLVII [f.14r] *Of disjoyning of cheke bones*: It happeth oft tymys that hendes of the cheke bonys ar out of her joyntes the which is known by this tokyn: the nether toth may not joyne with the owir closly as thei sholde do. And thus it is to be holpen: thou shalt take the pacient by both the jawes and bere the hendes of the gomes outwarde and lift up the pacient therwith fro the erth. And if it be out of joynte but on the on side, than shalt thou pull him fro the erth but by the on syde. And when the checke bone is in the joynt, than shalt thou anoynt it with dewte and make the pacient to use sowpyng and charge him that he put no grete morsel in his mowth at onys not within .viii. or .x. daies, for it schulde than lightly stert out agayn.

The preface to Book II runs as follows:

[f.16r] Here folowith the seconde boke of surgery. And for as moche as in the first boke is treatide of the hede with al maner of curis longing therto, therfor in þis the seconde boke folowing I purpose to shewe of sekenes and hurtis with the curys that long to the necke and the throte. And aftirwarde of kyrnellis and wennes beyng in þe same. And at the last of al maner of empostemys that myght happe to spring ther. And these chapturs folowing make mencion of the saide boke.

Then comes the 'kalendare' listing sixteen chapters and ending 'Explicit tabula secundi libri'. In some of the ensuing chapters the adaptor has succeeded in clarifying the original:

II,3 [f.17v] *Of a wounde in þe natrelle of þe hede wher throw3 vena organica is cutt asundr*: . . . first thou shalt sewe the mowthes of the veynes togedir with a smale nedyl and as thou shalt sewe the nidyr sede alway have a threde under the poynte of the nedyl to lift it up therwith to have thi nedyl ageyne at every puttyng . . .

Unlike the Anglo-Norman translator, the author of the Middle English adaptation preserves the Latin of certain quotations:

II,XII [f. 21v] *Of kankers gendride inwarde and outwarde*: . . . And thei that have kankers hidde it is bettir to be not helyde than helyde aftir the sayng of Ipocrase wurde: 'It is bettir to hem that hath cankers hide to be not helyde than helyde and thei that ar helyde schal senner perische and thei that ar not healide schal lyve longe tyme.' And these same wurdis are thus saide in latyn: *Quibusque cancri absconditi sunt* [f. 22r] *non curari melius est. Curati enim citius pereunt, non curati multum tempus perficiunt.*

Book III begins thus:

[f. 26v] Here folowith the thride boke of surgery in the which schal be treatide of remedesse for diseasese and hurtis that myght fortune in man from the ovir part of the scholder bladys unto the yerde. And these chapturs folowing maketh mencion of the same.

At the beginning of chapter VIII (*Of removing away dede flesch from a wounde*) there is an interesting addition:

[f. 30r] If it so be that ther waxith prowde flesch in a wounde for the which many leches usyn alumme calcynede or powdre of coperose, but we wil use these that ar more to preise in here werkingis as is the powdir of hermodactulus . . .

The celebrated passage dealing with treatment of the intestines runs as follows:

III,XXVII [f. 36v] *Of woundyng of þe bowellys and goyng out of hem:* . . . And thou schalt have a litil schort stycke of eldir the lengh of a large unce and a half and the gretnesse therof schal acorde with the gretenes of the bowellis that ar hurte. And take out the pytth of the sticke and make it as holowe and as thynne as þu may. And thou put in the same holowe pype in to [f. 37r] the broken hole of the bowell and gadir the sides that are broken togedir and that thei be evyn in the myddist of the lengith of the pipe. And than shalt thou sewe the sydes togedir with a small nedyl and threde. And be ware that thou sowe no thing of the bowell to the forsaide pipe.

Another detailed exploratory operation is described in III,XXXVI:

[f. 41r] *Of knowing of the ston be certayn tokens whedir it be in the bleddir or not:* If the ston be in the bleddir, in this maner thou shalt knowe it. Thou schal make the pacient to lye wyde open on cusschyns and thou schalt make him to holde up his fyeght stiffely into the firmament and knytt a roppe aboute hem and tye hem to a balke. And some man sitte upon the pacientis brest, than shall thou stoupe down and put thi .ii. fyngers of thi right hande, that is to say the lycpott and the longman, in to the hole of the pacientis arse and thou schal threste thi thombe of thi lyfte hande down on the pacientis schare and serche with thi fyngers hendys up-warde as ferr as thou may. And if [it] so be that thou fele any harde rownde thing in the maner of corluels ether or an hennes egg, than trust it fully that it is þe stone. And if it so be a neshe rounde gobett, than shal thou undirstande that it is a gobett of flesch congeylide in the bleddir and that it is that lettith the pacient some while to make watir.

Book IV begins:

> [f. 42v] Here folowith the fourth boke and the last of this werke of surgery in the whiche shal be shewede of remedese from the hippe bone upwarde unto the netheryst parte of the fote as the kalendre maketh mencion here aftir ensuyng.

After IV,11 there is a chapter on 'mormal' which corresponds to the final section of the Anglo-Norman translation but is not incorporated in Sudhoff's edition of Roger's Latin original:

> [f. 44v] *Of helyng of a mormale and the cause therof:* Ther is a certayn sore which is callede malum mortuum in latyn, that is to say in englische a dedde evil, and in French a mormal, and so it is callede in englische tonge also . . .

4. The Translations in MS Cambridge, Trinity College 0.1.20

MS Cambridge, Trinity College 0.1.20 (James 1044) is one of the earliest and most important collections of medical texts in the vernacular that we possess. It consists of 332 folios : ff.1–18 are foliated in one hand, ff.19–98 in an other; the folio after f. 98 was omitted and later numbered 99 in pencil and the rest of the MS refoliated in pencil by that same hand; f. 95b was missed by both the original foliator and the refoliator; there is also a f. 307a. The present foliation, therefore, actually runs to 330. The folios measure approx. 198 x 150 mm (the volume has been cut down) and are written in a variety of hands most of which are more or less contemporary with each other and may be placed in the period 1230–1260. The texts are distributed amongst these hands as follows:

1. ff.1r–52v
2. ff. 53r–98r
3. ff. 98v–102r
1. ff.102v–104v (l.10)
4. f.104v (ll.11–21)
1. ff.105r–194r
5. f.194r (extra receipt) (ff.194v–195v are blank)
1. ff.196r–213v (l.15)
6. f. 213v (l.16) – 215v
1. ff. 216r–239v
7. ff. 240r–249v
8. ff. 250r–292v
7. ff. 293r–299v
1. ff. 300ra–324va
9. f. 324vb (notes)
10. ff. 325r–330v.

The contents of the MS may be summarized thus:

1. ff.1ra–21rb the versified collection of receipts known as the 'Physique rimee', here amounting to over 1700 lines, written in double columns of approx. 22 lines per column. Some of the receipts are copied out as if they were in prose.[34]

2. ff.21rb–23rb [red rubric] *Les secrés de[s] femmes* inc. 'Ypocras dit et enseigne / les raisons de femme baraigne'. Verse fragments of a gynaecological treatise based on the *Trotula maior*, associated with 13 below.

3. ff. 23rb–24va miscellaneous prose receipts beginning with a charm, [red rubric] *Esperment a plaies* inc. 'Treis bons freres estoient ke aloient al mont d'Olivet . . .'[35]

4. ff. 24va–30rb a fragment of a prose translation of Roger Frugard's *Chirurgia* covering Bk. I,1–3, 5–8, 11–22, 26 and Bk. III,27. There is a red rubric *De tote manieres de froisseures* and the text begins 'Il avient ke li chief est naufrez en diverse manieres . . .' At the bottom of f. 24va there is a contemporary drawing of a man with a mace being struck on the head by a man with a staff which is obviously designed to illustrate the topic of head wounds with which the *Chirurgia* begins and is the work of the same artist who executed the drawings to the second translation of the *Chirurgia* (see 15 below)

5. ff. 30rb–32vb various prose receipts for the preparation of ointments beginning with Apostolicom cirurgicom.

6. ff. 33r–36v another set of medical receipts written in long lines across the page with red rubrics, beginning with *Poudre por la piere*.

7. ff. 37r–44v / 53r–55r (different hand) the collection of prose receipts known as the 'Lettre d'Hippocrate' followed by the Introduction and the sections on humours and urines (with red rubrics).[36]

8. ff. 45r–52v a medical treatise composed of prose receipts. After the opening rubric in red *A doner medicine* the first two and a half lines of the text have been erased (presumably because erroneous) and the work now begins 'quant vodrés doner medicine a malades'.

9. ff. 55r–194r a translation, acephalous, of the *Practica* of Johannes Platearius inc. 'Les signes iteles: l'urine roge ou sorroge . . .'[37]

10. f.194r a single prose receipt:

> Pernez une poiné de cikoré et une de cerelaunge et la terce de coupere et une des racines de persil et une des racines de fenoil et une de menu ache et une de l'achun et une de la semence de aniz et une poiné de l'escorche de saumbu et demi poiné de escroche [sic] de frene et deus poinés de pollipode.

---

[34] See Tony Hunt, *Popular Medicine in Thirteenth-Century England* (Cambridge, 1990), pp.142–203.
[35] See *ibid*. pp. 72–3.
[36] See *ibid*. p.104.
[37] See below pp. 149ff.

Folios 194v–195v are blank.

11. ff.196r–213v a prose translation of part of the Salernitan treatise *De instructione medici* with an opening red rubric *Issi comence le sotil enseignement Ypocras a ces disciples que mult li avoient requis coment il deusent visiter li malades*, inc. 'Li auctor dist au comencement de cest livre et parole a ses disciples . . .'[38]

12. ff. 213v–215v a series of brief descriptions in prose of the properties of herbs, beginning 'Olibanum ceo est encens. Il est chaud e seche el secunde degrei . . .'

13. ff. 216r–235v a gynaecological treatise in verse translated from the *Trotula maior*, beginning with a red rubric *Prologe* and 'Bien sachiés femmes, de ce n'aiés dotaunce, / ci est escrit por voir de lor science . . .'[39]

14. ff. 236r–239v a set of 172 octosyllabic verses on beauty treatments for women, many of which occur in MS Cambridge, St John's College D.4 (s.xiv[1]) ff. 84rb–86va.[40]

15. ff. 240r–299v An Anglo-Norman translation of Roger Frugard's *Chirurgia* accompanied by 47 scenes of medical consultations and / or activities in the pharmacy executed as elegant and refined line drawings, sometimes with a pale colour wash. On f. 273v there is an incomplete drawing by another artist.[41]

16. ff. 300ra–324va the Latin text of Roger's *Chirurgia* as far as Bk III,18.

17. f. 324vb four medical receipts, including a charm.

18. ff. 325r–330v an incomplete treatise on confession inc. '[Q]ui vodra bel e beaus vestu apparer devant la face Jesu . . .' There are blank spaces for coloured initials which were never entered. Folio 329v is blank.

The text of the Anglo-Norman translation of the *Chirurgia* has been copied by two scribes, the first responsible for ff. 240r–49v and 293r–99v, the second for ff. 250r–92v. These two hands are not found elsewhere in the MS. The quire structure is as follows: 10 + 12 + 12 + 12 + 8 (wants 7) + 6 + 2 (2 canc.) (James's quires 35–41). The second scribe's activity therefore coincides with quire divisions (quires 2–5) rather than text divisions, as was normally the case in lay scriptoria where scribes were remunerated according to the number of pages they had filled.

The outer leaves of the first quire are somewhat shiny and rubbed suggesting that they for some time formed an unbound 'booklet'. In the first quire there is no form of punctuation other than the stop (*punctus*). The initial rubric is in red. The opening capital A is illustrated by a different artist from the one responsible for the line drawings. Depicted is a typical uroscopy, the assistant holding up the vessel of urine for the doctor's inspection. The figures are depicted against a reddish-brown ground, with a green wash over their garments, some of the folds

---

[38] Edition forthcoming in Vol.2.
[39] Edition forthcoming in Vol.2.
[40] See Hunt, *Popular Medicine* pp. 204–16.
[41] The drawings are reproduced with commentary in Tony Hunt, *The Medieval Surgery* (Woodbridge, 1992).

being picked out in red. To the right of the capital there is red and blue saw-tooth
decoration and simple red ornamentation at the top. In the text the initial letter
of each sentence is splashed in red. On f. 240v there is a red rubric followed by a
blue initial, three lines deep, decorated in red. On f. 241r there are alternating red
and blue initials without decoration, but thereafter the coloured initials were
never executed and no guide letters are visible. There is an erasure after *mer* in the
last line of f. 241r : it looks as if the expunged letters were *ne*. On f. 241v the red
rubric *De la soudure de la plaie* is written over an erasure. On f. 243v line 12 the
word *spatumini* and the *f* of *chef* are written over erasures. On f. 249r the scribe has
left a blank for insertion of the name of the 'ostiliment cirugien'.

The second scribe writes a larger, fatter hand. He is more inclined to employ
long *s* at the ends of words, where the first scribe had a clear preference for short *s*.
The second scribe also makes greater use of superscript signs of abbreviation
('suspension'). His writing of *e* introduces a new form, not employed by the first
scribe, and where he does use the form common to the latter it is without the
central bar. His final – *z* is much firmer than the slight version used by the first
scribe. Some use is now made of the *punctus elevatus* (f. 263r line 12 and f. 271v
line 16). The rubricator remains the same, but the red splashes on initial letters is
more modest and also inconsistent (it ceases altogether on ff. 263r–273r). There is
more correction than in the case of the first scribe: f. 252r line 6 the scribe corrects
t'ois; f. 252v lines 9–10 *deverie* and *mania* are written over erasures; line 16 *epelen-*
psie is written over an erasure and emended from *apelempsie*; line 17 *le* before *col* is
written over an erasure; f. 253v line 11 the scribe has indicated the word division
aiote la dolur by a vertical stroke between the first word and the second; line 20 *a*
oes mettre is written over an erasure; f. 254r line 16 between *traire* and *de la plaie* an
e has been expuncted; f. 255r line 2 the scribe has inserted superscript *u* over
papires; f. 257r line 21 the scribe corrects *troiz* to *trois* by expunction of *z* and
addition of superscript *s*; f. 258r line 2 *plaie* and *l'oil* are written over erasures; f.
258r line 1 a revisor has entered at the top of the page a paragraph mark followed
by *o* and a superscript *i* has been added by the scribe to change *ignement* to
oigneiment – the same revisor has inserted a paragraph mark and *onement rumpant*
together with a pointing finger at the top of f. 272r; f. 259v line 9 by superscript
addition the scribe has converted *hors* to *aval*. In this second quire (ff. 250–261)
the surface of the parchment has been less well prepared than in the first quire. In
the next quire there are further corrections: f. 263r line 10 between *hors* and *e*
asuagist the scribe expuncts *a*; f. 265v line 8 in *oilie muscelin* the first *i* has been
expuncted; f. 266r line 10 *medlez* is corrected to *metlez* by expunction and superscript addition; line 20 *c* has been added before *este* together with a vertical
insertion mark; f. 267v line 13 in *signe cum dun signe pertus* the second *signe* has
been expuncted; f. 268v line 16 *colure* has been emended by erasure of *u* to *colre*; f.
268v line 1 the scribe has added *cu* to *es me* through superscript addition and
insertion mark; f. 270r line 3 the scribe has expuncted the second and third words
in *brusci del rosel e sparagi*; f. 272r line 20 the revisor has provided *cum oinement* as
a superscript addition after *quintement*; f. 278r line 10 *maulvaise* is corrected by
superscript addition of *e* over expuncted second *a*; line 12 a superscript *n* and
insertion mark are added to *e* before *ceste maneire*; line 18 *saf* is corrected from *sal*;

f. 279v a much blacker ink is employed, though the scribe remains the same; f. 280r line 8 *cure* is repeated and the first occurrence expuncted; line 17 *parcie* is corrected to *percie* by expunction and superscript addition; f. 280v line 11 *mestrie* is expuncted before *materie*; ff. 280v–281r the scribe clearly sharpens his pen here, and again on f. 284r and 286v; f. 283r line 2 *plai* is expuncted before *partie*; in the right-hand margin beside the line with the rubric *De la fermure* the revisor has written 'Nota' in pale brown ink and opposite lines 11–13 has drawn a hand with a pointing finger; he has also inserted *.i. colofonie* after *peiz grec* and corrected *chaut* over an erasure; f. 285r line 14 *soi* is followed by an erasure; f. 285v line 21 *faite* is expuncted before *sanez*; f. 287r line 20 after *survenunt* the scribe has corrected *ii* to *si*; f. 288r line 1 *grandur* has a final expuncted *e*; f. 289v line 5 *malade* has been expuncted before *mire*; f. 291v line 21 a superscript *s* has been added to *chitere*; f. 293v line 3 *sur* is written above the line before *ferme*.

At one point it is clear that the scribe of the Trinity text was working from a defective model or else from a set of unbound sheets which became incorrectly ordered. At line 11 on f. 253r the text suddenly changes from Sudhoff I,XXVIII (line 536) to I,LV (line 963). The missing material is found on ff. 255r line 1 – 266r line 11 and what ff. 253r line 11 – 255r line 1 transmit is Sudhoff I,LV (line 963) to II,3 (line 71). The scribe finally realised his mistake and made a clumsy attempt to patch up the error.

The language of the Anglo-Norman translation needs no detailed study in the present context, since the insular character of the copy is more strongly marked than in the case of the *Practica brevis* translation (see below pp. 149ff.). It seems likely that the translator was insular from the inclusion in his work of a number of words explicitly identified as English ('en englés'), namely *hannebaire* [corr. hannebane] (f. 261r), *hannebanne* (f. 265v), *maddokes* (f. 266v), *cockel* (f. 267r) and *popi neir* (f. 279r), though their gloss-like introduction does not preclude the possibility that they have been inserted by the copyist. The same gloss-like commentary is applied on f. 264r to serpigo "en franceais derte" which suggests that the procedure stems from the translator not simply the copyist. In tackling botanical names he occasionally has recourse to English as the language of the most familiar name form, at other times he admits defeat and simply retains the Latin original, with or without morphological adjustment, and for the great majority of cases, pleasingly, he finds vernacular French equivalents. Whilst none of these is exclusively Anglo-Norman, the converse is also true: none of the French names is limited to a continental dialect, as is the case with *bibuef* in the fragmentary translation on f. 27ra/rb (a prose receipt on f. 24rb has *blaunc bibuef*).

5. The Contents of the *Chirurgia*

Roger Frugard's *Chirurgia*, the 'Rolandina' of c.1230 and the 'Four Masters Gloss' of c.1250 agree in arranging their treatment of surgical pathology and therapy into four books, adopting the *a capite ad calcem*, i.e. topical, sequence. Book 1 deals with injuries to the head, Book 2 with those to the neck, Book 3 with the upper trunk including chest and abdomen, and Book 4 with the lower regions including the thigh and legs.

Book 1 deals at exceptional length with those injuries to the head and face which were a natural preoccupation of military surgeons who had to treat wounds inflicted by a variety of weapons such as arrows, maces, swords, sling stones, axes etc. The topics are distributed over the chapters of the Anglo-Norman translation as follows:

Damage to the meninges or cerebral membranes, namely the dura mater and pia mater [1]; cranial fracture [2]; removal of proud flesh on the dura mater [3]; a receipt for the preparation of the lenitive 'Ointment of the Apostles' [4]; assessment of the scope of the fracture, in the case of serious cranial fracture with a narrow wound, by digital palpation, and subsequent dressing [5]; method of ascertaining the existence of cranial fissure or hairline fracture penetrating to the inner surface of the bone, followed by directions for trephination and the making of burr-holes (the directions being much less comprehensive and useful than those found in Constantine the African or Paul of Aegina) [6]; similar directions for where part of the cranial fracture is depressed so that the fragment of bone cannot be easily removed [7]; treatment of headwound without cranial fracture [8] with an embrocation [9] followed by a receipt for an ointment [10]; treatment of a wound by incision [11]; symptoms of concealed cranial fracture in the patient's behaviour [12]; treatment of contusions without damage to the scalp or cranium, and the symptoms thereof [13] – the treatment involves the doctrine of 'laudable pus', a theory of the benefits of suppuration which goes back to Galen and was criticised by Teodorico Borgognoni (followed by Henri de Mondeville and Jean Pitard), who introduced a more rational idea of asepsis; the suturing of headwounds where there is a lesion to the scalp over a cranial fracture [14]; the preparation of 'red powder' for the consolidation of wounds [15]; the treatment of cranial fracture with a scalp wound which has not penetrated to within [16]; the treatment of superficial scalp wounds not involving the cranium [17]; head or facial injury caused by a bolt or arrow, not involving damage to the brain [18]; facial and nasal injuries [19]; facial injuries caused by a bolt or arrow [20]; removal of barbed arrow from wound [21]; injury to the brain, without cranial fracture or lesion of the scalp, through depression of the cranium [22]; tinea [23, 24]; scrophulous growths or cysts [25]; trephination to relieve mania or melancholia [26]; cauterization for epilepsy (*gutta caduca*) [25b]; inflammation of the eyes and eyelids [27]; inflammation of eyelids and eyelashes [28]; inflammation of eyes and eyelids [29]; irritation of the eyes [30]; ointment for destroying a web in the eye [31]; powder for consuming a web in the eye [32]; redness, swelling or web in the eye [33]; blood in the eye as a result of injury [34]; ectropium [35]; fistula beside the eye [36]; nasal growth [37,38]; nasal polyp and how it is recognized [39,40,41]; palatal polyp [42]; cautery for polyp [43]; tumour in nostrils, palate or gums [44]; powder for treating facial tumours [45]; splitting of the lips [46]; burning or pricking sensation in lips [48]; dislocation of the jaw [47]; fracture of the jaw, both mandibula and maxilla [50]; fracture of the jaw involving both bone and flesh wound [49]; fistula in the jaw [51]; toothache [52]; facial spots incl. impetigo, serpigo and morphew [53]; ear-ache [54]; auricular worm [55]; evacuation of foreign bodies from the ear [56].

Book 2 begins with a preface and continues with the following chapters: neck wounds [1]; neckwounds involving penetration (by arrow etc) [2]; injuries to the back of the neck caused by sword and similar instruments [3]; wounds to the back of the neck not involving severing of the main artery (Gurtl p. 710 declares it uncertain whether the *vena jugularis interna* or *externa* is indicated, but thinks probably the latter) [4]; wound to the back of the neck caused by an arrow or bolt [5]; throat wounds [6]; impostumes in the neck and nape of the neck [7,8]; anthrax or carbuncle [9]; impostume deriving from red choler [10]; impostume caused by phlegm [11]; tumour [12]; scrophula and glanders [13]; fistula [14]; goitre [15]; quinsy (retro-pharyngeal, -laryngeal and -oesophagal abscesses) [16,17]; 'branci' or tonsillitis, with use of gargles or surgical intervention [18]; inflammation of the uvula [19]; dislocation of the collarbone [20].

Book 3 deals with the upper regions of the trunk: injury to the shoulder blades [1]; injury to the scapulo-humoral or scapulo-clavicular joint (or collarbone ?) [2]; fracture or dislocation of the same [3]; wounds leading to dislocation of the shoulder [4]; arm injuries involving severed 'nerves' i.e. muscles, sinews or tendons [5]; swelling or hardening of the 'nerves' in the arm i.e. muscular contusion (or haematoma ?) [6]; cleansing of putrescent or suppurating wound [7]; removal of proud flesh [8]; erysipelas [9]; carbuncle [10]; flesh-wound in the upper arm [11]; injury to the muscles or tendons of the arm [12]; penetration of the arm by an arrow or dart [13]; injury to the bone or 'nerve' i.e. muscle or tendon in the hand [14]; contusion or haematoma in any anatomical member [15]; dislocation of the upper arm [16]; dislocation of the forearm or ulna [17]; dislocation of the hand [18]; fracture of the upper arm [19]; fistulas and humours in the arm [20]; chest injuries [21,22]; broken ribs [23]; injuries to lower part of the trunk [24]; injuries to the heart, lungs, liver, stomach or midriff [25]; intestinal injuries [27] – one of the most interesting chapters, which includes the apposition of a live animal e.g. a cat opened longitudinally, on protruding viscera to warm them and the suturing of an intestinal wound over a small tube of elder; fistulas and tumours in the same area and in women's breasts [28]; injury to the penis [29]; tumour or fistula in the penis and swelling and inflammation of the testicles [30]; injury to the peritoneum (sifac) and scrotum (osceum) [31–33]; hernias incl. sarcocele [35]; perineal litho-tomy, the removal of vesicular calculus or bladder-stone [36–38; incl. hypertrophy of the prostate in 36 ?]; spinal injuries [39]; injury to the rectum [40]; wounds in the kidneys [41]; perineal abscesses and fistulas [42]; haemorrhoids [43]; strangury [44]; cauteries [45].

Book 4 begins with a preface and chapter headings. It then deals with: injury to the 'vertebrum' [1]; injury to the hip [2]; injury to the knee [4–5]; injury to the leg [6]; injury to the foot [7]; dislocation of the hip-joint (vertebrum) [9]; dislocation of the knee [10]; fracture of the leg, with or without wound [11]; dislocation of the foot [12]; dislocation of the toes [13]; tumours and fistulas in the same area as the above [14]; blisters and ruptures (varicose ulcers ?) in the legs [16]; sciatica [17]; burns [18]; lepra [19]; tetanus [20]; mormal [–].

6. Chapter Headings in the MSS[42]

BOOK I

1.   S   Quot modis caput vulneretur et de signis lesionis panniculorum cerebri
       Sl2 Le chief est plaiez en diverses maneres
       Sl3 Quant li chiés est plaiez malement en plusors lieus
       T   De tote manere de plaies ke avenent al chef
       X   In howe many maners the hede is woundyde and of the tokyns of the hurtis of the too tees, that is to say the too skynnes of the brayne callide in latyn pia mater and dura mater

2.   S   De fractura cranei manifesta cum magno vulnere
       W   De vulnere lato cranei
       Sl2 De la briseure grant et aperte et de la plaie large
       Sl3 –
       T   De la depesceure del tes . . . Por emplier la plaie . . . Loez le naffré
       X   Of brekyng of the panne with a large wounde

3.   S   De dura matre si superflua caro super eam excrescat
       Sl2 A la morte char outier que croist sur la dure mere
       Sl3 De la morte char oster sus la dure mere
       T   Por morte char (twice)
       X   Of superfluite of flesch if it growe upon dura mater

4.   S   De apostolicon cirrurgico
       Sl   De apostolicon cyrurgico . . . De superfluitate carnis nate super iuncturam cranei
       Sl2 Pren demi livre de noire poiz
       Sl3 Apostolicon cyrurgien
       T   De la soudure de la plaie
       X   Of superfluite of flesche sprong upon þe joynt of þe panne . . . apostolicon

5.   S   De manifesta fractura cranei cum stricto vulnere
       Sl2 Se la briseure du test est grant et la plaie est [estroite]
       Sl3 Du test brisé a petite plaie
       T   Por asaier la grandure de la plaie
       X   Of greate breking of þe panne and the flesch above is straite holyde

6.   S   De fractura cranei facta in modum rimule
       Sl2 Se li tez soit fenduz en manere de fendeure
       Sl3 De la fendeure du test

---

[42] S = Sudhoff's text;   Sl = MS London, B.L. Sloane 1615 (s.xiii) ff. 70ra–83va;   Sl2 = MS London, B.L. Sloane 3525 (s.xiv) ff.180ra–208rb;   Sl3 = MS London, B.L. Sloane 1977 (s.xiv) ff.10ra–46ra;   T = MS Cambridge, Trinity College 0. 1. 20 (s.xiii) ff. 240r–299v;   W = MS London, Wellcome Hist. Med. Libr. 544 (s.xiv) ff.107ra–149ra;   X = MS London, B.L. Sloane 240 (s.xv) ff.1r–47v.

    T Por estre certifié si la test est fendue ou nun . . . De estroite plaie
    X ch. om.

7.   S De craneo quando est in altera parte depressum
     W De craneo depresso vel plicato
    Sl2 – (incorporated in ch.6)
    Sl3 –
     T De la depesceur del tes
     X Of breking of the hede panne when it is put in to the brayn warde

8.   S De vulnere capitis sine fractura cranei
    Sl2 De chief plaié sanz le test brisier
    Sl3 Du chief plaié sanz os brisier . . . De emplastre en yver
     T Por plaie del test sanz depesceur del tes . . . A faire embroke
     X Of a wounde of the hede without breking of þe panne . . . embrocacion for wynter

9.   S Embroca ad saniem provocandam in estate
    Sl De embroca ibidem ponenda pro temporis varietate
     W Embroca ad idem in tempore calido . . . Regula
    Sl2 Pren mauves en esté et fueilles de morelle une poigné
    Sl3 D'emplastre en esté
     T Autre embroke
     X Embrocation for somyr

10.   S De unguento fusco quomodo fit
    Sl2 Oignement a la plaie
    Sl3 Comment l'oignement fuse est faiz
     T Oignement a plaie novele
     X Unguentum fuscum

11.   S De humore capitis sine vulnere cutis quando manifeste craneum est lesum
    Sl2 –
    Sl3 Du chief feru qui est enflez sanz plaie
     T Por taillure de la plaie
     X Of swelling of the hede without any wounde of the flesch

12.   S Quando sine ruptura cutis craneum lesum est occulte
     W ch. om.
    Sl2 –
    Sl3 –
     T Conustre la depesceur del tes
     X –

13.   S Quando tumor capitis fit sine ruptura cutis et cranei
    Sl2 De chief enflez sanz plaie et sanz briseure . . . aluisne eguibuef . . . aluisne hermoise

S13 Du chief feru sanz plaie et sanz os brisier . . . D'emplastre por enfleure de
     chief . . . D'emplastre maturatif
T   A estre certein del tes . . . A faire emplaistre
X   –

14. S   De cura capitis quando cutis est incisa con craneo con ense vel alio tali
     W   De vulneribus capitis consuendis
     S12 A la foiz li chief est plaiez et li cuir et la char sunt trenchié o le test
     S13 A la plaie du chief dont la piece pent aval
     T   Del plaie del test
     X   Of heling of the hede when the flesch is cutt with the panne

15. S   De pulvere rubeo quomodo fit
     S12 La poudre est faite en tel manere. Pren de la grant consoude
     S13 De la rouge poudre la coutume
     T   A faire pudre ruge
     X   Pulvis rubius consolidativus

16. S   De cuti incisa cum modica parte cranei
     S12 Si un petit du test soit trenchié
     S13 De l'os entamé non pas tout outre
     T   Al tes de l'os
     X   ch. om.

17. S   De cuti sine craneo a capite segregato
     W   De cute separata a craneo et de sutura facienda cum sanguine recenti
     S12 ch. om.
     S13 ch. om.
     T   Si il avent ke le quir seit desevree de l[a] tes[te]
     X   ch. om.

18. S   De vulnere profundo facto in contumacia capitis
     S1   De vulnere profundo facto in continuitate [sic] capitis ante
     W   De vulneribus in concavitate capitis
     S12 Du chief plaié par devant ou deriere
     S13 ch. om.
     T   Por plaie de quarel en la face
     X   ch. om.

19. S   De curis vulnerum que per suturam fiunt in naso vel alia nobili parte
     W   De vulneribus in facie, in labiis et in naso
     S12 De plaie fete el nés ou es levres ou en aucun noble membre
     S13 De plaie de nés ou de levres
     T   Por plaie de la face u del neis . . . si le neiz est trenché en travers
     X   Of sewyng whech owght to be don in the visage and þe maners þerof

20. S   De vulnere teli facto in facie per nares vel iuxta oculum
     S1   De vulnere teli iuxta oculum per nares sive sit in profundo sive in angusto
          meatu et tortuoso et sit lignum in ferro vel non

W   De auricula cisa vel excoriata [extra material]
Sl2   De l'oreille trenchié [extra material]
Sl3   De l'oreille trenchié . . . De face plaiee
T   Por plaie de quarel
X   Of heling of woundys in the visage hurt with wode or iryn

21.   S   De vulnere sagitte barbulate
      W   [much new material]
      Sl2   Se la plaie est faite de saiete barbelee trai le fer [+ supplementary rubric, Ja soit ce que il n'avient mie sovent que li chief soit plaié de saite]
      Sl3   De la plaie de la saiete barbelee . . . Du chief plaié de dart ou de saiete
      T   Por plaie de sete barbelee
      X   Of a wounde made with a brode hokyde arwe

22.   S   De plicatura cranei sine cutis et cranei ruptura
      Sl   De curis capitis sine vulnere
      W   De craneo plicato
      Sl2   A la foiz est li chief feruz si que li test est enbasré [sic]
      Sl3   De l'os du chief enbarré sanz plaie
      T   –
      X   Of brusing of hede without any maner of wounde

23.   S   De cura capitis eorum que non perveniunt ex percussura vel vulnere et primo de cura tinee sine capillorum evulsione
      Sl   De cura tinee vel capillorum evulsione
      Sl2   Deus manieres sunt de taigne: l'un puet en curer [+ supplementary rubrics]
      Sl3   La cure de la tigne et la garison [+ supplementary rubrics]
      T   – . . . A faire silotrum . . . A faire oignement teingne
      X   Of heling of scallys with putting away of the heer

24.   S   De cura tinee sine capillorum [evulsione]
      Sl   De curis eiusdem sine emissione [corr. evulsione]
      W   Unguentum ad tineam sine evulsione capillorum [+ new material]
      Sl2   Pren avrone agreste et ruque sauvage [+ supplementary rubrics]
      Sl3   D'oignement + De l'ignoirre ou goutastre
      T   Autre oingnement a tegne
      X   Of divers superfluites of the hede

25.   S   De scrophulis que in capite oriuntur
      W   De superfluitatibus in capite
      Sl2   A la foiz avient que une[s] superfluite[z] nessent el chief qui semblent escroeles [+ supplementary rubrics]
      Sl3   Des escroeles . . . De la poudre des afodilles . . . De l'escroele qui ne se muet point
      T   Des escrolles ki avenunt en la teste . . . Autre
      X   Of scropules [sic] that ben in the hede

26.   S   De cauteriis que fiunt contra maniam vel melancoliam [+ 25b De cauteriis que fiunt ad epilensiam]

      Sl   De cauteriis que fiunt propter maniam, frenesim et epilensiam
      Sl2 De [MS Se] la maladie du chief qui est apelee manie et melancolie [+ 25b
           Por (MS for) le mal de coi en chet]
      Sl3 De la melencolie du chief [+ 25b Le mal dont on chiet]
      T   Al deverie . . . Por gute chaive
      X   ch. om.

27.   S   De egritudine oculorum et cura eorundem
      Sl2 A la foiz avient que les euz sunt roges plorant
      Sl3 Des peuls qui naissent es pauperes
      T   -
      X   ch. om.

28.   S   De pilis qui preter naturam in palpebris oriuntur
      Sl2 -
      Sl3 -
      T   -
      X   ch. om.

29.   S   De lacrimis oculorum quando pili preter naturam in palpebris non
           continentur
      W   De oculis lacrimantibus cum rubore
      Sl2 Se il avient que les euz sunt roge et plorant
      Sl3 Des iex rouges et plorans outre nature
      T   -
      X   For wateryng eyne

30.   S   Ad pruritum oculorum removendum
      Sl2 A la menjue des euz pren litargire demi unce
      Sl3 A la menjue des iex
      T   Por grature des oiz
      X   For akyng of the eyne and brennyng of hem

31.   S   Unguentum ad panniculum oculorum corrodendum
      Sl2 A la taie qui vient es euz
      Sl3 La garison a la toie des iex
      T   Por mancher la teie des oiz
      X   To frete away the webbe out of the eye

32.   S   Pulvis optimus qui valet ad panniculum oculorum corrodendum
      Sl2 A oster la taie des euz
      Sl3 Poudre por la toie des iex oster
      T   Autre bone puldre por la tei manger
      X   ch. om.

33.   S   De rubore oculorum et inflatione et panniculo
      Sl2 ch. om.
      Sl3 ch. om.
      T   Por rugeur des euz
      X   ch. om.

34.   S   De sanguine qui consurgit in oculis ex percussione vel ex tumore accidit extrinsecus sic subvenimus
    Sl2   Por hurteure des euz [+ supplementary rubric]
    Sl3   De plaie qui est sus l'oel
    T   Por sanc ke avent en l'oil par blesceure
    X   Of blode beyng in the eye

35.   S   De inversione inferioris palpebre et aliis
    Sl   De inversa carne inferioris palpebre et superfluitatibus
    Sl2   –
    Sl3   De plaie sus l'oel
    T   –
    X   –

36.   S   De fistula inter nasum et oculum nata
    Sl2   A la foiz vint festre . . . Oig[n]ement ruptoire est fet en tel manere
    Sl3   De flestre en vis . . . De l'oignement ruptoire
    T   Por festre en coste le oil
    X   ch. om.

37.   S   De curis nasus a superfluitatibus et de superfluitate carnis qui videtur esse polipus et non est
    W   De polipo in naso et de eius cura
    Sl2   A la foiz viennent unes superfluitez es narilles que en apele polipe . . . Pren celidoine et pain de cucu
    Sl3   A la superfluité des narines . . . Du vert oignement
    T   De superfluité ke aveint al nés
    X   Of a superfluite growing in the nose which semyth that it wer polippus and is not

38.   S   De carne que videtur esse polipus infra nares existentes
    Sl2   Por la char qui croist en la narille
    Sl3   Pour oster la char croissant es narines
    T   – . . . Oignement a ceo memes
    X   ch. om.

39.   S   De non polipo et signis curabilis polipi.
    Sl2   –
    Sl3   Du polipe
    T   De polippus ke aveint entre les narrilles
    X   Of polippus and his tokyns

40.   S   –
    Sl   De superflua carne que videtur esse polipus et non est
    Sl2   –
    Sl3   –
    T   –
    X   –

41.   S   De cura veri polipi cum ferro calido

    Sl   De curis eiusdem sine ferro
    Sl2 –
    Sl3 –
    T   –
    X   [included in 40 above]

42.   S   De polipo qui exit per foramina palati
    Sl   De curis polipi qui est per palatum
    Sl2 –
    Sl3 –
    T   A la feiz aveint polipus au paleis
    X   ch. om.

43.   S   Cauterium ad polipum urendum
    Sl2 –
    Sl3 ch. om.
    T   Por emflure del nés ke polipus est apelé
    X   ch. om.

44.   S   De cancro in naso, in labiis vel gingivis vel in alia parte faciei
    W   Diversa nomina apostematum, de cancro etc.
    Sl2 –
    Sl3 De chancre ou palais
    T   Por cancre a[s] narrilles e au paleis e as gencives . . . A taillir cancre
    X   Of kankir specialy beyng in the nose thirle

45.   S   Ad gingivas sive fuerit alibi cancer
    Sl2 Pren foilles d'olive et alun zacharin [+ supplementary rubrics]
    Sl3 De poudre a chancre . . . De poudre as gencives
    T   Pudre a ceo maus . . . Autre pudre pur cancre . . . Pur cancre
    X   –

46.   S   De fissura labiorum et cura eiusdem
    Sl2 As levres fendues pren la semence de la chenillé
    Sl3 –
    T   Por la fenture des lievres
    X   ch. om.

48.   S   De arsura labiorum
    Sl2 A l'arsure des levres pren amidum
    Sl3 De la porreture des levres . . . De l'arsure des levres
    T   Por arsure des levres
    X   For prickyng and chingyng of the lippys [new material]

49.   S   De disjunctura in mandibulis et causa eiusdem
    Sl2 La joe ist de son liu
    Sl3 De la dejointure de la joe
    T   –
    X   Of disjoynyng of cheke bones

50.   S   De fractura eiusdem sine vulnere
      W   De ruptura mandibule
      Sl2   De la joe route d'acune partie [=50 + 49]
      Sl3   De la routure (MS couture) de la joe [=50 + 49]
      T   –
      X   ch. om.

49.   S   De fractura eiusdem cum vulnere
      Sl2   [see above]
      Sl3   [see above]
      T   De la depesceur de l'os
      X   ch. om.

51.   S   De fistula ibidem in mandibula
      Sl   De fistula ibi nata, de brancis ibi natis
      Sl2   De festre qui nest a la joe . . . Si festre ait corrumpu os
      Sl3   De la flestre [sic] de la joe
      T   Por festre . . . Por char u os corumpue
      X   Of a fistule springing in the cheke bon

52.   S   De dolore dentium mitigando
      Sl2   De la dolor des denz et des gencives
      Sl3   Encontre la dolor des denz
      T   A dolur de[s] denz
      X   Of akyng of teth

53.   S   Ad pustulas diversas qui in facie oriuntur
      Sl2   As bruis qui naissent en la face [+ supplementary rubrics]
      Sl3   Des brues de la face [+ supplementary rubrics]
      T   As borbelettes ke avenunt en la face . . . De le cure devez faire por impetigo
            . . . Por oster serpigo . . . morphé blanche e neire . . . morphé neire
      X   Of doyng away of knwrzes in the visage . . . Of morphues and tetturs in the
            visage

54.   S   De doloribus in auribus et cura earundem
      Sl2   De la dolor qui vient el l'oreille . . . Pren aluine, calamente et eure savine
      Sl3   De la dolor des oreilles
      T   Por dolur des orailles
      X   ch. om.

55.   S   Ad vermem in auricula occidendum
      Sl2   –
      Sl3   –
      T   Por oscire vermine e hors metre . . . De verme ke est dehors
      X   ch. om.

56.   S   De quolibet alio in auricula habendo
      Sl2   –
      Sl3   De feve ou de pierre en l'oreille . . . Explicit la premere partie de ceste
            cyrurgie

    T   Se fev u peire u achune autre chose [. . .]
    X   ch. om.

BOOK II

1.   S   De vulneribus que fiunt in collo, ense vel alio simili
    Sl2 [A]laticor traitent en cest leu des plaies . . . De la plaie du col qui est fete d'espee
    Sl3 De la plaie de col faite d'espee ou de tel chose
    T   Des (MS Del) plaies del col
    X   Of disjoyning of the necke [new material]
         Of woundys made in the necke with a swerde and the cure of hem

2.   S   De vulneribus que fiunt in collo sagitta vel alio telo
    Sl2 Du col qui est plaiez tot outre de saiete
    Sl3 Du col percié tout outre de saiete ou de dart
    T   Si le col seit percié
    X   Of a wounde made throwȝ þe necke with arwe, dart or qwarell

3.   S   De vulneribus que fiunt in cervice cum ense vel aliis similibus
    W   De vena organica
    Sl2 – [supplementary rubrics]
    Sl3 De la vaine contreval trenchié du col d'espee [+ supplementary rubrics]
    T   De plaie en la atherel
    X   Of a wounde in þe natrelle of þe hede wher throwȝ vena organica is cutt asundr

4.   S   De eodem vulnere si organica vena non incidatur
    Sl2 –
    Sl3 –
    T   –
    X   incl. in 3 above

5.   S   De vulnere in cervice facto sagitta
    W   De vena perforata
    Sl2 Se dart ou saiete est fichiee en haterel
    Sl3 De saiete ou de dart fichié ou haterel
    T   Si le quarel seit afiché en la haterel
    X   incl. in 3 above

6.   S   De vulnere gutturis vel trachee arterie
    Sl2 Se la gorge est plaiee
    Sl3 De plaie faite en la gorge
    T   Por plaie en la corge
    X   Of a wounde in the throte

7.   S   De apostematibus circa collum et in cervice nascentibus
    Sl2 Tot autre sicomme diverses humors sunt en cors d'omme
    Sl3 Des apostumes

	T	De superfluité des humurs
	X	Of apostemes with here tokennes

8. S De cura apostematis quod fit ex sanguine
   W Maturativum in causa sanguine
   Sl2 –
   Sl3 Contre apostume de sanc
   T –
   X incl. in 7 above

9. S De cura antracis vel carbunculi
   Sl2 –
   Sl3 De entrace ou carbonele [sic]
   T De aposteme ke est apelé antrax
   X Of felowns and carbuncles . . . Of hote fyrie enpostemes [new material]

10. S De cura apostematis quod fit de colera rubea
    Sl2 –
    Sl3 Contre apostume de rouge cole
    T Autre aposteme . . . Por ameurer l'aposteme
    X ch. om.

11. S De cura apostematis quod fit ex fleumate
    Sl2 –
    Sl3 – . . . Emplastre pour apostumes
    T –
    X Of postemes gendrede of flewme + 11a Of certayn postemes that are undir the armeholys

12. S De cancro qui fit vicio interiorum vel exteriorum
    Sl2 –
    Sl3 De chancre comment ele vient . . . De chancre du col
    T Cancre ke aveint au cors des humurs . . . Oignement
    X Of kankers gendride inwarde and outwarde

13. S De scrofulis [et] glandulis circa collum et cervicem
    W De glandulis [extra material] + Differentia inter scrop[h]ulas et glandulas
    Sl2 A la foiz avient que boces naisent eu col qui sunt apelé (es) escroeles [+ supplementary rubrics]
    Sl3 Des escroelles [+ supplementary rubrics]
    T Des escroelles ke naissent en la gule . . . De tailliure . . . De superfluité des humors . . . Des apostumes
    X Of heling of glandules and scropules . . . Of helyng of scropules and wex kirnelles grete

14. S De fistula et cura eiusdem circa collum nata
    Sl2 Festre est une apostume qui a l'antree par defors est estroite e lee par dedenz
    Sl3 De flestre comment el est guerie . . . D'oignement precieus a flestre

      T   De festre . . . Oignement
      X   Of fistules with her diversites

15.   S   De cura bocii sine incisione
      Sl2 [B]ocion vient a la foiz desou la gole au quel tu feras cest espriment
      Sl3 De la cure de bociun sanz trenchier
      T   De bocium . . . De une boce tant sulement
      X   Of helyng of a pestelence botche

16.   S   De squinancia et quot sint eius species et que curabilis sit an non
      Sl2 Squinancie est uns apostumes
      Sl3 De squinancie
      T   De squinancie
      X   ch. om.

17.   S   De cura eiusdem a principio
      Sl   De cura sinantie
      Sl2 –
      Sl3 see above + Emplastre a squinancie
      T   –
      X   ch. om.

18.   S   De branciis interius tumentibus
      Sl2 A la foiz avient que les joues enflant dedenz
      Sl3 Des joes emflees par dedenz
      T   Des apostumes ke emflent dedensz
      X   ch. om.

19.   S   De cura uvule
      W   De passione epiglotti [new material] . . . De passione uve [new material]
      Sl2 A la foiz la luiete alonge et emfle
      Sl3 De la cure de la luete
      T   De emflure ke uvule (MS mule) est apelé
      X   ch. om.

20.   S   De disiunctura colli a capite
      Sl2 De l'os de la joe qui est issuz de son liu
      Sl3 De la desjointure du col
      T   De jugulare (MS tragulare)
      X   ch. om.

BOOK III

1.   S   De vulneribus que fiunt in homoplatis ense vel telo
      Sl2 De plaie qui est fete d'espee ou de tel chose
      Sl3 Des plaies faites es espaules d'espee
      T   Des cures homoplatis . . . De plais ke avenunt as homoplates
      X   Of woundes whech ar in the ovir part of schuldre bladis if thei be made
           with swerde or any such wepyn

2.   S   De vulneribus que fiunt in cathena gule
     Sl2 La chaiene de la gole
     Sl3 De la plaie qui est faite en la channole du col
     T   De la chaene de la gule
     X   Of woundes which be made in the chien of þe necke

3.   S   De ruptura eius con vulnere vel sine vulnere
     Sl2 Se li os qui est en la chaiene de la gole est brisiez
     Sl3 De l'os du col brisié
     T   De frainture
     X   Of breking of the chien of the necke with a wounde or withoute wounde

4.   S   De vulneribus que fiunt in humero quando disjungatur a superioribus
     Sl2 – . . . Se l'espaule n'est mie desjointe
     Sl3 A ce meismes
     T   De la disjungture de l'espaude (MS des espaude) . . . Si l'espaude n'est pas
         desjont
     X   Of woundyng of the schuldir with disjoynyng of hem

5.   S   De vulneribus brachii quando nervus est incisus
     Sl2 Se li os de braz et li nerf soient tranchié
     Sl3 De l'os du braz et du nerf trenché [+ supplementary rubrics]
     T   De l'os u le nerf del brace que est taillé
     X   Of hurting of þe arme with cutting of a senowe or ellis the bone

6.   S   De inflatione et duricie nervorum
     W   De dolore, inflatione, tumore et duricie nervorum
     Sl2 Se li ners sunt enflé . . . Pren racine de wismalve
     Sl3 De nerf emflé et dur . . . Comment diaute est faite [displaced to after 19]
     T   De dolur u de emflure u de duresce
     X   ch. om.

7.   S   De purificatione vulneris putrefacti
     Sl2 Se la plaie est malvesement curee si qu'elle porrist
     Sl3 De la porreture de la plaie [displaced to after 19]
     T   Si la plaie est malement sané
     X   Of rotyng of a wounde aftir that it is healyde

8.   S   De superflua carne a vulnere removenda
     Sl2 A morte char qui vient en la plaie
     Sl3 De morte char
     T   Si mavaisse char surveint as plaies
     X   Of removing away dede flesch from a wounde

9.   S   De herisipila superveniente vulneri
     Sl2 Por erispila, ce est feu ardant qui vient en la plaie . . . Pren un pastel
         d'estoupes, si le moille el jus de jubarbe
     Sl3 De erisipila
     T   De heresipilia . . . Por faire la char venire as plaius

  X Of herisupilla commyng upon a wounde . . . [IXa] Of restoryng of flesch in
    a wounde

10. S De carbunculo superveniente vulneri
  Sl2 Si carbonculus vieigne (MS meigne) en la plaie . . . Oingnement
  Sl3 De carbonele en plaie [in list of contents]
  T De carbunculo . . . Oignement a carbunculo
  X Of a carbuncle commyng upon a wounde

11. S De vulneribus brachiorum si os non est lesum nec nervus
  W De carnositate brachii vulnerata ita quod nec os nec nervus [. . .]
  Sl2 Plaie du braz
  Sl3 Du braz plaié sanz nerf
  T De la charnoseté del braz u entre l'espaude
  X Of wounding of the arme if þe bone be not hurt ne senewe

12. S De eodem si lacertus est lesus con nervo vel sine eo
  Sl2 Plaie de braz
  Sl3 Du braz plaiés avec le nerf
  T De la plaie del braz od sun nerf
  X Of hurting of the bught of the arme

13. S De eodem si telo est perforatum
  Sl2 Plaie de braz
  Sl3 Du braz plaiez de dart tout outre
  T Del braz ke est percé de dart
  X Of wounding þorwe þe arme with arwe, darte or qwarell

14. S De vulneribus manus si os est incisus vel nervus
  Sl2 Se li os et li ners sunt tranchié . . . Contre membre bleciez
  Sl3 De plaie de main quant l'os ou li ners est trenchiez
  T De taillure de la main
  X Of woundyng of þe hande if senowe or bone be hurt therwith

15. S De eodem si nullum illorum est lesum
  Sl2 incl. in above
  Sl3 Du menbre blecié
  T De la blesceur del menbre
  X Of brusing of þe membris throwgh fal or stroke

16. S De disjunctura humeri a superioribus
  Sl2 S'il avient que espaule soit desjointe [+ supplementary rubrics]
  Sl3 De l'espaule desjointe
  T De l'espaude ke est desjunte . . . Por metre le espaude en sun liu
  X ch. om.

17. S De disunctura cubiti
  Sl2 Se l'os del coute soit issuz de son lieu
  Sl3 De la desjointure du coute
  T –

X   Of disjoynyng of the bon that lieth in the elbowe

18.   S   De disjunctura manuum et digitorum
      Sl2   Se la mains est dejointe de son lieu [+ supplementary rubrics]
      Sl3   De la dejointure de la main et des doiz
      T   De la [de]jungture del main
      X   Of disjoynyng of the hande
            [18a] Of febillyng of membris to restor hem ageyn [new material]
            [18b] Of wronge setting in the joynt to sette it right [new material]

19.   S   De ruptura brachii sine ruptura carnis
      Sl2   incl. in above
      Sl3   De la briseure du braz et de l'espaule [+ supplementary rubrics]
      T   De l'os del braz u de l'espaude hors issu . . . De la frainture de l'os . . . De la
            fermure . . . De l'os ke ne est pas adrescé
      X   ch. om.

20.   S   De cancris, fistulis et apostematibus in brachiis nascentibus
      Sl2   Si cranque ou festre neisse en cest liu de la plaie et de la briseure
      Sl3   De chancre ou de flestre en cest leu neisent
      T   De festres u de cancres . . . De cancre sanz blesceure
      X   Of fistules and cankers breding in þe armes

21.   S   De vulnere thoracis et pectoris con ense vel alio simili
      Sl2   Se la plaie est faite en la chanole del col ou el piz
      Sl3   De plaie qui est faite en la channole du col ou ou piz
      T   De plaie en la forcele
      X   ch. om.

22.   S   De eodem facto con telo sive ferrum lateat interius sive non
      Sl2   Se aucuns fers est remés dedenz le piz
      Sl3   ch. om.
      T   Dedenz la substance de la forcele
      X   ch. om.

23.   S   De cura rupture costarum
      Sl2   De la coste ploiee par dedenz
      Sl3   De la coste plaiee la cure
      T   De la costee ke est plaié dedenz
      X   Of bresting or bowyng in of the ribbes

24.   S   De vulneribus quibuslibet a furcula pectoris ad inguinem
      Sl2   Se la plaie est entré en l'autre partie del cors
      Sl3   Des plaies faites de la forcele jusque as aynes . . . Du fer qui est entrez ou
            piz la cure
      T   Quant la plaie aveint en aucune partie del cors
      X   ch. om.

25.   S   De vulnere cordis, pulmonis, diafragmatis, epatis et stomachi

S12   Se li cuers ou li foies ou li pomons ou li vantrals ou la diaframe sunt plaiez . . . A la foiz li foies ist fors parmi la plaie

S13   De la plaie du cuer et du polmon . . . De la plaie de la ratele . . . Du foie quant il ist fors de la plaie

T   De plaie del quer u del pulmon . . . De l'esplein . . . De la (de la) foie ke est par estroite plaie

X   Of wounde of the herte, lunges, midryve and stomac . . . Of woundyng of the mylte

27.   S   De vulneribus intestinorum et si quod foras exierit qualiter ad suum locum est reducendum

S12   Se aucuns boiaus isse parmi la plaie

S13   De la plaie dont li boel issent fors

T   Des entrailles ke issent (MS est) par estroite plaie

X   Of woundyng of þe bowellys and goyng out of hem

28.   S   De fistulis, cancris et apostematibus ab homoplatis ad inguinem nascentibus

S12   Si festre ou cranque ou apostume naist en cest lieu, tu le guerras sicum nos avons enseignié devant [+ supplementary rubrics]

S13   De flestre et d'apostume en tel lieu [+ supplementary rubrics]

T   De festres e de cancres ke aven[en]t en cel liu . . . De cancre que avent as mameles . . . Achune foiz le chef de mamel est dedenz turné

X   Of fistules, cankers and postemes growyng in þes forsaide places . . . Of cankir beyng in womans tetes . . . Of aposteme in the tetes

29.   S   De vulneribus genitalium et cura eorum

S12   ch. om.

S13   De plaie de menbre d'omme et de la coille

T   Plaie sur le menbre, de cousture

X   Of wounding of the yerde or of the coddes

30.   S   De cancris, fistulis et aliis pustulis in genitalibus consurgentibus

S12   Se cranque nesse en cest lieu . . . Se li coillons sunt escorchié

S13   De chancre ou menbre de l'omme . . . De l'emfleure [et] de la rougor des coillons

T   Si cancre aveint al vit de l'home . . . Si le festre avent a l'avant (MS le vant) dit menbre . . . A le emflure dé coiz e eschorjeur

X   Of a cankyr beyng in a mannys ȝerde . . . Of swelling of the coddys

31.   S   De ruptura sifac sive sit magna sive parva

S12   Syfas

S13   De la routure de sifac

T   De siphac e de osceum . . . De rupture grande u petite . . . De rupture de siphac

X   Of tokenes of bresting of the syphac

32.   S   De cura rupture sifac con ligatura

S1   De cura eiusdem et ligatura per incisionem et incensionem

S12   De la routure qui est petite e novele . . . A la foiz la routure est petite

S13   incl. in above + De la cure par taillier et par ardoir . . . De ce meismes

    T –
    X –

33. S   De eodem si intestina in osseum ceciderint
     Sl2 Se li boiel chieent en la coille
     Sl3 Des boiaux qui chient en la coille
     T   Si le[s] boelle[s] cheent en osceum
     X   –

34. S   De hernia ex humoribus consurgente
     Sl2 Se la coille est enflee
     Sl3 De la hergne qui vient du mors
     T   ch. om.
     X   Of hernia aquosa or humorosa

35. S   De hernia que fit ex carnositate
     Sl2 De charnosité que se norrist delez le coillon
     Sl3 De la hergne de char
     T   De la maladie ke est apelé hernia
     X   Of hernia carnosa

36. S   De signis lapidis si fuerit in vesica
     Sl2 Se pierre est faite en la vesie
     Sl3 Du signe de la pierre en la vessie
     T   Quant la pere est en la vessie
     X   Of knowing of the ston be certayn tokens whedir it be in the bleddir or not

37. S   De lapide removendo a collo vesice
     Sl2 Se la pierre est el col de la vesie
     Sl3 De la pierre ou col de la vessie
     T   Deliverer la pere as funs (MS fans) de la vessie
     X   Of removing awey of the ston fro þe necke of the bleddir

38. S   De lapide abstrahendo a vesica
     Sl2 incl. in above + De morte char qui naist el col
     Sl3 De la pierre oster par taillier . . . La morte char qui est ou col de la vessie
     T   Por la pere hors traire
     X   Of drawing out the stone fro the bledder

39. S   De vulneribus que fuerint in posteriori parte hominis con lesione spinalis
          medulle vel nervi
     Sl2 Se plaie est faite entor le fondement
     Sl3 De la plaie faite entor le fondement
     T   De plaies ke avenunt al cors
     X   Of woundyng of the ryggebone in soche maner that the margh go oute
          therof

40. S   De cura longe si telo vel ense ledatur
     Sl2 S'il avient que longaon (ou) soit plaié de lonc d'espee
     Sl3 De la plaie de longaon

     T   Si le longaon est plaié
     X   ch. om.

41.   S   De vulnere renum
     Sl2   S'il avient que petit plaie [MS a. petit que plaie] soit faite en reignons
     Sl3   De la plaie du roignon
     T   De plaies as reins . . . Aposteme de carbunculo
     X   Of wounding of the reynes

42.   S   De fistulis et cancris in hiis locis nascentibus
     Sl2   Si flestre nesse en cel lieu
     Sl3   De flestre en ce lieu . . . D'apostumes entor le fondement
     T   –
     X   ch. om.

43.   S   De emorroidis
     Sl2   Emorodes
     Sl3   Des emoroides
     T   Cure des emerodes . . . U les emerodes sunt engrossi
     X   ch. om.

44.   S   De vulneribus pectinis
     W   De stranguria vesice ex vulnere pectinis
     Sl2   –
     Sl3   De stranguine
     T   De la grevance del penil (MS pis) [+ supplementary rubrics]
     X   ch. om.

45.   S   De cauteriis
     Sl2   –
     Sl3   Des cuitures
     T   Por quiturus a cors de l'home
     X   ch. om.

BOOK IV

1.   S   De vulneribus vertebri vel scie
     Sl2   Si plaie soit en l'os de la hanche qui est reons d'espee
     Sl3   De plaie de hanche faite d'espee
     T   A [l'os des] reins ke est apelé vertebrum
     X   Of woundis made in the wirleboon

2.   S   De vulneribus que fiunt in coxa ense vel alio simili
     Sl2   Se plaie soit faite en la cuisse
     Sl3   De plaie de cuise faite d'espee
     T   Por plaie en la quise
     X   Of woundyng of the thee with a swerde

3.   S   De eodem si fuerit con telo

Sl2 incl. in above
Sl3 incl. in above
T Si la quise est plaié de quarel
X incl. in above

4. S De vulneribus genuum sive patella sit incisa sive non
    Sl2 Se plaie est faite el jenoil
    Sl3 De plaie faite ou genoul
    T De plaie au genul
    X Of woundyng of the knee

5. S De eodem si fuerit con telo
    Sl2 incl. in above
    Sl3 Du fer oster de la paelete du genoul
    T Por quarel ke seit afiché
    X ch. om.

6. S De vulneribus cruris quocunque modo factis
    Sl2 A la plaie de la cuisse enseignons nos
    Sl3 A toutes plaies de cuisses
    T Des plaies de la jambe . . . Si la jambe seit perscé de quarel
    X ch. om.

7. S De vulneribus pedis con lesione nervi vel sine lesione eiusdem
    Sl2 incl. in above
    Sl3 De la plaie faite ou pié
    T –
    X ch. om.

8. S De disjunctura coxe a superioribus
    W De vertebro
    Sl2 Se li os de la hanche isse hors
    Sl3 Desjointure de hanche
    T Por le os ke est apelé vertebrum
    X Of disjoynyng of the hyppe

9. S De ruptura eiusdem con vulnere vel sine vulnere exteriori
    W De coxis
    Sl2 Se l'os de la cuisse est rout
    Sl3 De la cuisse route
    T Si le os de la quise seit debrisé
    X Of breking of the thee bone

10. S De disjunctura cruris a coxa
    Sl2 ch. om.
    Sl3 De la desjointure du genoul
    T Si genul seit dejointe
    X ch. om.

11. S De fractura cruris con vulnere et sine vulnere

Sl2   Por cuisse brisee
Sl3   ch. om.
T   Si la jambe seit debrisé od la char
X   Of bresting of the legge with hurting of þe flesch + Of helyng of a mormale
       and the cause therof [new material]

12.   S   De disjunctura pedis
       Sl2   Por pié desjoint
       Sl3   De la desjointure du pié
       T   Si le pé est dejoint
       X   Of disjoynyng of the fote or of the tees of hem

13.   S   De disjunctura digitorum
       Sl2   incl. in above
       Sl3   Du doit du pié desjoint
       T   Si les ortilles seint dejoint
       X   incl. in above

14.   S   De fistulis et cancris in hiis locis nascentibus
       Sl2   A la foiz avient que cranque ou festre naist en ce lieu . . . Encontre cranque
              qui croit sur l'os
       Sl3   De chancre et de flestre
       T   Des cancres e festris ke avenunt (MS aveint) a la fez en memes ces l[i]us
       X   Of cankers growing in thes places

16.   S   De pustulis et rupturis carnis que fiunt in cruribus
       Sl2   Se burues et escorcheures naissent es cuisses
       Sl3   De berues et d'escorcheure de cuisses
       T   De burbletes e de rupturus
       X   ch. om.

17.   S   De cauteriis que fiunt contra sciaticam passionem
       Sl   De cauteriis que fiunt in coxa et crure et pedibus
       W   De cauteriis in cya
       Sl2   Por l'asoagement de tot le cors fai .iii. cuitures en la jambe . . . Contre
              artetique
       Sl3   De goute de hanches . . . De cuitures pour assoagier tout le cors
       T   A sciatiche faites trois quiturus . . . Por gute artetiche
       X   ch. om.

18.   S   De combustione quocunque modo contingat
       Sl2   Contre arsure de membres
       Sl3   Contre arsure de fu et d'eue
       T   Por arsure
       X   ch. om.

19.   S   De lepra et quot sint eius species et quibus nominibus vocentur
       Sl2   Li sines par coi on doit conoistre le lieprus . . . Des .iiii. humors de liepre
              . . . Contre elephancie
       Sl3   De meselerie ou de liepre . . . Emplastre ou oignement

```
        T    De lepre
        X    ch. om.

20.     S    De spasmo vulneri superveniente
        Sl2  Contra spamus
        Sl3  De spasmes
        T    Por crampe ki avent
        X    ch. om.

[Mor mal]
        Sl2  Milmors
        Sl3  De mort mal
        T    Por la maladie que est apelé malum mortuum . . . Del limazun
```

TEXT

[BOOK I]

[f. 240r] [I] *De tote manere de plaies ke avenent al chef.* A feiz avent que li chef est plaié en plusurs maneirs; auchune feiz od la despesceur del test, auchune feiz sanz despesceur del test. La* despesceur del test est achune fie grande e aperte, achune feiz petite. Meis quant* [est] petite u grande, l'une est od graunde e large plaie e l'autre est od petite [e] estroite plaie. La despesceure del test quaunt aveint ele od la blesceure des toies del cervel est tutdis a criendre, kar alchune feiz est blescé la toie que defent le cervel del* test, que est apelé la dure meire, auchune feiz la teie que est sur le cervel, que est apelé la pie mere. Si la dure mere est blescé, ceo est la toie que defent le cervel del test, par ces signes le devez saver: la teste del plaié li doit duler, la face li doit roger, la veine des oiz li deit reesuer, e la lange li doit tote nercir. Enaprés quaunt la pie mere est blescé, ceo est la toie que est sur le cervel, par ces signes le devez cunustre: li naffré reevera, e sa voiz [f. 240v] li esgrevera que a peines parler pura, borbletes* li survendrunt en la face, e al commencement li doit core hors des orreales e des narrilles sanc e pureture, e si deit estre costivé, e pus ensuit, ceo que pis est, que li* plaié doit trembler troi[s] feiz u quatre* le jor, car ceo est certein signe de mort. Enaprés de trestuz icels, des quels ces signes que dit avum avendrunt, u si autres signes plus i avenunt, deveit[z] la mor[t] de cel attendre al plus jesque a cent jors. E pur ceo que de la despesceur del test auchune feiz en aveint la mort, dirrum avant par ordre coment hom poeet aideir a la despesceure del test.

[II] *De la depesceure del tes.* Quant la despescure del test est grande e aperte, sicum d'espee u de achune arme, issi que os u autre chose i deve estre fors treit, si mult sanc nel desturbe, u os u altre chose que deit estre trait hors, tut meintenant le trai[e]z hors e un drap de lin mult delié entre le test e la dure meire cointement en escleng metez dedenz. E dedenz le pertuz de la depesceure del test metez un drap de lin, u de soie* que mult melz vaut, issi que le[s] cheis del drap [f. 241r] de totes pars desuz le test seint mis proveablement, que la poreture que decurt des parties dehors ne decurge a la teie que dure meire est apelé e ensi blesce le cervel plus que ainz blescé ne fud. De l'espunge de la meir ben lavé e sechié poot hom meimes ceo faire, car ele, sicom la cose que mut beit, receit la pureture que cheit de[s] parties dehors. *Por empleir la plaie*: Tote la plaie seit emplie de peices linges u d'estupes que seint mis en albun d'oef e un plumaceol seit surmis*, e por la diverseté de la partie del chef cointement seit mis desure. E en iver soit la plaie dous feiz remuee e en esté troiz foiz, char en esté naist plus tost pureture en la plaie que en iver. *Loez le naffré*: Si devez loer al naffré que il gise de cele part dunt se dolt*, que les homurs

que decurrent a la tei que dure mere est apelé ne la blescent. E ceste cure deit
home faire jesque al plen reparraillement del test.

[III] *Por morte char*. Si il aveint que devant le reparrailement del test auchune
maleveise char e mort surcresse la teie que dure mere est apellé, l'esponge de la
mer, mult* ben [f. 241v] lavee mes ben secchié, metez desure, que par sa sause
mangusce la morte [char]. E tant metez la desure que tote la maufaisse char seit
amortie. *Por morte char*: [A]prés, si aveint que aprés le parraillement del test
malvaise char surcresse le test reparrallié, si metez seurement la pudre des hermodacles. Si deveiz garir la plaie dehors od sul drap linge u od cotun que res [est] de
[d]rap linge que est apelé charpie. *De la soudure de la plaie*: [E]naprés la soudure de
la plaie deveiz mettre sure le a[n]trait cirugien qui e[st] dit apostolicon, que si doit
estre fait: Pernez la peiz navaile, ceo est la neire peize, dimie livre, de sarapino,
armoniaco e opopanac uelment unce demie, de cire unce trois, de vin egre livre
demie.

[IV] E faites issi la confectiun*: Metez le vin egre en un* veissel d'estaim* od les
gumes devant dites, que ne deivent* pas estre tribleiz, ceo est asaver od galbano,
armoniac*, serapino e opapanac e la peiz navele, ceo est la peiz neire, [e] soi[en]t
mis od la sire sur le fue por fundre. E quant il serunt fundu, si meteiz un poi en
euue freide, e com ele devendra* tenve e sa culur muera, si metez peiz grec en la
grandur que devant dit avum, que seit triblé en puldre [f. 242r] od mastic e od
olibano uelement unce dimie e so[i]ent [mis] od les devant dites choses al vessel
estainé. E bein soient meu, que ben seint entremeszlez. E quant il devendra de
culur suzpale en culur citrine, si est signe que ben est quit. E dunc ostez le vessel
del fue e metez un unce dedenz de terebentine e amiablement le movez, que bein
se seint pres ensemble e entremetlez. E puis parmi un sac de drap linge le colez sur
eue freide, e voz* [meins] oignez d'olie lau[r]in u de autre liquor, e pois l'eschaufez
al fue e* mulez*, que le eue en seit issue e que vus en peuisiez* faire une ronde
confection que li especier apellent macdalions. Si cest entrait que est apelé cirurgicum apostolicum valt mult a l'esplein e a l'oinnier de l'os de* la plaie aprés la
soudure. E valt mult encontre la dolur del pisz e la depesceure.

[V] *Por asaier la grandure de la plaie*. [S]i la depesceure del test est grande e la plaie
desure estroite, si que vus nen poeez [estre] del tut certefié de sa graundur ne de la
pesceur del test, en la plaie devez belement mettre votre doi e asaieir* la depesceur
del test dedenz, kar e[n] nule manier ne put hom si ben asaieir la depesceur del test
cum al tastir del doi, e pois que saverez* la grandure de la depesceure, e en quele
manere e en quele part [f. 242v] le test est plus pescié, s[i] tailliez la plaie en croiz
od un rasor e* od auchun ostil cirugien si deseverez le quir del test. Si trop grant
sanc nel desturbet e si mestere est que os i deit* estre hors treit, si le treiez hors od
unes teneilles que soient a cel oes aparailliez. E s'il aveint que sanc li desturbe mult
u autre chose, ja seit ceo que par vostre* franchise en aiez pitié*, les choses que
funt a oster [ostez] sanz demorance. E un drap linge en esclenge entre le test e la
teie que est apelé dure meire od une penne dedenz metez. E totes les choses que
nus avum devant enseinnié si devez faire en la cure del test. E quant les [es]char-

neures s'entretienent* e sunt emsemble print, emplez tote la plaie dehors le test
d'un drap linge delié e blanc mis en albun d'oef e pois auches entre voz* meins
enprient. E devez bein espurgier* la plaie, que meuz peuissiez saner* la bleseure del
test. E si mestieirs est, les peices del quir que sunt sur le test deseverez e plaiez
aneire. E anaprés emplez la plaie en mi liu del pluimal de drap cum dit avum. E en
croiz sicum la plaie est talie metez un autre grant plumail dunt tote la plaie soit
coverte desure. E puis la liez e issi la leissiez del [f. 243r] matin jesque al vespre u
del vespre jesque al matin. E quant vus vendrez pur la plaie remuer e verrez les
peices del quir del test emfliez e accrés, si deveiz saver que ceo est bone signe. E si
vus le[s] trovez ausi cum amenuseez e amorties, si devez saver que ceo est mal signe.
E ceste cure devez faire dehors la plaie jesque vus vei[e]z que li test se soit reparrillé
e* asané*, e dunc laissiez* le drap e forciez le[s] peices del quir del test revenir el
liu u il devant furent, e issi le garrez jesque a la fin od drap linge u od carpie. E bein
devez saver que [en] les plaies de la pesceure del test le secunde jor ne le tierz* n'i
metum si drap nun ne nul oignement ne nule oigteuse chose. Mais quant la plaie
est atornee a garrir, si i devez mettre apostolicum cirugicum sur mol quir.

[VI] *Por estre certifié si la test est fendue ou nun.* [A]uchune feiz aveint que le test est
blescé en semblaunt de fenture, issi que cele part que* est blessé n'est plus haute
ne plus basse ne la blesceure ne put estre plus aparceu de cele part u la bleseur n'est
mie, e si cele fenture peirce* le test, ne pot pas legerement estre aparceu. Meis pur
estre de ceo certifié doit le naffré tenir sa buche e ses narrilles a sei, que aliene ne
s'en isse* e en re[f. 243v]tenant sa aliene suffler. E si fumee en ist par la fenture,
idunc saciez que le test est blescé jesque al cervel, e pois devez* li naffré issi garir.
De estroite plaie: [S]i la plaie est estroite, si l'eslargissiez e si sanc ne le desturbe u
autre chose, meintenant la garras. Dejuste la feinture d'ambesdeus parz parceras le
test par graunt queintise d'un ostil que est fest cum un perçur que est apelé
trepacium, e faites pertuz de une part e de autre tant cum vus verrez que mesteirs
est. Enaprés tailliez le test de l'un pertus a l'autre od un cisol cirugien que est a cel
oes fait que est apelé spatumini, que jesque al chef de la fenture vienge la taillure,
que vus puissiez hors traire la pureture que chauz est sur le cervel od cotun u od un
drap linge par un[e] penne mis en esgleng entre la teie e le cervel. E a cest plaie
devez meimes la cure faire que nus devant avum dit e siengné.

[VII] *De la depesceur del tes.* [S]i le test est en tele manere pescié qu'il seit deprient
en l'autre partie, que la piece del test ne pust de legier estre osté de cele part en
laquele ele sei teint, parciez le test, e* tanz* pertus i faites cum vus verrez [f. 244r]
que bosoigne est. E enaprés od le cisol e od les autres choses faites la cure sicum dit
est.

[VIII] *Por plaie de l[a] test[e] sanz depesceur del tes.* [S]i il i a plaie en la test[e] sanz
depesceur del test, meintenant emplez la plaie de totes pars de drap linge mis en
albun d'oef e pois print. E si ceo est en iveir, metez i emplastre que est apelé
embroche jesque la plaie quiture. E issi devez faire l'embroke. *A faire embroke:*
[P]ernez la malve que crest en curtil e de l'altre malve e un herbe que est apelé
branca ursina e de la parele e de voluble majore e pestelés ces* herbes bein. E les

folles de totes ces herbes si triblez bein od demie livre d'oint e ensemle le medlés bein. E enaprés metez tus ces choses en un vesel de terre od v[i]n blanc* e od trois unces de farine de frument e deus unces de semence de lin e dous unces de fenoil grece e bein ensemble le medlés e puis le metez sur petite fue lent e movez bein od une esclice. E tant sur le fu le laissez jesque il seit espesceis. E quant il est espessi, si metez en sauf*. E si ceo est en esté, si faites tele embroke.

[IX] Pernez les* fullus d'un herbe que est apellé solatrum, ceo est morele, e de malve une poingnie e depestelés* od trois unces de viel oint [f. 244v] que ne soit mie salé. E poz si pernez solatrum* e memitte, que est apellé celidoine salvage, e si vus ne poez aver memite, si pernez umblicum veneris e cassilaginem e le herbe violete. E ces herbes triblez et pernez hors le jus e metez od le devant dite recepcion e autant de vin* come de jus, e bein le movez e medlez ensemble. E derecheif metez trois unces de farine de frument e trois unces de vert mel e longement le movez od un' esclice sur le fue jesque il seit e[s]pessi, e puis l'ostez del fue e metez en salf. *Autre embroke*: [I]cés embrokes metum nus [as] plaies por le remuement del* tens jesque la plaie quiture, si metum les embrokes eslargiez sur drap linge. E quant la plaie quiture, si metez un drap sech en la plaie jesque la plaie seit desechié. E quant la plaie soit desechié, si metez cotum que est res de drap linge, que est apelé charpie, e aprés quant la char crest, si sustraét* le drap u le cotun. E des icel jor que la plaie comence a quiturer desque ele soit desechié i devez metre un neir oignement que si deit estre fait.

[X] *Oignement a plaie novele.* [P]ernez oile comun e sui de mutun oelement une livere, [f. 245r] e de la peiz neire que est apelé peiz navale dimi livere, de peiz grec unces trois, de cire unces trois, si ceo est en esté, e si ceo est en iver, si metez* unces dous, de mastic, de olibano, armoniaco, galbano, serapino, epopanac, te- rebentina, oelement unce e demie. E ensi le confisez: Metez en une paele d'estaim l'olie e le sui e la peiz neire od les gummes que ne deveint pas estre triblez sicum est galbanum, armoniacum, serapinum, opopanac, si metez sur le fue. Si faites puldre de mastic e de olibano e de peiz grec. E quant le sui e la cire e le peiz od les gummes serunt fundu, puis en movant o l'esclice i metez la puldre. Certein signe de la decoctiun est quant la gute de la decoctium mise sur marbre aeirt al doi e se ne deseivre mie, e quant iceo verrez, si ostez del fue, si metez terebentine e colez parmi un drap e metez en salf. Icest oignement valt a totes plais noveles, si fait nestre bone char, si atrait e fait quiture e si la gette. E des autres choses faites la cure sicum devant avum dite.

[XI] *Por taillure de la plaie.* [D]e ferure avent auchune feiz emflure en la test[e] sanz plaie, auchune feiz od le depesceure del test, auchune feiz sanz depesceure del test. Meis la depesceure del test [f. 245v] auchune feiz est celee a[l] taster. Quant la depesceure del test est aperte, si devez taillier le liu en croiz od un rasur e enaprés faites totes les autres choses que dit avum en la secunde cure del test.

[XII] *Conustre la depesceur del tes.* [S]i la depesceure del test est celee, tele come fenture, par les signes covenables del malade* le devez saver* jesque al quin[t] u al

septime jor, cum quant il [n']ad talent de manger ne* de beivere e malement se
porte e avisonques pisse ne va a sele e ad chalor* de fievre*. Dunc devez saver que
le test est depescé dunt tele doit estre la cure: tailliez la quir en croiz od un rasur e
les autres choses faites par ordre que dit avum en la teirce cure.

[XIII] A estre certein del tes. [Q]uant l'emflure del colp est sanz plaie e sanz entamure del test, par le demustrance del malade le devez conustre jesque al quint jor
u* al setisme, cum si il bein ma[n]gue, e beit, e ben se ad, e bein dort e vait a sele e
ben pisse e est sanz chalor de fievre. Dunc saiez certein que le test n'est mie
entamié e dunc i metez chose que oste le emflure e faites itele embroke. A faire
emplaistre: [P]ernez alonge e vinegre e armoise, rue e comin e cesste embroke metez
sur le emflure dous fez u trois u [f. 246r] quatre u plusurs foiz le jor al plus cha[u]t
que le malades le put suffrir. E si l'emflure ne se seit par cest emplastre reparrilez*,
[si faites] tele embroke: Pernez aloisne, aisil e armaise e la malve comune uelement
une poingné e triblez totes ces choses emsemble. E metez troiz unces de oint e trois
de farine de furment e od vin bein le medlez ensemble. E metez trois unces de mel
e puis le metez al fue e od l'eclice tant le movez que il seit e[s]pessez. E tele
embroke metez sur le emflur jesque il seit torné a maurer*, e enaprés ovrez le liu* u
la quiture plus pent od un ostil que est a cel ois fait, que est apellé sagittella. E tote
la quiture premez* ors od voz meins e, si mestere est, le doi metez dedenz. E les
autres coses faites que sunt aprés dites es* curez des clos* que sunt apostoemes*
apellez.

[XIV] Del plaie del test. [S]i* avent de la plaie de l[a] test[e] que la quir est entamé
od le test* par espee u par acun autre avent[u]re, sicum par colp de peire, issi que le
quir soit depescé u taillé qu'il pende, tailliez le quir parmi desque al test depescié. E
deseverez le quir del test od un ostil cirugien que est apelé rubigo. E jetez en voie
l'os del test e cusez le quir d'ambesdous pars, si comenciez a custre al chef desure e
fetes de une deliee agu[f. 246v]ille le puint od oun file de soie e athachiez bein le
puint desuz le doi e fermez l'autre puint aprés en meimes la maneier e tanz punz
faites par ordre cum vus veirez que mestierz est. E la plaie [desuz] d'ambesdous pars
laissiez overte, que par icés cheneals* peuse la plae plus avenantement garrir. E pus
sur la custure metez un puldre vermel que si doit estre fait.

[XV] A faire pudre ruge. [P]ernez la greinure consoude une unce, boilli une unce, de
peiz grec trois unces, de mastic e d'olibano uelement une demie unce, de sanc de
dragunt e de mumie uelement scruples dous. Trestutes ces choses emsemble triblez
e a oes* le gardez. Icest puldre e[st] bon pur sanc estancher e valt a la enfermure de
l'os e de la char aprés la depesceure e fait tost quir venir sur la plaie. E sur cele
custure devez mettre ceste puldre, sicum dit avum. E sur le pudre metez fulles de
plantaine. E es cheis de la plaie metez une tente e [u]n plumaceol de drap pur
depreendre la por[e]ture que ele decende contreval, e issi purez la plaie garrir plus
avenantement. E la devant dit puldre devez mettre desur dous foiz le jor jesque al
secunde jor que vus verrez que la char i surcresse e s'aferme. Idunc devez [f. 247r]
les poinz de la custure dellier e le fil hors traire e jesque a la parfite sodure de la
plaie le devez saner de drap u de charpie e de autre chose que dit avums. E en la

taillure* que li mires ad tailliez devez mettre un drap sech. E faites les autres choses dedenz le test [e] dehors que dit sunt as autres cures de la pesceure del test.

[XVI] *Al tes de l'os.* [S']il avent que le test seit desevré od le quir, qu'il n'atinge a la partie desuz, icele tantet de l'os devez* oster queintement e feire la cure sicum dit est de autres choses devant, nemés d'itant que le test ne doit estre fendu parmi, que vus pussez metre auchune chose entre le test.

[XVII] *Si il avent ke le quir seit desevré* de l[a] tes[te].* [S']il avent que le quir seit desevré de la test[e] sanz [le test] par plaie u par auchune autre aventure, si devez faire mes[mes] la cure que devant est dite.

[XVIII] *Por plaie de quarel en la face.* [S]i la plaie est en la test[e] devant u derere, issi que la plaie atinge al cervel, mortele chose est. Mes si [la] plaie decent d'amunt contreval, que ele n'ateinge a[l] cervel e par les orailles e les narrilles descende de autre part, [n'est mie mortele chose]. Cele* cure faites de ceste plaie que vus devez faire de celes que sunt avant dite.

[XIX] *Por plaie de la face u del neis.* [f. 247v] [S']il* avent que hom seit plaié en face u el* nes u el livre* u en auchune autre noble partie del cors que deit* estre cusu, al comencement joingnez l'une partie o* l'autre e al sumet del quir al plus deliément que vus poez. Pur tenir melz emsemble le devez custre od un delié aguille d'un file de soie lachant chescun point par sei, issi que l'un soit un poi desevré de l'autre. *Si le neiz est trenché en travers:* [E]naprés, si le neis est trenché od le levre* en travers, si devez checun pecie remettre en sun liu al plus avenantement que vus poez, e devez custre ensemble sicum est devant dite. E devez metre un plumaceol de drap d'ambes pars le nes e com de chevestre metez un apoial por le nes retenir en sun liu, qu'il ne ploie de l'autre part. E si mesters est, metez el nes un estoil, que la quiture meuz se purge par le[s] cheneals [. . .] Meis es lius la li os sunt tendre ne devez pas estoile mettre sicum en* le nes ne les orailles ne les autres menbres semblables a ces, que meimes le chanal se porge. Si devez mettre le vermeil* puldre desure e les autres que sunt dit devant.

[XX] *Por plaie de quarel.* [S]i auchun* est navré de dart en la face prés des nar[f. 248r]railles u juste le oil* u en la joue u en autre liu, issi que le fer seit entré en parfunt u en auchuns deliez e torteillus chaneiails, mes que grant travail* soit, si deveiz vus memes pener e purpenser coment vus pouissiez meuz le fere hors traire. E si le fust est od le fer en la plaie, si metez une tent[e] juste le fust jesque al fer. E quant vus savez que le fust se teint ferm al fer, si movez de poi en poi, remuant le fust od le fer e issi le devez par grant queintise hors traire. E [si] le fer n'at point del fust, si devez saver del navré coment il estut quant il fu naufré, u amunt u aval, u arere u en e[s]clenc. E en tele manere metez la tente* en la plaie e quaunt vus saverez la voie del fer, sil trahés hors. E si il ne put estre hors trait, issi qu'il se soet pris as neirs, meiz est que vus le laissiez, kar mult plaié un[t] retenu le fer en els e pois unt longement vescu. La cure doit estre itele. Quant vus avez le fer hors traite, si fetes un estoil de lard e metez dedeinz la plaie. E si la plaie est issi parfunde que lard n'i suffise a mettre, si faites une tente de drap linge e liez la plaie que la liure comence de[l] liu dunt la quiture deit venir, que si il i a dous pertus, que cele pertus se targe plus [que plus] pent, e* le pertus que desure est soit plus tost afermé. [f. 248v] E en tele manere gise li malades totesveis, que la quiture decure as parties dehors e nient as parties dedenz. E si vus* volez la plaie tost faire quiturer solunc la diverseté del tens, diverses embrekes i metez, l'une en esté, l'autre en iver, cum dit est en la quinte cure del chef. Si facés les autres choses que dites sunt es autres cures. Meis ceo ne seit pas lassié que quant la plaie comence a secher de la quiture e se commencera a fermer, si amenusiez l'estoil solum l'esporgement e la fermure de la plaie.

[XXI] *Por plaie de sete barbelee.* [S]i hom est plaié de saite barbelee, issi le devez hors traire. Vos devez prendre queintement od unes tenailles les eles de la sete barbalee e issi estreindre en retornant e a col de la saete replaer [e] meillez [purrez] aprés hors traire. E si ne la poez issi hors traire, si pernez un chalemel delié de fer u de areim e metre a l'une ele de la saite, issi que vus recevez* l'ele* dedenz le croiz* del chalmel e meimes ceo facés de l'autre part, e issi od grant estudie e od grant entent la saite hors tra[i]re. E meimes ceo poez faire de dous pennes d'oue. E des autres choses devez faire la cure sicum dit est devant. [f. 249r] [J]a soit ce qu'il n'avenge pas sovent que hom soit plaié sur la teste de saite u de chose semblable a sete, tut seit la cure greve, ele* ne* fait pas a trepasser. Quant la seite perce* le chef de l'un part e de l'autre par[t] le test ist hors a vene overte, cum si il avenit que* l'hom fut trait al chef devant e le dart venist hors derere, u trait fust derere e le dart venist hors devant, issi devez faire la cure. Si morteles signes al plaie n'avenunt*, la quir par unt que la sete s'en eist devez taillir, e od un ostiliment cirugien* que est apelé . . . devez le quir desevrer* del test. E si poez percier el test cent pertuz, que le chanel soit covenablement eslargi, e si devez le fer quintement e proveablement hors traire de cele part que vus verez que meilz porat issir. E de l'autre part trai[e]z hors le fust. E enaprés, si la sete u autre dart a ceo semblable ne perce le test de l'autre part e vus vei[e]z ben signe jesque al quint u al setisme jor, sulum le fer u le fust, sicum devant dit avum, devez le quir talier e del test desevrer. E en la devant dit manere devez le test percier od un perceur delié que trepaciun est apellé jesque a cent pertuz, e si devez la saite hors traire. E mei[f. 249v]mes la cure devez faire de cest que devant dit est de la despesceure del test.

[XXII] [A]uchune feiz aveint que del nafrure del cheif sanz depesceure del test u* del quir que li test est plaee dedenz sur le cervel. E par cele plaiure est le cervel desturbé de sun muver sicum a sun endroit mover se deit. Dunt les ovres del cervel* sunt enpescheez issi que le* plaié est en grant travail e en granz batailles en sun* dormant, e qu'il lieve en dormant e prent arme u ce qu'il trove, e si [se] demeine en dormant sicum fust en veillant. La cure deit estre tele sicum dit est desus. Vus devez le quir taillier en croiz* od un rasur [e escharnez] od un ostil cirugien que est rugine apellé. E de ambes partez [de] la plaure percez le test d'un perçur cirugien que est apellé trepacium e tut ceo que ploié est osteiz. E meimes la cure deveiz faire a cete plaie que dit est avant en la cure de la depesceure del test.

[XXIII] [L]a une teingne poeet garrir e l'autre num. La teignee que ne poeet estre garie par ces signes devez conustre. Le quir est divers e dur e met hors de sei muz escheirdes e mangue* les pellez. Icele teigne ne devez pas [f. 250r] recevre en cure. Si metez vostre cure es teignes que poent garir dunt il en i a deus manieres. La une est u muz pei[l]z creissent e uns peilz mult gros e le quir est gros e menu, si n'est mie dur; l'autre, od le quir gros e espés, si n'est pas od grant grature, e auchune foiz quiture. Meis la quele des does que ço seit, teile deit estre la cure. Raeiz primes les chevoilz. E puis pernez d'eleborum blanc unce une, de la peiz navale unce une, d'olie comun unces sis, des nuals autant. E triblez totes ces choses ensemble cum por feire oignement. E si mestiers est, en iver des noiz memes faites oile, si en faites od les choses devant dites oignement. E de cest oignement oig[nez] la teste al* malade noif jorz u unce, u plus u meins, tant cum vus verrez que mester est. E quant vus verrez que li quir serra enmolliz, si esrachiez les peilz od tote la racine*. E la part dunt vus les peilz esraciez [oignez] de* cel oignement. E quant li peil revendrunt, si faites la teste laver de leissive, e [f. 250v] quant li peil serrunt sechi, si oignez la teste d'un oignement que est apelé silotrum e tant le lessiez sur la teste jesque vus peussiez les peiz arachier legirement. A *faire silotrum*: [I]ssi devez feire silotrum. Pernez treis unces de vive chauz e metez en eue boillante e leissiez longement boillir. E metez dedenz dous unces arsenici mis en puldre e faites boillir. De ceste decoctiun est signe que quant la plume est enz mise e vus la traez hors, si poet hom la plume legerement oster. E pus que vus averez od tel oignement les chevoiz osté e [quant] verrez aucune rovor sur le* chef*, si oignez autrefeiz la tegne e memes la chose faites que dite est avant deske nule rovor n'i apirge en la teste. E si cele cure n'i vaut, si faites cest oignement. A *faire oignement [a] teingne*. [P]ernez la semence* de staphisagre une unce, d'ellebre blanc une unce, arsenici, vitreole e d'alum uelement unce demie, galle une unce, e metez totes ces choses en pudre e sis unces d'olie d'olive. E confisez les od une herbe que est apelé flaura e od avrone* salvage u damasche, e od senevé sa[f. 251r]vage que est apelé eruca e fumeteire e od espurge que est apelee titimalle e la lappace ague, uelement une javelee, e pestelez e traieiz hors le jus e medlez od la lie de l'oille, e puiz les metez al fu e faites boillir. E puis metez les avant dites* pudres e mellez ensemble e puis ajustez* trois unces de peiz liquide e de tel oignement oignez la teste. E faites des autres choses la cure sicum dit est en la prescene cure. E s'il i ad mult poiz, si mettez od l'oignement vif argent esteint od sage. E si li liu est velu, si l'oigniez de viel saim* e puis ostez les peiz, e puis si l'oigniez de silotro e faites avant la cure sicum avant dit est. E si la tangne est novele e neint* suranee, sance* arachier les chevoils la devez saner en ceste manire.

[XXIV] *Autre oingnement a tegne*: [P]ernez averone e flaure e senevé salvage e fumetere e armeise uelement une javelee e trib[l]ez bien e metez od oile jesque a trois jorz u, si vus plaist, a oit u plus. E puis boilliez les herbes en memes l'oille e ausi chaut cum le malade le puet suffrir les places de la teste en oignez al matin e al seir. E puis sur les placettes metez ceste pudre que si doit estre fai[f. 251v]te. Pernez staphisagre* e elebre blanc uelement une unce e faites puldre. E de ceste pudre mettez aseiz sur les malans aprés ço qu'il serrunt oint. [A l]a superfluté qui nest en la teste, que cil de Salerne apelent roigne*, devez icel oignement faire. Pernez de vif sufre unces deus, de argent vif unce une, d'ellebre blanc unce une, de comin*, de cheif d'espurge que est apelé staphisagre uelement unce dimie. E tut ço metlez ensemble. E metez od sis unces de oint e quant mestier est, si en oignez la teste. Esprovee chose est que ceste oignement valt a sausefleme e a une maladie qui est apelee malum mortuum e a malencolie, que avent es quises, e a chescune roigne.

[XXV] *Des escrolles ki avenunt en la teste.* Unes superfluitez qui avenent en la teste sunt* apelé escroilles dunt les unes sunt dures e les autres moles. E les unes sunt remuables e les autres nun. De celes que hom puit remuer doit tele estre la cure. Les chiés de la escroile tenez entre voz* deiz forement e li quir sur l'escrolle tailliez en lung e l'escroille pernez, od un cisol ben l'escharniez [f. 252r] e si vus ne poeez la pel aver, si le leissiez. E si ço est en esté, empleez la plaie de drap qui soit mis en albun d'oef, e si ço est en iver, od le moel d'oef. E un jor u deus i metez la puldre des affodilles en la plaie pur purir e manger la pel. Dunt la puldre doit issi [estre] fait. Pernez del juz des affodildis unces trois, de la chauce v[i]ve unces trois, arsenici unce une, e confisez issi. Faites le jus boillir en un pot e metez la chauz dedenz, ben les melez ensemble, e metez el solail e quant il est un poi desechié, sil metez en forme beslunge qui sunt apelé trocissi. E quant ben sunt dessechi, sis metez en sauf. E ceste puldre i devez mettre pur manger la pel de la escroele. E quant vus verrez la plaie emfler, dunc saciez que la pel est mangié. Enaprés devez mettre en la plaie un drap mis en aubun d'oef. E desure metez estupe* od un oef desque vus veez la pel tote aneintie e la plaie quiturer. Puis si faites la cure de la depescure del test. *Autre:* Si l'escroule que hom ne poet pas moveir entechist le quir od le test e espesist en un, issi que la tei que dure meire est apelé soit entechié de meimes le teche, issi [f. 252v] que semblant soit que l'escroelle naisse* del test e de la dure mere, tele serrat la cure. Deseverez tut le quir entur le test* entechi [e] de un perçur cirugien sagement perciez le test e od un cisol tut le test remuez. E por ce que cele ne puet partir de la dure meire si od grant greif nun, e pur ceo que grant peril en poeet avenir, si fait mult a criendre. Pur ceo valt mielz a lassier ceste cure que nus dium avant.

[XXVI] *Al deverie.* [A] la deverie que mania u melancolia est apelee al somet de la teste tailliez le quir en croiz* e bein faites le malade lier al primir. E puis si perciez le test od un ostil qui est trepanum apelé por aventer la materie de la maladie e que ele s'en isse. E la plaie sanez sicum dit est as cures des plaies devant.

[XXVb] *Por gute chaive.* [A] la gute chaive que est epelenpsie apelé faites une quiture al* malade sur le col al chief del test dereir.

[XXVII] E si al malade aveint que li oil li corent* u rogissent, [e] estre nature soent pel en sa papire que aucune foiz li mangusscent e issi funt les oilz lermer, e auchune feiz rogissunt e lerment [f. 253r] e nepurquant as pauperes n'ait nul peil contre nature. Si peilz i sunt, si devez saner al* malade.

[XXVIII] Si les peilz contre nature sunt es paupieres e plus i ait de la char[n]iteure, que li peil ne poent estre veu, si frotez primes les paupieres* dedenz des foilles de paritarie. E cum le sanc serra issu e la char averat seignié, si apparunt li peil. E puis od unes gignes que picicariolis* sunt apelees les devez od totes les racines esrachier. E si ceo est en esté, metez desure aubon* d'oef, e si c'est en iver, de la cire od l'aubun metez. E tant cum li peil iloec naissent devez [issi faire]. [Ceo est] chose esprové . . . [f. 255r] . . . E si mult char i ad, liez les paupires desure, qu'il seunt desure prient. E s'il n'i ad mult char, esrachiez les peilez e frotez les paupiers des devant dites foilles tant qu'il seignent e alez avant en la cure sicum devant dit est. A cel memes pernez les jus del chie[v]refoil e les cimes del buissum e de l'aloisne e medlez od aubun d'oef e od eue rosat e faites come emplastre e metez desure.

[XXIX] Si li oil lerment e rogissent e les peilz estre nature n'i soient pas [es] paupiers, tailliez les veines qui sunt el frunt e es temples. E quant il avront tant seigné cum vus savrez que mestiers est, si perciez la veine, si traeez de l'autre part un autre augule od un fil que a lui se teinge e od memes le fil liez la veine e ben la nuez*, que li sanc n'en isse. En la plaie metez treis jorz lard. Puis si metez dede[n]z char de porc megre salee dis jorz desque la plaie se soit ben espurgié. E quant ele serrat espurgié, si ostez la char e le fil. E puis, si mestiers est, si metez un drap u cotun qui est apelé charpie. Por restreindre les lermes metez le seun* en* la forcele, qui est apelé [. . .], en mi liu de l'oraille u el mol qui est desuz l'oraille. A memes [f. 255v] cest pernez olibanum, c'est gros encens, e mastic e ladanum fundu en chaut marbre od branches de loreir e metez sur les templus e sur les devant dites veines al plus chaut que li malade le poeet suffrir.

[XXX] *Por grature des oiz.* [A] la degrature des oiz oster pernez litargerie unce* demie, olibani e aloen* epatic la quarte partie de une unce. Triblez ces choses mut deliément en puldre e destemprez od olie violat e od jus de memite*, ço est celidoine salvage, e od agresta. E autrefeiz ajustez* oille violet e melez ensemble. E confissez cum oignement [blanc] e, quant mester est, od une penne metez es oilz sicum l'um fait collirie. E si morsure i est u arsure, si faites tel collirie: Pernez litargiri e aloen epatic, si en faites puldre e confiscez issi. Pernez les cimes* del boissun e aloesne uelement e traiez hors le jus e de cel jus e od ewe rosat parfiez les puldres devant dites del jus e de l'eue rosat e[n]tremedlez. E quant mester est, si metez es oilz.

[XXXI] *Por mancher la teie des oiz.* [P]or manger la teie des oiz devez fere tel oignement: Pernez une herbe que est apelé centrum galli e celidoine uelement une [f. 256r] javelé e pestelez bien. E puis lez metez en sis unces d'oli comun e lessiez iloec jesque a sis jorz u a oit u a plus, qu'il soient flaistri. E puis si metez buillir al fu e quant vus verrez que les herbes s'en irrunt al* funt*, dunc l'ostez del fu. E quant il serra bein colé, autrefoiz les metez al fu, si metez une unce de cire. E quant la cire ert fondue, si l'esprovez sur marbre, s'il est bien quit e s'il est un poi tenant. Dunc i metez dous unces del vert d'ereim e a len[t] fu le feites un poi boillir e autrefoiz l'esprovez sur la peire e s'il a verte colur, si l'ostez del fu e metez dedenz dous dragmus olibani triblié en mut delié puldre. E medlez od les devant dites choses e enaprés si metez le puldre de sarcocolle* mut delié dragmes* dous. E derecheif en muvant le metlez ensemble od oli* comun* e al derain totes ces choses metlez bein

ensemble od une esclice od oile comun* e od oculi licii e od aloen epatic, e issi les
metlez ensemble* od les devant dites choses, qu'il soent un poi tenve. E quant il
serrunt bien medlé ensemble, sis colez* parmi un drap e metez en salf. E quant
mester serra, sil metez od une penne delié es chiés des [f. 256v] oilz*. E quant la
teie serra auques degastee, pernez le jus de rue e de une autre herbe que est apelé
ipia, qui a une flur neire vermeille, e le jus d'un verm* qui est apelé pectinem e
metez ensemble en l'oil*. E cel memes verm* est mut bon a autre choses.

[XXXII] Autre* bone puldre por la tei manger. Pernez castore e olibanum e
sarcocolle* uelement dragmes dous e de la semence de champhore dragmes* dous
e de margarites ne mie perciés dragme* une e del vert de l'areint le pesant d'un
dener. E issi faites la confection: Triblez castoire e olibanum, ce est ancens gros, e
sar[c]ocolle e le vert d'areim tut ensemble e metez en un blanc marbre chaut e
[i]loc les demenez desque il soient sechi. E pois les tribliez mut delié e methez ben
ensemble les devan[t] dites puldre[s]. E enaprés les destemprez od ewe rosat en une
esquiele de terre* u en autre liu e ben les medlez. E puis si metez sechir al sola[i]l e
enaprés le tierz jor si destemprez autrefeiz od ewe roset. E faites autrefoiz secchir al
sola[i]l e ceo faites aprés dous jorz troiz foiz. E quant ces choses sunt desechiez e mis
en puldre e mené en un, sis metez en salf. Iceste puldre valt a la teie des oiz oster.

[XXXIII] *Por rugeur des euz.* [f. 257r] [S]i les oiz rogissent de sanc u de aucune autre
achaisun, issi que li oil soient enflé, u si tei[e] i est, tailliez la veine del frunt e li
malade en maniere de chevest[r]e mette sa main el sumet de sun nes e de cele part
que la main est jointe al braz e u li greingnur doit poeet sur le frunt atendre,
poigniez la veine, mes qu'il ait desainz la teste rese. E enaprés mesurez de l'une part
e de l'autre trois dois de la main al malade e merchiez d'ambes parz e de cel signe
qui est sur le oreille jesque al signe qui est sur l'autre oreille merchiez od enke u od
auchune autre chose. Derecheif de cel signe que est sur l'oraille traiez l'autre signe
d'entravers, que doit estre loinz de lui. E faites de l'un signe jesque a l'autre
d'ambesdous parz merc d'enche. E sur le devant dite signe taillez le quir od un ostil
que est apelé sagittella e laissiez la quiture hors cure. E enaprés metez un fer chaut
sur le quir, mes metliez est que les veines soient tailliez que vus devez issi mut
avenantement taillier. Si li malades est si febles qui ne poeet mutes plaies suffrir*,
si merchiez le malade sicum devant dit est. E en la mesure de trois doiz de la main
al malade tra[f. 257v]ez* une ligne od enke d'entravers de l'un signe jesque a
l'autre e tailliez sur le signe. E puis embrasez le* liu od un fer tut ardant. E puis
metez desure un drap mis en albun d'oef jesque le fu soit hors alé e enaprés i metez
autres choses asuageantes* e que repriement l'esbraszement del fu e puis metez
desure un plumaceole. E la liure doit estre semplable a la liure qui enseigné est es
autres parties del cheif. E qua[n]t le fu serra hors issu, si metez desure une corde de
drap e tenez la plaie overte noef jorz u vint. E quant vus osterez la corde, si laissiez
la plaie affermer.

[XXXIV] *Por sanc ke avent en l'oil par blesceure.* [S]i de coup u de autre chose a ce
semblab[l]e avinge sanc en l'oil u emflure dehors, issi devez a l'oil suvenirement
aidier. Pernez cire novele e bele e eschaufez al fu e pernez comin* e tribliez en delié

puldre e medlez od la cire. E cele emplastre* metez desure meintefoiz e sovent. Altre cure a cel memes: Pernez verveine e aloisne e traieiz hors le jus e medlez od ewe rose e metez desure od estupes. E si ceo est en iver, si metez saffran oveoc.

[XXXV] S'il aveint que la pau[f. 258r]piere desuz l'oil covient estre taillié, que auchune feiz aveint par aposteme u plaie desuz l'oil, sur la plaie malement sané le taillez en* esclenc [e] cusez une plateine de plum od la paupiere u soient troiz pertuz. E puis metez un plumaceol en miliu. E puis quant mester est, ostez la plateine e sanez la plaie sicum les autres plaies.

[XXXVI] *Por festre en coste le oil.* [A]uchune feiz est enfestré le liu que est juste l'oil u le nes, issi que de tres petite* plaie ist quiture. Dunc devez l'oil metre* de l'autre part e feire plus large le pertuz, sil devez tailler en droit. E une penne mise en aubun de oef metez jesque as funz de la plaie. Enaprés, si li malades est tendre, par les pertuz metez jesque a[s] funz de la plaie, si vus poez, un chalmel de fer u de araim e parmi memes le chalmel metez un fer ardant por quire les racines del festre. E si li malades crient le fu, si metez dedenz le chalmel une pile que si deit estre feit: Pernez vive chauz e metez en une corde dunt vus devez faire saim qui est apelé capitel[l]um e laissiez ileoc des la tierce ure del jor jesque a vespr[e]s. E puis i metez la penne od aubun de oef jesque le fu decheize e soit hors alé. Enaprés [f. 258v] sil sanez sicum les autres plaies. [O]ignement* rumpant devez issi faire: Pernez capitellum e metez vive chauz dedenz e fundez e metlez cum vus voissez feire oignement. U faites le issi: [Pernez] le gros [encens], sil metlez en puldre od os de chien. E metez od aubun de oef destempré desure* l'aposteme*, ço est clo u qualque maniere d'enflure, e ceo le depescera. E al derain si l'aposteme* est de sausefleume, metez i lancelette triblié od chardun velu.

[XXXVII] *De superfluité ke aveint al nes.* [U]ne superfluité qui aveint al nes sovent est une manire d'aposteme* qui vient dedenz le nes que est apelé polipus. Auchune feiz nen est mie, meis, [sicome] polipus, avient en la plus large partie del nes e sanc [ist] hors auchune feiz e demure sur la livre, dunt cele doit estre la cure. Esrachiez jesque au funz od un ostil cirugien qui est apelé sagittella e la tailliez perfies. E si aucune chose remaint dedenz le nes, si metez une tente od l'oignement rumpant dedenz qui doit estre fait de chauz e de saim sarazin. E enaprés i metez le moel de oef qui soit metlé od oile commun e quant le fu s'en serra issu, sil sanez sicum les autres plaies od oignement vert e od autres choses. *Oignement a ceo memes:* [f. 259r] [P]ernez celidone la racine e d'une herbe qui est apelé aleluia e les foilles centrigalli e luveesche salvage uelment une javelé, e autant d'une herbe que est apelé scabiosa. E triblez ben totes ces herbes od une livre de siu de mutun e od une liv[r]e d'olie e issi les laissiez set jors u noef. E puis les metez en un pot e quisez ben jeske les herbes s'en aillent as funz*. E pois sis colez e* la culure metez en une* chaudire. E si c'est en esté, si metez trois unces de cire e si c'est en iver, si n'i metez point. Mes aprés ce qu'il ert fundu, si metez de la puldre del gros encens e de mastic e del verd de l'araim unce demie, e de aloe epatic mis en puldre e medlé puis od oile comun*. E quant serrat* ensemble ben fundu, puis le metez en sauf. E ben pernez garde, que cest oignement valt a totes plaies e feit bone char venir e mangue la mavaise.

[XXXVIII] E s'il i a nule mavaise char entre les narrilles [. . .] une foiz si metez u dous u trois. E si mestir est, sil curez od chaut fer u od oignement sicum dit est devant en la prescene cure.

[XXXIX] *De polippus ke aveint entre les narrilles.* [U]ne aposteme vent entre les narilles qui est polipus apelé. Le greignur avent entre les nar[f. 259v]illes e crest en grandur e autre[feiz]* decent aval e meine le eir devant sei. De ces sunt dous manires dunt l'une pot hom garrir e l'autre nun. De cele que ne pot estre sanee ces sunt les signes: le liu de l'em[f]lure est neir e le nes est gros e dur e la char ne decent pas contreval. De polipe que pot* estre sané ces sunt les signes: le nes est mol e traitable, que vus poeez par taillier issi saner.

[XL] Pernez meintenant la char od unes deliees tenailles e, tant cum vus poeez, sil traeez aval e si tute* vient, tote la traeez hors. E si ele ne veint tote hors, tant cume hors vient si tailliez. E si ele ne pot par les tenailles estre hors trait, si l'eslargiez od une tente faite de malo terre, que un estrument crois faite cum un rosel qui est fait de fer u de areim pusse estre mis dedenz les narrilles eslargiez. E enbrasét le liu covenablement. E puis metez desure un moel d'oef od oile comun jesque le fu seit issu hors e puis la sanez sicum les autres plaies.

[XLI] E si li maledes dute le chaut fer, metez un estoel de drap qui soiet mis a l'oignement rumpant e metez desure un moel de oef od oile comun. E puis si faites memes les choses que dites sunt en la devant dite cure.

[XLII] *A la feiz aveint polipus au paleis.* [f. 260r] [A]ucune foiz avient polipus par le[s] pertus del palais par la force de nature, que, s'il issi avient, sur aventure le devez mettre e sur la force de nature. E devez al nes mettre une tente de cire por faire la bone char creistre.

[XLIII] *Por emflure del nes ke polipus est apelé.* [A] l'emflure del nes que polipus est apelé saner par arsure vus devez mesurer de la main al malade trois dois [sur] sun frunt* e iloeques li faites quichun en tele maneire que l'arsure del quichun nen vait pas a la char, meis al* suriz* qui est musculus apelez, sicum dit est al chapittle de la rovor des oilz. Puis si faites la cure que est ditte en cel memes traitié.

[XLIV] *Por cancre a narrilles e au paleis e as gencives.* [A]uchune foiz avient le chancre es narrilles e el paleis, auchune feiz as gencives e si mangue le liu u il est e la char dedenz. Si la char est dure, perse e anercie, icel cancre n'est mie legir a garir, meis si la maladie est novele e ne soet pas suranee, si le devez issi garir. A *taillir cancre:* [T]ant come le cancre dure tailliez le tut jesque al vif*. Enaprés od un chaut fer le bruillez e solonc la diversité del tens, sicum dit est, le devez saner od un muel de oef que vus metrez sure. E s'il aveint qu'il ait man[f. 260v]gé les livres u les narrilles, tut le menbre pori desque al vif* tailliez e puis sil sanez avenantement. E quant il aveint al palais, que suvent avient, si l'ardez d'un chaut fer u d'or chaut. S'il avient es gencevus, lavez primes le liu od vin egre e trois jors le frotez od alum e puis le lavez d'un lavore que zemarinum est apelé, que si doit estre fait. Pernez vin quit u miel* od eisil uelement e boilliez en cest les racines d'une herbe que est apelé tapsus barbastus e de chevrefoilles e de pomme gernette e pelectre e gingivre. Meis primes i metez cest que nus vus dirum ore.

[XLV] *Pudre a ceo maus.* [P]ernez alume zucré e foilles d'olive e roses e poliol roial* e les escorces de pommes gernettes e des pieres des dates e de pelectre e del canele e del gilofre e noiz muscate ouelement. E totes ces choses metez en puldre e metez desure, sicum dit est. Meis* primes lavez le cancre de vin egre u calment soit enz boilli e mis desure e que* le malades ait maschié entre ses denz lovesche salvage. E si vus laissiez nule [de] ces choses que dites sunt, icest traitié le vus enseignerat. *Autre pudre pur cancre:* [P]ernez girofre e comin e l'escorce de pomme gernet[f. 261r]te e les pieres des dates e les foilles d'olive e faites puldre e metez sur les gencives ben* lavez od vin egre e un oef metez desure en la maniere que devant dit est. *Pur cancre:* [P]or manger le cancre pestelez sel od farine de* frument e od jus de ache e persille e metez desure. Derecheif por manger le cancre ostez l'aubun de l'of, si retenez le moel e emplez l'eschale de sel. E ardez, si en faites puldre e lascive e roille. Metez le moel e emplez e de tut faites puldre. E si ceste puldre est al premir trop forte, si metez en* la puldre de l'albon de oef, sicum dit est.

[XLVI] *Por la fenture des lievres.* [A] la feinture des lievres faites tele la cure. Pernez de la semence jusquiami, que en englés est apelé hannebane*, e metez sur charbons u sur breses ardantes. E metez i un chalemel pe[r]cié parmi de seu u de autre chose pur la fume recevre es lievres par le pertus del chalmel qui est apelé embotum e issi sanerunt le[s] livres. Derecheif autre cure a cel memes: Le noel del nois ars mis en puldre metez desure. Uncore a cel memes: Pernez aloen epatic e litargire e vitreolum* od olibanum uelement e de ce faites puldre mut delié e metez desure. Autre cure: Pernez une herbe que est apelee flau[f. 261v]ra e fumeterie uelement une javelee e traiez hors le jus e destemprez de cest jus la devant dite puldre e medlez ensemble e metez i oile violat u olie comun. Derecheif del jus e de l'oille parfiez entremedlez, hore de l'un, hore de l'autre, sicum vus voissiez faire oingnement e ben metez ensemble* e entremetlez. E quant mester serra, si en oignés le liu.

[XLVIII] *Por arsure des levres.* [A] l'arsure* des livres pernez alum zucari[nu]m e metlez od le mel e parfies en reposant i metez meil e metlez ensemble cum pur faire oingnement. E quant mester serra, si metez sur le liu. As pointures des levres: Pernez anis e zucre e destempreez od oile violat u sirop rosat e oignez le liu. Icest oignement asuagist. Nus metum desure oignement blanc, mes pur le vin egre i metum ewe rosat e por olie commun violat.

[XLVII] Si* avient aucune foiz que les joes issent hors de lur propre juncture, que vus devez conustre par ço que les denz* desuz ne se jungnent pas been as denz desure, ainz tendunt a la partie dehors* u a la partie dedenz, [e] la mole desuz, ja soit iceo que ele soit junte par nature, si [ne] puet ele esbrissir, e ja soit de l'autre dessevré, si [ne] la put hom assembler. E issi la devez aidier. Vus devez pren[f. 262r]dre les chiés des joes desuz les oreilles e sis remenez un po as parties dedenz, que le[s] denz desuz soient aloiné as denz desure e qu'il seint mis proprement en sun liu, chescun par grant quintise. E dunc pernez une esplente, si la levez sus. E puis oingnez le liu de diauté u de marciaton. E issi liez l'esp[l]ente, que les denz d'ambesdeus les joes se tingent en lur* droite partie e que les joes ne se puissent mover. La diete doit estre mandé* qui doit estre unie, que li malade ne move la joe.

[L] Si la joe est rute de l'une part e de l'autre, li mires* doit amiablement cerchier le liu e quant il avra conu le liu de la pescure, si doit avenanment* mener* chescune partie a sun liu qu'il* doit conustre par les choses que dites sunt en la presseine cure de la desjointure* de la joe. E issi la devez lier jesque ele soit sanee. E dietez le sicum dit est en la cure devant.

[XLIX] *De la depesceur de l'os.* [S]i la despescure avient de l'os e de la char, rendez a la premor chascune part a sa partie covenablement. E puis cosez la plaie cointement* sicum devant dit est en la custure del nes. E lassiez la plaie desuz overte e metez dedenz un estuel* covenable e la puldre vermaille, sicum devant dit est, metez sur la [f. 262v] custure e enaprés un plumaceol e[n] la plus basse partie de la joe devez mettre [e] al desus e liez le liu sulunc la diverseté del tens. E puis en[j]oingnez al malade sa diete – viande que puisse estre humee – e solum la maniere del tens en la plaie metez puldre e autre[s] choses does foiz u trois le jor.

[LI] *Por festre.* [L]a festre l'une est a [e]stroite pertus, ce est la festre qui est dite mandibula, e l'autre a un pertuz large e ample. Meis quant la festre est od le pertus estroit, si metez tente dedenz del jus mali terre. E quant le pertus est grant, si metez oignement rumpant jesque la festre soit amortie. E quant la festre est amortie, si metez tente dedenz [d']un drap qui soit mis en aubun de oef. E quant le fu serra chaeet, si faites la cure od oignement vert [e] od les autres choses qui devant dites sunt. *Por char u os corumpue:* [S]i la plaie ad corumpu la char e les os, amiablement devez esgarder si nule chose i est que deive estre osté, sil devez taillier jesque al vif. E si vus veez qui aucune quiture en ist, dunc saciez est amortie. E si ceo que vient hors est auches cler [e] euus, dunc fait a criendre que la festre se soit araciné as racines de[s] denz e si issi avient, dunc devez les denz hors traire. E puis metez dedenz le festre u[f. 263r]ne tente od oignement vert. Si devez faire en ceste cure sicum devant dit est jeske a la fin. E metez la puldre, qui devant dit est as gencives, quant cancre n'i est.

[LII] *A dolur de[s] denz.* [A] la dulur de[s] denz e des gencives faites une quichun en la funteinele* derere en la char qui est dereire l'oraille e en ce metez un petit nu. E puis si pernez la semence [d'une] herbe que est [apelé] cassilago e de la porete e metez uelement sur les charbons. E li maledes receve la fumee par un chalmel* qui est apelé embottun. Cele* [fumee] la reume* qui [fait] la dulur merveillusement deslie e met* hors e asuagist.

[LIII] *As borbelettes ke avenunt en la face.* [A]s burbleites qui aveinent en la face oster pernez unces trois de miel, de* lait, de ficz* unces dous, del jus de mal[o] terre unce une. E ses choses metlez ensemble e metez en la pome de terre croissi e metez sur lent fu boillir. E metez ces puldres ovec que rechoit tartar* [de vin] blanc, de senevé unce une, de peivre u de alum zucré uelement unce demie, boracis unces dous, del gros encens e de l'os de la seche uelement unces dous. E ces mis en puldre metez en tele liquor e longement movez ensemble e metez en un. E quant mestier serra, eschaufez le liu, si l'oingnez. E quant les burblettes creverunt, [f. 263v] sis oingnez d'un oingnement blanc, meis por aisil si metez eue rosat e por olie commun violat. Autrement: Pernez mastic e gros encens uelement unce demie, de litargire e de plum ars uelement unce une, de ceruse unces trois. Totes ces choses metez en puldre e issi les confissez. Metez un poi de aisil en un morter e puis les devant dites puldres destemprez. E enaprés i metez un poi* de l'aisil e medlez ensemble e puis de l'oilie e puis de l'aisil e issi metez parfiez, ore de l'une, ore de l'autre, e metlez ensemble. Le signe de la decocsion est quant l'ungement est tenve e decort uelement. Icest oignement vaut a tute maneire de roigne que avient de saucefleme e pur asuager arsure que avent de mauvais humurs. E pur ceo que mutes superfluitez avenent en la face, sicum est dit*, e morphea e un autre maladie qui est apelé impetigo, qui, ja soit iceo que tut le cors purprenge, plus est en la face veue, pur ceo dirrum une partie de ces maladies. *De le cure [que] devez faire por impetigo*: [B]ele cure devez faire. A une sollure que avent sur le quir de l'home qui est apelé impetigo pernez froment e metez sur un enclume* de fevre e bruillez le frument od un fer chaut [f. 264r] e pus si primez fort le frument. E de ceo qui de cel frument ist chaut oignez la maladie suvent. Icest oignement vaut ensement a sausefleume. *Por oster serpigo*: [P]or oster une maladie que est apelé serpigo e en franceais derte* faites tel oingnement. Pernez litargire e [tartar de] blanc vin* e plum ars e l'escorce de la brioine arse e mis en puldre e un po de lasive uelement unce une. E confisez* issi: od le jus d'un herbe qui est apelé ciclamis* e od oile metlez les devant dites puldrus, e[n] metant ore de l'un, ore de l'autre, e parfiez les metlez ensemble, que bein se soient pris en un. E puis les metez en salf. E quant mestier serra, si en oignez le malade* e par troiz jorz le teinge sur sei e ne lave pas sei*. Enaprés le teirz [jor] si faites baingnier e ce face jesque il soit sein. *Morphé blanche e neire*: [M]orphé l'une est blanche e l'autre est neire, si est une espece de lepre. De ces dous l'une put estre sanee, sicum la blanche, e la neire nun. Cele que doit estre curee devez issi esproveir. Pernez une agulle e poiniez dedenz le quir del malade; si sanc en ist, si pot estre garri; si ewe blanche en ist, ne pot estre sanee. A la blanche morphé faites tel oingnement: Pernez tartarum e sulfre vif* e orpiement, sel* bruilliez, cristal, nitre*, savon sarazin, argent [f. 264v] vif, mirre, e litargire* e cire blanche, olie commune, olie musceline, oillie laurine, gresse de geline, pe[i]vre e mastic, olibanum, ladanum, euforbium, storacum calamite. E issi confisez. Ces qui sunt a triblier triblez e metez ensemble od sulfre e savon e oile e faites bollir. Mes la cire e la gresse de geline fundez par soi e pois metez olie laurin e muscelin* e metez od les devant dites choses e assemblez. E cest oignement chaut does foiz le jor metez desure. Autre oignement a cel oes: Pernez tartarum, suffre chenellié, argent vif e orphiment, sel ars, roil e oculum licium, totes ces choses od olie pestelez e metez ensemble e quisez e puis en oignez le malade* jesque il soit sein. Autre: Pernez suffre vif e savon franceis e nuz* ben tribliez uelement unces trois, de roil unces dous, de fumeterre e de lappace ague e de flaure uelement une javelé. E traiez hors le jus e confissez le jus od les devant dites puldres e lungement les metlez ensemble. E pur tote la maladie qui est impetigo apelé faites cest oignement. Pernez les racines des affodilles e de orpiement e des foilles d'olive, vif argent e litargire e oile commun e ensemble issi confisez. Ses qui sunt a triblier triblez e des [de]vant dites racines* traez le[s] jus e la devant dite puldre od ces jus metlez e puis i metez olie e parfiez metant l'un [f. 265r] od l'autre. Mes l'argent vif, qui doit estre mis en cest oignement, doit estre estent od sauge u od chevols moilliez que meuz vaut. Od les devant dites choses metlez issi le jus de cent-chiés e triblez od sel e od ces choses ensemble triblez frotez forment le liu. E puis faites le malade baigner troi[s] jorz e quant il serra del bagne issu, si l'oignez de l'oignement jesque il soit seins. *Morphé neire*: [J]a soit iceo devant dit que* hom ne poet la neire morphé saner, totesveies* i metrum la cure que nus savum e espruvé avum. E memes la cure i mettum que nus fa[i]sum a la derte* e ancuntre chescune grature de rongne. Si doit estre tele la reception. Tartarum e suie uelement unces dous, del cel gros e de suffre vif uelement unces trois, d'orpiment e de alum unce demie, e tut ceo tribliez en un mortir. Derechief pernez la fumeterre e de l'averone salvage uelement une javelé, e de la lappace ague e de une herbe que est apelé panis porcinus uelement e pestilez bein e traét hors le jus. E puis pernez savaon [. . .] sarazin uelement unces sis e metez od les devant dites puldres e medlés ensemble bein. E puis i metez del jus e medlez e puis de l'oile e en demenant* [metez] ore de l'un e ore de l'autre e medlez ensemble bein. E puis metez en saf.

[LIV] *Por dolur des orailles.* [f. 265v] [D]olur naist en l'oraille auchune foiz de la discursion* des homurs issi que en l'orelle* nest chose estre nature, auchune foiz que ver vient de hors en l'oreille* e nen ist pas, ainz est* certain acheisun de dolor. Meis quant la dolur vient en l'oraille de la discursion* des humurs, devant que li humor se soit afermé issi les solums aider. Pernez l'oingnun e pus d'entravers le tailliez parmi e al liu que crous est dedenz metez olie muscelin e metez sur les bresus lentes e lassiez ilec lungement boillir. E puis al plus chaut que li malade le poet suffrir, metez sur le oraille. Autrement: Pernez rue e l'aubun de l'oef e triblez ensemble e prinez hors le jus parmi un drap. Puiz tailliez l'oingnun d'entravers parmi e al crois de l'oignum le devant dit jus metez e faites quintement boillir al fu. E metez* sur l'oraille autrisi chaut cum li malede le poet suffrir. Autre cure: Pernez aluesne e calement e olie feit de la semence de chenillé, qui est apelee hanne-banne, e savine e metez en un covenable vaissel e faites bein builler. E sur le vessel metez un tuel percez* parmi que est apelé embotum. E li malede receive longe-ment en sa oreille [la fumee] que istra par le pertus del tuel e bein ait sa teste coverte. E si la dolur ne s'alegge par ses choses [f. 266r] ne ne se* muet, dunc sachez qu'il i ad verme* en l'orail u que li humurs se sunt afermé, dunt les signes doivent estre teles: li liu enfle e rogist e chalur en ist. Meis si poreture en ist e est torné por maurer, dunc devez faire la cure que dit est en la partie del traité des apostemes. E si les devant [dites] signes n'i aperunt, dunc sachez que verme est en l'oraille e[n]gendré.

[LV] *Por oscire vermine e hors metre.* [P]or le verm oscire e hors traire si ajustums ceste cure. Pernez une herbe que est apelé persicaria* e les nuals* des peires de peschier e des cerices e pestelez ben ensemble e traez hors le jus e metlez ovec autant d'olie de lin* e metez chaut en l'oraille . . . [f. 253r] . . . E quant le verme* serra mort, sil traez hors od unes mul[t] desliés tenailles que pincecarioles sunt apelé. Hom i met la ventuse aucune foiz por traire hors. *De verme ke est dehors:* [S]i verme* est dehors venu e entré en l'oraille, metez oli[e] od les foilles capparis e de callement e bein entremetlés, si degutez en l'orail. Ceo met hors le verme e asu[a]ge la dolur. E si verm naist en autre menbre, elebre blanc bein triblé od vin metez dedenz le liu. Ce ocit* le veirm meintenant.

[LVI] *Si fev u peire u achune autre chose* [. . .] [f. 253v] [S]i fev u piere u auchune autre chose cheieit en la oraille, li malade doit de cele part sun cheif apueir. E puis metez la ventuse as orailles. E puis sil feites esternuer*, que la ventuse se suchant traie a sei les esperiz que denz sunt e par mut atraire les face venir as parties de ors. E uns autres envolupent bombes*, ço est cotun, entur un fer u entur un fust e metent* en terebentine [u] en autre glumuse chose, que ceo que cheit en l'oraille aprés se aeirde a* itel estrument [e] est ors treit. Meis pur ceo que nus dotums que tele chose mise dedenz l'oraille plus i aoite la dolor que ne suage, pur ceo laissum ceste cure.

[BOOK II]

Si parole li mestre de cures de cirugie. [N]ul ne me doit blamer de parole lunge, quant mutes paroles brevement dites plus tornent* a nunsaver que a profit a cels qui l'oient e nent ne l'antendunt. Meis pur ceo que nus volums le profit as petiz sicum as granz, ne voil metre les escriz par ordre que apris ai de mun mestre menuement e privément, ainz voil issi overtem[en]t dire que vus le puissez entendre e a oes mettre. E pur ceo que dit avum de la teste brevement, [ore dium del col], primes des plaies, al se[f. 254r]cund liu des apostemes, al teirz liu des escroilles e des glandres, al quart liu de[s] festres, [. . .] al sisme de l'oil e al setime liu des choses qui dedenz avinent e les signes. Ore dirum avant des plaes que aveint al col e a l'aterel e en la corge e des cures tant cum apent* a cirugie.

[I] *Des* plaies del col.* [A]s plaes que avenunt el col d'espee u de aucune autre arme semblable a espee tele medicine i sulum fere. As premiers lius amiablement [devez] esgarder e ver s'il* i a os u auchune tele chose qui deve estre hors trait. E od le doi devez bein ce[r]chier e puis tut meintenant traire hors. E enaprés si cusez la plaie e metez desure la puldre roge e tut cest meimes devez faire en ceste cure que dit est desainz es autres. E si sanc i abunde u auchune autre chose, que vus nel puusiez errantement hors traire de la plaie, si cusez une partie de la plaie e une partie lassiez overte, que quant tens demustra, peusez meiz oster les choses qui funt [a] oster*. E quant averez trait hors de la plaie ço que doit estre osté, si cusez le liu, e le chief de la plaie que plus est pendant laissiez overt. E les autres choses qui dit[es] [f. 254v] sunt desainz en la custure devez faire en ceste cure.

[II] *Si le col seit percié.* [S']il avent que li col seit percié de l'une part jesque a l'autre, sicum de la destre part jesque a la senestre, si metez lardon, l'un de l'un part e l'autre de l'autre part, juste la buche de la plaie. E issi le laissiez jesque al teirz jor que la plaie comence a quiturer. E le devant [dit] lardun pur le var[i]ement* [del tens] por la plaie faire quiturer seurement i metez. E quant la plaie quiture, si metez un estoel de drap en la manere des autres plaeies. E puis la sanez. E bien devez es autres plaies semblables esgarder que la part de la plaie que [plus] pent soit plus am[i]ablement sanee. E al derain la targiez plus a fermer e en menusant l'estoel qui desure est chescun jor ne hastez pas la plaie pur trop tost garir.

[III] *De plaie en la atherel.* [S]i la plaie vient a l'haterel d'espee u de auchune tele arme semblable, que la veine soit taillié que est apelé organale, issi la devez aidier. Cosez tute la veine od une aguille, issi que la veine ne soit percié. E de l'autre part metez l'aguille od un fil, que le fil s'[i] aerde*, e od cel fil bien l'atachez* [e] estrainiez que sanc n'en issie, si n'emplez pas la plaie de drap. E si ceo est en [f. 255r] iver, si metez embroche sur . . . [f. 266r] . . . la plaie. E si ceo est en esté, si metez moel d'oef jesque la plaie comence a quiturer. E quant la plaie comencera a quiturer, drap sec mis en neir oignement metez sure e autres choses qui funt bone char venir. E faites memes la cure qui est a fere as autres plaies. *Por conustre le[s] chefz de la plaie:* [Q]uant vus conustrez que les chiés de la plaié veine desuz e desure se teinent ensemble, desliez le[s] fil[s] de cel liu e ostez e cosez avant sicum dit est. E si li nerf est taillez en lung u en esclenc, e ne mie d'entravers, en ceste manere le devez saner. Pernez les verms qui desuz tere naissent qui sunt lunges e rundes e resemblent [f. 266v] les verms qui issent hors del ventre de l'home e que li Anglés apelent 'maddokes' e triblez e en olie commun confusement les boilliez al fu e nule autre chose ovec. E quant vus averez mestier, si metez desure trois foiz u quatre u plus. E s'il est taillié d'entravers, ne deit pas de cele medecine estre sanee, ainz doit estre garri par medecine de nature. Car hom doit custre le quir que est sur le nerf e puis mettre la puldre ruge desure. E si le liu rogist, metez desure embroke* que dit est en la premiere partie pur emflure oster.

[IV] E si la veine organale [n']est taillé par le devant dite plaie, dunc metez sur la plaie un drap mis en albun d'oef. Mes nen emplez mie mult la plaie e metez sur ceste plaie tele embrok sicum dit est par ordre en l'autre cure.

[V] *Si le quarel seit afiché en la haterel.* [E]naprés si il avient que la dart soit afichié a l'aterel e [ait] percié la veine e le artere*, que la plaie seigne mut, meintenant quant l'arme est ors trait, cosez la plaie sicum dit est en la tirce partie desure. E puis metez la puldre ruge u la puldre de la fiente de l'asne [ars], que s'il aveint que vus nen aiez de la fiente de l'asne ars, si pernez de la fiente de l'asne que sul avient de l'asne veirt e prinez [f. 267r] parmi un drap. E metez desure cel jus: Pernez d'encens unces dous, de aloe unce une, e de aubun de l'oef e* les peilz del lievere e confisez issi. Ceo que est a triblier triblez e destemprez od l'aubun de l'oef e en confisant i metez les peilz del lievre e puis metez ce sur* les* auteries tailliés e tant illoc le laissiez desque il chiece aval par soi. A ceo valt gipsus, qui est en englés apelé 'cockel', od les grains des grapes delieement* triblez. E a ceo vaut le flur laureole e les foilles de l'ieble mises desure. E a ceo vaut le grain del froment maschié e mis desure. Ceo estanche sanc e esprové chose est. A ceo vaut chauz* [e] capiteils metlé e mis desure. E quant le sanc serra esstanché, sil sanez sicum dit est es autres cures devant.

[VI] *Por plaie en la corge.* [S]i la plaie aveint en un liu en la gorge qui est apelé ysophagus u en la veine que est apelé trachie arterie*, issi que l'arterie* soit percié e taillié, itele plaie est mortele. De quelque chose que la trachie arterie est plaié, si est chose mortele. E s'il aveint que li petit quir que la est soit plaié, feites la cure sicum as autres plaies.

[VII] *De superfluité des humurs.* [S]icum en home sunt quatre humurs devisé[s], issi i a quatre collections* que vienent des superfluetez des quatre humurs [f. 267v] e a chescun sun nun par soi. E tuz generalment sunt apelé apostemus, dunt il en ad quatre maneirs. L'une que avient de sanc est apelé flegmon e cele* que aveint de colre naturele est apelé herpes hestiomenus*, que li franceais apelunt lu, e cele qu'avient de colre de melancolie est apelé cancre e cel[e] que veint de flegme* est un clou que est apelé zima u palus pur ceo que mut quiture en ist. E chescune de ces doit estre coneu par ses propres signes. Si l'aposteme avient de sanc boillant, le puls* doit estre fort e li malede doit suffrir dolur e chalur e emflur. E si l'aposteme avient de fleme, si doit le clo estre blanc e mol; si vus metez le doi desure e auques primez, si en avendra signe cum d'un pertus. E si aposteme vieint de colere roge, ces sunt les signes: color vermeil metlé od colur citrine*. E s'il avient de colure u de melancolie neint naturele, si doit ensure grant duresce od ner d'encre*. Ore alum as cures. Si fasium* la cure issi.

[VIII] Pernez rue e comin e lardon e farine de forment e l'oinun e quisez en olie e longement les demenez. Si metez desure jesque quiture i avienge. E quant l'aposteime est* meure, ce part u le liu* plus pent tailliez desuz en lunge e, si vus poeez [f. 268r] mettre vostre dei dedenz, e al plus ducement que vus poeez, tote la quiture metez hors. E quant la pureture serra hors priente, si metez dedenz un estoel de drap dous foiz le jor. E enaprés le sanez sicum es autres cures.

[IX] *De aposteme ke est apelé antrax.* [S]i l'aposteme qui est apelé antrax u carbunculus soit aucune foiz avenu as reins, issi les devez saner od fraides choses cum od ólie e od le jus de la morele e de aisil e del jus de chevrefoile e de memite* [e] vermicularis. De ces choses devez oster la chalur entur les lius qui suff[r]unt. Si antrax* u carbunculus avient de sanc boillant, si metez sur le liu scabiosam triblié od oint. Ceste chose est espruvé. Consoude triblié entre deus pieres par devin miracle ocist l'aposteme qui est apelé antrax e en un jor issi la cure, que plus de cure mester ne avra fors que la plaie soit sanee. E memes ceo fait un herbe que est apelé pié de columb.

[X] *Autre aposteme.* [S]i l'aposteme avient de colre neire e trop chaut soit e espés e en autre part s'est asis, ausi le devez descolure[r] cum les autres plaies. E saner li devez sicum dit est en la cure desure de antrace*.

[XI] E si l'aposteme avient de fleume, feites ceste emplastre qui recet geuimalve les racines trois unces, de veil oint de porc, ostez* les dous parties colees, si i metez olie [f. 268v] e puis i metez de l'escume d'argent e litargire e cire e metez al fu boillir e faites cum enplastre e metez desure. U faites l'emplastre que feire solium as apostemus por fere maurir. *Por ameurer l'aposteme.* [P]ernez les racines des lis e quisez en eue e puis tribliez od oint* e puis l'eschaufez al fu. E quant il eirt un poi rosti, puis i metez les foilles de celidoine salvage e de cholez quit en vin e autres choses qui faient maurir e quiturer. Tut[es] ces choses ensemble metlez e metez desure e quant l'aposteme quiture, si [le] li[u u] plus pent* [tailliez e] faites les choses qui dites sunt en la cure des apostemus de sanc.

[XII] *Cancre ke aveint au cors des humurs.* [C]ancre avient al cors auchune foiz par le vice* des humurs qui dedenz sunt, aucune foiz par le vice des choses forens: par le vice de[s] choses foreines* sicum par plai qui est* malvaisement garie, par les vices des choses qui dedenz sunt sicum des humurs dedenz corrumpuz. Car quant la plaie quatre meis u demie an aveine de la gent nun curé* e puis turne a sursanure, ne l'apelun meis plaie, ainz fasium cancre u festre. Icestes maneires de cancres auchune foiz avienunt en lung tens, auchune fois en poi de tens. E aveint auchune foiz que le cancre s'est ahers [f. 269r] es lius nervus pleins de deversus veines e de arteries. Icele maneire de cancre n'est pas a saner par taillier ne par ardier: dunt Ypocras dit "A tuz icels es quels le cancre est muciez, cum es veines u es nerfs e es arteries, mielz est qu'il ne soit curez, car li curé plus tost perissent e li nun* curé vivent lung tens". E pur ceo que entur le col e le aterel e la gorge sunt neirs e plusurs arteries e habundance de veines, nes devez pas tailler ne ardoir, meis sanum les sicum nus poum. E si le cancre est de lung tens e al col, si faites tel oignement. *Oignement.* [P]ernez les racines de la lange de boef unce une, de canele unce une, de gingevre unces dous, de zucre unces dous, de vif argent unces dous, de cire [e] reisine unces quatre, e de viel oint cinc unces, que si devez confire. Les racines des herbes tribliez en un morter e puis i metez l'oint e medlez amiablement ensemble. E des autres choses faites puldre e medlez od les devant dites choses. E metez vif argent en un vessel de terre od le reisine e fundez al fu. E quant il est fundu, sil metez en salf. E si cest oignement ne suffist, si metez ceste puldre por mangier le cancre. Pernez ellebre blanc e aristologiam* rotundam e metez en puldre e puis metez desure. E s'il est esteint od tele puldre, si metez desure estupes [f. 269v] od olie e od oef. Pus* i metez oignement vert. E des teles choses le poeez saner jesque a la fin. Ore dirum del cancre qui est as lius* charnus*.

[XIII] *Des escroelles ke naissent en la gule.* [E]scroeles naissent en la gule, desuz les aiseles e es illers, e unes* glandres qui ne sunt pas escroeles*. E si volez saver que ele est glandre u escroele, issi le poeez esprover. Pernez iere terrestre e les branches citri e quant il sunt ben pestelé, sis boillez en olie e metez desure trois jors. E si les glandres amenusent, si feites memes la cure. S'il rougissent e volent quiturer, dunc

metez choses pur maurir. E quant l'aposteime est mauree, dunc la tailliez en la
manere que la quiture s'en isse. E s'il endurcist* e creist plus [d']un mois u demi an
e issi porisse*, si faites cest oignement. Pernez les racines tapsie e la racine de la
raiz salvage uelement e quant les racines serunt ben porgié*, dunc les triblez e
metez en olie boillier. E autant metez de l'olie cum des racines e faites boillir
desque meitié u plus. E de cel olie degutez trois gutes u quatre sur l'apotesme e
laissez ester. E si l'oil de l'apotesme enfle, que quiture en isse, dunc sachez que li
malade garra par tele medicine. E s'il nen emfle, dunc ne* garra il mie. E si [signe]
de garison i avent, faites [f. 270r] la cure de memes la oile [e] derechief faites cest
beivre* que par mai est trové, que si doit estre fait. Pernez les racines del rosel e
mali terre, e les racines brusci e sparagi, e les racines de la raiz salvage e de la
damasche, e de scrophulare e d'ellebre blanc, e trois racines d'aristologie* e roses e
fabe lupini, e les racines spatule fetide*, e les foilles lauriole uelement ben porgiez*
e ben tribliez ensemble [e] boilliez en tres bon vin desque a la meitié. E de cest vin
boive li malades une foiz la simaine par matin. E s'il est viel* home, sil beive pur e
s'il est joiefne, si beve le pesant de dragmes* quatre medlé od autre vin plein
hanap. E s'il est trop orible a bevre, si i metez dedenz zucre. E le malade bein se
garde cum s'il eust pris medecine [laxative], car il irra le jor trois feiz a sele u quatre
u plus. Derecheif faites quichum sur le tendrum de l'oreille en miliu tant cum les
glandres sunt fresches. A cel meimes: Al decurs de la lune quant la lune est de
noef* [. . .de] la racine spatule fetide e de la raiz salvage, un jor dis, un autre jor
noef* e issi desque al definement* de la lune chescun jor une. E si ço ne vaut, si
recorez a la cirugie. Meis ceo devez ben noter, que nule glandre ne escroele nen
devez taillier que vus ncn puissez ben tenir [entre] vos meins. [f. 270v] *De tailliure*:
[I]ssi tailliez l'escroele u la glandre. Primes les devez tenir entre vos meins e puis le
quir desure taillier en lung e oster la char de tus parz [e] od un fer rebuchié traire
hors. E si altres choses i ensivent, tut trai[e]z hors e tant cum il sunt od lur peals
traez hors. E si mut* [sanc] ensuit*, par l'espace de trois jors u de quatre les traez
hors. E le secund jor emplez la plaie d'un drap qui soit mis en albun d'oef. E si le
foillet de la escrelle remeint dedenz, metez desure la puldre de affodilles que
devant dit est en la cure del cheif en memes le chapitle des escrolles qui naissent
en la teste. Enaprés traiez hors la charunge o la quiture e itele pudre metez dedenz
por manger la pel de l'escrolle. E quant vus verrez la plaie emflee e deschié, dunc
devez mettre en la plaie un drap qui soit mis en albon d'eof. E desure metez une
estupe od un oef jesque vus verrez le drap porri e corrumpu e la plaie quiturer. E
enaprés curez la plaie de oignement vert que dit est [en le chapitle] al title de la
cure de la superflueté del nes, e des autres choses dunt hom sane les autres plaies
devez [faire] la cure. *De superfluité des humors*: [S]uvent sot avenir as eisceles* e as
illieirs une superfluité de humor e faire iloc une dure* assemblee grande [f. 271r] e
hors aparissante. E quant se aieirt en parfunt fermement, si est une aposteme que
apelé est bubo dunt il en i ad dous maneires, e l'une puet estre sanee, l'autre nun.
Si li malede ad chalur continuele e soi, e mut est ateint, e l'asemblé des humurs est
megre, e sent dolur el piz el parfunt, iceste sout avenir suz les aisseles, si ne put
estre sané. E s'il avent en la grandur d'un oef u de meindre e li malade n'ait nule
dolur el piz ne autres mavaises signes, mes poi de force en sei e poi de chalur, ceste
pot estre sanee, meis que dur aeirdement i ait. *Des apostumus*. [A]s apostemus, si

tost maurissent* u nun, quant il sunt maur*: Covent les apostemus si tost percier* e si n'atendez pas desque il crevent par sei. E si vus nel faites, a peines u jammés nel garras. E quant li malades taillié serra, sil devez saner en la maniere des autres plaies.

[XIV] *De festre.* [F]estre est aposteme que ad le pertus estroit e [le fund] parfunt [e] large*, que aucune foiz avent de la vice* des choses foreines, aucune foiz par la vice des humurs qui sunt dedenz, u dehors sicum dit est en la cure des plaies. Itele maneire de festre aucune foiz [f. 271v] avient de lung tens, aucune foiz de po de tens, e l'une aveint as lius nervus e es lius u veinus sunt e les autres avienent* es lius charnus; e aucune foiz corrumpunt le[s] festre la char sulement, aucune foiz l'os, auchune foiz les neirs. E chescune en a ses propres signes par que[les] ele doit estre conue. Icele que la char mangue met* hors quiture cum ewe blanche e od escume; e si l'os est blescié, si en ist quiture come lavure* de char; e si le nerf est blescé, si en ist neire quiture e mut pudlente. E par signes les poez conustre e pur ceo que la festre feirt issi en diverses parties del cors diverses medicines coveint faire. E pur ço que el haterel ne el col ne en la gorge n'i osum mettre fu ne taillier, pur ceo le aiderez en tele maniere. Si le pertus de la festre est estrait, si l'eslargiez od une tente de malo terre e en ceste maniere devez fere. Faite[s] tente de malo terre sec e par le tuel de la festre le metez en[z] que tut le tuel soit empli e laissiez del matin jesque al vespre u del vespre jesque al matin. E quant le tuel iert ben eslargi, si metez enz oignement rumpant [. . .] La u le liu est mut aempli de veinus ne d'auteries une partie des affodilles metez dedenz. E s'il est home tendre, si faites a ceste cure un precius oignement que si doit estre fait. *Oignement:* [f. 272r] [P]ernez pelectre e pevre e orpiment e alum e senevé, elebre blanc e neir, e del vert de l'areim, e de vive chauz autant cum de tuz e confisez issi. Tribliez ceo qui est a tribler e metlez amiablement od savun sparantic e enaprés formez de se une tente e metez ensz jesque as funz de la festre. Icest oignement decurt dedenz le festre, si l'ocit e desseche. Enaprés jesque le fu soit chaut i metez stupe od muel d'oef u aubun od olie. E puis metez oingnement vert que dit est en la cure de l'aposteme que est apelé polipus e de autres oignemenz jesque a la fin. E quant le festre met hors quiture sicum ewe, dunc est la festre morte. E si ceo n'est pas festre entre les veines e les nerfs, meis entre le quir e la char, e si soit mis en lung u en esclenc, si le pertus de la festre est estroit, si l'eslargissez issi que la tente soit mis en parfunt* [. . .] E puis metez dedenz un drap mis en aubun d'oef e issi le laissét del matin jesque al vespre u del vespre jesque al matin. E puis metez desure la pudre des amfodilles. E quant vus verrez* que la plaie emphle, dunc sacés* que la festre est morte. E puis la sanez quintement cum oinement vert e des autres choses cum dites sunt en la cure des plaies.

[XV] *De bocium.* [f. 272v] [U]ne maladie que est apelé bocium* avient en la gule*. A ce fait hom tel esperement. Pernez les foilles de la tres petite* noiz e ses racines od tute la sustance e bein pestelez ensemble od dous censz grainz de peivre e boillez en bon vin e de cel vin beve li malade chescune matine jesque il soit delivre. U facés tele medecine. Pernez les racines viticelle* e la racine cucurbite* salvage, ciclaminis, polipodie, sparagi, brusci, aristologie ronde*, cucumiscelle*, yari*, palam marine e l'esponge de la mer, brancam ursinam, burith, lait de scroppha les primeres* fils* prodiente e les racines tapsi barbasti e conficés issi. Totes ces choses desechiez [e] tribliez e saciez parmi un sac* e metez fu sur pallam e l'esponge de la meir e tribliez en puldre e cum por fere eletuarie les metlez ensemble. E quant li malade irra dormir, si metez suz la lange. Enaprés pernez polipodie e malum terre e vetonie e les racines tapsi barbasti e quisez en ewe tant que trois fiolees d'ewe [se degastent] en une* fiole. [Metez] en la devant dite puldre le seir, e al matin dunez a beivre al malade de cel ewe e de la culure ensement. E cel jor ne beive li malade point d'eue [e] jesque al teirz jor ne prenge puldre ne potun. [f. 273r] E del tierz jor en avant la puldre sicum dit est aparaillé li metez desuz la lange. E faites issi jesque al disme jor u a l'unzime. E la devant dite potun donez al malade de l'unzime jor jesque a l'uncime a beivre. E si par ces espermenz nen est li malade delivre, si recurez [a la] cirugie. *De une boce tant sulement.* [S']il i a une boce tant sulement, od un fer chaut i metez un seun* en lung e un autre en lé. Puis metez desure un drap mis en oint. E chescun jor al matin e al seir traeiz le seun* hors, que la char soit d'els trenché. E quant ce ieirt fait, si remeint* [rien] de la boce, si metez desure la puldre des afodilles. E quant le liu serra purgié, sil sanez sicum les autres plaies. E si la boce ne s'est aeirs as arteries, si la pernez ferme en vostre main e quientement tailliez le* quir en lung e pernez la boce od ustil cirugien qui est apelé uncus e de l'une part e de l'autre ostez bein la char del quir, e vostre doi metez dedenz e la boce od tut sun foillet traeez hors. E puis emplez la plaie legerement de drap linge. E si mut sanc i survent, si faites les remedies qui devant dites sunt al capitle qui est antitlé de la plaie qui est faite el haterel de sete e lassiez la plaie ester od ces remedies trois jors. E puis si rein i remeint, si i metez desure la pul[f. 273v]dre des affodilles e enaprés si l'aidiez od* le oef. E enaprés alez avant come en la cure de la plaie. Mes de ceo pernez bein garde, que le foillet de la boce soit de tut en tut esracié, que rein n'i soit lessié, char si nule chose i est laissié, ja si petit ne seit, si recrestera la boce. E quant le liu est porgié parfitement, si mete[z] desure la pudre ruge. E si devez faire ceste cure sicum dit [est] as autres. E si la boce est grande e li malade est veil e feble par vostre jugement, ne vus entremetez pas, char aucune foiz solet avenir en tele maniere de boce que mot ad partie[s] que ne poent pas de legir, si a grant guarance ne soit, estre arachié. E dutum a mettre fer chaut ne taillure, que nus* ne bleçum les arteries u les nerves* u la boce se est aeirs. E cels qui nus* aidium de ceste maladie faisum bein lier sur un banc* e forment tenir.

[XVI] *De squinancie.* [S]quinancie est une aposteime qui naist en la gorge dunt i ad trois maniers. La prime ceo est apellé squina[n]cie, si comprent le nun de tuz. Iceste naist entre la trachie arterie e ysophagum* en un liu en la gorge qui est apelé ismon. Iceste espece est mortele, si ne le put nul garir si Deu nun. La secunde est apelee sinancie que tint une partie de la materie dedenz e une autre partie [f. 274r] dehors, issi que vus poeez veir le emflure dehors, e ceste est meins maliciose. La terce partie est apelé quinancie, iceste met* sa materie tut de[h]ors, e la maladie de ceste est meins a criendre, la quele espece des trois est meilur a curer. Ces sunt les generaus signes: grevance pur atraire sa aelene e de mettre* la hors, si ne put le malade manger ne bevre ne parler ne sal[i]ve transgluter ne machier. Eissi el comencement li devez aidier.

[XVII] Si force e age li suffre, si seinez le malade al bras* de la veine de la teste u de la veine que est desuz la lange. Si li faites tel gargarisme. Pernez gallas e balaustias e roses e lentes e faites boillir en ewe e de ceste eue gorgoie li malades suvent. Car iceste gargarisme reprent les humurs decuranz al liu doillant. E dehors le oingnez de dialtee u faites une emplastre* qui sane le secunde e la terce espece que si doit estre fet. Pernez la racine de ieble e aloesne e chardun* beneit e senationes a vostre pleisir e pestelez ben ensemble e traez hors le jus. E puis si pernez la farine de l'orge e de la semence de lin* e destemprez od le devant dit jus e medlez ensemble issi qu'il soit aquis tenve. E puis si pernez oint de porc e fundez en une paele e metez i autant de miel e faites boillir od l'oint. Enaprés metez le jus od [f. 274v] la farine en la paele e medlez od les devant dites choses. E tant les laissiez boillir desque il venge a s'espesir*. E en la maneire d'embroke tele emplastre metez sur le liu trois foiz u quatre le jor e tutdis chaut. E si le posteme quiture dedenz, od vostre doi u od autre chose depesciez l'aposteme, que la quiture curge hors. Mut est profitable chose. Issi ai jeo auchun[s] curé* par ma main.

[XVIII] *Des apostumes ke emflent dedensz.* [U]nes apostemus qui branci* sunt apelé enflent dedenz sicum dous alemandes, dunt grief est l'atrait de l'aleine al malade, di atraire e mettre hors. A ceste maladie devez faire gargarisme e si le* malade n'est par ceo delivre, si recorez a la cirugie. E primes metez le malade par devant vus e pernez la lange desuz e primez od un covenable estrument e li malade tinge sa buche overte, que vus peussiez celes amigdeles veeir, e od un ostilement de fer nescessarie tailliez - les paleetes qui* sunt dejuste els nient* entamez laissiez. Puis si faites gargarisme de ewe rose e de aisil ensemblement od le jus a[r]naglosse. E si vus veez que mut sanc i decurge, si metez meiz, e s'il quiture, dunc le tailliez en cele maneire. Taillez le quir en lung e od estrument fait a cel oes le traiez hors e od la racine del tut en tut les erachiez. E [f. 275r] puis quisez le liu od estrement d'or u de fer.

[XIX] *De emflure ke uvule* est apelé.* [U]ne emflure que uvule* est apelé crest en lung e emfle. Iceste devez desecchir od puldres destrainanz e od gargarismes e od ceste puldre qui receit galle*, balaustie, peivre, pelectre e canele, e metez desure od un chaut fer crois. E faites gargarisme de cest qui receit vin duz e meil e aisil uelement e les devant dites choses mises en puldre faites boillir od le[s] liquors. E s'il issi n'est desechi, tailliez le od unes tenailles a cel oes faites dejuste le paleis al plus sutil liu, meis de ceo vus gardez que vus n'adesez les racines de l'uvule*. E faites la gargarisme qui deseche dunt li malades gargoie nuit e jor. E ben se gart li malades qu'il ne gise suvin. E gargarize sovent de l'ewe u geline grasse est enz quite. E ben se gart li malades que trois jorz ne trois nusz gueres ne dorme. U ainz qu'il soit tailliez, l'ardez de un dener d'or e feites le gargarisme sicum devant dit est.

[XX] *De jugulare*.* Jugulare* est un os qui ist auchune foiz de sun liu e pur ceo desjuint le col e vice en avint e[n] la juncture del col, que, si le maledes n'est tost aidié en haste, purra murir. A cele maladie poeez issi aideir. Faites al malade ovrir la buche e metez un fust enz, qu'il tenge sa buche overte, e me[f. 275v]tez desuz la jhoue une esplente. E vus en levant sus fermement de voz mains ambesdous les chés de l'esplente [tenez] e metez vostre un pei sur l'une esplaude e l'autre sur l'autre, que od voz piez aval primant, od vos mains le chef forment sustraiant, faciez l'os revenir a sa propre joincture. Puis si oingnez le liu od diautee u od marciaton* e* leine muste de soi metez sure u estupe. E ces fomentacions e ces oignemens faites chescun jor e la seingné del terce jor i solet mut valer.

[BOOK III]

Des cures homoplatis. [D]es cures* homoplatis e de la chaine de la gule e de tutes les choses qui de ce avienent jesque a la coillie voldra[i] tra[i]tier.

[I] *De plais ke avenunt as homoplates.* [D]es plaies que avenunt es homoplates par espee u par autre arme semblable issi les devez aidier. Si la plaie est fresche, porgiez le[s] superfluetez e meintenant la cusez e lessiez* les chiez overz, e metez la puldre ruge desure. E faites aprés les autres choses que dites sunt en la secunde partie des custures. E si la plaie n'est pas fresche, primez la purgiez ben, que sanc en isse*. E enaprés la cusez sicum dit est desus. E s'il est percié [de] dart*, si metez dedenz lardun e faites les autres choses sicum dit est desus en la secunde partie en la cure del col quant plaié est e percié de dart.

[II] *De la chaene de la gule.* [S]i la chaene de la [f. 276r] gule est taillié, issi la devez aidier. Emplez primes la plaie de un drap qui soit mis en albon d'oef e hors prient e metez desure moel de oef od estupe. E puis metez un drap sec od embroke desure por le variement* del tens e pur quiturer. E quant verrez os u autre chose que covenge estre hors trait, sil traeez sagement hors. E puis si fetes la cure cum od neir oignement e les autres choses faites sicum as cures des plaies.

[III] *De frainture.* [S]i l'os qui est chaene de la gule est fraint u en autre manere embaissé, levez le braz u l'espaude al malade od une vostre mein e de l'autre mein pernez le part dehors qui munte en haut, primez en bas, e une plateine e un plumaceol mis en albun d'oef metez en croiz desure e une lunge* esplente liez de tutes parz. E liez le braz al malade a sun col, qu'il pende, e un plumaceol metez desuz les aisseles, que li braç* ne puisse chair aval, e en nule maniere ne l'ostiez mie jesque il soit sain. E si la fraiture avient de la plaie, n'i metez pas lunge esplente desure, meis la u la fraiture est laissiez [le] liu overt, que vus en memes cel liu puissiez mettre estoel por saner sicum les autres plaies. E metez la liure de cele part sur une esplente lunge.

[IV] *De la disjungture de* l'espaude.* [S]i l'espaude par plaie des parties desure est des[j]ointe, issi faites la cu[f. 276v]re. Al commencement anettez la plaie. E si la plaie n'est fresche, mundez la plaie, que sanc en isse. E si auchune chose i est a oster, primes l'ostez. E puis si cusez la plaie en ceste maniere. Rendez la part a la partie covenablement e en la sovereine partie de l'esplaude ambedous les parties de la plaie porpernez bien od une aguille, que li fil que [a l']aguille s'aeirt s'a[n]volupe a memus la auguile, e laissiez la auguille en ceste custure jesque al fermament de la plaie. E faites en ceste maneire autant de poinz cum vus verrez* que mester est e la[i]ssiez la auguille en chescun point. E puis metez la puldre ruge desure e un plumaceol, meis les cheis, sicum dit est es autres cures, leissiez oveirt e faites ceo que dit est as autres cures*. E quant vus verrez que la plaie serra afermee, si ostez les auguilles e les filz, si metez enz un estuel, sicum es autres plaies, e amenusez. Aprés fetes la cure cum as choses semblables desque a la fin. *Si l'espaude n'est pas desjonte.* [S]i l'espaude n'est pas desjointe des parties desure, premerement en sustraiant soit remué e enaprés la sanez jesque a la fin sicum dit est es autres cures.

[V] *De l'os u le nerf del brace que est taillé.* [S]i l'os u le* nerf del braz est taillié d'entravers, primes emplez la plaie de drap mis en albun de oef e enaprés si metez [f. 277r] un drap sec od embroke por le deverseté del tens. E si de l'os doit rein estre hors trait*, sil traez hors. E al nerf feites la cure que dit est en la secunde partie. Enaprés le sanez od oignement neir e od les choses qui devant dit[es] sunt.

[VI] *De dolur u de emflure u de duresce.* [S]i dolur u emflure u duresce se prent as nerfs dunt il soient contrait, sis devez oindre de diautee que si est fait. Pernez les racines de la gumalve livres dous, de fenugrec e de lin* uelement livre une, squille livre demie, de oile livres quatre, de cire livre une, de terebentine, de galbano, de la gumm[e] de ire uelement unces dous, colofonie e de raisine uelement livre demie. E tutes les racines lavez bein e tribliez e ensement la semence de lin e le fenugrec e squille. E quant serrunt triblié, si metez en sis livres* de eue jesque a trois jorz. E le quart jor metez sur le fu e laissez boillir jesque il venge a s'espessir. E puis metez petit e petit en un sac [e] quant vus vodrez culer, si metez un po d'eu[e] boillante. E al traire hors si metez dous livres del jus e de sisun e metez en quatre livres d'olie e boilliez desque le jus soit degasté, que vus devez conustre par ceo que point de jus nen ait desus. E puis i metez une livre* de cire e quant ele serat fundue, si i metez terebentine e puis i metez la gumme de l'iere e galbanum e al derain i metez la pu[f. 277v]dre de colofonie e la reisine. E quant il serra quit, si l'ostez del fu. Ceo est le signe de la decoctiun: quant la gute mise sur marbre espesist. E puis quant il serra colé e refredi, sil metez en salf. Cest oingment vaut a la dolur del piz qu'avient de freidure e al pleuresie, meis que primes soit eschaufé al fu en une eschale d'oef e puis soit mis chaut sur le piz. Ceste eschaufe les lius enfrediz e amollist e amustit.*

[VII] *Si la plaie est malement sané.* [S]i la plaie malement sanee porrist, od icest oingnement la devez saner que si doit estre fait. Pernez d'olie une livre, de siu de mutun livre demie, de blanche sire unces dous, de peiz greic unces trois, de sauge e de sisimbrio*, ce est basme euage, e levistici* e de savine e de anet e rue. E enaprés metez tutes ces herbes de chescune une poingné e confissez issi. Le siu fundez en l'olie e colez e enaprés metez les choses tribliez e ben metlez ensemble, que bein si soiunt pris ensemble, sil gardez. A ces [memes] pernez salge savage e damasche e lancelee, centinerve* e pimpernelle, armeise, lange de boef uelement une javelee e pestelez bein od une livre de siu de mutun. E puis en formez* magdaliuns e laissiez desque il soient flastri. E puis si metez les magdaliuns e une livre d'olie en un veissel estaimé e faites boillir al fu desque les [f. 278r] herbes augent a funz. E puis ostez del fu*, e les devant dites herbes e l'olie colez parmi un drap e metez autrefoiz al fu. E quant il commencent a boillir, si ceo est en esté, si metez treis unces de cire, e en iver dous, e quant la cire serra fundue, si metez mastic e gros ancens e colophonie uelement unce une e qui soi[en]t mis en pudre e en demenant od une esclice les metlez ensemble*. E puis metez en salf. Icest oignement vaut mut a la plaie porrie por aneitir* e por faire bone char venir e por bone char nurir.

[VIII] *Si mavaisse char surveint as plaies.* [S]i maulveise char survient es plaies, si i devez mettre la puldre des hermodaccles en ceste maneire. Metez cotun en sauge e metez desure la puldre des hermodacles e puis metez desure. Autre cure. Pernez quatre unces de vive chauz, d'orpiment unce une e de eue chaut tant qui suffit e metez al fu. E od une esclice le medlez ben ensemble e puis sil metez blanchir al solail e laissiez tant qu'il soent desechi. E puis si metez en delié puldre e metez en sa[l]f. U faites tele pudre que nus avum usé sovent que receit hermodacles, aristo-logiam* rotundam* e li vert de l'arim. Tutes ces choses metez en puldre e metez en salf. Iceste puldre pusantment mangue la maufaise char e nient violentement. [f. 278v] Autre pudre. Pernez la chauz e destemprez od miel cum* paste e faites cum un pain e metez sur la tiule chaude e quisez e puis metez en puldre. Iceste puldre vaut pur manger la char morte e osist le cancre.

[IX] *De heresipilia.* [P]or ceo que un aposteme que est apelé herisipila seult* avenir as plaies e autres choses achantes, por ceo i metums differrences entre els e lur signes e lur cures. Erisipila avient auchune foiz en la plaie sicum borbleites e li liu est atempré e bein traitable e ceo est bone signe en la plaie. Auchune foiz avienent* borblettes neires e le liu de la plaie est dur e malement traitable e ceo est maufais signe. Les lius u teles apostemus vennunt devez od freides choses aidier. E metez dunc desus une plateine mis el jus* de la jubarbe e le jus de la morele, vermicularis, umbilici veneris, e de la chenellié e od ceo devez medler l'aubun de l'oef e olie rosat e violat, sandali blanc e ruge. E si vus ne poeez tuz ces choses aveir, si metez une partie. E quant ele revendra a sa propre nature, si leissiez la medicine ester. *Por faire la char venire as plaius*: [N]us veums que les plaius auchune foiz sunt crosses. Por feire la char venir faites tele medicine. Pernez de siu colé une livre de[f. 279r]mie, de cire unces trois, d'olie fioles dous, de mastic, olibanie e de mirre* uelement unces trois e confisés issi la cire e le siu fundez en olie. E puis i metez des choses qui sunt a tribler e quant il sunt ensemble pris, sis metez en salf.

[X] *De carbunculo.* [Q]uant l'aposteme que est apelé carbunclus survent* en la plaie, sil devez oindre de populeon que si doit estre fait. Pernez les oilz del poplier livre e demi e des foilles papaveris [nigri], qui est apelé en e[n]gleis popi neir, e des foilles de la mandrage e les cimes* del boissun e des foilles* de la chenillié e de la morele, umbilici veneris, vermicularis, lettues, jubarbe, bardane, violes, centum-cellie* uelement unces quatre, de freis oint de porc u de vi[e]l ben lavé livres trois. E faites en ceste manere. Pestelez bein les oilsz del poplier e autrefoiz le[s] pestilez bein [. . .] od les magdaliuns e metez en salf oit jurz. E puis depescés les magdaliuns par peicces en une chaudiere de trebein olant [vin] e metez sur le fu boiller jesque

le vin* soit anenti en movant totesfoiz od un esclice. E enaprés le cuilez parmi un
sac e laissiez refredir e metez en un veissel. Icest oignement vaut al* chaut de la
fievre ague e a cels qui ne poent dormir quant le puls* e les templus e les plantes
des peiz e des mains en sunt oint. E cest [f. 279v] oignement medlé od oile rosat u
violat si li malade est enoint, mervelusement oste la chalur. E si l'unblil* del
malade en est oint, si fait la suur venir. *Oignement a carbunculo*: [P]or l'aposteme
que carbunculus est apelé metez cest oignement qui receit peivre e orpiement
uelement e fies* secches tant cum vus plest e tribliez ensemble e confiscez od miel
e quisez jesque il soit espés. E puis le metez sure, ce amortist le charbuncle. E quant
il serra amorti, issi que la char mauvaise chece, dunc metez cest oignement desure.
Pernez la gummalve e brancam ursinam uelement, tribliez od oint de porc e laissiez
trois jorz flaistrer. Puis si quisez e colez [e] en la culure* metez un po de cire e de
mastic e autrefoiz le quisez e puis metez en salf.

[XI] *De la charnoseté del braz u entre l'espaude [. . .].* [S]i la charnoseté del braç est
plaié devant u entre l'espaude* e le cute, u la funte del braç est, de mauvaise e
neint cointe cure i pot [peril] avenir. Meis si la plaie est es autres parties del braz,
ne fait mie a duter. E si neires* burbelettes survenent as parties devant dites e
enflure munte* amunt, si est mal signe. E si blanches burblettes i survenunt e
l'emflure decende aval, ço est bon signe. [f. 280r] E faites la cure en teles plaies
sicum en l'os que n'est fra[i]nt ne pescié.

[XII] *De la plaie del braz od sun nerf.* [S]i le braz est plaié od sun nerf u od sun suriz,
si est mortel signe. E si le nerf ne la suriz n'est plaié e la plaie est en lung, l'une
partie e l'autre en enprimant a la partie joigniez e quintement la cusez e laissiez le
liu overt par unt la plaie se puisse purgier plus avenantement. E puis si faites la
cure avant sicum dit est es autres cures. E si l'aposteime que erissipila est apelé i
survient, faites la cure sicum devant dit est. Meis ço notez amiablement, que si le
brace est ensemble trait d'aucun fer en esclenc, si est mortel signe, e si en lung est
plaié, si faites la devant dite cure.

[XIII] *Del braz ke est percé de dart.* [S]i le braz est percé de dart de l'une part jesque a
l'autre, si metez un lardon de l'une part e un autre de l'autre part, e issi devez al
malade aidier sicum dit est en la secunde partie, quant le col est percié parmi de
l'une part jesque a l'autre. E si de l'une part est percié, si metez un lardon dedenz e
faites la cure enaprés sicum es plaies semblables que dites sunt desure.

[XIV] *De taillure de la main.* [S]i l'os u le nerf de la main est taillié, metez un drap
dedenz sicum [f. 280v] es autres plaies. Enaprés, sicum dit est desus en la cure del
braz* quant l'os u le nerfs est blescié, faites la cure.

[XV] *De la blesceur del menbre.* [A]uchune foiz avient que le membre est blescé par
colp u par fraiture u par autre aventure dunt emflure avenge. E issi porisse[nt] la
char e les ners e les os. Primes i devez mettre choses molliantes [e] pur [mettre hors]
quiture el* commencement primez la quiture hors suef entre vos mains e joignez
l'un menbre a l'autre sicum il avenist es junturus del braç, si rendez le braz a

l'espaude* e s'il avient en la quisse, si joingnez la jambe a la quisse. E issi faites des autres e ço faites desque tute la materie en soit issue, e puis le sanez sicum les autres plaies.

[XVI] *De l'espaude ke est desjunte.* [S]i l'os de la spaude est desjont, issi devez al malade aider. Faites le malade gesir sovin e pernez une peire u fust roond de l'une part e agu de l'autre part e pernez la partie plus ronde, si metez fils, qu'il i ait un torsun de fils, e cele chose roonde metez desuz l'aissiele al malade e li mire*, fermement premant, mette sun calcain sur sele chose e de ses meins lieve l'espaude por mettre l'os en sun dreit liu. E anz que le luiscel* del fil soit osté, une pecce mis en aubun d'oef [od] une longe esplente [f. 281r] liez desure de totes parz e laissiez illoec le luiceol* e liez d'un autre esplente e un plumeceol metez desure e ce soit pendu e levé en haut. Aprés trois jorz, s'il n'est pas bien atorné, si l'atornez e [o]ignez e liez en memes la manere. E si auchune collection d'umurs i avient, sil seigniez de l'autre* part. *Por metre le espaude en sun liu:* [A]uchune foiz avient que la chose ne put estre atornee en la maniere que dit est e dunc aturnez un lung fust e aquus emple e feites en miliu un pertuz, issi que li torsun del fil i puust entrer, si i metez le torsun del fil enz* la plus aimple partie [e] tiengent dous hommes fort le fust. E li malade munte sur un eschamel e li torsun li soit mis desuz les aiseles e li mires tenge ferm le bras e sil qui tenent le fust eslievent* de l'autre part l'espaude. E un autre soit qui coille l'escamil desuz* le[s]* peiz del malade e endementires qu'il pent, si metez l'e[s]palde en sun liu e puis le liez sicum dit est. E si ce est enfant, ne covent, nemais que li mires met son poing desuz l'eissele de l'enfant e tenge l'espaude de l'autre part e susleve* de l'autre main. Issi revendra l'os a sa propre jointure e garra. E si mestiers est, faites primes foment d'eue u [. . .] ces herbes semblables. E puis si oigniez le liu de diauté u* de marciaton* e puis [f. 28lv] metez desure estupes. E quant il serra revenu parfitement a sa propre jointure, si li faites tele constrictorie. Pernez pudre roge od aubun d'eof e medlez ben ensemble e envolupez [le liu] desure od un lung lignoel e puis le liez sicum devant. E leissiez issi plusurs jorz desque la jungture se soit afermee. E quant vus verrez l'enflure del constrictorie reprint, dunc baingniez le malade en ewe chaude e fomentez*, le constrictorie sus* levez* e quant vus verrez que mestiers est, si metez desure spadadrappum que si doit estre fait. Pernez le pudre de mastic e gros encenz, de peiz grec, boilli* e fundez od cire e od siu de mutun sur le fu. E metez une peize dedenz e metez tiedve sur cel liu. E si mestiers seit, si metez apostolicon cirugien.

[XVII] Si l'os de la cute* est desjont de sun propre liu, issi li devez aidier. Li mires desuz la pleüre del braz mete* une esplente e tenge sun pé sur l'esplente e[n] primant desuz e od sa main lieve le brace [a l']espaude. E issi doit remener l'os en sun propre liu e tro[i]s feiz u quatre le jor leve le braz e avale e puis le releve e lie, issi que le braz soit levé e pendu al col del malade, qu'il nel peust plaier. E aprés po jurz doit li malade asaeir d'avaler e de lever sun braz e puis soit issi lié, que le valer ne le lever del braz [ne] soit desturbé.

[XVIII] *De la [de]jungture del main.* [S]i la jungture de la main est [f. 282r] issue hors de sun propre liu, li mires prenge le braçz al malade a une sue main, e sa main, e

legerement e suef ramaine l'os del liu contrarie a sun propre liu. E puis face les
fomentations e les* oignemenz e, si mestiers est, metez esplente de l'une part e de
l'autre e puis liez. En memes ceste maneire devez mettre les doiz en lur propre liu
quant issu serra de sa jonture.

[XIX] *De l'os del braz u de l'espaude hors issu.* [S]i l'os del braz u de l'espaude est issu
hors, al comencement le devez remettre en sun propre liu. E s'il avient sanz ruture*
de la char, si devez prendre le membre de une part e de l'autre [e] sueif estendre* e
[primer] od voz* mainz sicum la franture fust al braz. Li mires face sun deciplie
tenir la main al malade por bein estendre ses doiz e sun braz tut. E un hom soit de
l'autre part qui teinge ferme le malade par l'espaude. E li mires joigne les os
ensemble e remeine a sun propre liu. E quant vus averez ceo fait, pernez une
plateine ample de quatre dois pur lier le braz qui soit mise en albon d'oef e metez
desur le braz e ben le liez. E puis pernez un autre peice e liez desure e ausiez de
chescune part. E puis metez sure les esplentes aparailliés e liez od un cordele e
leissiez issi jesque al teirz jor. Al chef de trois jorz faites ausi e a l'autre jor e al teirz.
E enaprés le novime jor aparil[f. 282v]lez une pudre constrictorie*, sicum dit est
desus en la teirce cure, e de cele constritorie enoigne li malade le brace e l'esplente
en la devant dite manere e ben se garde li malade qu'il ne s'apue sur sun membre*.
E si le leissez jesque a plusurs jorz jesque l'os se soit afermé ben. E iceo devez
conustre quant le constri[t]orie se lasche. Puis bainez le malade en ewe chaude e
eslevez le strictorie e ben le fomentez* de ewe u* quite soit malve e teles herbes a
lui en sa nature semblables. E puis sil terdez ben. E si l'os est afermé, dunc oingnez
de dialtee u de maciaton e puis metez desure estupus* e liez od esplentes e fil. E si
vus veez que li os ne s'est ben afermé, faites constrictorie de memes la maniere e
atendez u[n] po. E s'il est afermé, chescun jor feites fomentation e oignement e
liures desque il soit seins. E s'il avient que erisipila i avienge par destresce de liure,
desliez le liu tant lungement cum ele i est, e curez sicum dit est. *De la frainture de
l'os:* [S]i la fraiture de l'os est od la plaie, al commencement i soit aucun qui tenge
forment le membre al malade de l'une part et de l'autre e li mires asaie a sun doi si
l'os est frait u desevré de sun liu. S'il est frait, ço que est a oster ostez e [j]oignez os
a l'os e remenez a sun propre liu. E quant ceo ieirt fait, si liez desure une esplente
estroitement, en la maneire devant dite, mis en albun d'oef, [f. 283r] nequedent
que l'esplente soit percié sulun la maniere de la plaie. E puis i metez esplentes de
tutes parz, issi que la partie de l'esplente soit taillié de l'une part e de l'autre. E puis
metez dedenz un drap linge mis en aubun de oef. Chescun jor le sanez sicum les
autres plaies. E ne deliez pas les esplentes nemés del teirz jor el teir[z], sicum dit est,
desque la plaie soit sanee. E enaprés faites voz fomentations e autres adjutorius
sicum devant dit est. *De la fermure:* [A]uchune foiz avient que l'os ne puet estre
afermé u par vellesze u par fieblesce de vertu, qui ne pot duner nureture* as
membres e, ja soit iceo que l'os soit afermé, si* sent le malade granz dulurs. A ceste
maladie feites tele emplastre qui receit peiz grec .i. colofonie e peiz navale e
raissine uelement. E fundez al fu e al plus chaut que li malade le pot suffrir sil metez
desure e liez suef. *De l'os ke ne est pas adrescé:* [S']il avent que l'os ne soit pas
adrescié trois meis u quatre ainz que li malade venge al mire, si temprez primes

trois foiz u quatre od les devant dites* foment[at]ions meinte foiz e suvent. E quant ben serra fomenté, sil depesciez autrefoiz e puis faites la devant dite cure.

[XX] *De festres u de cancres.* [D]e festres e des cancres divers memes ce [diums] en ces parties que dit avom desainz. S'il avient [f. 283v] a alchum de plaie, metez le devant dit oignement desure. E s'il avient* es parties nervus del braç, si metez la puldre des amfodilles, e l'oignement devant dit metez a ceste cure que dit est del festre. Kar quant il avient es lius nervus*, mielez est qu'il ne soit pas curé que curé. *De cancre sanz blesceure.* [S]i cancre avient en tele partie sanz blescure del braz, si n'est pas a duter, ainz tailliez le cancre jesque al vif od un fer. E quisez amiablement od un fer chaut. E puis metez desure moel de l'oef mellé* od olie jesque le fu cheice. E puis le sanez od oignement vert sicum les autres plaies. E si festre est es charnus lius del braç, metez dedenz oignement rumpant e faites memes [les] incensiuns e les incisiuns seurement. E des autres choses faites la cure sicum dit est desus. E si os est [co]rumpu u porri par festre, si devez tut le os porgier e ço que corrumpu est devez traire hors. E puis alez avant sicum dit est en la desus. Des apostemus diom nus ice que dit est desainz e de memes la cure doivent li malade estre medicinez.

[XXI] *De plaie en la forcele.* Si plaie en vient en la forcele del piz u el piz d'espee u de autre maneire arme semblable, issi que la plaie soit d'entravers u en pendant, si cusez la plaie en lung* e feites la cure sicum dit est desus. E s'il perce les [f. 284r] choses dedenz, si metez un drap dedenz e faites la cure sicum as autres plaies. E si sanc u pureture peirce les choses dedenz, se mette li malade as genulz tornant soi ore de l'une part e ore de l'autre e issi mette hors le sanc e la pureture par le chanal de la plaie e ceo face li plaié tantes foiz quantes foiz il girra de cele part desque il soit seins. E si tele maniere de plaie avient en lung, n'i devez pas fere custure, meis* od drap e od autres choses jesque a la fin le devez curer.

[XXII] *Dedenz la substance de la forcele.* [S]i dedens la sustance de la forcele u del piz atapist fer, perciez l'os del piz en rooant e issi le traez hors. E si le fer atapist desus les costes u entre les dous costes, metez* un coinet entre dous pur tenir le liu overt e issi le traez hors legerement. E s'il ne put covenablement estre hors trait, melz est que vus l'i laissiez. E si le fer ne perc[e] mie jesque dedenz, traez le fer e metez lardun dedenz e faites ausi cum dit est es autres cures des plaes. E encore s'il ne perce mie dedenz, metez lardon u estoel oint de lard e as autres choses aidiez sicum dit est desus. E si devez ben noter que vus issi alez e metez l'estoel en teles plaes, que vus puissiez, quant mestiers est, avenantement hors traire e qu'il ne remaigne dedenz. [f. 284v]

[XXIII] *De la costee ke est plaié dedenz.* [Q]uant la coste se est plaié auchune foiz dedenz, dunc devez le malade mener al bang e oignez voz mainnes od miel u od terebentine u od auchune autre glamuse chose e metez vostre mein desur le malade en primant e levez meintenant e issi faites plusurs fiez jesque la costee soit remené en sun propre liu. E memes ceo solt* faire la fentuse mise od fu. E enaprés metez apostolicon desure u auchune emplastre semblable.

[XXIV] *Quant la plaie aveint en aucune partie del cors* [. . .] [S]i plaie avient en auchune partie del cors jesque as illieirs u as buals, qu'il nen issent ne blescié ne soient, en memes la maneire faites la cure que dit est en la plaie del pis e de la forcele, od fer u sanz fer, meis sul d'itant que quant le fer tapist dedenz, qu'il ne doit estre taillié en rooend meis* en long.

[XXV] *De plaié del quer u del pulmon.* [S]i auchune est plaié al quor u al pulmun u al foie u en diafragmate*, iteles plaies ne devez pas recevre en cure que en teles lius avien[en]t. E par ces signes poent estre conuz. Si li quors est plaié, neir sanc en doit issir od grant habundance. E si le pulmun est plaié, sanc espumés i doit issir od grant habundance e l'aleine* al plaié doit muer. E si pla[f. 285r]ie avient en diafragmate*, li plaié doit aver grant e espés hanellissement. E si le foie est plaié, conustre le* devez par les blesceures des ovremenz* que en lui sunt. E si l'estomac est plaié, la viande doit issir par la plaie. Tutes iceles maneires des plaies sunt morteles e pur ceo que les genz ne quident que li plaié perisent* par nus, pur ço laissums iteles cures ester. *De l'esplein:* L'esplien est servil membre e de ceo avient que de legier suffre taillures e arsures par quei, si nul[e plaie] i a*, par la cure que devant dit est seurement ieirt delivré. U tailliez de tut en tut la partie blescié. *De la foie* ke ist* par estroite plaie:* [A]uchune foiz avient que la foie ist hors par estroite plaie e nus dutums la blesceure de la plaie e pur ceo ne l'osum eslargir. A ceste blesceure devom issi aidier. Li malade gise sovin bein estendu e li mires de la partie desus d'entravers prenge le quir entre ses mains e sun deciple prenge la partie desus en meimes la maneire. E issi li mires e sun deciple, tenant le quir, hastivement esli[e]vent tut le cors, que li malades par siudein atraction de l'air e[s]force le foie a venir en sun propre liu.

[XXVII] *Des entrailles ke issent* par estroite plaie.* [S]i les entrailles issent hors par auchune plaie faite* [en] le cors, en lung u en escleng, [f. 285v] issi que la greinure* partie remaint seine, al premir le poum issi aidier. Si les boials par demurrance* de[h]ors sunt refredi, fendez auchune vive beste parmi e metez sur(e) les entrailes e tant la lessiez illoec qu'il soient eschaufé e de chalur naturele avivé [e] enmolliz. Enaprés aparilliez un chalmel percié de seu* en la maneire de la plaie del boel, issi que de sa lungur surmunte la lungur de la plaie une unce. E le challem[el] soit mut delié [e] en la plaie del boel soiet enz mis. E soit cosu de une delié aguille [e] d'un fil de soie. E issi soit mis le chalemel, que la superflueté del boel puise par lui passer e qu'il ne soit desturbance a la custure de la plaie. E quant ce est faite, si terdez les ordures del boel suef od une esponge mise en ewe e quant il serrunt ben espurgié, sis metez enz parmi la plaie dunt il s'en isserunt. E pus soit le* plaié mis sur une table tut quais, que les buaus repairent en lur propre liu. E si la plaie nen* est si grande qu'il poussent estre enz mis, si soit feit plus ample. E quant il serrunt enz mis, si laissiez la plaie overte jesque le buel se soit pris ensemble. E dunc sur la custure del buel metez la puldre roge chescun jor. E puis que le boel serra afermé, si sanez la plaie dehors od cus[f. 286r]ture e od autres choses faites la cure sicum dit est desus. E s'il avient que la plaie soit grande, iceste i ajustum, que une piece asez lunge soit mise en la plaie en lung, que de l'une des chiés passe en l'autre. E sur cele* memes piece la partie dedenz quintement soit cusu. E la puldre roge soit sure mis, que la piece que remaint dedenz chescon jor soit traite vers la partie pendante, que le drap de la plaie chescun jor soit osté. E quant vus verrez la plaie estre afermee, dunc ostez la piece e as chiés que ne sunt pas ben afermé faites la cure sicum es autres plaies. E li malades gise enclin e nient sovin, que la porreture ne vienge as entrailles dedenz. E sa diete soit mut tenve* e legiere.

[XXVIII] *De festres e de cancres ke aven[en]t en cel liu.* [D]es festres e des cancres qui en ces memes lius naissent memes soit la cure que dit est es lius charnus*. E faites memes les arsures e les taillures e les oignemenz violenz* dedenz. Meis ce i ajustum nus desure, que, si le festre perce le ventre, n'i devez mettre oignement ne puldre, que vus ne blesciez les entrailles. E si le pertus est estroit, od une tente de malo terre l'eslargissez. E li plai[é] s'encline, que la pureture qui dedenz est peusse issir. E puis metez dedenz un estuel enoint de oignement rumpant. Enaprés fa[f. 286v]ites la cure sicum desus dit est. *De cancre que avent as mameles:* [D]el cancre qui as mameles avient dium nus que, si la mamele est dure e tosté* e luisante, si la lessiez ester, car ele ne pot estre sanee si la mamele n'est arachié od totes ses racines. Meis quant la mamele est dure entur le col del [l]iu e* es autres parties est ben traitable, si la devez curer od le pudre des affodilles e od oignement rumpant sicum devant dit est. E bien avieint que aposteime survient es mameles de sanc que surhabunde en femme chescun [mois e] que illoc* avient. Car la mamele est membre espungus, dunc il avient que ele atrait a sei sanc menstruus [e] iloec se turne en lait, que, quant il n'ist mie a l'enfantement, si remaint iloec e endursist, si fait iloec grant dulur. A ceste maladie devez issi aidier. Metez i choses por amaurir sicum malve, brancham ursinam e les autres choses que devant dit[es] sunt. E quant le menbre est ben amolli, si tailliez sulunc la maneire [devant dite] e metez un estoel ben coé dedenz e primez hors tote la quiture. E pur ço est dite tente coee, que les tentes que remeinunt dedenz sunt acheisun de grengnur dulur, dunc le reconvent taillier por traire hors [f. 287r] la tente. *Achune foiz le chef de mamel[e] est dedenz turné.* [A]uchune foiz avent que le chef des mameles as juvenceles novelement mariees est dedenz torné, que l'enfant ne put recevre, dunt le devant dit mal ensuit. Pur ceo i devez mettre une ventuse de voire al cheif de la mamele por atraire a sei e suchir. Puis curez la plaie sicum dit est.

[XXIX] *Plaie sur le menbre, de cousture.* [S]i sur la membre d'umme avient plaie, od custure saner le devez e od autres choses sicum devant dit est. E memes ço devez faire des coilz, que si del* fuillet s'en ist, sil remetez en sun propre liu e cusez la plaie e metez desure la pudre ruge e sanez aprés sicum les autres plaies.

[XXX] *Si cancre aveint al vit de l'home.* [S]i cancre avient el vit de l'homme e purprenge tut le membre, tut le cancre tailliez hors, issi qu'il i ait un po del vif taillié, puis sil quisez od chaut fer. E puis le sanez sicum dit est desus. *Si le festre avent al [d]evant dit menbre.* [S]i festre avient el devant dit membre, faites la cure od oignement rumpant e od les autres choses sicum devant dit est. E si burbelettes i survenunt, si metez oignement blanc, meis pur aisil i metez rosat ewe e por olie commun olie violat.[f. 287v] S'il avient que le fil est rumpu u eschorchié par le quel il emfle, engrossist e endursist, si devez mettre dedenz olie medlé od aubon de l'oef. Enaprés si le tuel est estroit, si metez dedenz une tente de cire u de tel semblable, que la quiture mieuz venge as parties dehors. Autre cure a cel* memes: Pernez aloen e le jus de l'ache e olie violat e albon d'oef medlé ensemble e metez sur le liu. A *le emflure de[s] coiz e eschorjeur.* [A] la eschorcheure e a la rovur des coilz e a l'emflure pernez chimoleam, vernice e mirre e colophonie e vetonie e raisine* e tribliez ço que fait a triblier e medlez od oile chaud e puis i ajustez la ra[i]scine e medlez ben ensemble. E lavez primes les coilz de ewe chaude e puis metez tel oignement sur le liu. U pernez vermicularem e ciphulam e olie violat e triblez primes les herbes e medlez ensemble od l'aubun d'oef. A ço memes vaut* l'aubun de l'oef medlé od olie violat.

[XXXI] *De siphac e de osceum.* [S]iphac est une pelecte qui reteint les entrailes en un liu que est apelé osceum e de cele pelecte avient sovent que ele est eslachie e rumpue, auchune foiz plus, auchune foiz meinz. E s'il avient qu'il i eit petite ruture, si en ist ventosité [f. 288r] e empfle a la grandur d'une noiz u de un oef. E si la rupture est grande, le* buel decent parmi altre liu qui est apelé duodenum e par le pelecte que est siphac apelé cheit es coilz.

[XXXII] E si la rupture est petite e de po de tens e li malade soit enfés, faites en primant une liure sur la rumpure, si li donez trois foiz crepes de la greignure consoude noef e quant noef jorz se sunt passez, si manjuce en demenusant un*. *De rupture grande u petite.* [S]i la rupture est petite u grande e li malade soit cum de age de bachiler u auques de age u enfant e la rupture ne soit mie de lung tens, meintenant par taillier e par quiture quire le solium issi aidier. El commencement metez le malade sur un banc, la teste e ses espaudes issi que les entrailles li descendunt al piz, e ses jambes e ses quisses teinge li malade eslevé. E metez la coile quintement de cele part u la rupture est al plus que vus poeez, si merchiez* entur d'enche u de charbun. Enaprés pernez tote la roonddesce od dindimo e puis si metez le fer chaut de l'un signe jesqu'a l'autre e en memes la manere metez le fer en lé. E puis un autre maneire de fer, e les fers issi [en croiz] remanants*, metez desure une esplente mut delié e liez bein. Quant ce serra fait*, si ardez trois quitures [f. 288v] bein prés jesque al fer. *De rupture de siphac:* [A]uchune foiz est la rupture de siphac petite e dunc devez prendre la peleite od dindino e merchiez en memes la maneire que dit est. E metez le fer chaut de l'un signe jesque a l'autre e ben menez le fer e sa e la, amunt e aval, e ço en trois quiturus. Quant sur cel memes liu est la p[e]lecte trovee, si la tailliez en lung e faites quiture sur deindimum de ça e la e metez desure un oef od estupe. E li malade en eslevant ses jambes e ses quisses soit porté sur sun lit e liez bein ses jambes a* ses quisses qu'il ne se destende*. E quant le fu serra chaut, si metez desure la pudre ruge e autres choses que destreinunt. E quant il serra sanee, si metez apostolicon pur aorner la plaie. E sa diete* soit tenve e legere. E aprés cest faites la liure sicum dit est e li malade se tienge de fenme dous mois u trois.

[XXXIII] *Si le[s] boelle[s] cheent en osceum.* [S]i li buel cheent en osceum, sis remetez en lur propre liu. E s'il ne poent legerement estre arire mis, faites deslier e metez choses mollificatifs. E quant les entrailles serrunt mis enz e afaitiez sicum dit est, li diciple mette sa main la u la rupture est e li mires taille la pel qui est [f. 289r] sur la coille de cele part. E quant la coille est hors trait, si escarnez dindinum sicum devant dit est. E quant ce est fait, od un estrument qui est cloua* apelé, si nule ventosité est en dindimo, retenez dedenz e soit dunkes cusu ad* une esplente e bein liez dindinum. E laissiez pendre l'un cheif e l'autre de l'esplente par soi hors e, les tables surmises [al] dindimo, sil quisez de trois quitures e tailliez jesque a l'esplente. E quant vus averez ce fait, si metez desure estupe od oef e faites le malade porter a sun lit, sicum dit est, [e] desque al nofime* jor metez desure oef od oile. E aprés noef jorsz chiet le fu. E puis le fomentez od ewe u soit quit enz branca ursina e paritaria e aloesne e teles choses. E puis le* sanez sicum dit est desus.

[XXXV] *De la maladie ke est apelé hernia.* [U]ne maladie que est apelé hernia* auchune foiz avient de une carnosité* qui neist estre nature dejuste la coille. E quant cele pelecte est taillié, si doit estre escorchié de l'une part e de l'autre e quant icele carnosité* est descoverte, si devez dindimum taillier par quichun del quir dehors jesque amunt e jetez envoie. E puis si cusez* osceum sicum dit est desus.

[XXXVI] *Quant la pere est en la vessie.* Si piere est en la vessie, [f. 289v] de l'home, issi en poez estre cert. Auchune foiz hum se siece sur un banc e tinge sun pé sur un eschamel e li malade siece* sur ses quisses e ait ses quisses lié od un fachol a sun col u ben afermé as espaudes del suzseant. E dunc estoist li mire devant le malade e dous doiz de sa main destre mette en sun cul*, issi que le pui[n]g senestre emprient sur le penil* [e] od les doiz enz mis esleve tote [la] veissie* en sus. E si vus trovez auchune ronde chose dure, dunc saciez que la peire i est. E si vus i trovez mole* chose e charnuse*, charnosité est que desturbe la urine.

[XXXVII] *Deliverer la pere as funs* de la vessie.* [S]i vus volez delivrer la piere as funz de la vessie qui est al col de la vessie, primes faites vos fomentations e vos oignemenz e petroleon* [metez] par le tuel* del membre. E en po d'ure aprés metez siringe el col de la veissie e belement e suef la peiere del col de la vessie butez as funz. U faites ço que est plus seure chose e plus legere, sicom nus solium faire. Od les vomentacions e les enoingtions faites totes les choses por conustre si piere i est en la vessie e od les dois enz mises e le puing senestre enpreissié sur le penil od memes les dois traitiez le col de [f. 290r] la veissie. E la piere que iloec est movez un petit e issi amiablement le menez as funz. E issi poeez devant gar[ir] le malade qui est grevé de tele passion.

[XXXVIII] *Por la pere hors traire.* [S]i vus volez la peire hors traire, si devez dieter le malade* e einz qu'il soit curé doit jeuner* douz jorz e poi manger. E le teirz jor faites totes les choses que dites sunt por conustre si pieire est en la veissie [. . .] E pois le tailliez en lung od un estrument en la funteinele, dous dois sur le cul, e traiez hors la peire. E [aprés] la taillure e le osture de la peire desque a nof jorz matin e seir faites les fomenz de ewe [u] quit soit enz bransa ursina e paritaire e malve. E en iver metez desure estupe od muel de oef e en esté aubun od tut le moel. E le malveise char qui nest el col de la vessie tailliez hors od un rasur e la taillure cusez de dous u de trois puinz*. E puis la sanez sicum les autres plaies*. Ce devez ben saver, que, si la peire est grande, ne devez pas faire la cure par taillir, meis al devant garder le malade devez einz preendre la peire del col de la ve[f. 290v]issie as funz.

[XXXIX] *De plaies ke avenunt al cors.* [D]es plaies que avenunt el cors as parties dereire dium nus que dit avum desus. Coment qu'il avienge en l'eschine del dos, iceo ajustum nus, que s'il est plaié en lung sanz blessure de la meule dedenz, sicom achun nerf i fust blescez, si porra estre sané. Meis si l'eschine est plaié d'entravers, issi que la meule s'en isse u dedenz remaint corrumpu, a vis u unchus u jamais ne creum qu'il puis[se] estre garri par cirugie.

[XL] *Si le longaon est plaié.* [S]i [le] longaon est plaié par espee u par arme semblable, sil sanez sicum dit est en la cure del braz. E s'il est plaié d'entravers* e desevré de l'eschine es chiés, u de l'un chief jesque a l'autre u de l'un chief sulement, liez [le] longa[o]n fermement. E de auchune forte esplente de cele part u ele se teint bein l'estreigniez, que [a] la dereine partie n'avienge* nul nu[r]issement. E issi la laissiez jesque la dereine partie porrisse. E puis le tailliez od un rasur. Puis si faites la cure sicum es autres plaies. E si ele n'est del tut taillié, de maveise cure avient auchune foiz peril. E si la plaie avient [f. 291r] de dart, faites memes la cure que del braz dit est.

[XLI] *De plaies as reins.* [R]element avient que plaies aveinent as reinz e s'il avient, la cure del liu a la peusance de Deu maimes [laissum] que [a] la nostre cure. E nequedent solun la manere e la grandure de la plaie li overier ententif mant medicine en ceste partie sicum [es] cures des autres plaies.

[XLII] Des cancres e des festres qui naissent* en ces lius dium ceo qui desainz* est enseignié. *Aposteme de carbunculo*: Entur le fundement nest auchune fois aposteime issi cum carbunculus e est iloec une enfleure e auchune foiz el meis l'oste li malade od sa main e aprés [re]naist e par negligence n'est pas curé e issi enfestrit le liu. E pur ceo que plus soiez certifié demandez al malade si [quant] ventosité li ist par le cul, une partie* [ist] de l'autre part. Dunc saciez a vier que festre i est percié al chief longaonis. Issi devez al malade aidier. Al premeir le plus long doi enoint d'olie metez el cul del malade, si metez une tente parmi le festre e tastez de vostre doi al chief longaonis si la tente s'en ist par le pertus. E dunc i metez une peice sicum seon al cheif de la tente od une [f. 291v] aguille, metez parmi e liez la char e dunc laissiez. E a l'autre jor tailliez la char jesque a la peize. E si vus ne la volez taillier, si metez de l'une part de la peice unguent rumpant tant que sufist desuz la char [e] traiez la piece ainz. E quant l'ungement avra la char degasté, si garissez sicum les autres plaies.

[XLIII] *Cure des emerodes.* [E]morroides avien[en]t en trois maneires. Auchune foiz sunt dedenz e envoient sanc e funt* dolor. Auchune foiz sunt dehors, si en ist quiture, tel ure, se est, nule chose ne metent hors, e engrossissent e avien[en]t fiez e mut s'estrainunt e funt grant dulur. S'il sunt dedenz e sanc en ist, faites primes foment por asuager la dulur de la racine tapsi barbasti e de maruil* neir e de mentastrum*. Puis si pernez l'escor[c]e des chasteinez e l'escorce cucurbite e vielz* soles* e peiz grec* e metez sur les carbuns alumé. E le malade en estant sur un eschamel receive la fumee. E ceo face li malade dous foiz u trois le jor deske le sanc soit estanchié e la dulur amenusé. Puis, si vus volez [que] charrunt come fis, par auchun estrument semblable a clistere* i metez dedenz [f. 292r] le jus de la brionie e laissiez iloec une ure u dous e ceo faites desque l'ardur chiece. E puis l'oignez de l'oignement blanc sanz aisil e puis le fomentez desque il soit sein. *U les emerodes sunt engrossi.* [S]i les emoroides* sunt engrossi e quiture nule n'en ist, pernez les foilles de l'armeise e de l'aloisne tribliez e quit od olie de linois e metez desure al plus chaut que le malade le poit suffrir desque al tersz jor u al quart. E si ço fait bin, si faites memes la medicine. E si vus veez que eles ne descrescent mie, pernez le fruit caprifici* e metez en un pot sur le fu jesque il soit torné en charbuns e en faites puldre e, [le liu] enoint de meil, metez la pudre sur leine od la suur de sei meimes bien en primant od vostre main u od vostre pié. E quant il serrunt refreidi, metez desure l'autre pudre e ce faciez desque il soient amenusé. Enaprés, si par ceo ne sunt bein curé, liez chescun d'un fil de soie, si le malade le poet suffrir [. . .] e laissiez iloec le fil jesque il cheit*. E puis metez sure chescun oignement rumpant en une chaiseite de cire e puis metez [sure] chescun* le fer chaud. Enaprés si sanc [f. 292v] [n']en ist mais u quiture, asaiez od une tente s'il tent vers l'os u envers longaonem: s'il torne [envers longaonem], [si] laissiez ester; si envers l'os, si i metez un chaud fer u l'oignement rumpant. Enaprés i metez l'oef e sanez sicum les autres plaies.

[XLIV] *De la grevance del penil*.* Por ce que par plaie entur* le penil e es autres parties veisinez a la veissie avient* [u]ne grevance de pissier que est apelé stranguria*, dirum coment il puet estre aidié. Faites ceste emplastre qui receit [la cendre] des* foilles e la racine de l'ieble e faites la cendre longement boillir. E enaprés metez en un sachelet e metez sur le penil al malade tant chaud cum il le porra suffrir. Meintenant rendra la urine al malade.

[XLV] *Por quiturus a cors de l'home*. Por ceo que quitures funt bein al cors d'ume, si dirrum d'els en quels lius il deivent* estre fait e a quei il valent, de homeplates jesque as [c]oilz. A *l'emflure del braz*: [A] l'encision u a l'emflure del braz e de la juncture de la main* quisez le malade el braz trois dois ariere le nois. A memes l'emflure [f. 293r] e al dulur de la main faites entre dous dois de l'autre part. A memes ce faite[s] quiture* el crois. *Al dolor des espaudes*: [A] la dolur des espaudes e por la defaiture des oilz faites quichum al noit de[l] braz dedenz e en la funteinele dehors*. *Por dolur que est apelé asma**: [A u]ne maladie qui est apellé asma*, ce est quaunt hume ne put atraire sa alaine ne hors mettre, faites quiture sur le piz desuz un liu qui est apelé epiglaco, ce est la forcele. *Por dolur de l'estomac*: [A] la dolur de l'estomac metez un seon desuz la forcele del piz. A la vice de la foie feites quiture sur le foie. A l'esplein metez un seon al senestre costee sur l'esplein. E uns i mettent dous, le un remué de l'autre. A la dulur de l'umblil faites seon trois dois suz l'umblil. A la dulur des reinz suz memes les reinz en la funteinele faites seon al* noet. A la dulur de l'echine* faites trois seons, l'un en miliu de l'eschine e l'autre trois dois desure e le terz trois dois desuz. A la dulur des coilz metez seon desuz les coilz en osceo.

[BOOK IV]

O[r] ai purposé par la grace de Deu de mettre fin a cest ovre. Meis pur ceo que jo ne ai cest o[v]re tresté par parooles colurees ne acemees ne par ordre, si demande pardon a ce[f. 293v]lui qui cest livere volenteres lirra, que* il volenteirs entende par queles paroles e par quel* ordre jo ai ce livere endité e mette estudie sur ceo de bein dire sicum sur ferm e estable commence[me]nt por aver los e glorie. Des cures qui sunt plus haut des reins dit ai en sus. E ore traiterai de scia e de ses cures e des menbres qui sunt plus aval. A *plais qui sunt en scia, ce est le os runde:* [I] [D]es plaies qui sunt en cia, ce est l'os rund u le liu. [II] De plaies qui venunt en la quise par espee u par acune arme semblable. [III] De cele memes od dart. [IV] [D]es plaies del gunil e si la paele* soit taillié u nu[n]. [V] [D]es* plaies des genuz od dart. [VI] [D]es plaies des quisses en quelcunques maneere faites. [VII] De* la plaie del pié* od blescure des neirs u sanz blescure. [VIII] [D]e la desjonture de la quise des* parties sovereines. [IX] [D]e la rupture* de cel meimes od plaie u sanz plaie. [X] [D]e la desjongture de la quisse e de la jambe. [XI] [D]e la rupture* de la quisse od la rupture* de l'os u de la char e sanz rupture de cel memes. [XII] [D]e la desjong-ture del pei e de la jambe. [XIII] [D]e la desju[n]gture des ortilz*. [XIV] [D]es cancres e des festres que neissent en memes ces* lius. [XVI] [D]es borbletes e des rupturus de la char que avenunt as quisses de sausefleime u [f. 294r] de melancolie. [XVII] [D]es quichuns qui avenunt en la quise e es jambes e es pez. [XVIII] [D]e l'arsure de fu e de fer chaud e de euue chaud. [XIX] [D]e lepre e quantes e[s]peces sunt e de quels nuns il sunt apelé. [–] [D]e cauncre e male mort que est apelé malum mortuum.

[I] A *[l'os es] reins ke est apelé vertebrum.* [S]i l'os qui est es reinz qui est apelé vertebrum, ce est le os qui se turne el liu que scie est apelé, est* blescé d'epee, issi que une partie de scie remeinge, si* auchune chose deit estre ors treit, sil traiez hors. E faites es custures e es autres choses la cure sicum devant dit est. E s'il s'est pris al dart e ne puisse seurement estre hors thrait, taillez la char jesque a l'os pur meilz traire hors. E s'il ne put estre hors trait, od un delié perçur qui est apelé trepacium en la devant dite manere perciez e isi le traiez quintement hors. E enaprés faites la cure sicum devant dit est. E si l'os n'est blescee, si est la cure aperte.

[II] *Por plaie en la quise.* [S]i plaie aveint en la quise* d'espee u de acune autre arme semblable, s'il est blescié u nun, memes la cure devez faire que dit est desuz en la cure del braz.

[III] *Si la quise est plaié de quarel.* [S]i la quise est plaié od dart, nule chose n'i faites plus que dit est en la cure del braz desure.

[IV] *De plaie au genul.* [f. 294v] [S]i aveint al genild que la paele* del genild soit sevré en grant partie, par custure festes la cure en la manere que devant dit est. Memes ce dium nus si la paele del genild est blescé u nun.

[V] *Por quarel ke seit afiché.* [L]e dart qui se eirt a la paele deit estre hors trait par grant quintise sicum devant dit* est e ensengné. E puis faites la cure sicum es autres plaies.

[VI] *Des plaies de la jambe.* [D]es plaies de la jambe dit avum sicum des autres choses, meis ice i surajustuns que* si la plaie avent trois dois* desuz le genul u del genul amunt [u] en la carnosité de la jambe u e[st] l[e] menbre organal, si est peril e si fait mut a duter, dunt vus devez faire la cure sicum de[s] braz. Mes ce notez, que si emflure avent od duresce e od grant dolur munt amunt, si est mortele signe. E si l'emflure avale, n'est pas signe mortel. *Si la jambe seit perscé de quarel.* [S]i la jambe est depescié de dart, faites les devant dites cures.

[VII] Si la plaie aveint el pié od la blescure des ners, faites memes la cure que dit est es plaies des mains, e si el talun, si faites quinte cure.

[VIII] *Por le os ke est apelé vertebrum.* [S]i l'os qui est vertebrum apelé ist* hors del liu qui est apellé scia par cop* u par autre aventure e le nerf [f. 295r] qui joint les os est rumpu, li mala[des] sera tutdis clop, e si hoem le peut amender. Primes gise li malade sovin* e li mires seit* cuntre lui od ses pez tresturnez en primant od ses peiz cuntre lui e tenant sa jambe entre l'une quise e l'autre*. E un forte home teinge le cors e li mires en traiant od ses mains les parties dessus e en primant od ses peiz si remaine vertebrum en sun propre liu. E si mesterz est, liez le malade de dous cordes dejuste la jointure. E li mires seant encuntre lui teinge le chef de cele cordele de l'une part e un autre soit de l'autre part qui face icel memes, e issi en traiant oelement soit l'os refaitié*. E mesurez les peiz, que vus saciez si estut bein u nun. E soit li malade turné, que li mires ne soit deceu, e mesure[z] ses taluns. E si ambesdous les nates gisent uelement, si est bein. E dunc i metez une pece mis en aubun d'oef e un plumaceol metez desure e liez od une grande esplente. E li malade gise en un estroit liu, que les quisses ne peussent vagir. E suvent fa[i]tes enuncions e fomentacions sicum dit est.

[IX] *Si le os de la quise seit debrisé.* [S']il aveint que l'os de la quisse soit rumpu, el commencement le metez en sun liu. E si rupture de la char par plaie aveint, si devez prendre le menbre de l'une part e de l'autre [f. 295v] e suef estendre e preendre od les mains. E puis si faites la cure sicum dit est en la rupture de char* del braz. Meis ice i ajustum que a la mesure de l'autre quisse, jambe e pié soit efaitié. E il covent que vos leissiez espace a la mesure de une unce entre les chiés de l'os. E pur lier* une plateine ample metez e puis une autre sur cele e de la plaie faites sicum des autres plaies.

[X] *Si le genul seit dejointe.* [S]i la jambe est desjuncte de la quise, faites memes la cure que dit est en la disjuncture del braz. E la cure des fomentacions e des enuncions faites avant od la devant dite estupe*. E remenét l'os en sun liu e liez sanz tables. E puis contrait, puis estendu, se move li malade e bein se acustume d'aler.

[XI] *Si la jambe seit debrisé od la char.* [S]i rupture de la jambe e de la char est od plaie, memes ce dium que en la rupture del braz e[st] dit, e nule chose n'i ajustum ne meis d'itant que une unce d'espasce soit leissié entre les os sicum dit avum en la rupture del braz. E plateine de sis dois liez desure. Ne ce ne lessum nus mie, que si la rupture aveint en la quise u en la jambe [e] est l'espace de tro[i]s unces desuz le genuld u desure e malveis signes avienunt, si est mortel signe.

[XII] *Si le pé est dejoint.* [f. 296r] [L]e pé est achune foiz desjont de sun liu, ore ça, ore la, ore envers la plante, or envers le* talun. Faites primes vos fomentacions e vos enuncions e puis trahez le pié forment. E por la varieté de la [des]juncture destrainiez le nu* de venir a sun propre liu e liés tables desure de totes pars.

[XIII] *Si les ortilles seint dejoint.* [L]es ortilles del pié aucune foiz sunt esluissié. En memes la manere les remenez a la jungture sicum dit est de[s] dois.

[XIV] *Des cancres e festris ke avenunt* a la fez en memes ces l[i]us.* [L]es cancres e les festrus que avenunt en memes ces l[i]us achune foiz corumpunt la char e purissent* l'os e corumpunt par ce que ces parties sunt charnus. E s'il ne sunt prés as veines u as neirs u as auteries, si devez taillier e arder e mettre les oingnemens violenz*. Icele manere de cancre auchune fois s'eslargist e runge en coste, issi le devez par tallier saner. Quant cancre est en eslargant, si taliez les livr[e]s de tutes pars e p[r]imez hors le sanc. E puis si l'ardez jesque as funz. E puis curez od eoef mis sur e od autre[s] choses sicum devant dit est. E s'il aveint que cancre avienge en liu ossuus* [e] sur os [. . .], si fetes issi la cure. Faites une chassette de cire ausi grant come le cancre est, si emplez de oingnement rumpant e metez sur le [f. 296v] cancre u faites un cercle de cire veire u de paste autrisi graunt cum le liu est, si metez desure por garder la bon char, e le liu emplez de oingnemenz rumpant, que malvaise [char] soit amortie, [co]rumpue e mangué. E laissiez issi del* matin jesque al vespre [u del vespre] jesque al matin. Puis si metez oef al fu. E quant le fu serra chaeet, si tailliez la char que est malement creu jesque a l'os e raez l'os amiable-ment. E tant cum vus verrez que l'os est entechi de cancre, par vostre engin ostez. E quant vus verrez que la bone char crest sur l'os, si faites la cure sicum es autres plaies. E si vus veez que l'os est de[l] tut amorti, icele [manere de] cancre* ne peet estre sané. Derecheif cancre avint as parties deraines qui poet estre ocise od la puldre psilotri. E cancre pullente e neire amortist par la pudre des affodilles.

[XVI] *De burbletes e de rupturus.* [B]urblettes e ruptures qui avenunt as jambes sunt curé en memes la manere que dit avum de la feinture de la test, meis que taunt i ajustum que le malade lieve sa jambe entur le liu de la rupture de sa urine matinale e puis la terde e oigne del devant dit oignement. E quant vus verrez que les borblettes s'en vunt* e que les rupturus sanunt, dunc metez oignement blanc [f. 297r] e[l] quel por aisil soit mis ewe roset e por olie comun* olie violat.

[XVII] A *sciatiche faites trois quiturus*. [A]l passion sciatiche faites trois quiturus sur le liu de scie, ce est de l'os rond, e une quiture al remedie de tot le cors. Faites dous quiturus trois dois desuz [le genul e trois dois] desure le talon e faites une quiture desuz la jambe que mut vaut a artetike e a la dulur des parties sovereines. *Por gute artetiche*. [A] la gute artetiche* faites quiture al crois desuz le pié.

[XVIII] [A]rsure avient de fu [u] de ewe ch[a]ude, dunc al primez devez prendre oli conmun e metler od ewe freide e quant bein se serrunt entrepris, si i metez autrefoiz ewe e lungement [metlez] ensemble, e puis de celes choses oingnez le liu. Derecheif pernez herbes freides, crassulam la graunde e la mendre, e umbilicum* veneris, solatrum e jubarbe, de checun une poigné e pestelez od une livere de novele oignt. E quisez tut en un pot e ço quullez parmi un drap [e] metez cire e mastic. Icest vaut mut. Derechef pernez le sumet del seu e triblez od oint e od siu de porc e laissés trois jors pur flestrir. E puis le quisez en ewe e quullez* e puis sil metez en salf. *Por arsure*: [S]i arsure en veit parfunt, si fetes ceste oignement qui receit letargerie, plum ars, de mastic, de gros ancens [f. 297v] uelement unce e demie, gresse de porc unces trois, tu[tes] ces choses tribliez* e metez en puldre. E puis si pernez le jus vermicularis, umbilici veneris, solatri e cimus de buissun uelement demi unce, de olie violat unces quatre, e demenez longement le jus od l'olie e medlez bein ansemble. E puis i ajustez les devant dites puldres e autrefoiz ewe rosat e faites sicum oingnement blanc el mortieir e metez cest oignement sur la fole del cholet u de la plainteine e metez desure. Derecheif pernez la vive chauz e metez en ewe e lavez forment e laissez en pais trois foiz* as funz e jetez l'eue. Enaprés pernez olie violat u rosat u conmun e medlez* od la chauz mult bein e autrefoiz lavez e ostez e gardez. E el comencement i seult mult valer savon sarazim si le liu en est oint*.

[XIX] *De lepre*. [L]e lepre* avient en cors d'ume de humurus corumpuz e de quatre humurs, dunc quatre manieires de lepre* sunt: l'une est apelé alopicia, l'autre elephancia, la terce leonina, e la quarte* tiriasis. Allopicia est de fleume qui est semblable a gupil, char uns gupilz sunt depilez, si sunt cil qui cele maladie unt*. Elefancia est de sanc, de l'olifant nomee, [f. 298r] char sicom l'olifant est greing-nure de[s] autres bestes, issi est sanc des autres humurs. Leonina est de colore ruge e si a nun de liun qui plus est chaude de autre beste. Issi est ceste passion plus chaude de autre u pur ce que* lium est de diverse colur, issi est cele maladie de diversus colors. Tyriasis est de melancolie, si est semblable a un verm que est apellé tirus, kar sicum tirus par sa compression e par sa confricacion* pert s'espuille, issi cels qui unt cele maladie se defrotent e degratunt tuz jorz, as queles nus fesum cest oignement. Pernez savum franceais unces trois, picule l[i]vre une, de cire unces trois, de* la farine lupinorum amarorum e fulliginis uelement unces quatre, del jus panis porcini unces trois, de fumeterre unces trois, de viel oint de porc unces quatre, d'olie e de capitel tant que suffise. Totes ces choses metez en un vesel de tere al fu e quant il serrunt fundu, estre les choses que ne devent estre fundu, si metez cire e puis la puldre des choses qui tribliez sunt. E de ce tiedve oignez le malade chescun jor desque al setisme jors. E puis al[t] li malade al ba[i]ng, si se leive. E quant ceo eirt fait, le teir[z] jor aprés li coupez les coilz e entre l'espaudle* e la cute, u la fontaine est ditte, le* quissez e es fonteines que sunt desuz [f. 298v] l'une e l'autre oraille. Icest oignement* vaut encontre elefancia. E ancontre allopicia faites tel oignement. Pernez peivre e vif suffre e de pelestre unce une, de olie de violette [fiole] une, del jus de la burnette fiole* une, de savon franceais lifre une, e confissez issi. Ce ke doit es[tre] triblé triblez e boillez en olie. E puis metez savvon e metlez ensemble e* un pou le fundez al fu. E pus frotez le* malade forment o leine e puis vet li malade au bain sec ausi cum estuve e bein se oingne e su[e] al bain. E issi face del teir[z] jur al* terce jesque il soit [sein] e fet garde ki il soit* res.

[XX] *Por crampe ki avent.* [L]a cra[m]ppe qui aveint en la plaie puet um saner en ceste maneire. Unnez de cel oignement que si doit estre fait. Pernez oile muscelin unce une, petteroile unce une e demi, d'oile comun e de bure de mai uelement dragmes quatre, de cire unce une, storascis blanc* e ru[g]e uelement dragmes dous e demi, de mastic e olibanum uelement unce e demi, de la gume d'eire* scruples quatre e demie e confissez. Tut medlez ensemble e metez sur le fu od les choses qui devent estre [fundu] e od une esclice les pudrez en demenant medlez. E a derain quant il ven[f. 299r]dra a l'espescir e bein serra quit, dunc i metez storacim e oignét le malade entre dous feus a l'haterel e el col e en l'eschine e par tut le cors. Icest oingnement vaut mult a checune gute crampe qui vient de replecion. *Por la maladie que est apelé malum mortuum.* [C]este maladie malum mortuum est apelé* commun[em]ent. Si il vient de malancolie e naist as dereines parties del cors, dunt ces sunt les signes. Il a lee cruste e dure e sante moisture e od grature e ceo doit estre la cure. Epurgiez* la matire quinze jurs d'oximel e sil porgiez puis od beneite medlé od yeralogodion agusié de ellebre neire*. E le teirz jor aprés estuvez* les jambes od herbes boillies en vin fort. E puis oignez le malade de neir oignement e de oignement qui soit a sauseflegme medlé ensemble e aguissez d'elebre e par sis jors checun* jor dous foiz. *Del limazun*: [P]ernez limazun, triblez en fort vin u quisez en lascive e pernez la gresse qui sornoe* e oignez les jambes. Pernez le test de grand nois e metez en pudre od fulugine e od crote de cheifre e desstemprez od saim d'oie*. Pernez la tettesuriz* e le sel bruilli e destemprez od le jus de [f. 299v] la parele. E puis [en] triblant e en pestelant mellez od mel oint de porc. E faites enplastre e eschaufez sur une teule al fu e metez sur le mal al plus chaut que li malade le poet suffrir.

NOTES AND REJECTED READINGS[1]

[BOOK I]

I. od la despesceũr d.t. est quant la plaie est a.f.   quant la plaie p. u g.   est del   blor-
bletes   la   quarte

The opening shows signs of disorder including dittography ('od la despesceur' and 'quant la plaie') and failure to distinguish the subjects 'fractura' and 'vulnus' of the Latin. I have emended a number of readings (see above) to produce a text which more accurately renders the original. In the list of symptoms of damage to the *dura mater* AN omits 'alienatio' (122) (glossed in some MSS 'id est loquitur aliena') and renders 'oculorum incensio' (122) with 'la veine des oiz li deit reesuer' (ME 'swelling of the eyen'). Under symptoms of injury to the *pia mater* AN curiously renders 'defectu virtutis' (124) with 'li naffré reevera'.

II. soie u de alchune   e de une plume seint s.   doit

In AN 'cose que mut beit' renders '(res) bibula' (142). At 145 AN adds an explanation that pus forms in the wound quicker in summer than in winter, so that it needs more frequent dressing. The description of the patient's position in the penultimate sentence is an addition probably prompted by an insertion in the source (cf. the 'ut sanies declinet ad exterius' of MS M, Sudhoff p.159, n.19).

III. mie

The Latin has 'spongia marina bene lota exsiccata' (150, cf. 140) and so I have restored 'mult' where the scribe wrote 'mie' (probably as the result of misreading the abbreviation *ml't*): ME has 'sotyl powdre of pomyshe wel waschide and dried befor'. AN supplies a number of explanatory phrases e.g. 'E tant metez . . . amortie', 'que res est . . .' (cf. Renzi p. 430 'Nota quod carpia est carpitura panni sive rasura' and *Rolandinus* ed. Daremberg 'carpia, id est rasura panni vetusti'), 'ce est la neire peiz'. In the list of ingredients of the receipt 'picis grece libram .i., galbani' (156) is omitted, but restored in the following preparation (IV below).

IV. conflecciun   eun   estain destaim   devient   annoniac   defendre   noiz
en   mulexz (x expuncted)   penuisiez   e a

The receipt for *apostolicum cirurgicum* is probably not part of the original text of the *Chirurgia* and even here is not rubricated. Typically, AN accompanies a technical expression, 'magdaleones' (171), with a brief explanatory phrase ('une ronde confection . . .'). In the penultimate sentence 'l'oinnier' translates 'coequationem' (172). The final sentence ('valet etiam ad dolorem ex fractura pectoris, que fit ex contusione, casu, percussione', 173–74) is not accurately rendered.

V. saieier (second e expuncted)   ne saverez   u   deveit   nostre   picie
sentrecientent   voiz   escurgier   saver   a   asaner   il laissiez   treiez

The 'ostil cirugien', not further identified in AN (cf. ME 'some crokyde instrument that is

---

1 For translations and sigla see Introduction and note 42. Corrected readings are indicated in the text by asterisks.

scharpe'), corresponds to the 'rugen' of the Latin (181), and the 'tenailles' (ME 'pynsons') to 'picicariolis' (var. *piscanolis, picigarolo, picicando, picitariolo* etc.) (183). The phrase 'ja seit ceo que par vostre franchise en aiez pitié' does not accurately render 'licet tuo beneficio differas quousque illa [sc. removenda] cessaverint' (184). 'E pois auches . . . e plaiez aneire' constitutes an addition to the Latin (190, following 'impleatur'). The Latin 'quartarios' (var. *quarterios*) (192, 195) is rendered by 'les peices del quir del test'. For the reference to 'en croiz' cf. the marginal note in MS M 'plumaceolus etiam in modum crucis imponas intra quartarios carnis, ne ipsi possint conglutinari' (Sudhoff p.161, n.6).

VI. que cele   peirge   issi   le devez

AN makes no attempt to find a vernacular equivalent for the surgical chisel or to adapt the Latin morphologically to the grammatical context, Latin 'spatumine' (212) being reproduced as 'spatumini'. Similarly, 'trepacium' is probably also Latin, arising from a misreading of 'trepanum' ('trepano', 211).

VII. en   traiz

AN 'od le cisol' renders 'con spatumine' (var. *spatumino*, 222).

VIII. ce ces   blane   saufi

The plant 'parele' for 'paretaria' (228) is probably the result of confusion with 'paratella'.

IX. la   depestelesie   solaciun   vim   del del   sustraet la drap linge que est apelle charpie e apres quant la char crest si s.

AN 'des icel jor que la plaie comence a quiturer' translates Latin 'a die vero reumatis' (247) which is glossed in M 'id est ex qua sanies incipit generari' (Sudhoff p.162, n.23), which is probably the source of the translation.

X. m. de mastic unces dous de olibano

The Latin has 'picis grece .ii. uncias' (251) and, at the end of the list, 'ana unciam semis' (252). At the end of the receipt the penultimate clause in AN ('si fait nestre . . .') reflects a reading like the marginal insertion in MS M 'et malam corrodit et saniem generat et eandem attrahit et educit' (Sudhoff p.163, n.7 and C [TCC 0.1.20] f. 303vb).

XI. The phrase 'la secunde cure' reflects the reading of M 'in secunda cura capitis' instead of 'in fractura capitis' (Sudhoff p.163, n.17). C f. 304ra and Renzi p. 433 also have 'in secunda cura'.

XII. malada   sanoier   ue   achalor   ficure

XIII. i   si reparrilez   mairier   lin   pernez   e es   dos   apostoeines

AN omits the first ingredient, 'arthemisia' (284), and a later one, 'cepe' (284), omits the preparation (284–85), and paraphrases 'si ab istis non repellitur materia' (287). In the second embrocation AN adds 'aisil'. The Latin has 'quatuor uncias de farina frumenti' (291).

XIV. ii   la teste   cheveals

In AN 'rubigo' is an error for 'rugen' (303 'con rugine'). The Latin specifies 'con acu subtili quadrata' (305). The phrase 'desuz le doi' is apparently an attempt at rendering 'sub mensura unius uncie' (306) i.e. leaving a finger's breadth between stitches. In a Florence MS there is the instruction 'non fiat continua sutura, sed fiat per intersticium unius digiti' (Sudhoff p.164, n.11). At the end of the instructions the Latin specifies that 'inferior vero pars' (308) should be left open, whereas AN has simply 'la plaie' which muddles the sense. I have therefore supplied 'desuz' (cf. ME 'leve the nedirest place of the sor open that the gore and filth may rene out').

XV. ces   trailleur

AN 'aprés la depesceure' does not correspond to the Latin 'post suturam' (315) and 'jesque al secunde jor' seems to be an error (320 'usque ad ix dies' cf. ME 'and so do tyl .ix. or .x. daies ende untyl the flesch grewe fair above').

XVI. que devez

AN 'tantet' renders Latin 'tantillum' (330), whilst 'queintement' is an addition to the source, probably the result of reading 'a cuti' (330) as 'caute'.

XVII. desevree

I have added 'le test' in accordance with the Latin 'sine craneo' (335).

XVIII. mes c.

The Latin 'in contumacia capitis' (337), variously glossed 'id est in summitate' and 'id est eminencia' (Renzi p. 436 'id est in conjunctione cellularum'!) is not rendered by AN, probably because the meaning of 'contumacia' was not recognized. The introduction of 'quarel' is an addition.

XIX. il il   del   livres   deveit   ol   od le nes   es   marmeil

AN 'sumet del quir' renders the Latin 'superficiem cutis' (347). In the source the nose-stall is described as 'sustentaculum in modum capistri' (353) and also as 'retinaculum' (354), which is not included by AN. ME has 'sett .ii. litill pellows on every syde to kepe the nose stedfast and have the maner of an heltir with a spelk to bynde up the nose'. Also missing from AN is the matter corresponding to 'In omnibus quoque suturis extremitates apertas relinquimus, quo et stuellum ibidem inmittere valeamus et per illos meatus saniem effectam purgemus' (355–57), most likely as the result of a palaeographical 'saut du même au même' from 'per illos meatus' in 355 to 'per illos meatus' in 357. The phrase 'es lius la li os sunt tendre' corresponds to 'in cartillaginosis locis' (358) (ME 'in a gristilly place'). In 'les autres menbres' AN subsumes 'et virga et labiis et similibus' (359–60). In the Latin, treatment with the powder is prescribed 'usque ad nonam <vel plures> dies' (360–61).

XX. auchum   oile   travaild   entente   en   vuos

AN omits 'angustos' (366) applied to 'meatus' ('chaneiails'). The phrase 'mes que grant travail est' corresponds to 'licet laboriosum sit extrahere' (366) and 'devez vus memes pener' to 'secundum ingenium quisque laboret' (367). 'E si il ne put estre hors trait, issi qu'il se soet pris as neirs' is an explanatory amplification of 'si absque multa molestia non possit extrahi' (374). In the cure the Latin specifies that the tent 'sagimine ungatur' (379) and that 'desuper plumaceolum de panno lineo ponatur' (380). These details are omitted by AN as the result of another 'saut du même au même' (from 'de panno lineo' in 379 to 'de panno lineo' in 380). I have added 'que plus' in accordance with the Latin 'plus retardetur ad consolidandum quod magis pendet' (382). At 387 Sudhoff's text ought to read 'non praetermittimus' (C f. 304vb 'non pretermittamus').

XXI. reveez   sele   troiz   ne   le   pente   quil h.   naavenunt   cirugien talier descurere

At the beginning AN omits 'si forcipes ibi large immittere possumus' (391–2). The phrase 'a col de la saete' renders a gloss to 'ad stipitem' (393), namely 'id est collum sagitte' (Sudhoff p.167, n. 6). AN 'a vene overte' renders 'manifeste' (403). For the surgical instrument in the cure the Latin has simply 'con rugine' (406), whereas there is a blank left in AN. The notion of 'cent pertuz' results from a mistaken interpretation of Latin 'in modum .c. perforamus' (407) where '.c.' signifies 'crucis' (cf. Renzi p. 437 'in modum litterae C'!). AN repeats this detail and again renders Latin 'trepanum' with 'trepaciun' (see VI above and XXII below}.

XXII. ue   cerver   la   fu   en en troiz

AN omits 'vel casu' (416) and embroiders 'motui cerebri non modicum repugnare' (417). Latin 'hostiles inpugnaciones [var. *pugnas*] imaginatur' (418) is reduced to 'granz batailles'. I have added 'e escharnez' on the basis of the Latin 'con rugine scarnetur' (420–21). AN again renders 'trepanum' (421) by 'trepacium', but the context is hopelessly garbled in the MS which actually reads: 'od un rasur e si l'ostez del test d'un perçur cirugien que est apellé trepacium. E tut ceo que ploié est osteiz. E meimes la cure deveiz faire a cete plaie que dit est avant en la cure de la depesceure del test od un ostil cirugien que est rugine apellé e de ambes partez la plaure percir le test'.

XXIII. mavgue (superscript v)   a la   r. e la part dunt vus les peilz esrachiez les peilz od tote la racine   e de   les   chevoilz   semeie   auroue   a. de ces p.   la iustez   de miel e de saim   meint   sance les

For 'le quir est divers e dur' the Latin has 'cutis densa et dura', suggesting that AN misread an abbreviation of the first adjective. Concerning the incurable case of *tinea* the Latin has 'Huius curam pro derelicta habeamus' (428), AN 'Icele teigne ne devez pas recevre en cure'. In the first of the curable types AN 'menu' appears to render 'non continua' (430). In the description of the skin as 'gros e espés' AN has read 'spissam' where Sudhoff's text has 'scissam' (431) and 'si n'est pas od grant grature' presupposes the attested variant 'non multo pruritu' as opposed to the 'con multo pruritu' of Sudhoff's text (431). In the receipt 'olie commun' followed by 'des nuals autant' reflects the reading of the Florence MS of the *Chirurgia*, which has 'olei' with an interlinear addition 'vel nucis'. In the receipt for the depilatory (*psilotrum*) the Latin specifies '.iiii. uncias calcis vive' (446). For 'dous unces arsenici' the Latin has 'de auripigmento quartam partem uncie' (447). AN by its repetition of 'plume' does not very clearly render the Latin 'penna inmissa et statim extracta de facile depilari potest' (449). I have emended AN to 'rouor sur le chef' in accordance with the Latin 'ruborem aliquem super caput' (450). In the second receipt for 'galle' the Latin has 'galluce' (456). AN 'vif argent esteint od sage' rests on a misreading of 'extinctum con saliva' (462) as 'con salvia'. AN 'nient suranee' renders 'non . . . inveterata' (465) by which is understood 'de novo velud infra annum' (465).

XXIV. staphisagne   toigne   c. unce une

AN 'a oit u plus' diverges slightly from Latin 'ad .ix. dies vel etiam plus' (470). 'Les places de la teste' and 'les placettes' are inaccurate renderings of the Latin 'discrimina' (471/73) (cf. Renzi p. 439 'id est per segregationes capillorum'). AN 'les malans' is a clarification by the translator. The appearance of 'malum mortuum' is explained by a gloss to 'melancoliam' (484) in one of the Latin MSS, 'id est malum mortuum', though the translator has made of it a distinct illness, probably correctly.

XXV. qui sunt   voiz   escupe   naissiez   t. remuez e pur co e.

AN 'od un cisol' renders Latin 'con spatumine' (491). AN omits the detail that the skin be 'unco prius apprehensa' (491) and the whole of the phrase (after 'escharniez / scarne-tur') 'et, si fieri potest, con ipso panniculo, inter quem nata est, abstrahatur' (492–93). AN's phrases 'si ço est en esté' and 'si ço est en iver' are additions to the Latin. In the receipt 'juz des affodildis unces trois' diverges from 'succi affodillorum uncias .vi.' (497). In AN 'E quant vus verrez la plaie emfler, dunc saciez que la pel est mangié' the second clause is an explanatory addition to the Latin 'cum vulnus tumefactum esse videris et desiccatum' (502). AN 'aneintie' stands for Latin 'decoctum et corruptum' (504). The 'perçur cirugien' corresponds to the Latin 'trepano' (512) and 'cisol' to 'spatumine' (512).

XXVI. troiz

AN slightly rearranges the elements of this chapter. For 'lier' the Latin has the more explicit 'in vinculis teneatur' (519). AN's reference to the trepan stems from a variant not recorded by Sudhoff, e.g. C f. 306vb 'perforetur cum trepano'.

XXV[bis]. a la

The chapter number is a mistake by Sudhoff. The Latin makes no reference to 'gutta caduca' (AN 'la gute chaive'). In the Latin the cautery is applied 'ad nodulum in fontanella supra collum, hoc est in extremitate occipicii' (522–23).

XXVII. coumt   al al

Latin 'preter naturam' (525, 528) is rendered by 'estre nature' and 'contre nature'. Sudhoff's punctuation of the Latin in this chapter is faulty. The last sentence in AN unhelpfully abbreviates the Latin 'si in eis [sc. in palpebris] pili preter naturam contineantur' (528).

XXVIII. pauperieres   compicicariolis   ambon

The scribe of AN understood 'con picicariolis' (534) as one word. In the remedy 'de la cire' is a misreading of the Latin 'de croco' (535). Owing to misplaced folios in AN's exemplar (see Introduction above p. 21) there is disruption of the continuity of the chapter, which is continued on f. 255r. AN 'les jus del chie[v]refoil' and 'od eue rosat' are additions to the last receipt as given by Sudhoff, though 'cum albumine ovi vel aqua rosata' is found in C f. 307rb.

XXIX. miez   seim   un en

AN addresses the physician-user of his work as 'vus' whilst the Latin has, more impersonally, 'quod medico videatur sufficere' (547), though C f. 307rb has simply 'quantum videbitur sufficere', which may be at the base of AN's reading. AN 'si perciez la veine' is the result of a misunderstanding of the Latin which has 'vena illa tota diligenter con acu subtili apprehendatur, ita quod vena non perforetur' (548–49) as is 'de l'autre part un autre agule' for 'ex alia parte acus ipsa' (549), though here again C may offer the source reading by its omission of 'ipsa'. At C f. 307rb 'caro porci salsa macra' explains the appearance of 'salee' in AN (cf. Sudhoff p.172, n.5). AN's reference to 'charpie' is also explained by C f. 307va 'si opus fuerit carpiam vel aliud' (see Sudhoff p.172, n.6 & Renzi p. 441). AN 'forcele' renders 'fontanella' and what follows in AN combines 'cartilaginis auris' (561) of Sudhoff's text with a gloss found in some MSS 'in ea scilicet que est in medio auris' (Sudhoff p.172, n.9), though 'mol' is not an accurate rendering of 'cartilago'.

XXX. une unce   e de lorier   meminte   iaustez   cuues

The Latin has 'litargiri unciam unam' (566). AN 'jus de memite, ço est celidoine salvage e od agresta' misunderstands 'agresta' (568) which apparently stands for 'celidonia agrestis' which is added in the margin of MS M (see Sudhoff p.172, n.21). After 'oile violet e melez ensemble' AN omits the Latin 'et ita vicissim, modo de isto modo de illo ponendo' (568–69). In the receipt AN omits the third ingredient, 'masticis' (573).

XXXI. e   sunt   sanocolle   dragnes   olile   comin   comin   ensembles
colorez   des des o.   verin   boil   verin

For 'a sis jors u a oit' the Latin has 'per .v. dies vel .ix.' (580) (C f. 307vb has 'per .v. vel .viii. dies'). For 'dous dragmes' Sudhoff prints '.iii.' (588) but notes the variant '.ii.' (see also C f. 307vb). AN 'oculi licii' reflects an attested variant of 'oculi lucidi' (590, see Sudhoff p.173, n.17). Both forms are common and denote a variety of honeysuckle (*Lonicera* spp.). The spatula ('esclice') is introduced earlier in AN than in the Latin (593). AN 'un poi tenue' translates 'parum liquida' (592) and 'es chiés des oilz' 'in oculorum extremitatibus' (595). AN has misunderstood the Latin in 'quant la teie serra auques degastee', since 'consumptus' (595) refers to the medical preparation. AN's 'ipia' is a common Latin synonym for 'morsus galine' (596). For 'pectinem' Sudhoff's text offers 'pectinelongus' (597) with the variants 'pecten' and 'pectine' (Renzi p. 442 'pictine') and specifies 'valet etiam ad alia, id est ad maculam' (598).

XXXII. autrefoiz   sanocalle   de graines   de graine   terit

After the first three ingredients the Latin has 'dragmas .ii. et semis' (601) and the fourth is given simply as 'camphore dragmas .ii.'. AN omits the second reference to 'camphoram quoque et margaritas' (605). AN 'u en autre liu' is a curiously inaccurate rendering of 'vel alio simili' (607, following 'in parapside terrea'). AN does not correctly render the indications of time, 'hoc fiat ter. Post novem dies . . .' (610).

XXXIII. suffur   tra traez   lez   asuaintes

For 'la veine del frunt' the Latin has 'in quatuor [var. *in tribus*] venis frontis' (614). The translator has understood a different punctuation from Sudhoff's, where it is the 'incisio' that is made 'in modum capistri' (615). AN 'trois dois de la main' corresponds to '.iii. unciis manu' (618) (in at least one MS 'digitis' is written over 'unciis'). The sentence 'de cel signe qui est sur le oreille . . . sur l'autre oreille' erroneously telescopes the Latin 'signa . . . ab eo signo, quod est supra auriculam, usque ad signum, quod est super frontem, et a signo, quod est supra aliam auriculam, signum de incausto vel alio simili protrahas' (619–21). In the next sentence AN fails to specify the distance, 'distet ab eo uncia et dimidia' (622) and truncates ll.623–24 of the Latin. The Latin makes no mention of the 'sagittella', having simply 'con rasorio' (625), and has 'sanguinem manare permittas' (625), whereas AN has 'laissiez la quiture hors cure', which rests on the reading *emanare* (Renzi p. 443). AN 'mes metlez . . . tailliez' is an addition to the Latin, whilst 'as autres parties del chief' presupposes the attested variant 'capitis' for the 'corporis' printed by Sudhoff (634). The indication of time 'noef jorz u vint' diverges surprisingly from the Latin 'usque ad .xxx. vel .xl. dies' (635).

XXXIV. comun   emplasture

AN 'suvenirement' may have entered as a misunderstanding of the Latin 'subvenimus'.

XXXV. e en

AN does not specify the condition of the eyelid, 'inversatio / inversio inferioris palpebre' (649). AN 'trois pertuz' diverges from Latin 'quatuor foraminibus' (651) and after 'en miliu' AN omits Latin 'et pellicula ligaminibus ad superiora conprimatur et ita per .ix. vel .xi. dies dimmittatur' (652–53).

XXXVI. pente   metre en destre par del autre p.   igneiment   defure   la posterine
la posterne

In the Latin the eye is to be moved 'con aliquo instrumento' (658). For 'penne' the Latin has 'pecia' (659, 665) and the 'pillula' is specified as 'de unguento ruptorio' (664). The Latin has 'a tercia usque ad nonam et [var. *vel*] a nona usque ad vesperas' (664–65). The Latin has a receipt for 'capitellum' which is absent from AN and is not found in all the Latin MSS. The second receipt is not in the Latin at all. AN 'en une corde' seems to derive from a text like Renzi p. 444 where there is the following addition: 'Capitellum autem sic fit: Accipies duas partes cineris fabarum et tertiam calcis vivae et pulverizatas insimul misce: et in cophino vel in corba solum faciendo, pedibusque calcando, et parum aquae instillando, et sic faciendo solaria, cophinum vel corbam impleas, foveam rotundam desuper cultello facias ad mensuram medii brachii: illam foveam ter in die aqua impleas, mane, meridie, et sero: concha ponatur inferius: et quod extrahitur a prima die usque ad viii collige, et repone, et hoc est forte capitellum: Medium dicitur quod ab secunda die postea colligitur. Si vis scire utrum sit forte, medium ovum *in filo ligatum* in capitellum mitte: si non receperit medium, forte est capitellum'.

XXXVII. de posterne   sunz   en   tine   comin   bein s.

The phrase in AN 'meis polipus avient' does not accurately render the Latin which speaks of a growth which is sometimes a polip, 'aliquando non, sed videtur esse, nam in ampliori parte . . .' (679–80). I thus emend to 'meis sicome polipus avient'. In the Latin the eradication is performed with the 'spatumen' (681) and the cutting with the 'sagitella' (681). For AN 'saim sarazin' the Latin has only 'sapone' (683). AN 'set jors u noef' inverts the Latin 'per .ix. dies vel .vii.' (689) and 'colez' simplifies 'coletur per petiam [C f. 309rb caciam]'. AN's directions for preparation in winter contradict the Latin 'in hyeme vero .ii. uncias' (692). After 'verd de l'araim unce demie' AN omits the Latin 'Sed antequam mittatur viride eris, probetur si se tenuerit, et postea apponatur viride es et iterum temptetur et, si colorem mutaverit, ita quod viridis videatur, deponatur ab igne' (693–96), which specifies that a half-ounce of aloes is to be added. It is clear that the omission is caused by a 'saut du même au même' involving 'unciam semis' (693, 696).

XXXVIII. AN omits part of the Latin (and displaces 'si necesse fuerit'): 'Si vero fit infra nares tota caro et magna sit opilatio, primo secundum modum foraminis intromittatur per medium tenta de malo terre sicco semel vel bis vel ter, si necesse fuerit, postea curetur ferro calido vel unguento, ut supradiximus in proxima cura' (701–04).

XXXIX. lautre   ne pot

The opening sentence 'Une aposteme . . . polipus apelé' is an addition to the source. AN 'entre les narilles' presupposes the variant 'intra' for 'infra' (706; see Sudhoff p.177, n.4; C f. 309va has 'inter'). AN 'crest en grandur' seems to have been prompted by Latin 'nares adamplat' (707). AN omits 'per incensionem' (710).

XL. cute

AN 'une tente faite de malo terre' renders the variant 'tenta de malo terre' (715; Sudhoff p.177, n.11 and C f. 309va). Through another 'saut du même au même' ('inmittatur', 717, 718) AN omits 'per ipsam vero cannam ferream vel eneam ferrum candidum mittatur' (717–19).

XLI. The Latin specifies 'per nares stuellus . . . intromittatur' (723).

XLII. AN 'sur aventure le devez mettre' renders 'casui imputetur' (727). Once again (see XL above) Sudhoff's text has 'tasta' for AN 'tente', with similar meaning (C f. 309vb has 'tenta'). For AN 'char' the Latin has 'pellis' [var. *cutis*] (728).

XLIII. frundet   as   surcilz

The direction that the cautery 'nen vait pas a la char' rests on a misreading of 'craneum' as 'carnem' (732). In AN the reference to the chapter on redness of the eyes (see XXXIII above) comes later than in the Latin and 'traitié' is used to render Latin 'paragrafo' (734). AN 'suriz' (MS *surcilz*) is a literal translation of 'musculus'.

XLIV. aval   aval   e novel

AN unaccountably omits 'labiis' as a site of the growth from both the rubric (735) and the opening sentence (736) and also fails to render 'locus . . . corroditur in circuitu et rubet aliquando locus et inversatur cutis et cutem non corrodit' (738–39). AN's 'ne soet pas suranee' is not an accurate rendering of 'ne locus sit corrosus multum'. My correction 'al vif' ('to the quick') renders 'ad vivum' (743, 749) of the Latin. AN omits 'con rasorio' (743). Apart from the (displaced?) phrase 'la diverseté del tens' the translator has failed to render some five lines of his source (744–48). For AN 'alum' the Latin has 'con alumine zucarino' (752) which a gloss in one MS explains as 'quedam species . . . aluminis albissimi, que ad modum zucari potest pulverizari' (Sudhoff p.178, n.13). AN's 'zemarinum' describing the 'liquor' (753) may have arisen from a misunderstanding of 'zucarinum'. The final sentence in AN does not render the Latin 'postea' (755) and 'loco prius absterso' (756).

XLV. faial   meis que   qui   beu   od   de

MS 'alum e zucre', which I have printed 'alume zucré', renders 'aluminis zucarini' (758). AN omits 'ossium cancri' (759) and, after 'lovesche salvage', 'vel etiam pulvis eorum, que relinquuntur in sacello post factum claretum' (762–63). In the second receipt AN omits 'aluminis' (764–65). The receipt 'Pur cancre' is an addition to the source.

XLVI. hannebaire   metreolum   ensemble ensemble

AN understandably drops Roger Frugard's explanation of 'scissura labiorum' as 'que vulgari nostro dicitur setlium, aput alios dicitur setula' (769–70) (Renzi p. 447 'quae italice dicitur setula'), but in the next sentence introduces a new vernacular element in the description of 'jusquiamus', 'que en englés est apelé hannebane [miscopied by the scribe as 'hannebaire']'. AN 'chalemel pe[r]cié de seu' renders the Latin word 'embotum' (771) which AN also incorporates in the text. The next receipt is an addition to the source, though it resembles an insertion recorded by Sudhoff p.179, n.16 (see also Renzi p. 447).

XLVIII. larsere

I follow Sudhoff's chapter numbers even where they are erroneous, as here. This time AN correctly renders Latin 'alumen zuccarinum' (781), but has not understood 'mel ponendo' (782) ('en reposant'). In the next receipt 'anis' must be the result of a misreading of 'amidum' (or 'amilum', 785) as 'anisum'. AN 'od oile violat u sirop rosat' is an extension of 'con syrupo' (785).

XLVII. li   deuz   desuz   lur liu d.p.   unie mande (unie expunged by underlining)

The Latin records that it sometimes happens 'nec inferiorem molam licet male coniunctam segregare vel male segregatam coniungere' (793–94), 'nor is it possible to disengage the lower jaw if it is badly aligned or to align it if it is badly dislocated'. AN has not understood this and the addition of 'ne' at two places is indispensable. AN's 'par nature' may have arisen from a misreading of an abbreviation representing 'male'. In the reference to the condyls of the jaws ('chiés des joes') MS 'dedenz' contradicts the Latin 'ad exteriora' (795) and has been corrected to 'dehors'. AN's 'les joes ne se puissent mover' is also erroneous, since the unexpressed subject of the Latin (800) is the teeth.

L. mures   avenaument   mensure   e quil   deseinture

The incorrect numbering is Sudhoff's.

XLIX. contenuat   ostiel

AN's 'la diverseté del tens' seems at first to be a mechanical error for 'pro partis varietate' (814), but some of the Latin MSS (e.g. C f. 310vb) have 'pro temporis varietate'. The diet is explained with an addition to the source, 'viande que puisse estre humee'.

LI. AN has obviously misunderstood 'fistulatur aliquando mandibula' (818), falsely distinguishing two types of fistula. Not rendered are 822–24 which are missing in many Latin MSS. The Latin speaks of 'putredinem albam' (827) ('aucune quiture').

LII. funteinrele   chaval   ceo la   zeume   nient

AN 'petit nu' renders Latin 'nodellus' (837), which is glossed in M by 'de cera vel radice absinthi[?]' (Sudhoff p.181, n.17). AN 'en ce' appears more explicitly in the Latin as 'in hac ustura' (836). The Latin specifies that the patient is to receive the fumes 'super dentem patientem' (839).

LIII. u de   fiez   tartan   potel   dite   euelume   deite   blanc verte
confizez   ciclanus   la maladie   nel luve pas en veie   vis   sil   veice   litargite
musge   la maladie   muz   dites choses racines   d. soit que   totesveirs   terre
demandant

For 'unces trois de miel' the Latin has '.vi. uncias mellis' (843). AN 'la pome de terre' renders 'malum terre' (844) which normally denotes the earthnut (*Conopodium majus* (Gouan) Loret) or sowbread (*Cyclamen hederifolium* Aitken). The contents 'de peivre e de alum zucré uelement unce demie, boracis unces dous' renders material not included in Sudhoff's text but recorded by him in a note (p.182, n.8; see also C f. 311r and Renzi p. 449). For the application of the ointment the Latin specifies 'loco calefacto ad ignem inunge' (848). In the preparation of the white unguent the Latin specifies 'con oleo miscendo distempera' (855). AN uses 'decocsion' where Sudhoff's text has 'confeccionis' (858), but other Latin MSS e.g. C f. 311va have the reading 'decoccionis'. AN's 'tute maneire de roigne' is an addition, as is 'Tele cure devez faire ... impetigo'. The next heading '[P]or oster ... oignement' is also an addition to the source. It is interesting that the insular translator gives the vernacular alternative to 'serpigo' 'en franceais'. The opening of the receipt substitutes 'litargire e blanc vin' for Latin 'tartarum vini albi' (872) and omits 'succum cyclaminis', 'pulverem fuliginis, piretrum, oleum commune' (872–3). The phrase 'un po de lasive' is an addition. In the section on morphea 'si est une espece de lepre' is an addition to the source. AN 'sanc en ist' reflects a variant 'sanguis exit' recorded by Sudhoff p.183, n.19. In the receipt some Latin MSS have 'vitrum' (cf. AN MS *veice*) for 'nitrum' (887). AN's 'euforbium, storacum calamite' is an addition to the source. In the next receipt 'suffre chenellié' is apparently a literal rendering of Latin 'sulphur cannellatum' (896), which one Latin MS glosses with 'id est infusum in canna'. AN's 'roil' presupposes a reading 'rubigo' for the 'fuligo' (896, 901) of the source. For 'oculum licium' one should read 'oculum licii' or 'oculum lucidum'. In the next receipt AN omits 'saponis sarracenici' (900), 'tartari' (901), 'auripigmenti, salis communis, ellebori albi ana uncias .ii., aluminis scissi unciam semis' (901–02). In the following receipt 'des foilles d'olive' is an addition to the Latin which has 'auripigmentum foliatum' (907; C f. 312rb has 'auripigmentum solatrum'). Once again, in the phrase 'estent de sauge' AN has misread 'saliva' (912) as 'salvia'. AN's 'u od chevols moilliez que meuz vaut' is an addition to the source. AN omits the Latin instruction concerning the patient's bath, 'pro viribus ibi moretur' (915). In the next receipt AN's introduction of the word 'reception' is worthy of note. For 'cel gros' the Latin has 'salis nitri' (922) followed by the quantity 'unciam .i.'. AN omits 'ellebori albi et nigri' (923) and 'herbe flaure et eruce agrestis' (924–25). AN renders only one half of 'saponis spatarenti et sarracenici' (927) and has 'unces sis' for Latin 'uncias .iii.' (927).

LIV. discussion   brelle   breille   en certain   discussion   metez boillir   pernez
su   verine

MS 'discussion' (twice) is emended in accordance with the Latin 'discursu' (932) and 'decursu' (935). In the last of the receipts the translator omits 'juniperum' (948) and adds 'e olie feit de la semence de chenillé, qui est apelee hannebanne'. AN's 'tuel percez' renders 'embotum inversum [var. inversatum]' (949). The phrase 'si porreture s'en ist e est torné por maurer' seems garbled, probably owing to the omission of several words. The Latin reads 'subveniendum est con saniem provocantibus et ad maturitatem ducentibus' (955).

LV. persicana   mals   liu   verine   verine   um

AN's 'des cerices' is an addition to the source. The displaced folios in the translator's exemplar seem to come to an end here and the text is continued on f. 253r without loss of any of the Latin original. For the surgical forceps the Latin has 'picicariolis' (963) and the cupping-glass, 'cufa' (964), is glossed in some MSS 'ventosa'.

LVI. estreiner   dombes   metez   e od

AN's 'de cele part sun cheif apueir' rather loosely renders Latin 'caput supra dolentem partem flectatur' (972–73). In accordance with Latin 'tali instrumento inherendo [var. adherendo] abstrahatur' I have emended AN by a simple relocation of the conjunction 'e' and replacement of 'od' by 'a'.

[BOOK II]

Preface. torment   atent

AN rather loosely renders Latin 'cum multa paucis implicita obscuritatem potius et confusionem quam compendii commoditatem parere soleant' (2–3), adding the commonplace distinction between hearing and comprehending. In the next sentence, 'ne voil . . .', AN has misunderstood the Latin, which lacks any negative (5–7), and subsequently substitutes 'brevement' for the quite contrary 'compendiose' (8) of the Latin. AN's rendering of 'quinto botii' (11) has obviously fallen out and accordingly I print [. . .]. On the other hand, 'al sisme de l'oil' has no correspondence in the Latin, which has 'sexto eorum [misunderstood as 'oculorum'?], que interius surgunt' (11) which AN transfers to seventh place in a rearrangement of the final part of the preface which has necessitated editorial intervention. The whole preface is missing in MS C.

I. del   sul   de la plaie o.

AN omits a largely redundant line (43) of the Latin and seems to follow a text like that of Sudhoff's Fl. (p.188, n.8).

II. narement

The text of AN is somewhat disordered at the beginning and has been emended in accordance with the Latin. The MS reads '[S]'il avent que li col seit percié de l'une part jesque a la senestre, si metez lardon de la destre part jesque a l'autre, l'un de l'un part e l'autre de l'autre part juste la buche de la plaie . . .' AN's 'le devant [dit] lardon' corresponds to Latin 'pultem [var. *pulverem*]' (56) and 'targiez' presupposes the reading 'tardius relinquatur' (Sudhoff p.188, n.16; C f. 313vb).

III. a. a la veine   la sacez   embroke pur lemflure oster

AN's 'organale' is a rendering of 'organica vena' (65–66). Latin 'acus con filo ei inherente' (67) has been misunderstood (AN attaching the thread to the vein) and the MS reading corrected. AN makes two omissions which seem to have been occasioned by another 'saut du même au même' (from 'emittat' in l.68 to 'inmittatur' in l.70). AN furnishes the rubric 'Por conustre le[s] chefz de la plaie'. The phrase 'se teinent ensemble' does not accurately render Latin 'putruisse' (75) and 'd'entravers' mistranslates the Latin 'ex toto' (78), possibly in anticipation of 'ex obliquo' in l.82. AN takes a long phrase, including the English word 'maddok', to render 'terrestres lumbrici' (80). Further, AN 'ne deit pas de cele medecine estre sanee, ainz doit estre garri par medecine de nature' mistranslates '(minime consolidabitur), predicto tamen remedio, natura coadiuvante, sepe conglutinatur' (84). In the final sentence 'rogist' seems to be an error for 'emfle' ('tumet', 87).

IV. AN's 'veine organale' translates 'vena organica' (91).

V. arcele   e en   suffre   ses   delicement   cessant

AN 'la tirce partie' translates 'tercia particula' (98). The following procedure, here coordinated by 'et', is related by the conjunction 'aut' in the Latin. For 'la fiente de l'asne [ars]' the

Latin has 'stercoris asinini sicci' (99). AN's 'fiente . . . veirt' corresponds to Latin 'stercus . . . viride' (100), which in one MS is glossed 'id est recens'. AN seems to have understood that the compressed dung would yield 'jus', though this is not suggested in the Latin. The reference to English 'cockel' is, of course, an addition by the translator. In the next receipt 'laureole' corresponds to a variant of the Latin 'lanceole' (105; Sudhoff p.189, n.28) and the phrase 'esprové chose est' also corresponds to a variant recorded by Sudhoff (p.189, n.29; C f. 314rb has 'probatum est').

VI. aitrie   laitere

AN 'percié e taillié' ('perforetur vel incidatur', 112) shows the translator's habit of substituting 'e' for the 'aut / vel' of his source. AN omits a sentence (113–14) from the Latin.

VII. sollections (first l expuncted)   flegmon e que avient de colre est apele serpigo
hestimomenus   flegnne   plus   ncine (superscript i)   verdentre   fassiis

AN specifies 'quatre humurs' for Latin 'humores diversi' (116; is AN 'devisé[s]' an error for 'diverses'?) and 'quatre collections' for 'collectiones' (117), but this may reflect a variant reading of his source (see Sudhoff p.190, n.4). AN omits 'colera vero alia naturalis et dicitur rubea, alia innaturalis et dicitur melancolia' (120–21). AN's addition '[cele] que avient de colre est apelé serpigo' is clearly both erroneous and intrusive and I have accordingly cleared it from the text. The references to 'lu' and 'palus' are also additions. Of the symptoms of 'apostema de sanguine' AN omits 'rubor' (124) and in the case of 'apostema . . . ex colera rubea' renders 'calor, rubor, mixtus citrino colori' (127) as 'color vermeil metlé od colur citrine', thus misreading 'calor' as 'color'. In the next case 'ner d'encre' (MS *verdentre*) renders 'nigredine' (128).

VIII. i avienge est   la quiture

In the Latin the opening ingredients include 'vino albo' (133), omitted by AN. I have emended 'u la quiture plus pent' in accordance with Latin 'ubi locus magis pendet' (134–35). The Latin specifies that the incision is to be made 'con sagitella' (135).

IX. mente   antrix

The phrase 'aucune foiz avenu as reins' is an addition of the translator. AN 'olie' is less specific than 'oleo rosarum' (141). I have emended MS 'mente' to 'memite' in accordance with the Latin (142) – the confusion is a common one. AN rarely modifies the syntax of the original in a radical way, but 'de ces choses devez oster la chalur entur les lius qui suff[r]unt' is an uncharacteristically free rendering of 'similibus calorem reprimentibus' (142). The addition of 'od oint' to 'scabiosa' is not authorised by Sudhoff's text (144), but MS C, for example, has (f. 314vb) 'scabiosa contrita cum lardo'. One of the effects specified by the Latin, 'ex toto [antracem] concavat' (146), is omitted by AN. The final reference to 'pié de columb' is not found in Sudhoff's text.

X. ancraee (cr superscript abbreviation)

AN 'colre neire' apparently renders 'colera rubea' (149). The phrase 'le devez descolure[r]' appears to be a misunderstanding of 'exulcerat' (150) as 'excolorat' and 'les autres plaies' a misreading of 'alta vulnera' (150) as 'altera vulnera' (an error attested by MS C f. 315ra).

XI. oster   oint e autre   ne pent

AN 'emplastre' here translates 'cataplasma' (153). In the Latin the quantity of marshmallow roots is given as eight ounces (154), to which is added '.xviii. uncias adipis porcini' (154) and 'olei veteris sextariis duobus' (154) followed by 'sublatis radicibus et colato oleo' (155). It looks as if this passage was garbled in AN's source. It has certainly been completely misunderstood.

AN 'litargire' seems to have entered the text from a gloss in the Latin (see Sudhoff p.192, n.1 and MS C f. 315ra 'argenti spume .i. litargiri'). AN adds 'cire', whilst omitting details of quantity and preparation (155–56). AN omits entirely the receipt found in Sudhoff ll. 159–63. AN's 'quant il eirt un poi rosti' is a misunderstanding of 'post adde cepe assatum, memithe' (166; Sudhoff's 'menuthe' is an error) – perhaps 'cepe' was missing in the translator's exemplar. AN omits part of the Latin (167) as the result of a 'saut du même au même' ('cocta . . . coctam'). AN's 'quant l'aposteme quiture' corresponds to Latin 'cum autem maturum [sc. apostema] fuerit' (170) and I have emended what follows in accordance with the Latin 'ubi locus magis dependet' (170).

XII. les vices   forcines   est apele   gent est close   uin   austologiam   puf
luns   channus

AN reverses the order in which he exemplifies the 'vicio interiorum' and 'vicio exteriorum' (175). The Latin has 'postquam .iiii. vel .v. menses' (176). I have emended MS 'est close' in accordance with Latin 'incuratum' (177). AN seems to have followed a text like Sudhoff's J, 'et nota quod cancer quandoque fit in nervosis locis . . .' (Sudhoff p.192, n.12), but owing to yet another 'saut du même au même' ('plenis arteriis' 179, 182) part of the relevant source material is omitted. On the other hand, AN's 'cum es veines u es nerfs e es arteries' is an addition. The quotation from Hippocrates is found in *Aphor.* VI, 38. For 'al col' the Latin has 'circa loca predicta' (188–89). In the receipt for the unguent the Latin specifies 'lingue bovine uncias .iiii.' (191) and adds 'radicis bardane uncias .v., radicis celidonie unciam .i.' (191–92) omitted by AN. The Latin also specifies 'in mortario marmoreo tere' (194). In the receipt for the powder AN seems to follow a reading like Sudhoff's Fl. which specifies 'aristologiam rotundam' (not 'longam', 201).

XIII. umes   esqoelers   endust   proisse   porrigie   nes   beuure   damstologie
fende   porgrez   mel   grames   noef estroeleste   dis   desinement   tut
nensuit   feisceles   dore   maniessent   m. e ainz que il soient maur   perciez

The Latin has 'folia citri' (209). AN's 'sil rougissent e volent quiturer' is an inaccurate rendering of 'si autem rubescant, ita quod videatur quod debeant duci ad saniem' (211–12). For 'oignement' at the head of the first receipt the Latin has 'oleum' (215; var. *emplastrum*, Sudhoff p.194, n.11). AN omits 'et oleum quantum de omnibus' (216) and 'et hoc in vase posito in caldario pleno aqua bulliente supra ignem' (217–18). For 'l'apotesme' and 'l'oil de l'apotesme' the Latin has 'auris (illius partis)'. AN omits 'fracta fuerit' (220) and adds the phrase 'par mai est trové'. I have assumed a haplography and corrected 'signe de garison' in accordance with the Latin 'signum liberationis' (222). In the receipt for the beverage the order of the ingredients has been changed by AN which omits the black variety of hellebore (225, see var. in Sudhoff p.194, n.21) and misinterprets 'ro.' after 'aristologie' as 'rose' instead of 'rotonde' (226; cf. II, XV below). AN has quite misunderstood 'semel in mane in ebdomada, si fuerit puer, si fuerit juvenis bis .iii. uncias' (230). The sentence 'Derecheif . . . fresches' is an addition to the source. In the next receipt the Anglo-Norman text is clearly corrupt. The Latin has 'undecim' (235) for 'noef', which is followed in the MS by 'entroeleste' which may be a corruption of 'crespeletes' ('crispellas', 236). AN has not understood that the 'crispelle' are reduced daily by one ('undecim . . . decem . . . novem', 237) and has 'noef . . . dis . . . dis', which makes no sense, though the Latin is perfectly clear. In the next receipt, dealing with surgical intervention, 'fer rebuchié' translates 'unco' (244) and 'tant cum il sunt' 'quotquot fuerint' (246). For 'par l'espace de trois jors u de quatre' the Latin has simply 'per intervalla' (247). The phrase 'e le secund jor' ought, according to the Latin (248), to be attached to the following sentence, which is itself a misconstruction of the Latin, which has 'si quid de folliculo suo vel de scrofula ipsa remanserit' (248–49). AN 'charunge o la quiture' translates 'carnositas et pinguedo' (251), apparently reading the last word as 'putredo'. The sections 'De superfluitate des humors' and 'Des apostumus' are additions to Sudhoff's text but correspond to passages found in MS C. MS C f. 316va has 'De bubone: Solet plurimum humorum fluxus incidere sub ascellis et unguinibus et duram faciunt collectionem extra eminentem et in profundo firmissime coherente que bubo vocatur. Est autem quedam curabilis, quedam non. Si enim fere continuum calorem paciatur, inde corpus et sitim et vehementer extenuetur et minus magna fuerit collectio et dolorem pectoris in profundo idem sentiat, quod cum contingit sub ascellis, incurabilis est. Item cum predictis lignis [corr. signis] in quoda[m] loco aliquantulum sit mollis, ita quod aliud videatur in profundo et circumquaque immoderate sit dura, incurabilis est. Item erupta sanie quoquo modo caro sit interius multa superflua et plurimum dura que aliquando mollis que appositis corosivis plus crescat quam di [f. 316vb] minuatur, incurabilis est similiter. Si autem fiunt quasi ovum anserinum vel eo minor et dolore pectoris omnino careat et a reliquis predictis sinthomatibus immune sit, licet modicam enim habeat sitim et calorem, possibile est curari dummodo dictam superius non habeat coherenciam. Cura putredinem generantibus et aliis maturativis indiget ex quo maturatum fuerit flōmab̄ [?] amplo vulnere nullam rationem expectamus donec per se crepet, quod si non feceris vix aut nunquam de cetero curare valebis. Incisione vero facta ad instar aliorum vulnerum curabis'.

XIV. aucune feiz large   mite   neient   ist   lavere   parfunt jesque al pertus de la
festre comunit   metez   faces

AN has telescoped the opening sentence as a result of a 'saut du même au même' ('vicio interiorum' 201, 262; cf. the reading of MS J, Sudhoff p.195, n.25) with consequent loss of clarity. AN's 'neire quiture e mut pudlente' presupposes the reading of MS M 'putredo nigra fetoris multi' (269), where the last two words are an interlinear insertion (see Sudhoff p.196, n.2). In dealing with growths on parts of the neck and throat AN omits the qualifying phrase 'que implicita sunt et intricata nervis vel arteriis' (272). The application of the 'oignement rumpant' has been obscured by an omission due to another 'saut du même au même' ('nervis et arteriis' 277, 279). In the receipt for the ointment the sentence 'E puis metez oignement vert ... a la fin' is displaced from its position in the Latin (290–92). AN 'savun sparantic' renders Latin 'sapo spatarenus' which is explained in MS M as follows: 'Nota sapo spat. gallicum album idem est. Sapo spatarenus sic fit: Accipe calcem et cinerem ana et ponetis in aliquo vase, bene conprime, ut aqua superposita vix exeat. Superpone aquam, sicut fit de lixivia, et fiat capitellum. Preterea accipe sepum arietinum vel hircinum, liquefiat, coletur et colatura commisceatur con capitello et equaliter et bulliat ad ignem usque ad spissitudinem et deponatur ab igne et, ut magis inspisetur, adde ibi aliquantulum de cinere bene cribellato, qui magis valet, qui fit de corticibus fabarum conbustis. Dicitur autem spatarenum a spata, quia incidit ad modum spata'. AN has misrepresented the sign that the fistula is dead by omitting the crucial phrase 'emittit saniem spissam' (290). After 'la tente soit mis en parfunt' AN has omitted 'et sic aliquantulum cuticula talis ad superiora levetur et a fundo fistule usque ad os eius super tastam usque ad ipsam findatur' (295–96), a relic of which is found in the MS reading 'jesque al pertus de la festre (?) comunit' which follows 'parfunt' and which I have omitted from my edited text.

XV. botru (with nasal bar over u)   cuire gule   trespecte   urticelle   enturbite
roses   enmiscelle   yan   e les primetes   foilles   sanc   cine   serin   seim
remuent   li   cum od   mis   vermes   uus   blanc

AN omits the ritual 'cantando Pater Noster' (302–03) and the detail 'nucem, que nondum fecit fructum' (303). In the receipt AN has once again (see II, XIII above) misunderstood 'ro.' after 'aristologia' (309) as 'rose'. The reading 'palam marinam' is an attested variant of 'pilam marinam' (310), which is described in MS M as 'quod invenitur in littore maris ad similitudinem pile de pilis animalium facte' (Sudhoff p.197, n.15). The translator or copyist completely misunderstood 'scrofa primo filios producente' (311), apparently misreading 'filios' as 'folios' (MS 'foilles') and left the original reading ('prodeunte'? see Sudhoff p.197, n.17) as 'prodiente'. At the end of the receipt the Latin has 'usque ad undecimum vel duodecimum diem facias potionem' (320). In the treatment of the 'botium' AN omits 'sicut in aliis suturis diximus' (342).

XVI. ysphosagum   ad   dementre

In the description of 'quinancie' 'maladie' is probably an error, the Latin having 'malicia' (357), though Sudhoff records (p.196, n.6) the variant 'de cuius malo'. The phrase 'la quele espece des trois est meilur a curer' is a misinterpretation of the phrase which in the Latin opens the next sentence, 'Quecunque vero istarum specierum fuerit . . .' (359). Amongst the general symptoms 'ne parler' is a laconic rendering of 'vox etiam quandoque denegatur ex toto' (360) and 'machier' an inaccurate one of 'sputum emittere' (361).

XVII. albrusaz (superscript u)   esplastre   tarchardun   liu   al espesir   cire

AN omits the first gargle, presumably as a result of a 'saut du même au même' ('gargarismum, -us 364, 365). Also omitted is 'sumac' (365) from the list of ingredients. In the second receipt there is the omission of 'porrorum folia' (371–72). AN's 'issi qu'il soit aquis tenve' hardly renders 'quod multum remaneant liquida' (375). The first person testimony in the last sentence follows the Latin (384).

XVIII. tranci   la   u celes qui   un poie

The Latin has 'unde difficilis est excreatio et anxia spiritus attractio' (387–88). AN's 'un covenable estrument' renders the text of MS Fl. 'instrumento apto' (Sudhoff p. 200, n.5 and MS C f. 318vb). The phrase 'e li malade tinge sa buche overte' should logically come after 'devant vus', as in the Latin (389). For 'un ostilement de fer nescessarie' the Latin has 'unco ferreo vel eneo capere et conpetenti ferro incidere' (390–91).

XIX. mule   mule   puldre galle   mule

In the receipt AN omits 'stafisagrie' (401) and 'piper, piretrum, stafisagriam, balaustiam' (403). At the end of this section AN follows the text of the Latin, not as it is punctuated by Sudhoff, but taking 'vel ante incisionem' (410) as beginning the next sentence.

XX. tragulare   e tragulare   marioton   od

AN substitutes the personal pronoun 'vos' for the impersonal 'medicus' (416) of the Latin.

[BOOK III]

Preface. curel

Most of the preface and the whole of the table of contents are omitted by AN which retains the final sentence of the preface as an indispensable guide to the contents.

I. lesisseiz   issi   darc

II. vanement

III. linge   bruc

AN 'en autre manere embaissé' renders 'aliquo modo residerit' (97), whilst 'plateine' and 'plumaceol' render 'plagella' (98) and 'plumaceolo' (99) respectively. AN has made no attempt to tackle 'ferule' (99), which according to one gloss means 'stellas factas in modum crucis' (Sudhoff p. 204, n.12).

IV. des e.   uuerrez   cures leissiez overt

AN 'laissiez la auguille en ceste custure' corresponds to a variant reading of the Latin 'in hec sutura relinquatur' (115; Sudhoff p. 205, n.1 and MS C f. 320vb). At the end of the chapter

AN's 'en sustraiant soit remué' does not accurately render 'si aliquid est abstrahendum, removeas' (126).

V.   les   trait sil trait

Here AN 'embroke' renders 'pultes' (131), glossed in MS M by 'id est embrocas' (Sudhoff p. 205, n.23).

VI. liu   livros   lieive   amustic

In the receipt the opening reference to 'lin' is an addition, whilst the Latin specifies the seed of fenugreek (138). In the directions to boil water prior to straining AN omits the explanation 'ad abstractionem viscosissimi succi' (144–45). AN 'e de sisun' is an addition to the source. The Latin has 'omnia loca infrigidata et desiccata' (154) at the end.

VII. filunbrio   lentifi   cent' menue   p. enfermez   liu   ensemble e puis metlez ensemble   aneintir

The Latin has 'sisimbrii' and 'balsamite aquatice' (159), both of which may denote *Mentha aquatica* L. It seems probable that the former here denotes horsemint (*Mentha sylvestris* L.). AN omits the quantity ('manipulum unum', 160) of the last six ingredients. At the end of the receipt there is another omission owing to yet another 'saut du même au même' ('incorpora' 173, 174).

VIII. anstologiam   roses   cunte

AN 'maulveise char' translates Latin 'superflua caro'. AN's 'blanchir' is an addition to the source (cf. 180). 'Metez cotun en sauge' is a misreading of 'inficiatur bombax saliva' (179). In MSS 'salvia' and 'saliva' are frequently confused. For the third time (see II, XIII and XV above) the abbreviation 'ro.' is expanded to 'rose' instead of 'rotunde'.

IX. seuit   avienit   jus de la cenillie e od ces medlez la aubun doef e olie rosat la jubarbe
e le jus de la m.   mirte

AN 'achantes' is a hapax rendering 'accidentia' (194). AN 'entre els e lur signes e lur cures' diverges from 'inter ea signa et curas' (196), but at least one Latin MS has 'inter eam et signa et curas'(Sudhoff p. 207, n.23). Amongst the signs of the worst form of erysipelas AN omits 'tostus' (198). The list of ingredients (200–02) is disordered in the AN MS. The phrase 'por faire la char venire as plaius' probably derives from a rubric which has been lost from the text printed by Sudhoff. In the following receipt 'colofonie uncias .iiii.' (208) is omitted.

X. survenent   cumes   f.m̄. mā.   centunicellie   vein   a la ch.   puis   lu (with
nasal bar) unblil   seis   cultre

In the list of ingredients 'umbilici veneris' is an addition to the source. The enigmatic MS reading 'foilles m̄ mā' may have originated in 'tenerrimarum' (215). AN 'centumcellie' corresponds to Latin 'scarumcelle' (217), itself a corruption of 'scatumcellus' (*Umbilicus rupestris* (Salisb.) Dandy). The Latin specifies three ounces (217) of this and the preceding ingredients. There is an omission in AN as the result of a 'saut du même au même' ('magdaliones informentur', 219 and 'magdalionibus informatis', 221).

XI. lespande   neirces   e m.

AN 'funte' translates Latin 'affinitas' (240) but AN omits the following phrase 'spacio trium unciarum infra vulnus fuerit' (240). I have added 'peril' to render the Latin 'periculum' (241).

XII. AN 'suriz' translates Latin 'musculo' (248). The second sentence follows a reading like Sudhoff's Fl. 'utraque pars parti iungatur, comprimatur' (Sudhoff p. 209, n.14). The Latin specifies that part of the wound should be left open 'ubi vulnus magis dependet' (251), a detail omitted in AN.

XIV–XV. braez   e el   lespande

Half of ch. XIV and the beginning of XV are omitted by AN, apparently as the result of a 'saut du même au même' ('cura diligens exhibeatur' 265, 'cura exhibeatur' 272). Some of the symptoms in XV ('et humorum . . . emittatur', 277) are omitted in AN.

XVI. ultire   muncel   del lautre   linceol   enz e   esliaveint   de desuz   se   susuene   he u   martraton   so metez   e sus   le nesz   e boilli

The Latin has 'filis superpositis sit quasi globus filorum' (286). AN does not make it clear that the subject of 'ce soit pendu e levé en haut' is the patient's arm ('illud [brachium]', 291). AN later misunderstands the Latin ('medicus vero firmiter teneat brachium et humerum ex altera parte et tenentes lignum elevent' (300–01) according to which the physician holds the arm and shoulder, whilst the two assistants raise the wooden plank. The omission in AN indicated by square brackets in the text corresponds to 'ubi bullierint malva, branca ursina' (307). In the receipt there is an omission due to a 'saut du même au même' ('misce' 312, 'commisce' 313) followed by the omission of 'ex eo locum inunge' (313). AN 'l'enflure del constrictorie' refers to 'tumor . . . qui ex strictorio supervenerit' (316). AN next changes the word order, anticipating 'aqua predicta fomentetur' (318). In the receipt for 'spadadrappus' the scribe writes 'boilli' for 'boli' (321), as he does also in I, XV above.

XVII. c. del os   metez

AN omits the phrase 'et ex ea [sc. plicatura] quasi taffam [var. *staffam, stupam*] faciat' (326).

XVIII. ses

AN's 'e sa main' is rather awkwardly placed, the Latin having 'brachium con una manu et manum con altera' (335). Similarly, 'si mestiers est' is displaced. In the Latin it qualifies the preparation of fomentations (336). In the final sentence the switch from plural ('les doiz') to singular ('serra') is not reflected in the Latin which maintains the plural.

XIX. recure   e e.   ses   constructorie   meinbres   sometez   uc   estupuis   mureture   si il   dites choses

AN 'sicum la franture fust al braz' is taken to refer to the directions for dislocation 'sine carnis ruptura' (341), whereas according to Sudhoff's punctuation, which seems right, it begins the next sentence (343). We should read 'Cum la franture est al braz li mires . . .' AN 'les esplentes aparailliés' translates 'ferulas primo paratas' (349–50; see III, III above). AN has misunderstood the time of application, which is every three days ('tercio die . . . et postea similiter alio tercio', 351). For 'constrictorie' the Latin has 'strictura [var. *strictorium*]' (352). AN's 'quant le constri[t]orie se lasche' abbreviates the Latin 'quando tumor, qui ex strictorio venerat, desinit' (357), whilst 'od esplentes e fil' seems to rest on a misunderstanding of 'con fascia et ferulis' (361), or perhaps the source read 'filis' for 'ferulis'. For 'fractura con vulnere' the Latin envisages two assistants (369). Omitting a phrase which is also missing from Sudhoff's MS M (373–74), AN botches the direction 'ferule apponantur undique, nisi quod supra vulnus medietas ferule ponetur ex una parte et alia ex altera' (374–75).

XX. avient   eiflius uernus   uielle

AN presupposes a reading in the Latin 'in ea parte brachii in qua de nervi vel lacerti lesio non sit, non sit timendum . . .' (400–01).

XXI. lungur   neis il soit seins e si tele maniere

The Latin has 'ex transverso et vulnus dependeat' (413). AN's 'en lung' is an addition to 'suatur' (413). AN has misunderstood and abbreviated 'hoc fiat [sc. patiens] quotiens ipse [sc. vulnus] mutatur et supra illam partem ad iacendum . . . semper locetur' (418–19; see Sudhoff p. 215, n.17).

XXII. e metez

AN omits 'intra costam et costam incidatur' (426) and there is a further omission, probably due to a 'saut du même au même' ('superius' 429 and 432). In contrast 'e encore s'il ne perce mie . . . sicum dit est desus' is an addition to the source. The Latin MSS display some confusion (see Sudhoff p. 216, n.3).

XXIII. soit

AN's 'u od auchune autre glamuse chose' replaces 'vel visco vel pice' (438).

XXIV. ne

AN presupposes the reading 'vel intestina et non exierint' (445, see Sudhoff p. 216, n.19).

XXV. diafstagmate   ia ine   diastragmate   les   ornemenz   pescisent   s.n. la de la de la f.   est

AN omits 'stomacho' (451) and the detail that the patient wounded in the diaphragm 'cito moritur' (455–56). The section on the spleen (470–72) is placed by AN before that on the lung and liver (460–69). AN's 'u tailliez de tut en tut la partie blescié' is an addition to the Latin. AN followed a source which had 'epar' instead of 'pulmo' (see Sudhoff p. 217, n.5 and 12).

XXVI. Sudhoff erroneously omits this chapter number.

XXVII. est   face   greiture   denunciance   feu   la   uen   cole   tendie

According to Sudhoff's numbering of the chapters there is no XXVI. AN omits 'incisum fuerit' (476–77), erroneously taking 'in longum vel ex obliquo' (476) to refer to the position of the wound (omitting 'et', 475) and hence also obscuring the sense of the 'ita quod' clause (476). AN also omits 'ex utraque parte' (482). The 'unciam unam' of the Latin (482) is glossed in one MS by 'digitum unum' (Sudhoff p. 217, n.31). According to the Latin the sponge is to be dipped into 'aqua calida' (496). The subject of 'serrunt / isserunt' is 'buel' taken in the plural (cf. 'intestinis' 497 and 'intestinum' 501). AN's 'tut quais', which would mean 'completely still', is probably an error for 'quaissé' = 'shaken' (see 'conquatiatur', 499). AN's 'sur cele memes piece la partie dedenz . . .' presupposes the reading 'interior pars' (see Sudhoff p. 218, n.21), not the 'exterior pars' of Sudhoff's text (507). The sentence 'E li malades gise enclin . . . dedenz' seems to be an addition to the source, but is in fact referred to in the Latin of the next section (see 520–21).

XXVIII. charmus   molenz   coste   ces autres   chloc

AN does not render 'apostematibus' (513, 515) in the rubric and first sentence. AN has misunderstood the syntax of 'idem dicimus, quod et superius, quia, cum sint in carnosis locis . . .' (515–16), presumably by omitting 'quia'. AN's 'luisante' is an incorrect rendering of 'livida' (misread as 'lucida' ?). AN's 'entur le col del [l]iu' assumes a variant reading in the Latin (see Sudhoff p. 219, n.8). In the treatment itself AN omits 'vel etiam incensione' (527) and 'et locum purifica' (535). In the explanation of the 'tente coee' it should be noted that Sudhoff's base MS often has 'tasta' for 'tenta' ('teste' in 535 seems to be an error) in the other MSS (see Sudhoff p. 219, n.23). AN renders 'primariole' (540) but not '[mulieres] in partu nove' (540). AN 'cheif de la mamele' renders the variant reading 'caput mamille' (see Sudhoff p. 219, n.31) for the 'capitellum' of the text (542).

XXIX. le

AN took 'folliculum' (547) as subject. The correction 'del foillet s'en ist' assumes the use of a singular verb with the plural subject 'coilz', a phenomenon frequently attested in our text.

XXX. tel   rasinie   vait

The Latin specifies 'con ferro calido vel auro' (553). In MS M 'filum' (558) is glossed 'que coniungitur pellicula con membro virili' (Sudhoff p. 220, n.13). AN's 'le tuel' renders Latin 'orificium' (560). AN omits the short receipt 'Ad idem valet fabba excoriata et parata, ut comedi debet et superposita' (570–71). The final sentence of this chapter follows an extra passage recorded by Sudhoff in another Latin MS (Sudhoff p. 221, n.2).

XXXI. e le

AN's 'en un liu que est apelé osceum' is a misunderstanding of 'retinet intestina, ne cadant in osseum' (575). AN's 'duodenum' is preferable to the Latin 'dindimum' (579). AN omits 'et hernia fit' (580) at the end.

XXXII. iiii   merchier   remanance   foit   e   descende   diote

For 'noef' the Latin has '.xi.' (584–85). AN simplifies 'quando .xi. dies supersunt de luna, ita quod quolibet die usque ad finem lune comedat de eisdem [unum] diminuendo' (586; cf. Sudhoff p. 221, n.13). AN seems also to have evaded the problem posed by 'caput et [var. ad] humeros habens depressos' (591). Like MSS Fl. & J. AN omits 'Deinde . . . intromittatur' (595–96). The 'autre maneire de fer' renders 'alius stilus' (597) and 'une esplente mut delié' 'spagus subtilis' (598). AN's 'dous mois u trois' renders a variant reading of the Latin (see Sudhoff p. 222, n.12).

XXXIII. docia   de   nofue   la

AN's 'faites deslier' does not correspond to the Latin which has 'fiat clistere vel purgetur' (613). The phrase 'usque superius' (617), glossed in one MS by 'id est usque ad inguen' (Sudhoff p. 222, n.23), has been misunderstood as 'ut superius', 'sicum devant dit est'. In the Latin 'cloua' sometimes appears as 'clava', 'gioua' and is glossed 'instrumentum est quod assimilatur tenaculis' (Sudhoff p. 222, n.24). 'Esplente' translates 'spago' (618). AN's 'nofime jor' corresponds to an attested variant in the Latin (Sudhoff p. 222, n. 30).

XXXIV. This chapter ('De hernia ex humoribus consurgente') is omitted by AN.

XXXV. herina   camosite   carmosite   currez

XXXVI. fie ce   col   peril   ireisse   male   charnisse

AN 'auchune foiz hum' is an error for 'auchun forz hum' ('aliquis fortis' (640)).

XXXVII. fans   petroloneon   ruel

AN 'tuel' (MS 'ruel') appears to be a translation of 'syringam' (651), but it is not clear how 'del membre' can be accommodated to the Latin 'petroleum per syringam immitatur' (651), and it is best taken here to mean 'outlet' i.e. the anal orifice.

XXXVIII. maladie   jenier   puniz   p. meis al devant garder

The Latin has 'dieta precedat tenuis' (661). Owing to a 'saut du même au même' ('vesica', 'vesice' 664) AN has omitted 'inveniatur lapis et ducatur ad collum vesice' (664). Also misunderstood is 'ibi in fontanella duobus digitis supra anum incidatur in longum et deinde con instrumento lapis extrahatur' (665–66; see Sudhoff p. 224, n.12).

XXXIX. The Latin has 'quocunque modo contingat de spinali medulla' (678) and 'veluti nervus poterit conglutinari' (680).

XL. destravers   naivienge

The rubric corresponds to Sudhoff's MS J 'De vulnere longaonis' (Sudhoff p. 225, n.2). Some MSS have 'longia', others 'longaon'. One expects 'plaié en lung' for 'in longum vulneretur' (684) to provide the contrast with 'd'entravers' ('ex transverso' 685). AN omits 'et quasi per se cadat' (689–90).

XLI. The Latin has 'curam potius divine gratie beneficioque nature committimus' (696), although 'beneficioque nature' is omitted in MS Fl., as it no doubt was in AN's source.

XLII. uaissent   desaniz   e une partie

The Latin has 'fit ibi quandoque ampulla per mensem, et paciens . . .' (704) and 'ut ergo de eius principio melius certificari valeas' (706). AN has misunderstood the Latin 'interroga si quando [var. quandoque] per anum ventositatem emittit, pars [var. et pars] illius ventositatis per fistulam exeat' (707–8), 'de l'autre part' being substituted for 'per fistulam'. In the following sentence AN substitutes 'dunc' for 'Quod si constiterit' (708), and 'a vier' reflects the 'verum est' of MS J. AN omits the adverbial phrase in 'si tenta de facili exeat' (711–12) and misunderstands 'velud acus missa' (713) as 'cum acu missa'.

XLIII. sunt   matuil   menstrarum   medlez   solos   gros   chistere   emorosces   caprisiti   cheint   ch. oigne

The apparently intrusive 'se est' reflects the 'scilicet' of MSS Fl. and J (Sudhoff p. 226, n.13). After 'si vus volez' AN omits 'ut atrici cadant' (729). AN's 'l'ardur chiece' is a mistranslation of Latin 'ardor inceperit' (731), perhaps misread as 'ceciderit'. AN imitates the absolute construction of 'inuncto loco' (738), but with 'si par ceo ne sunt bein curé' diverges from the Latin 'si penitus vis curare' (741). There has evidently been an omission (by the copyist ?) corresponding to the Latin 'incidantur, quod si non sustinuerit . . .' (742). AN's 'le fer chaud' presupposes a reading 'ferrum calidum' (cf. 747), whereas Sudhoff's text has 'parum calidum' (744). AN 'l'os' does not adequately render Latin 'os natium' (745–46).

XLIV. del pis   entut   aument   stranguiria   les

Confusing 'pectus' and 'pecten', the translator wrote 'De la grevance del pis' for 'De vulneribus pectinis' (749).

XLV. devient   de la main de la iuncture   q. faite   al noit en la funteine le de braz de-denz e dehors   asina   asina   od   del sechine

AN 'a l'encision' is an addition to the source, whilst 'et ad dolorem manus' (761) is omitted the first time it occurs (cf. 763) and 'uratur in concavitate manus et ex alia parte inter digitos' (763–64) is obscured. AN 'epiglaco' is for 'epiglotto' (771) and 'forcele' renders Latin 'furuncula / furcella' (cf. 773). For pain in the kidneys the Latin has 'fiant in fontanellis usture ad nodulum' (781) with a superscript addition in MS Fl. 'con setone' (Sudhoff p. 228, n.12) which is reflected in AN. AN omits 'cauterium contra emorroidas: ad emorroidas mittatur seton supra anum retro' (788–89).

[BOOK IV]

Preface. e   quele   plaie   ols   en   piz   e des   runture   rinture   rup od la   rupture   orcilz   cel

In the list of chapters Sudhoff's 15th chapter-heading (*De apostematibus in hiis locis nascentibus*)

is here combined with the 14th (cf. Sudhoff p. 229, n.19). In fact there is no chapter 15 in Sudhoff's edition, chapter 14 (pp. 232–33) bearing the rubric *De fistulis et cancris in hiis locis nascentibus* (p. 232, l.120). The final chapter heading is not in Sudhoff's edition which has XX. *De spasmo*.

I.   en   li

The explanation of 'vertebrum' is an addition to the Latin source. AN has reversed the Latin 'si telum ei [sc. scia] inhereat'. In the Latin the drill or borer is a 'trepanum' (39) (cf. I, VI). AN does not render 'circa ferrum' (39).

II.   quisee

IV.   plaie

AN does not render 'si ex transverso fiat' (51).

V.   dit devant est

VI.   qui   doie

In MS M the phrase 'spacio trium unciarum' is glossed 'nota quod uncia est mensura unius digiti' (Sudhoff p. 230, n.21). AN does not mention the blackening ('nigredo', 61) of the swelling.

VII.   AN omits 'vel ossis vel sine lesione eorum' (67–68).

VIII.   est ist   copu v   socum   feut   q. e lautre entre lautre   refanie

AN omits 'propter rumorem ibi discurrentem' (71–72). In the Latin the strong assistant holds the patient's body 'a superiore parte' (76), but this phrase has been transferred by AN to the actions of the doctor. AN's 'corde / cordele' are not accurate translations of 'fasceolus' (78 / 79). After 'esplente' AN omits 'fascia' ('ita quod ambe coxe comprehendantur con fascia' (84–85)).

IX.   ch. par plaie aveint si devez prendre del braz   l. par

The Latin has 'plagellam per semissem amplam imponere' (94).

X.   estupes

The appearance of 'genul' in the rubric is not justified by the Latin which has 'crus', correctly translated in the text by 'jambe'. AN's 'estupe' translates 'stupha' (see Sudhoff p. 232, n. 3), where Sudhoff's text has 'stapha' (99). AN does not render 'cubiti' (99) and 'violenter' (100).

XI.   In MS M 'spatium uncie' (106) is glossed 'unciam vocat grossiciem digiti' (Sudhoff p. 232, n.9).

XII.   la   lui

AN does not render 'a medico' (114).

XIV.   aveint   puriissent   molenz   officius   des   cure

AN omits 'se constringit' (125) through a 'saut du même au même' ('aliquando', 125). The omission in the text corresponds to 'aliquam eminenciam fecerit' (130). AN 'grant come le cancre est' renders 'ad modum loci' (131) which is glossed in MS M by 'ubi cancer est' (Sudhoff p. 233, n.7). AN truncates 'deinde ovum ad ignem tollendum ponatur' (135) and 'entechi de cancre' abbreviates 'nigrum, infectum et mortificatum' (138).

XVI. iuut (second u with nasal bar)   comin
Sudhoff's numbering is erroneous as no chapter XV appears in his text.

XVII. artechie

AN omits 'ad nodulum vel fiat ibi cauterium triangulatum' (152–53). AN's 'une quiture desuz
la jambe' is an addition to the source.

XVIII. umblicium   quillez   trubliez   noiz   m. bein   en fut enci

AN omits a whole receipt ('Item recipe . . . inungatur locus', 164–66) and also 'sifulam' (167)
after 'crassula la mendre'. AN also replaces 'sepo arietino' (171) by 'siu de porc'. In the receipt
for the ointment 'unce et demie' diverges from Latin 'unciam semis' (175) and 'gresse de porc'
appears to be an error for 'gerse' (175). In the receipt the Latin has 'cimarum rubi uncias .iii.'
(177).

XIX. peire   lepres   quatre   unt depilez   qui   confuscacion   da   e. la fonteine
la   o. pernez   foille   en   la   e al   ne soit

AN omits 'spume nitri uncias .iii.' (204). AN's 'estre les choses que ne devent estre fundu' is a
reformulation of 'preterea que teri debent' (206–07). For 'inter cubitum et humerum' (211)
AN has 'la fonteine e la cute'. In the receipt for the ointment AN has omitted 'ana uncias .iii.'
(214) as the quantity of the first two ingredients and also 'succi porri' (214–15). AN has also
omitted 'sed prius lanuginem, ubi est, abradas' (217).

XX. chaut   gmendeire   a apele   epurgier   ellebrentire   estivez   checum   sor-
noee   dois   terce suriz

The change of units to 'dragmes' and 'scruples' is introduced by AN. For AN's 'dous feus' the
Latin has 'inter tres ignes' (230). The rest of AN is an addition to the source.

GLOSSARY

The glossary is designed to meet the needs of readers who have little specialist knowledge of Old French and Anglo-Norman and is therefore as comprehensive as practicable, registering variant forms and omitting only those words which are identical with familiar modern French forms. Where possible the equivalents in the Latin source are given in brackets at the end of each entry. Plant identifications conform to the nomenclature adopted in A.R. Clapham, T.G. Tutin and D.M. Moore, *Flora of the British Isles*, 3rd ed. (Cambridge, 1987).

ABUNDER v.n. to abound, be plentiful, be present in large quantity (superhabundare)
ACEMÉ a. flowery, polished (of language) (sublimus)
ACHAISUN, ACHEISYN s. cause (causa)
ACHANT a. accidental (accidens)
ACHE s. smallage, wild celery (Apium graveolens L.) (apium)
[ACREISTRE] v.a. to increase (augmentare) ACCRÉS p.p.
ADESER v.a. to touch (tangere)
ADJUTORIUS s.pl. medical aids, remedies (adiutoria)
ADRESC(I)É p.p. set (of bone) (rectus)
AEIRDEMENT s. adhesion
AELENE s. breath
[AERDRE] v.a. and refl. to adhere, stick (adherere, inherere) AEIRT, SE AIEIRT, SE (A)EIRT ind.pr.3 AEIRDE, AERDE sbj.pr.3 AHERS, AEIRS p.p.
AFAITIER v.a. to arrange, fit (aptare)
A(F)ERMER v.n. and refl. to become firm, harden, consolidate, heal (consolidari, esse confir-matus, confirmari) AFERMÉ(E p.p.
AFFODILLE, pl. AFFODILDIS, AMFODILLES s. ramsons, wild garlic (Allium ursinum L.) or crow garlic (Allium vineale L.) (affodillus, centum capitum)
AFICH(I)É p.p. embedded, stuck (infixus)
AGRESTA s. yellow horned-poppy, 'celidonia agrestis' (Glaucium flavum Crantz) (agresta; else-where can mean verjuice)
AGU a. acute, sharp (acutus)
AGUILLE, AUGULIE, AGULLE, AUGUIL(L)E s. needle (acus)
AGUIS(I)ER v.a. to render tart, pungent AGUISSEZ imper.5 AGUSIÉ p.p.
AIDIER, AIDEIR v.n. to aid, assist (subvenire)
AIMPLE a. broad, wide (amplus)
AINZ, EINZ adv. earlier, before; rather, on the contrary, but (immo); therein, into (it) (interius) A(I)NZ QUE, EINZ QUE conj.loc. before (antequam)
AIS(S)ELE, AISSIELE s. armpit (ascella)
AISIL s. vinegar (acetum)
AJUSTER v.a. to add (addere, superaddere)
ALAINE s. breath
ALBUN, AUBON D'OEF s. white of egg (albumen ovi)
ALCHUM pr. anyone
ALEGGER v. refl. to be relieved, to ease
ALEINE, ALIENE, ALAINE s. breath
ALELUIA s. wood sorrel (Oxalis acetosella L.) (allelulia)
ALEMANDE s. almond; tonsil (amigdala)
AL(L)OPICIA s. alopecia, falling out of hair (allopicia)
ALOE, ALOE(N EPATIC s. aloes (Aloe L. spp.); liver-coloured form of aloes (aloe, aloe epaticus)
ALOINÉ p.p. aligned (adequare)
ALOISNE, ALOESNE, ALUESNE s. wormwood (Artemisia absinthium L.) (absinthium)

ALONGE see ALOISNE
ALUM s. alum ALUM ZUCARINUM (I,48), ALUM ZUCRÉ (I,53) powdered alum (alumen)
AMAURIR v.a. to bring to maturity
AMBE a. both D'AMBES PARS on both sides (ex utraque parte)
AMBESDEUS, AMBESDOUS a. both D'A. PARZ on both sides (ex utraque parte)
AMENU(I)S(I)ER v.a. to diminish, lessen, reduce (diminuere, essere diminutus, minuere) AME-
    NUSÉ, AMENUSEEZ p.p.
AMEURER v.a. to bring to maturity, to a head (of boil)
AMIABLEMENT adv. carefully, gently (diligenter)
AMIGDELES s.pl. tonsils (amigdale)
AMOLLIR v.a. to soften (mollificare)
[AMORTIR] v.a. to destroy (mortificare) AMORTIST ind.pr.3 AMORTI(E p.p.
AMUNT adv. upwards (sursum) D'AMUNT from above (a superioribus)
AMUSTIR v.a. to moisten, wet (humectare)
AN s. year DEMI(E A. six months (dimidium anni)
ANAPRÉS adv. next, afterwards (postea, deinde)
ANE(I)NTI p.p. destroyed (corruptus); consumed (consumptus)
ANEIRE adv. forthwith
ANERCI p.p. blackened (denigratus)
ANET s. dill (Anethum graveolens L.) (anetum)
ANETTER, ANEITIR v.a. to cleanse, clean up (mundificare)
ANGLÉS a. English
ANIS s. aniseed (Pimpinella anisum L.) (anisum)
ANTENDRE v.a. to understand ANTENDUNT ind.pr.6
[ANTITLER] v.a. to intitle (intitulare) ANTITLÉ p.p.
A(N)TRAIT s. poultice
ANTRAX, ANTRACE s. anthrax, malignant growth, carbuncle (antrax)
ANVELUPER v.refl. to be wrapped round
AOITER v.a. to increase
AORNER v.a. to dress (a wound) (conponere)
APARAILL(I)ER, APARILLIER v.a. to prepare, arrange (parare, preparare)
APENDRE v.n. to belong to, relate to, concern APENT ind.pr.3
APIRGE sbj.pr.3 of APARER to appear
APOIAL s. support, supporting device (sustentaculum)
APOSTE(I)ME, APOSTOEME, APOTESME, POSTEME pl. APOSTEMUS, APOSTUMUS s.
    aposteme, boil, ulcer (apostema)
APOSTOLICON, A. CIRUGIEN, APOSTOLICUM CIRUGICUM s. 'ointment of the
    Apostles' (apostolicum cirurgicum)
APUEIR v.a. to lean (flectare)
APUER v.refl. to lean (se appodiare)
AQUIS, AQUUS adv. somewhat, a little (aliquantulum)
ARACHIER v.a. to pull out (removere, enervare)
ARACINÉ p.p. rooted (in)
ARDANT a. red hot (ardens, candens)
ARDIER, ARDOIR v.a. to burn (incendere)
AREIM, ARAIM, ARIM, AREINT, EREIM s. brass, bronze (eneum)
ARERE adv. back(wards)
ARGENT s. VIF A. quicksilver (argentum vivum)
ARIRE adv. back (again), back(wards)
ARISTOLOGIE, ARISTOLOGIE RONDE, ARISTOLOGIA ROTUNDA, ARISTOLOGIAM
    s. aristolochia, birthwort (Aristolochia L. spp.) (aristolochia)
ARME s. arm, weapon (arma)
ARMOISE, ARMAISE, ARMEISE s. mugwort (Artemisia vulgaris L.) (arthemisia)
ARMONIAC(UM, ARMONIACO s. gum ammoniac (Dorema ammoniacum D.Don. and D. au-
    cheri Boiss.) (amoniacum)
A[R]NAGLOSSE s. plantain, waybread (Plantago major L.) (arnoglossa)
ARS p.p. burned (incensus)
ARSENICI s. (yellow) arsenic (auripigmentum)

ARSURE s. burning sensation; burn; cauterization (arsura; incensio)
ARTER(I)E, AUTERIE s. artery (arteria) see also TRACHIE ARTERIE
ARTETIKE s. gout (artetica passio)
ASAIER, ASAIEIR, ASAEIR v.a. to examine, test; to try, attempt (temptare)
[ASANER] v.a. to heal, cure ASANÉ p.p. (curare)
ASAVER, CEO EST to wit, namely
ASEIZ adv. freely, plentifully (habundanter)
ASIS see ASSEIR
ASMA s. asthma (asma)
ASNE s. ass
ASSEIR v.refl. to be seated ASIS p.p.
ASSEMBLÉ(E s. gathering (into a lump)
ASUAGEANT a. soothing (mitigans)
ASUAGIR, -ER v.a. to soothe (mitigare) ASUAGIST ind.pr.3
ATACHER, ATHACHIER v.a. to fasten (nectere)
ATAPIR v.n. to lie hidden, concealed (latere)
ATARGIER v.n. to be slow to (II,2 tardius relinquere)
ATEINDRE, ATENDRE v.a. to reach, touch, afflict (contingere, procedere ad, terminare ad)
ATEMPRÉ a. soft, yielding (temperatus)
ATEREL, ATHEREL s. nape of neck (cervix)
ATINGE sbj.pr.3 of ATEINDRE
ATORNER, ATURNER v.a. to arrange, prepare (aptare) ATORNÉ p.p. ready
ATRACTION DE L'AIR s. intake of breath (aeris attractio)
ATRAIRE v.a. to attract, draw to (trahere)
ATRAIRE s.v. attraction
ATRAIT s. drawing, intake (of breath) (spiritus attractio)
AUCHES, AUQUES adv. a little, somewhat (ex parte, aliquantulum)
AUGENT sbj.pr.6 of ALER
AUQUES DE AGE getting on in years (provecte etatis)
AUSIER v.a. to make even (adequare)
AUTREFEIZ adv. again, once more (iterum); sometimes (aliquando)
AUTRESI adv. A. CHAUT just as hot AUTRISI GRAUNT as big as
AVAL adv. downwards (deorsum)
AVALER v.a. to lower (deponere) cf. VALER; v.n. to descend
AVEIR v.refl. with A (I,13) to behave, conduct oneself
AVENANTEMENT adv. fittingly, well (conpetenter, diligentissime, diligenter) AVENAN-
     MENT carefully, well (caute)
AVENIR v.n. to occur (contingere) AV(I)ENT, AVIEINT, AVEINT ind.pr.3 AVINENT, AVE-
     NENT ind.pr.6 AVENDRUNT fut.6 AVENGE, AVINGE sbj.pr.3 AVENIT sbj.imp.3
AVENTER v.a. to release, allow to escape (by exposing to the air)
AVENTURE a. chance, accident (casus) SUR A. METTRE to ascribe to chance (casui imputare)
AVISONQUES adv. scarcely (vix)
AV(E)RONE s. southernwood (Artemisia abrotanum L.) A. SALVAGE (I,23;I,53) A. DAMA-
     SCHE (I,23)
AVIVÉ p.p. revived (iuvare)
BACHILER s. young man
BAGNE, BAIN, BANG s. bath (balneum)
BAINGNIER v.n. to take a bath (balneare) BAINEZ imp.5
BALAUSTIA, BALAUSTIE s. pomegranate (Punica granatum L.) (balaustia)
BANC s. bench (banca, bancus)
BARBELÉ, BARBALÉ a. barbed (barbulatus)
BARDANE s. great burdock (Arctium lappa L.) (bardana)
BASME EUAGE s. water-mint (Mentha aquatica L.) (balsamita aquatica)
BEIVRE v.a. to drink BEIT ind.pr.3
BELEMENT adv. carefully, sensitively (diligenter, leviter)
BENEITE s. 'herb bennet' (Geum urbanum L.) or hemlock (Conium maculatum L.) or cowbane
     (Cicuta virosa L.) (benedicta)
BESLUNG a. oblong

BIN = BIEN

BLAMER v.a. to blame, criticize (crimen opponere)

BLANCHIR v.n. to go white

BLESCER v.a. to injure, wound, harm (ledere)

BLES(C)EUR(E s. wounding, damage, lesion (lesio)

BOCE s. boil, ulcer (bocium, botius)

BOCIUM s. swelling (bocium); goitre, bronchocele (II,15)

BOEL, BOELLE pl. BOIALS s. bowel(s) (intestinum, -na)

BOILLI (I,15;III,16) s. fine earth (containing iron oxide) (bolus)

BOILL(I)ER, BOILLIR v.a. to boil (bullire)

BOISSUN, BOISSON s. bramble (Rubus fruticosus sens. lat.) (rubus)

BOMBES s. cotton (bombax)

BORACIS s. crude borax (borax)

BORB(E)LET(T), BURBLEITE, BORBLEITE, BURB(E)LETTEE s. pustule, pimple (pustula)

BOSOIGNE s. ESTRE B. to be necessary

BRAC(E, BRAZ, BRAÇZ s. arm (brachium, lacertus)

BRANCA URSINA, BRANSA URSINA, BRANCHAM URSINAM s. bear's breech (Acanthus mollis L.)

BRANCI s.pl. swellings (causing sore throat), tonsillar abscesses (branci)

BRESES, BRESUS s.pl. embers (prunae)

BREVEMENT adv. briefly

BRIOINE, BRIONIE s. var. cucurbitaceae incl. white / red bryony (Bryonia cretica L. subsp. dioica (Jacq.) Tutin)

BRUILLER v.a. to burn, cauterize (urere, comburere) BRUILLIEZ p.p. (tostus)

BRUSCI s. butcher's broom, knee holly (Ruscus aculeatus L.) (bruscus)

BUALS, BUAUS s.pl. intestines, bowels (intestina)

BUBO s. bubo, boil

BUCHE s. mouth (os)

BUISSUM, BOISSON s. bramble (Rubus fruticosus sens. lat.) (rubus)

BURE DE MAI s. May butter, unsalted butter

BURITH s. soapwort (Saponaria officinalis L.)

BURNETTE s. one of the burnets (Sanguisorba officinalis L., Pimpinella saxifraga L., Sanguisorba minor Scop. subsp. minor)

BUTER v.a. to push, thrust (impellere)

ÇA ... LA adv. here ... there (hac ... illac)

CALCAIN s. heel (calcaneum)

CAL(A)MENT, CAL(L)EMENT s. calamint (Calamintha L. spp.) (calamentum)

C(H)AMPHORE s. camphor (camphora)

CANCRE, CAUNCRE, CHANCRE s. sore, tumour, cancer (cancer)

CANELE s. cinnamon (cinnamomum)

CAPITELLUM, CAPITEL, CAPITEILS s. lye, alkaline detergent (capitellum)

CAPPARIS s. honeysuckle (Lonicera caprifolium / periclymenum L.)

CAPRIFICI s. honeysuckle (Lonicera caprifolium L. / periclymenum L.) (caprificus)

CAR, CHAR conj. for, because

CARBUNC(U)LUS, CARBUNCULO, CHARBUNCLE s. carbuncle, boil (carbunculus)

CARPIE see CHARPIE

CASSILAGO s. henbane (Hyoscyamus niger L.) (cassilago)

CASTO(I)RE s. castoreum (made with scent glands of beaver) (castoreum)

CEL s. salt C. GRAS (1,53 sal nitri)

CELÉ a. concealed, hidden (occultus)

CELIDO(I)NE, C. SALVAGE s. greater celandine (Chelidonium majus L.) or yellow horned-poppy (Glaucium flavum Crantz) (memitha, agresta)

CENDRE s. ash (cinis)

CENILLIÉ s. henbane (Hyoscyamus niger L.) (jusquiamus)

CENSZ a. hundred

CENT–CHIÉS s. ramsons, wild garlic (Allium ursinum L.) or crow garlic (Allium vineale L.) (centum capita)

CENTINERVE s. ribwort plantain (Plantago lanceolata L.) (centinervia)

CENTRUM GALLI, CENTRI GALLI s. clary (Salvia pratensis L.) or cockle (Agrostemma gi-
    thago L.) or darnel (Lolium temulentum L.) (centrum galli)
CENTUMCELLIE s. pennywort (Umbilicus rupestris (Salisb.) Dandy) (scarumcella)
CERCHIER v.a. to investigate
CERICE s. wild cherry (Prunus avium L.)
CERTEFIÉ, CERTIFIÉ p.p. ESTRE C. to be certain, sure, assured (certificari)
CERTEIN a. certain, sure (certus)
CERUSE n. white lead (cerusa)
CERVEL s. brain (cerebrum)
CHAEÉT p.p. of CHAIR
CHAINE, CHAENE DE LA GULE, s. collar-bone (cathena gule)
CHAIR v.n. to fall (cadere) CHARRUNT fut.6 CHAEÉT p.p.
CHAISEITE, CHASSETTE s. casket, small container (casula)
CHAL(L)(E)MEL s. tube, pipe (can(n)ellus, embotum)
CHALOR s. heat (calor)
CHANAL, CHANEL, CHENEAL pl. CHANEIAILS s. channel (meatus)
CHAPIT(T)LE, CAPITLE s. chapter, section (capitulum, paragrafus)
CHAR s. flesh, meat MORTE C. proud flesh
CHARBONS s.pl. coals (carbones, prunae)
CHARDUN s. thistle CH. VELU CH. BENEIT blessed thistle (Cnicus benedictus L.) (cardo
    benedictus)
CHARNITEURE s. fleshy growth (carnositas)
C(H)ARNOSETÉ, CARNOSITÉ s. fleshy part, fleshy growth (carnositas)
CHARNU a. fleshy (carnosus)
CHARPIE s. lint (carpia)
CHARUNGE s. dead flesh or skin (carnositas)
CHASSETTE see CHAISEITE
CHASTEINE s. sweet chestnut (Castanea sativa Miller) (castanea)
CHAUDI(E)RE s. cooking-pot (caldarium)
CHAUZ s. lime VIVE CH., CHAUCE V. quicklime (calx viva)
CHAUZ, CHAUT p.p. of CHAOIR to fall (cadere)
CHEET p.p. of CHEIR to fall
CHEIF D'ESPURGE s. stavesacre (Delphinium staphisagria L.) (cappurgium = caput purgium)
CHEIR v.n. to fall (cadere) CHEIT ind.pr.3 CHEENT ind.pr.6 CHEIEIT ind.imp.3 CHIECE,
    CHECE, CHEICE sbj.pr.3
CHEIS pl. of CH(I)EF
CHENEAL s. channel (meatus)
CHENILLÉ, CHENILLIÉ s. henbane (Hyoscyamus niger L.)
CHEVESTRE s. halter, stall, muzzle (capistrum)
CHEVOI(L)Z, CHEVO(I)LS s.pl. hair (capilli)
CH(I)EF, CHEIF, pl. CHEIS, CHEFZ, CHÉS, CHIEZ s. head, end (caput, extremitas)
CH(I)EVREFOIL(E s. honeysuckle (Lonicera caprifolium / periclymenum L.) (caprificus, caprifo-
    lium)
CHIMOLEAM s. fuller's earth (chymolea)
CHOLET s. cabbage (Brassica oleracea L.) (caulis)
CIA s. hip-bone, ischium, socket of femur (scia)
CICLAMI(NI)S s. earthnut (Conopodium majus (Gouan) Loret), sowbread (Cyclamen hederifo-
    lium Aiton) (ciclamen)
CIME. pl. CIMUS s. tip (of shoot) (cima)
CIPHULA (III,30) s. unidentified plant (sifula, scicula, simphula)
CIRE, SIRE s. wax (cera)
CIRUGIE s. surgery (cirurgia)
CIRUGIEN a. surgical
CIRURGICUM APOSTOLICUM s. 'ointment of the Apostles'
CISOL s. chisel (spatumen)
CITRI (II,13) s. probably a cucurbitaceous plant (citrus)
CITRIN a. lemon yellow (citrinus)
CLISTERE s. clyster, enema (clistera)

CLO(U s. boil, carbuncle, aposteme
CLOP a. lame (claudus)
CLOUA (III,33) s. surgical instrument (cloua)
COCKEL (ME) (II,5) s. gypsum
COÉ a. with a string attached (for withdrawal) (caudatus)
COILLE sbj.pr.3 of COILLIR to remove (auferre)
COIL(L)(I)E s. scrotum, testicle (testiculus)
COI(L)Z s.pl. testicles
COINET s. small wedge (cuneus)
COINTE a. skilful, careful (caute) NEINT C. unskilful, negligent (incaute)
COINTEMENT adv. skilfully, dexterously, carefully (caute, provide)
COL s. neck (collum; stipes)
COLER v.a. to strain, sieve (colare)
COLLECTION (III,16) s. abscess, humour, gathering (collectio)
COLLIRIE s. eye salve (collirium)
COLOFONIE s. colophony (colofonia)
COLP s. blow (percussura, percussio)
COLRE s. choler, bile (colera)
COLURE, CULURE s. strained material (colatura)
COLURÉ a. highly-coloured, high-flown (coloratus)
COMENT QUE conj. however, in whatever way (quocunque modo)
COMIN s. cumin (Cuminum cyminum L.) (cyminum)
COMPRENDRE v.a. to include, embrace
COMPRESSION s. compression (compressio)
CONFECTION s. preparation, mixture, product
CONFIRE v.a. to make up, concoct, prepare (conficere) CONFIS(S)EZ, CONFISCEZ imp.
CONFRICACION s. rubbing (confricatio)
CONFUSEMENT adv. all together, in a mixture
CONSOUDE s. GREINURE, GREIGNURE C. consound, comfrey (Symphytum officinale L.)
     (consolida maior)
CONSTRI(C)TORIE s. and a. constringent, styptic (strictorium, strictura)
CONTINUEL a. continual
CONTRAIT a. contracted (contrahere)
CONTRARIE a. opposite (contrarius)
CONTREVAL adv. down (ad inferiora; inferius)
CONUSTRE, CUNUSTRE v.a. to know, recognize (cognoscere)
CORDE s. rope, cord (corda)
CORDELE s. string, cord
CORGE s. throat (guttur)
COR(R)E v.n. to run, flow (fluere, lacrimare)
COROMPRE v.a. to cause to fester (corrumpere)
COR(R)UMPU a. festering (corruptus, putrefactus)
COSE = CHOSE
COSEZ see CUSTRE
COSTE(E s. side, rib (costa) EN C. beside (iuxta)
COSTIVÉ a. constipated
COTUN, COTUM s. cotton (bombax, carpia)
COVENABLE a. appropriate, relevant (idoneus, competens, aptus)
COVENABLEMENT adv. suitably, properly (convenienter, diligenter, competenter)
COVENGE sbj.pr.3 of COVENIR to be necessary, fitting
CRAMPE s. cramp (spasmus)
CRASSULAM LA GRAUNDE s. orpine (Sedum telephium L.) (crassula maior)
CRASSULAM LA MENDRE s. common stone crop (Sedum acre L.) (crassula minor)
CRE(I)STRE v.n. to grow (crescere, excrescere)
CREPE s. pancake, fritter (crispella)
CREU p.p. of CRESTRE to grow
CREVER v.n. to burst (crepare)
CRIENDRE v.a. to fear (timere) CRIENT ind.pr.3

CRISTAL s. crystal (cristallum)
CROIS a. hollow pl.fem. CROSSES (III,9) (concavus)
CROIS, CROIZ s. hollow, hole (concavitas)
CROISSI p.p. hollowed out (concavatus)
CROIZ s. cross EN CROIS in the shape of a cross (cruciform incision; in modum crucis)
CROTE DE CHEIFRE s. goat dung
CROUS a. hollow (concavus)
CRUSTE s. scab
CUCUMISCELLE s. squirting cucumber (Ecballium elaterium A. Richard)
CUCURBITE s. var. cucurbitaceae incl. Cucumis sativus L., Citrullus colocynthis (L.) Kuntze,
    Lagenaria siceraria (Mol.) Standl, Lagenaria vulgaris Ser. C. SALVAGE (II,15) (cucurbita)
CUL s. anus (anus)
CULUR s. colour (color)
CURE s. cure, medical treatment (cura)
CURER v.a. to cure, heal
CURGE sbj.pr.3 of CURRE
CURTIL s. vegetable garden
CUSTRE v.a. to sew, stitch (suere) CUSEZ, COSEZ imp.5 CUSU p.p.
CUSTURE s. stitch, suture (sutura)
CUTE s. elbow (cubitum)
DAMASCHE a. domestic; cultivated (of plant) (domesticus)
DART s. javelin, throwing spear (telum)
DATE s. date (Phoenix dactylifera L.) (dactilus)
DEBRISER v.a. to break, fracture
DECHEIR v.n. to diminish, decline, die down (of fire) DECHEIZE sbj.pr.3 (cadere)
DECIPLE, DICIPLE s. assistant (discipulus)
DECOCTION, DECOCTIUN, DECOCTIUM, DECOCSION s. decoction, liquid; coction,
    completion of cooking (decoctio)
[DECRESTRE] v.n. to decrease, diminish (decrescere) DECRESCENT ind.pr.6
DECURE v.n. to run down, flow (from) (decurrere) DECORT ind.pr.3 DECURGE, DECURE
    sbj.pr.3 DECURRENT sbj.pr.6
DECURS s. waning (of moon) (diminutio)
DEDENZ adv. within, inside (interius)
DEFAITURE s. failing, weakness (defectus)
DEFINEMENT s. end (finis)
DEFROTER v.refl. to rub oneself (confricare)
DEGASTER v.a. to consume (consumere)
DEGRATER v.refl. to scratch oneself (scalpere)
DEGRATURE s. itching, irritation (pruritus)
DEGUTER v.a. to pour drop by drop (instillare)
DEHORS adv. outside, without (extrinsecus)
DEI pl. DEIZ s. finger (digitus)
DEJUSTE prep. beside, next to (iuxta)
DELIÉ a. fine (of texture of cloth), delicate (delicatus)
DELIÉMENT adv. dextrously, subtly (delicatius, subtilissime)
DELIV(E)RER v.a. to dislodge (stone in the bladder)
DELLIER v.a. to unbind, unfasten (dissoluere)
DEME(I)NER v.refl. and v.a. to behave, conduct oneself; to shake, agitate (agitare)
DEMENUSER v.a. to reduce (diminuere)
DEMORANCE, DEMURRANCE s. delay PAR D. at intervals (per intervalla)
DEMUSTRANCE s. indication, evidence (iudicium)
DEMUSTRER v.n. to indicate (ministrare)
DENER s. penny (denarius)
DENZ adv. inside, within
DEPESC(I)ER v.a. to break, fracture, damage, smash (incidere, dilanire)
DEPESTELER v.a. to crush or pound (with a pestle) (pistare)
DEPILÉ a. hairless
DEPREENDRE v.a. to squeeze (conprimere)

DEPRIENT p.p. of DEPRIENDRE to press, compress (depressus)
DERAIN a. furthermost (extremus) AL D. finally, in the end (in ultimo, postremo, ad ultimum)
DERECHEIF adv. again, furthermore, in the same way, next (iterum, deinde, item)
DERERE, DEREIR(E adv. and prep. behind
DERTE s. tetter, skin eruption (serpigo)
DES prep. from, since
DESAINZ adv. previously, earlier (prius)
DESCOLORER v.n. to drain of colour (see notes to II,10)
DESECHIR v.a. and v.n. to dry up (desiccare)
DESEV(E)RER v.a. to separate, cut away, detach (separare, segregare); v.refl. to become unstuck
    (dissolvere)
DESJOINTURE, DESJONGTURE, DEJU[N]GTURE s. dislocation (disiuntura)
DESJUINDRE v.a. to dislocate (disiungere) DESJUINT, DESJO(I)NT, DESJUN(C), DEJOINTT
    p.p.
DESLIER v.a. to relieve, loosen, untie (dissolvere)
DE(S)PESC(E)UR(E s. fracture (fractura)
DESQUE adv. and prep. as far as, until
DESTEMPRER v.a. to mix with, dissolve in liquid (distemperare)
DESTENDRE v.refl. to stretch out (se distendere)
DESTRAINANT a. constrictive, constringent (constrictivus)
DESTRAINDRE to constrain, constrict (constringere) DESTREINUNT ind.pr.6 DESTRAI-
    NIEZ imper.5
DESTRESCE s. tightness (strictura)
DESTURBANCE s. impediment, hindrance (impedimentum)
DESTURBER v.a. to hinder, impede, obstruct (impedire)
DESURE adv. on top
DESUS adv. above
DESUZ prep. under, beneath
DEU s. God
DEVERIE s. madness, mania (mania)
DEVERS a. diverse, varied
DEVIN a. divine (divinus)
DEVISER v.a. to distinguish (distinguere)
DEVOIR v.n. to owe (debere); to be accustomed to (I,1 solere) DEVEIT, DEVEIZ imp.5 DE-
    VEINT ind.pr.6 DEVE sbj.pr.3
DIAFRAGMATE s. diaphragm, midriff (diafragma)
DIAUTÉ(E, DIALTEE s. dialtea (preparation of marshmallow) (dialtea)
DIETE s. diet (dieta)
DIETER v.a. to put on a diet (dietare)
DINDIMO, DINDINO, DINDIMUM, DEINDIMUM, DINDINUM s. perineum, 'didymis' or
    'epididymis'
DIOM ind.pr.4 of DIRE
DISCURSION s. flow, course (discursus, decursus)
DISJUNCTURE, DISJUNGTURE s. dislocation (disiunctura)
DIVERSETÉ, DIVERSITÉ, DEVERSETÉ s. difference, diversity, variety (varietas)
DOES a. two
DOILLANT a. sore, painful
DOI(T) pl. DOIS, DOIZ s. finger (digitus)
DOLEIR v.n. to ache, be painful, hurt (dolere)
DORMANT, EN SUN in his sleep
DOUS, DOUZ a. two
DRAGME pl. DRAGMUS s. drachm, dram
DRAP s. cloth D. LINGE linen cloth (pannus lineus)
DROIT, EN straight (in rectum)
DULER v.a. to ache, be painful, hurt (dolere)
DULUR s. pain, ache (dolor)
DUODENUM (III,31) s. for DINDIMUM ?
DURESCE s. hardness (duricia, duricies)

DUTER v.a. to fear (timere) D. A (refugere)
EFAITIÉ p.p. of EFAITIER to fit, make match
EIR s. air (aer)
EIRT fut.3 of ESTRE; see also AERDRE
EISSELE, EISCELE s. armpit (ascella)
ELE s. feather, flight (of arrow)
ELEBORUM s. E. BLANC white hellebore (Veratrum album L.) (elleborus albus)
ELEPHANCIA s. elephantiasis, severe form of leprosy (elefancia)
ELETUARIE s. electuary (electuarium)
EL(L)EBRE s. hellebore E. BLANC white hellebore (Veratrum album L.) (elleborus albus) E.
    NEIR black hellebore (Helleborus niger L.) or bear's foot (Helleborus foetidus / viridis L.) (el-
    leborus niger)
ELS pron. m. pl. them
EMBAISSÉ p.p. lowered
EMBOTTUN, EMBOTUM s. funnel (embotum)
EMBRASER v.a. to cauterize (incendere)
EMBROCHE, EMBROKE, EMBREKE s. wet poultice (embroca)
EMFL(I)ER v.n. to swell (tumefacere, inflare, intumere, tumescere) EMPHLÉ, ENFLIÉ p.p.
EMFLUR(E s. swelling (tumor, inflatio)
EMOR(R)OIDE, EMERODE s. haemorrhoid (emorroida)
EMPLASTRE s. plaster (embroca, emplastrum, cathaplasma)
EMPLEIR v.a. to fill (implere, inplere) EMPLEEZ imp.5 EMPLIE, AEMPLI p.p.
EMPRIENT p.p. of EMPREINDRE to press upon
ENAPRÉS, ANAPRÉS adv. next, afterwards (postea, deinde) ENAPRÉS DE on the occasion of
ENBRASER v.a. to burn, cauterize (incendere)
ENCENS s. GROS E., ANCENS GROS frankincense (Boswellia thurifera L.) (thus)
ENCISION s. gash, cut
ENCLIN a. prone
ENCLINER v.refl. to bow, stoop, bend (se inclinare)
ENCLUME s. anvil (incudis)
ENDEMENTIRES QUE conj.loc. while (dum)
ENDITÉ p.p. of ENDITER to compose (redigere)
ENDURCIR v.refl. to harden, grow hard (indurescere,indurare)
ENDURSIR v.n. to harden, grow hard
ENFANTEMENT s. childbirth (partus)
ENFERMURE s. setting, mending (of bone) (consolidatio)
ENFÉS s. child (puer)
ENFESTRÉ p.p. afflicted with ulcer, fistula (fistulare)
[ENFESTRIR] v.a. to afflict with ulcer ENFESTRIT ind.pr.3
ENFLER v.a. to swell (tumere)
ENFLEURE s. swelling (ampulla)
ENFREDI p.p. chilled, cold (infrigidatus)
ENGENDRÉ p.p. caused, engendered (generatus)
ENGIN s. skill, art (ingenium)
ENGLÉS s. the English language
ENGROSSIR v.n. to swell (ingrossari)
ENJOINDRE v.a. to enjoin, impose on ENJOINGNEZ imper.5
ENKE, ENCHE, ENCRE s. ink (incaustum)
ENMOLLIR v.a. to soften (mollificare)
ENOINGTION s. application of ointment (unctio)
ENPESCHER v.a. to impede, interfere with
ENPREISSIÉ p.p. of ENPREISSIER to press upon (imprendere)
ENPRIENT p.p. of ENPRIENDRE to compress
ENSEINNIER v.a. to show, indicate (docere) ENSEIGNIÉ, ENSENGNÉ p.p
ENSEMBLEMENT adv. together
ENSEMENT adv. likewise, similarly (similiter)
ENSU(I)RE v.a. to follow, ensue ENSUIT ind.pr.3 ENSIVENT ind.pr.6
ENTAM(I)É p.p. of ENTAM(I)ER to damage, injure, fracture (ledere)

ENTAMURE s. damage, injury, fracture (fractura)

ENTECHI(E)R v.a. to infect (inficere)

ENTENT s. care, attention (diligentia)

ENTENTIF a. assiduous (diligens)

ENTRAILLES s.pl. bowels (intestinum)

ENTRAIT s. poultice

ENTRAVERS a. crosswise D'E. transversely, across (ex transverso, ex obliquo)

ENTREMEDLEZ, ENTREMETLÉ, ENTREMESZLÉ p.p. of ENTREMELER to mix together (incorporare)

ENTREMETRE v.refl. to undertake, concern oneself with

ENTREPRIS p.p. of ENTREPRENDRE to mix (incorporare)

ENTRETENIR v.refl. to unite, knit together, grow together

ENTUR, ENTOR adv. and prep. around

ENUNCION s. application of ointment (unctio)

ENVOLUPER v.a. to wrap, cover (obvoluere, involvere)

EN(S)Z adv. therein, inside (intus)

ENVOIE adv. away

EOEF s. egg

EPELENPSIE s. epilepsy (epilempsia)

EPIGLACO s. abdomen

EPOPONAC see OPOPONAC

EREIM see AREIM

ERIS(S)IPILA s. erysipelas (aposteme) (herisipila)

ERRANTEMENT adv. immediately, forthwith (statim)

ERUCA s. charlock (Sinapis arvensis L.) (eruca)

ESBRASZEMENT s. burning sensation, inflammation (incendium)

ESCHALE s. shell (of egg) (testa ovi)

ESCHAMEL, ESCAMIL s. stool (scamnum, sella)

ESC(H)ARNER v.a. to remove the skin from (scarnare)

ESCHARNEURE s. scar, scar tissue (scarnatura)

ESCHAUFER v.a. to heat (calefacere)

ESCHEIRDE s. scale, scab (scama = squama)

ESCHINE s. spine (spinalis medulla)

ESCHORJEUR, ESCHORCHEURE s. sore, excoriation (excoriatio)

ESCLENC, ESCLENG(E, ESGLENG, EN aslant, obliquely, sideways (ex obliquo, in obliquo)

ESCLICE, ECLICE, SCLICE s. spatula (spatula)

ESCORCE s. outer skin, peel (cortex, testa)

ESCORCHIER v.a. to strip off the skin, excoriate (excoriare)

ESCRIT pl. ESCRIZ s. writing, written composition (scripta)

ESCROEL(L)E, ESCRELLE, ESQROELE, ESCROULE, ESCRO(I)L(L)E s. scrofulous sore, scrofula (scrophula)

ESCUME D'ARGENT s. spume of silver, litharge (spuma argenti, gl. litargirum)

E[S]FORCER v.a. to force, compel (compellere)

ESGARDER v.a. to look at, examine (intueri, attendere)

ESGREVER v.n. to become hoarse (ablatio vocis)

ESLACHIÉ p.p. relaxed (relaxare)

ESLARGI(E)R v.a. and refl. to widen, enlarge, spread out (elargare, ampliare) ESLARGIEZ (dilatus) EST EN ESLARGANT is in the course of spreading out (est in elargando, id est quando se elargat)

ESLEVER v.a. to lift, take off (elevare)

ESLUISSIÉ p.p. of ESLUISSIER to dislocate, put out

ESPA(S)CE s. space (spatium)

ESPAUD(L)E, ESPLAUDE, ESPALDE s. shoulder (humerus)

ESPECIER s. spicer

ESPER(E)MENT s. test, trial, experiment, treatment (experimentum)

ESPÉS a. thick (spissus)

ESPESCEIS p.p. of ESPESSIR to thicken

ESPESSIR v.a. ,v.n., v.refl. to thicken (inspissare, condensare) ESPESSI, ESPESCEIS, ESPESSEZ
　　p.p. ESPESCIR sbst.v.
ESPLEIN, ESPLIEN s. spleen (splen)
ESPLENTE s. splint (fascia, fasceolus, spagus)
ESPONGE, ESPUNGE s. sponge (spongia) E. DE LA ME(I)R sea sponge (spongia marina)
ESPORGEMENT s. purging, cleansing (purgatio)
ESPROVE(I)R v.a. to test (experiri, probare)
ESPUILLE s. skin (spolium)
ESPUMÉ a. frothy (spumosus)
ESPUNGUS a. spongy, soft (spongiosus)
ESPURGE s. spurge (Euphorbia L. ssp.) (titimallus)
ESPURGIER v.a. to clean out (purificare)
ESQUIELE s. bowl, dish (parapsis)
ESRAC(H)IER, ERACHIER v.a. to pull out, eradicate ((radicitus) evellere)
ESTABLE a. solid, reliable (stabilis)
ESTAIM s. tin, pewter
ESTAIMÉ, ESTAINÉ a. made of tin (stagnatus)
ESTANCHER v.a. to stanch, stop flow of (constringere) ESTANCHIÉ p.p.
ESTANT pres.p. (stando) of ESTER to stand
ESTÉ s. summer (estas, tempus estivum)
ESTEINDRE v.a. to extinguish (extingere) ESTENT, ESTEINT p.p.
ESTERNUER v.n. to sneeze
ESTOIL(E, ESTOEL, ESTUEL s. tent, seton (stuellus)
ESTOIST sbj.pr.3 of ESTER
ESTRAIT see ESTROIT
ESTRE prep. beyond , in addition to, more than E. NATURE abnormally (praeter naturam)
ESTREINDRE v.a. to grasp, hold tightly (comprehendere, stringere, constringere) ESTREIG-
　　NIEZ imper.5 v.refl. S'ESTRAINUNT ind.pr.6 ESTRAINIEZ imper.5
ESTROIT, ESTREIT a. narrow (strictus, arctus)
ESTROITEMENT adv. tightly (stricte)
ESTRUMENT, ESTREMENT s. instrument (instrumentum)
ESTUDIE s. care, attention, application (studium) METTRE E. DE to take care to, to apply one-
　　self to (attendere)
ESTUPE pl. ESTUPUS s. (fibres of) tow (stup(p)a)
ESTUT ind.pr.3 and pret.3 of ESTER
ESTUVE s. vapour bath (stufa)
ESTUVER v.a. to treat with vapour bath
EUFORBIUM s. spurge (Euphorbia L. spp.)
EU(U)E s. water E. ROSAT, ROSET rose water (aqua rosarum / rosata)
EUUS a. watery (aquosus)
FABE LUPINI s. dwale, deadly nightshade (Atropa bella-donna L.) (faba lupina)
FACHOL s. bandage (fasceolum)
FAIENT ind.pr.6 of FAIRE
FARINE s. flour F. DE FRUMENT wheat flower (farina tritici) F. LUPINORUM AMARORUM
　　flour made from Lupinus albus L. (yields a bitter glucoside)
FEBLE a. weak, feeble (debilis)
FEIRT ind.pr.3 of FERIR to strike, attack
FE(I)Z s. time A FEIZ at times, sometimes (quandoque) AUCHUNE F. sometimes (aliquotiens,
　　aliquando)
FENDU p.p. of FENDRE to split, pierce (frangere, findere, scindere)
FENOIL s. fennel (Foeniculum vulgare Miller)
FENOIL GRECE for FENUGREC
FENTURE, FEINTURE s. crack (rimula, fissura, scissura)
FENTUSE s. cupping glass (cufa)
FENUGREC s. fenugreek (Trigonella foenum-graecum L.) (fenugrecum)
FER s. iron (ferrum)
FERM adv. firmly, fast
FERMAMENT s. closing, healing (of wound) (consolidatio)

FERMER v.a. to secure, fasten v.n. to mend, heal (firmiter nectere; consolidari)
FERMURE s. mending, healing (consolidatio)
FERURE s. blow (percussura)
FEST p.p. of FERE
FESTRE pl. FESTRIS, FESTRUS s. sore, fistula (fistula)
FEV s. bean (fab(b)a)
FEVRE s. blacksmith (faber)
[FI] pl. FIS s. ficus, tumour, fig-shaped pile or haemorrhoid
FIC pl. FICZ s. fig (Ficus carica L.)
FIE s. fig (ficus), tumour
FIE s. time A(U)C(H)UNE F. sometimes (aliquando)
FIEBLESCE s. weakness (debilitas)
FIENTE s. dung (stercus) F. DE L'ASNE ass's dung (stercus asininum)
FIL(E s. thread (filum)
FIOLE s. phial (fiala, fiola)
FIOLEE s. contents of a phial
FLAISTRER v.n. to wither (marcescere) FLAISTRI p.p.
FLAURA, FLAURE s. ? lady's mantle (Alchemilla vulgaris sens. lat.) or fumitory (Fumaria offici-
    nalis L.) (flaura, herba flaura)
FLEGME s. phlegm (fleuma)
FLEGMON s. phlegmon, suppurating ulcer (fleumon)
FLESTRIR v.n. to wither (marcescere)
FO(I)LLE pl. FULLUS, FULLES s. leaf (folium)
FOILLET, FUILLET s. follicle; scrotum (III,29) (folliculus)
FOLE s. leaf (folium)
FOMENT s. fomentation (fomentum)
FOMENTACION s. fomentation (fomentatio)
FOMENTER v.a. to foment; (III,19) to treat with fomentations (fomentare)
FONTAINE, FONTEINE s. fount; fontanelle (hollow between two muscles) (fons)
FORCE s. strength (virtus)
FORCELE s. fontanelle (fontanella); thorax (thorax); abdomen (epiglaco, furuncula, furcella);
    collar-bone
FORE(I)N a. outer, exterior (exterior)
FOR(E)MENT adv. firmly (firmiter)
FORS prep. except (nisi); conj. except that (nisi quod)
FRAID a. cold
FRAINT p.p. of FRAINDRE to break
FRAINTURE, FRANTURE s. break, fracture (ruptura)
FRAITURE s. break, fracture (fractura)
FRANCEAIS s. the French language
FRANCHISE s. benevolence, considerateness (beneficium)
FREIDURE s. chill, cold (frigiditas)
FROMENT, FRUMENT s. wheat (frumentum)
FROTER v.a. to rub (fricare)
FU(E s. fire (ignis)
FULLE see FO(I)LLE
FULUGINE s. soot (fuligo)
FUME s. fumes, vapour
FUMEE s. breath, vapour
FUMETERRE, FUMETE(I)RE, FUMETERIE s. fumitory (Fumaria officinalis L.) (fumus terre)
FUND, FUNT, FUNZ s. bottom (fundum, profunditas)
FUNDEMENT s. anus or perineum
FUNDRE v.a. and v.n. to melt (liquefacere, resolvere) FUNDU p.p.
FUNTE DEL BRAÇ s. ending of the upper arm (lacerti affinitas)
FUNTEINELE s. fontanel; (III,38) outlet
FUST s. wood, piece of wood, wooden shaft (lignum)
GALBANO, GALBANUM s. galbanum (gum resin) (galbanum)
GALLE pl. GALLAS s. oak-apple, gall-nut (galluca, galla)

GARGARISME s. gargle, mouth-wash (gargarismus, gargarisma)
GAR(R)IR v.a. to cure (curare); v.n. to heal (curari)
GELINE s. hen (gallina)
GENCIVE pl. GENCEVUS s. gum (gingiva)
GENILD, GENULD s. knee (genu)
GENULZ s.pl. knees
GESIR, GISIR v.n. to lie (iaceo) GIRRA fut.3 GISE sbj.pr.3
GETER v.a. to eject, get rid of (educere)
GIGNES s.pl. tweezers, small forceps (picicariolus)
GILOFRE s. cloves (Eugenia caryophyllata Thunb.) or clove gilliflower (Dianthus caryophyllus
    L.) (gariofilus)
GINGIVRE, GINGEVRE s. ginger (zinziber)
GIRRA fut.3 of GISIR
GLAMUS a. sticky
GLANDRES s.pl. glanders, swollen glands (glandule)
GLUMUS a. sticky (glutinosus)
GORGOIER v.a. to gargle (gargarizare)
GRAIN s. grain (granum)
GRANDUR(E s. quantity, size (quantitas)
GRAPE s. grape (uva)
GRAS a. fat
GRATURE s. itching (pruritus)
GREF, GREVÉ a. difficult (difficilis)
GREIF s. difficulty
GREINGNUR, GREINUR(E, GRENGNUR a. larger (maior)
GRESSE s. animal fat, grease (pinguedo)
GREVANCE s. difficulty (difficultas); damage, injury, harm
GREVÉ p.p. of GREVER to afflict
GRIEF a. difficult, awkward (difficilis)
GUARANTE s. A GRANT G. with great care
GUMALVE, GEUIMALVE, GUMMALVE s. marshmallow (Althaea officinalis L.) (malva viscus)
GULE s. throat (gula)
GUM(M)E, GUMM s. gum (gummi)
GUMM(E DE IRE / L'IERE / D'EIRE s. gum ivy (Hedera helix L.) (gummi hedere)
GUNIL(E s. knee (genu)
GUPIL s. wolf (vulpes)
GUTE s. drop (gutta)
GUTE s. gout G. ARTETIKE gout (artetica), arthritis G. CHAIVE epilepsy (epilempsia) G.
    CRAMPE stomach cramp (spasmus)
HANAP s. goblet (ciphus)
HANNEBANE (ME) s. henbane (Hyoscyamus niger L.) (jusquiamus)
HANELLISSEMENT s. breathing (hanelitus)
HASTE, EN speedily (festinanter)
HASTER v.n. to hasten (festinare)
HATEREL s. nape of neck (cervix)
HERBE s. herb H. VIOLETTE violet (herba violaria)
HERISIPILA, HERESIPILIA s. erysipelas (aposteme) (herisipila)
HERMODAC(C)LE s. autumn crocus (Colchicum autumnale L.) (hermodactilis)
HERNIA s. hernia, swelling in the scrotum or testes (hernia)
HERPES HESTI(M)OMENUS s. devouring herpes, vesicular or pustular condition of the skin,
    'lupus', 'wolf' (herpes estiomenus), gangrene
HOMOPLATE pl. HOMOPLATIS s. shoulder-blade (homoplata)
(H)ORE . . . (H)ORE adv. now . . . now
HORS adv. out
HUMER v.a. to swallow
HUMOR, HOMOR, HOMUR s. humour (humor)
IDUNC adv. then, in that case (tunc)
IEBLE s. danewort, dwarf elder (Sambucus ebulus L.) (ebulus)

IEIRT fut.3 of ESTRE

IERE TERRESTRE s. ground ivy (Glechoma hederacea L.) (hedera terrestris)

ILLER pl. ILLIEIRS s. groin, flank (inguen)

IL(L)O(E)C, ILEC, ILOEQUES adv. there, in the same place (ibidem, ibi)

IMPETIGO s. impetigo, morbid condition of the skin (impetigo)

INCENSIUN s. cauterization (incensio)

IPIA s. chickweed (Stellaria media (L.) Vill.) or scarlet pimpernel (Anagallis arvensis L.) (morsus galline)

ISMON s. isthmus (of throat), thin tissue between larynx and oesophagus (ismon)

ISSI QUE conj.loc. with the result that

ISSIR v.n. to leave, go out (exire, provenire) IST ind.pr.3 EIST pret.3 ISSE sbj.pr.3

ITANT   SUL D'ITANT QUE except that (excepto quod)

IVE(I)R s. winter (hyems, tempus hyemale)

JA SEIT CEO QUE conj.loc. although (licet)

JA SI PETIT NE SEIT however small it be

JAMMÉS adv. ever; (with negative) never

JAVELÉ(E s. handful (manipulum)

JESQUE adv.   J. A up to, as far as; conj. until; prep. as far as (quousque, usque)

JEUNER v.n. to fast (ieiuanre)

JOE, SHOUE s. jaw (mandibula)

JO(I)EFNE a. young (juvenis)

JUBARBE s. houseleek (Sempervivum tectorum L.) (semperviva)

JUGULARE s. clavicle, collar-bone (os jugulare)

JUINDRE v.refl. to join

JUN(C)TURE, JUNGTURE, JOINCTURE, JONTURE s. joint (iunctura)

JUSQUIAMI s. henbane (Hyoscyamus niger L.) (jusquiamus)

JUSTE prep. next to (iuxta)

JUVENCELE s. young woman (primariola)

LA conj. where

LACHER v.a. to lace, intertwine (nectere)

LADANUM s. ladanum (ladanum)

LAIT DE SCROPPHA s. milk of breeding sow (lac de scrofa)

LANCELEE s. ribwort plantain (Plantago lanceolata L.) (lanceola)

LANCELETTE s. ribwort plantain (Plantago lanceolata L.)

LANGE s. tongue (lingua)

LANGE DE BOEF s. alkanet / bugloss (Anchusa officinalis L. / arvensis (L.) Bieb.) (lingua bovina, lingua bovis)

LAPPACE AGUE s. dock (Rumex L. ssp.) (lappatium acutum)

LARD s. lard (lardus)

LARDON, LARDUN s. piece of bacon fat (lardo, lardus)

LASCHER v.refl. to desist (desinere)

LAS(C)IVE s. lye

LASSIER v.a. to abandon, overlook, omit (praetermittere)

LAUREOLE, LAURIOLE s. bay, laurel (Laurus nobilis L.) or spurge laurel (Daphne laureola L.) (laureola)

LAURIN a. OLIE L. oil of bays (oleum laurinum)

LAVURE s. cleansing lotion (liquor); wash, waste washing water (lotura) L.DE CHAR water in which meat has been boiled

LAXATIF a. laxative (laxativus)

LÉ, EN laterally (in latum)

LÉ(E a. wide (latus)

LEGIER a. easy DE L. easily (de facili)

LEG(I)EREMENT, LEGIREMENT adv. easily; gently (de facili; leniter, leviter)

LEINE s. wool (lana) L. MUSTE s. unwashed wool, with its suint (lana succida) L. OD LA SUUR DE SEI (III,43 lana succida) unwashed wool, with its suint

LEISSIVE s. lye (lixivium)

LENTES s. lentils (lentes)

LEONINA s. leontiasis, a kind of leprosy leading to thickening of the skin (leonina)

LEPRE s. leprosy (lepra)
LERME s. tear (lacrima)
LERMER v.n. to water (of eyes), weep (lacrimari)
LETTUE s. lettuce (Lactuca L.) or sow-thistle (Sonchus oleraceus L.)
LEVISTICI s. lovage (Levisticum officinale Koch) or scotch lovage (Ligusticum scoticum L.)
   (levisticum)
LEVRE, LIVRE s. lip (labium)
LIE s. lees (feces)
LIER v.a. to bind, fasten (ligare)
LIEVE ind. pr.3 of LEVER to stand up, arise (surgere)
LIEV(E)RE s. hare (lepus)
LIEVRE s. lip (Labium)
LIFRE s. pound (weight) (libra)
LIGNOEL s. linen (linum)
LIMAZUN s. snail
LIN s. flax (Linum usitatissimum L.), linen, linseed SEMENCE DE L. linseed
LINOIS s. linseed
LIQUOR s. liquid (liquor)
LIS s. lily (lilium)
LITARGERIE, LITARGIRI, LITARGIRE, LETARGERIE s. litharge, lead monoxide (litargirum)
LIU s. place (locus) EN MI L. in the middle
LIUN, LIUM s. lion (leo)
LIURE s. bandage (ligatura, ligatio)
LIV(E)RE s. pound (weight) (libra)
LIVRE s. lip (labium)
LOER v.a. to advise (locare x laudare)
LONGAON, LONGAONIS, LONGAONEM s. rectum (longa, longia)
LONGEMENT adv. for a long time (diu)
LOREIR s. laurel, bay (Laurus nobilis L.) (laurus)
LOS s. praise (laus)
LU s. wolf, erysipedes (lupus)
LUISANT a. shining (see notes to III,27)
LUISCEL, LUICEOL s. skein, hank (globus)
LUNG a. long EN L. lengthwise (in longum)
LUVE(E)SCHE, LOVESCHE (SALVAGE) s. lovage (Levisticum officinale Koch) or scotch lov-
   age (Ligusticum scoticum L.) (levisticum agreste, levisticus agrestis)
MACDALION, MAGDALIUN, MACDALION s. magdaleon, cylindrical plaster (magdalio)
MADDOKE (ME) s. maddock, worm
MAI = MOI
MAINNES s.pl. hands
MALAN s. sore, ulcer
MALEDE s. patient (patiens)
MALEMENT adv. with difficulty (male)
MALE MORT s. gangrene (malum mortuum); necrotic flesh
MALENCOLIE, MELANCOLIA s. illness deriving from excess of black bile (melancolia)
MALICIOS a. malignant (maliciosus)
MALUM TERRE, MALO T., MALI T. s. earthnut (Conopodium majus (Gouan) Loret) or sow-
   bread (Cyclamen hederifolium Aiton) (malum terre)
MALUM MORTUUM s. gangrene, necrotic flesh
MALVAIS fem. MALEVEISE, MAUFAISSE a. bad M. CHAR (caro superflua)
MALVE s. marshmallow (Althaea officinalis L.) (malva) M. QUE CREST EN CURTIL (malva
   ortolana) M. COMMUNE common mallow (Malva sylvestris L.)
MAMELE s. breast (mamilla)
MANDER v.a. to order, recommend (diet)
MANDIBULA s. type of ulcer, sore, fistula (see notes to I,51)
MANDRAGE s. mandrake (Mandragora officinarum L.) (mandragora)
MANEIR(E, MANIRE, MANIER s. manner (modum)

MANG(I)ER, MANCHER v.a. to eat, eat away (corrodere, occidere) MANGUE ind.pr.3 MAN-
  GUSCE, MANJUCE sbj.pr.3 MANGUÉ p.p.
MANIA s. mania (mania)
MARBRE s. marble (marmor)
MARCIATON, MACIATON s. marciaton, a green ointment (marciaton)
MARGARITE s. pearl (margarita)
MARUIL NEIR s. black horehound (Ballota nigra L. spp. foetida Hayek) (marrubium nigrum)
MASCHIER, MACHIER v.a. to chew (conmasticare)
MASTIC s. (gum) mastic (mastix)
MATERIE s. matter, pus (materia)
MATINAL a. morning (matutinus)
MAURER, -IR v.n. to come to a head ESTRE TORNE A MAURER (devenire ad maturitatem)
MEDICINE, MEDECINE s. medicine, medical treatment (medicamina, remedium)
MEDLER v.a. to mix (incorporare, miscere)
MEGRE a. lean (of pork); thin (macer)
MEILLEZ see MELZ
MEIMES a.invar. same M. CEO the same thing M. LA CURE the same cure EN M. LA
  MANERE in the same way
MEIN s. hand
MEINDRE a. lesser, smaller (minor)
MEINTEFOIZ adv. many a time (indesinenter)
MEINTENANT adv. at once, immediately (ilico, statim)
ME(I)RE s. DURE M. 'dura mater' (dura mater) PIE M. 'pia mater' (pia mater)
MEIS QUE conj. except that
MEITIÉ s. half (medietas)
MEIZ see MELZ
MEIZ s. drink made of two parts wine and one part honey (mellicratum)
MEL, MIEL, MEIL s. honey (mel)
MELZ, MEIZ, MEUZ, MEILZ, MIELEZ, MEILLEZ, METLIEZ adv. better, more (melius)
MEMIT(T)E s. yellow horned-poppy (Glaucium flavum Crantz) (memitha, memithe, agresta
  (I,30 see above))
MENER v.a. M. A UN to reduce to a single substance (in unum redigere)
MENSTRUUS a. menstrual (menstrualis)
MENTASTRUM s. horsemint (Mentha sylvestris L.) or water-mint (Mentha aquatica L.) (menta-
  strum)
MENU a. small, ? patchy (I,23 non continua)
MENUEMENT adv. in detail
MENUSER v.a. to reduce, diminish (minuere)
MERC s. mark, stamp, sign (signum)
MERCHIER v.a. to mark, stamp (signare)
MERVEILLUSEMENT, MERVELUSEMENT adv. wondrously, exceedingly (mirabiliter)
MES QUE conj. although (licet); provided that
MESTER(E, MESTIEIRS, MESTEIR, MESTIERZ s. ESTRE M. to be necessary
MESTRE s. master (doctor)
MESURER v.n. to measure (mensurare)
METLER, MEDLER v.a. to mix (incorporare)
METLIEZ adv. better (melius)
MEU p.p. of MOVEIR to stir
MEULE s. marrow (medulla)
MEUR a. ripe, mature (maturatus)
MIELEZ see MELZ
MIRE s. doctor, physician (medicus)
MIRRE s. myrrh (mirra)
MOEL, MUEL s. yolk (of egg) (vitellum)
MOISTURE s. moisture
MOL s. soft flesh (I,29 cartilago)
MOL a. soft (mollis)
MOLE s. jaw (mola)

MOLLIANT a. emollient (mollificativus)
MOLLIFICATIF a. emollient (mollificativus)
MORELE s. black nightshade (Solanum nigrum L.) or deadly nightshade (Atropa bella-donna L.)
   (solatrum)
MORPHÉ s. morphew, scurfy eruption (morphea)
MORPHEA s. morphew, scurfy eruption (morphea)
MORSURE s. smarting (of eyes), stinging sensation (mordicatio)
MORTER, MORTIEIR s. mortar (mortarium)
MOT adv. very, much
MOVER v.n. to move (movere)
MUCIÉ(Z p.p. hidden, concealed (absconditus)
MUER v.a. and v.n. to change, alter (mutare)
MUMIE s. mummy (mummia)
MUNDER v.a. to cleanse (mundificare)
MUNT ind.pr.3 of MUNTER to rise, ascend
MUT pl. MUTES a. many
MUTUN s. sheep SIU DE M. mutton fat (sepum arietinum)
NAF(F)RER, NAUFRER v.a. to wound, injure (ledere)
NAFRURE's. wound, injury (percussura)
NAR(R)(A)IL(LE s. nostril (nares)
NATES s.pl. buttocks (nates)
NATURE s. ESTRE, CONTRE N. abnormally (praeter naturam)
NAVRER v.a. to wound, injure (ledere)
NEIRS s.pl. nerves (nervi)
NE(I)S, NEIZ s. nose (nasus)
NEMÉS, NEMAIS prep., adv. except, unless N. QUE except that N. D'ITANT QUE except that
   (excepto quod, nisi quod)
NEQUEDENT QUE conj. although
NER s. black, blackness (nigredo)
NERCIR v.n. to turn black, blacken (nigrescere)
NERF s. nerve; muscle, sinew (nervus)
NERVUS a. muscular, sinewy (nervosus)
NES s. nose (nasus)
NESTRE v.a. to form, come into existence NEST ind.pr.3 NESSENT ind.pr.6
NITRE s. nitre (nitrum)
NOEL s. kernel (nucleus)
NOET s. knot (of muscle) (nodellus)
NOIF a. nine
NOIS, NOIT s. knot (of muscle) (nodus)
NOIZ MUSCATE s. nutmeg (Myristica fragrans Houtt.) (nux muscata)
NOTER v.a. to note, observe, remark (prenotare, notare)
NOVIME, NOFIME a. ninth
NU s. ball, knot (of muscle) (nodellus, nodus)
NUAL s. kernel (of walnut) (nux, nucleus)
NUER v.a. to tie (nectere)
NUN adv. not   SI . . . NUN except
NUNSAVER s. ignorance, confusion (II,1 obscuritas et confusio)
NURETURE s. sustenance (nutrimentum)
NURISSEMENT s. nourishment (nutrimentum)
NUSZ s.pl. nights
NUZ s. nut (nux)
OCULI LICII, OCULUM LICIUM s. honeysuckle (Lonicera caprifolium / periclymenum L.)
   (oculus lucidus)
OELEMENT adv. in equal measure (ana, equaliter)
OES, OIS s. use (usus)
OIE s. goose (anser)
OIGNEMENT, OINEMENT s. ointment, unguent O. NEIR (unguentum fuscum) U. VERT (un-
   guentum viride)

OIGTEUS a. greasy (unctuosus)

OIL pl. OIZ s. eye OIL(S)Z DEL POPLIER poplar buds (oculi populi)

OINDRE v.a. to anoint, rub, smear (ungere, inungere) OIGNEZ imper.5 OINT p.p.

OINGNUN, OINUN s. onion (cepe)

OINNIER subst. vb. healing (coequatio)

OINT s. animal grease, fat (anxungia)

OIR v.a. to hear, listen to OIENT ind.pr.6

OIT a. eight

OLIBANUM, OLIBANO, OLIBANI s. frankincense (Boswellia thurifera L.) (olibanum)

OLANT a. sweet smelling (odoriferus)

OLIE, OILE s. oil (oleum) O. COM(M)UNE (oleum commune) O. LAURIN(E oil of bays
    (oleum laurinum) O. MUSCELINE oil of musk (oleum muscellinum) O. ROSAT oil of roses
    (oleum rosarum / rosatum) O. VIOLAT oil of violets (oleum violarum)

OLIFANT s. elephant (elephans)

OPOPONAC, OPAPANAC, EPOPONAC, EPOPANAC s. opoponac (opoponax) (Opoponax
    chironium (L.) Koch)

ORDRE s. PAR O. in order

ORDURE s. dirt, filth (sordes)

ORGANAL a. VEINE O. external jugular vein (organica vena) MEMBRE O. principal member

ORIBLE a. disgusting (horribilis)

ORPI(E)MENT, ORPHIMENT s. yellow arsenic trisulphide (auripigmentum)

OR(R)EILLE, ORREALE, ORAILE s. ear (auris, auricula)

ORTIL(LE s. toe (digitus pedis)

ORS adv. outside

OS s. bone OS DE CHIEN (I,36)

OSCEUM, OSCEO s. scrotum (osseum)

OSCIRE v.a. to kill, destroy OCIT, OSIST ind.pr.3 (occidere)

OSSUUS a. bony (ossuosus)

OSTER v.a. to remove, withdraw (removere, repellere) OSTE(I)Z imper.5

OSTIL, USTIL s. tool, instrument

OSTILEMENT, OSTILIMENT s. instrument, tool, appliance (instrumentum)

OSTURE s. removal (abstractio)

OUE s. goose (anser)

OVEOC adv. therewith, in addition, as well

OVERIER s. (medical practitioner) (operator)

OVRE s. operation, function, working (I,22 of brain)

OVREMENZ s.pl. workings, operations (operationes)

OXIMEL s. oxymel, preparation of vinegar, herbs and honey

PAELE s. pan (patella); knee-cap (patella)

PALAIS, PALEIS s. palate (palatum)

PALAM MARINE s. ? lungwort (Pulmonaria officinalis L.)

PALEETE s. membrane (pellicula)

PALUS s. pustule, boil

PANIS PORCINUS s. sowbread (Cyclamen hederifolium Aiton) (panis porcinus)

PAPAVERIS s. poppy (Papaver L.) P. NIGRI (papaver nigrus)

PARCIEZ see PERC(I)ER

PARELE s. dock (Rumex L.)

PARFIEZ, PERFIES, PARFIES adv. at intervals, in turn (vicissim, per intervalla)

PARFIT a. complete, full (perfectus)

PARFUND, PARFUNT a. deep EN P. deeply

PARITARIE, PARITARIA, PARITAIRE s. pellitory-of-the-wall (Parietaria judaica L.) (paritaria)

PARMI adv. through the middle; prep. through

PAROLER v.n. to speak

PARRAILLEMENT see REPARRAILLEMENT

PART s. DE TOTES PARS on all sides (undique) DE CELE PART where

PAPIRE, PAUPIERE pl. PAUPIERS s. eyelid (palpebra)

PASTE s. paste (pasta)

PEAL s. ? follicle (II,13 folliculus)

PECTINEM s. type of worm
PEI s. foot (pes)
PEIC(C)E, PECIE, OIECE, PECCE, PEIZE s. piece (pecia, frustulum) P. LINGE piece of lint
    (pecia linea)
PE(I)L pl. PEI(L)Z, PEILEZ s. hair (pilus)
PEIRE, PERE, PIERE, PEIERE, PIEIRE s. stone (lapis)
PEIZ(E s. pitch (pix) P. NAVA(I)LE naval pitch (pix navalis) P. GRE(I)C Greek pitch (pix greca)
PEL s. skin, hide (pannus, panniculus)
PELECTE, PELEITE s. membrane (panniculus, pellicula)
PELECTRE s. pellitory (Anacyclus pyrethrum DC) or pellitory-of-the-wall (Parietaria judaica L.)
    (piretrum)
PELLE s. hair (pilus)
PENER v.n. to strive, exert oneself, take trouble (laborare)
PENIL s. penis (pecten)
PENNE s. feather, quill (penna)
PERC(I)ER v.a. to pierce (forare, perforare, penetrare) PEIRCE ind.pr.3 PARCERAS fut.2 PAR-
    CIEZ imper.5
PERÇUR, PERCEUR s. drill, borer (trepanum)
PERIL s. danger (periculum)
PERS a. blue, livid (of flesh) (lividus)
PERSICARIA s. persicaria (Polygonum persicaria L.) or water-pepper (Polygonum hydropiper L.)
    (persicaria)
PERSILLE s. parsley (Petroselinum crispum (Miller) A.W. Hill)
PERTUS, PERTUZ s. hole, opening, orifice (os, foramen, meatus)
PESANT s. weight (pondus)
PESCEUR(E s. fracture (fractura, ruptura)
PESCHIER s. peach-tree (Prunus persica (L.) Batsch) (persicus)
PESCIER v.a. to fracture (frangere)
PESTELER, PESTILER v.a. to crush or pound (with a pestle) (pistare)
PETIT E PETIT adv. little by little
PETROLEON s. petroleum, mineral oil (petroleum)
PETTEROILE s. petroleum, mineral oil (petroleum)
PEUSANCE s. power (gratia)
PEUSE sbj.pr.3 of POER
PICICARIOLIS s.pl. tweezers, small forceps (picicarioli)
PICULE s. pitch (picula)
PIÉ DE COLUMB s. (dove's-foot cranesbill) (Geranium L. spp. esp. G. molle L.)
PILE s. pill (pillula)
PIMPERNELLE s. scarlet pimpernel (Anagallis arvensis L.) or burnet saxifrage (Pimpinella saxi-
    fraga L.) or great burnet (Sanguisorba officinalis L.) (pimpinella)
PINCECARIOLES s.pl. pincers, forceps (picicarioli)
PIS adv. worse (deterius)
PISS(I)ER v.n. to urinate (urinare)
PI(S)Z s. breast (pectus)
PLACE s. affected spot (discrimen)
PLACETTE s. affected spot (discrimen)
PLA(I)E, PLAI pl. PLAEIES, PLAIUS s. wound (vulnus, plaga)
PLAIER v.a. to wound (vulnerari) PLAIÉ, PLAEE p.p. PLAIÉ subst. p.p. wounded person ; (I,5)
    to depress, push down; v.n. to bend (plicari, replicari)
PLA(I)URE, PLEÜRE s. depression, dent (plicatura)
PLANTAINE, PLAINTEINE s. great plantain (Plantago major L.) (plantago)
PLANTES DES MEINS s.pl. palms of the hands (plantae manuum)
PLANTES DES PEIZ s.pl. soles of the feet (plantae pedum)
PLATEINE s. plate; pledget-like strip (plagella)
PLEST ind.pr.3 of PLESIR to please
PLEÜRE DEL BRAÇ s. bend of the arm (plicatura brachii)
PLEURESIE s. pleurisy, abscess in the diaphragm (pleuresis)
PLOIER v.n. to bend, move (out of place), depress (vagari)

PLUIMAL, PLUMAL s. small pad (plumaceolus)

PLUM s. lead (plumbum) P. ARS calcined lead (plumbum ustum)

PLUMACEOL(E, PLUMECEOL s. small pad (plumaceolus, pulvinar de pluma . . . fit ex pannis lineis triplicatis)

PLUME s. feather (penna)

POER v.n. to be able POE(E)T, PUIT ind.pr.3 POUM ind.pr.4 POEEZ ind.pr.5 PUREZ fut.5 PUUST, PEUSSE sbj.pr.3 PEUIS(S)IEZ, PUISSIEZ, POUISSIEZ, PUUSIEZ, PEUSEZ, PUISSIEZ sbj.pr.5 POUSSENT sbj.pr.6

PO(I, POU adv., pr.indef., s. little (parum, modicum, aliquantulum); a. few

POIGNIER v.a. to grasp POIGNIEZ imper.5

POINGN(I)É s. handful (manipulum)

POINIEZ imper.5 of POINDRE to pierce, prick (pungere)

POINT pl. POINZ s. stitch (punctus)

POINTURE s. stinging or pricking sensation (punctura)

POIS adv. then, next (deinde)

POIS QUE conj. after (postquam)

POIZ s.pl. lice (pediculi)

POLIOL ROIAL s. pennyroyal (Mentha pulegium L.) or wild thyme (Thymus serpyllum L.) (origanum)

POLIPE s. polypus, nasal growth (polipus)

POLIPODIE s. polypody (Polypodium vulgare L.) or oak fern (Gymnocarpium dryopteris (L.) Newman) (polipodium)

POLIP(P)US s. polypus, nasal growth (polipus)

POME DE TERRE s. earthnut (Conopodium majus (Gouan) Loret) or sowbread (Cyclamen hederifolium Aiton) (malum terre)

POMME GERNETTE s. pomegranate (Punica granatum L.) (malum granatum)

POPI (ME) s. poppy (Papaver L.)

POPLIER s. poplar tree (Populus L.) OIL(S)Z DEL POPLIER poplar buds (oculi populi)

POPULEON s. ointment made with poplar buds

POR CE QUE conj. because (quia)

PORGE see PURGER

PORETE s. leek (Allium porrum L.)

PORPRENDRE v.a. to take hold of (capere)

POR(R)IR v.a. and v.n. to rot, decay (tabefacere, putrefacere) PORRISSE sbj.pr.3 POR(R)I p.p.

POSTEME s. aposteme (apostema)

POTUN s. potion, drink (potio)

POZ adv. then, next

PREISSE sbj.pr.3 of PRENDRE to take

PREMEZ imper.5 of PREENDRE to press

PREMOR s. A LA P. first (primo)

PRESCEN, PRESSEIN a. next, following (proximus)

PRIENDRE, PREENDRE v.a. to press, squeeze (coartare, exprimere, conprimere, impellere) PRIMANT pr.p. PRINT, PRIENT p.p. PRIMEZ, PRINEZ imper.5

PRIMER, PRIMIR s. AL P. to begin with, at the beginning (primo)

PRIMES adv. first (primitus)

PRINEZ imper.5 of PRIENDRE to press

PRINT p.p. of PRIENDRE to press

PRIS ENSEMBLE p.p. joined together (conglutinatus)

PRIVÉMENT adv. privately (privatim)

PRODIENTE see note to II,15

PROVEABLEMENT adv. properly, clearly (provide)

PSILOTRI s. depilatory (psilotrum)

PUINT pl. PUNZ, POINZ s. stitch, suture (punctus)

PUDLENT a. foul, filthy

PUING s. fist (pugnus)

PULLENT a. stinking (fetidus)

PULMON s. lung (pulmo)

PULS s. pulse (pulsus)

PURETURE, PORETURE s. pus, matter (sanies, putredo)
PURGER v.a. to purge, cleanse (purgare) PORGE sbj.pr.3
PURIR v.a. to rot (putrefacere)
PURPENSER v.n. to take thought (cogitare) P. COMENT to work out how
PURPOSER v.n. to intend, arrange to (disponere)
PURPRENDRE v.a. to invade, take hold of, occupy (occupare) PURPRENGE sbj.pr.3
PUS see POIS
PUSANTMENT adv. powerfully, strongly (potenter)
QUAI(S a. still, calm (see notes to III,27)
QUANT conj. whether (I,1); a. how much, how many
QUAREL s. bolt, quarrel (telum)
QUART(E a. fourth (quartus)
QU(E)INTEMENT, QUIENTEMENT adv. skilfully, carefully (caute)
QU(E)INTISE s. skill, dexterity (cautela)
QUER, QUOR s. heart (cor)
QUICHUN, QUICHUM s. cautery, cauterisation (cauterium, coctura)
QUIDER v.n. to think
QUINANCIE s. type of quinsy, inflammation of various parts of the throat (II,16 quinancia)
QUIN(T) a. fifth
QUIR s. hide, skin (cutis, corium, pellis) PETIT Q. (cuticula)
QUIS(S)E s. thigh (crus)
QUITURE s. pus, discharge, suppuration (sanies, putredo); cautery (ustio, ustura, cauterium)
QUITURER v.n. to suppurate (saniem facere, saniem emittere)
QUULLEZ = CULEZ imper.5 of CULER to strain, sieve
RAEZ imper.5 of RERE to shave
RAIS(S)INE, RA[I]SCINE, RASINIE s. resin (resina)
RAIZ s. radish (Raphanus L.) R. DAMASCHE radish (Raphanus sativus L.) (rafanus domesticus)
    R. SALVAGE white radish, white charlock (Raphanus raphanistrum L.) (rafanus agrestis)
RASOR, RASUR s. razor (rasorium)
REBUCHIÉ a. hooked
RECEIT ind.pr.3 of RECEIVRE to receive
RECEPCION s. medical receipt, prescription
RECONVENIR v.n. to be fitting, appropriate (oportere)
RECORRE A v.n. to have recourse to
RECRESTRE v.n. to grow again
REESUER v.n. ? error for r(o)uver, to become red (oculorum incensio)
REFAITIER v.a. to mend, put back in place (reaptare)
REFREDIR v.n. to cool down (frigescere, infrigidare) REFREDI p.p. (infrigidatus)
REIN pron. anything; (with negative) nothing
REINS, REINZ s.pl. kidneys (renes)
REISINE s. resin (resina)
RELEMENT adv. rarely (raro)
REMAINE ind.pr.3 of REMENER to bring back
REMEDIE s. remedy, cure (remedium)
REMEINGE sbj.pr.3 of REMEINDRE to stay
REMENER v.a. to replace, bring back (to original position) (reducere)
REMUABLE a. changing, variable (mobilis)
REMUÉ a. separate, distinct (semotus)
REMUEMENT s. change, variety (diversitas)
REMUER v.a. to change dressing or bandage of (mutare); to move about (movere)
REPARRAIL(L)EMENT s. restoration, repair (restauratio, reparatio, reparamentum)
[REPARRALLIER] v.a. to restore, cure (reparare) REPARRALLIÉ, REPARRILLÉ, REPARRILEZ
REPLAER v.a. to bend (plicare)
REPLECION s. repletion (repletio)
REPOSER v.a. to place in turn
REPRIMER v.a. to suppress (reprimere)
REPRINT p.p. of REPRIENDRE to repress, check
RERE v.a. to shave (radere) RES p.p. RAEZ, RAEIZ imper.5

RESTREINDRE v.a. to restrain (constringere)
RETORNER v.a. to twist, turn (retorquere)
REUME s. rheum, mucous discharge (reuma)
ROGER, ROGIR v.n. to redden, become red (rubeo)
ROIGNER, RONGNE s. scabies (runa var. ruma, rufa; scabies)
ROIL s. rust (see notes to I,53)
ROILLE s. ? round slice
ROOANT, ROOEND a. round (rotundus)
ROONDDESCE s. roundness (rotunditas)
ROSE s. rose (rosa)
ROSEL s. reed (canna, harundo)
ROVOR, ROVUR s. redness, inflammation (rubor)
RUBIGO s. error for 'rugen', surgical instrument (see notes to I,14)
RUE s. rue (Ruta graveolens L.) (ruta)
RUGEUR s. redness, inflammation (rubor)
RUGINE s. surgical scraper (rugen)
RUMPANT a. caustic OIGNEMENT R. (unguentum ruptorium)
RUNGER v.a. to gnaw, eat into (corrodere)
RUT(E a. broken (rupta)
RUTURE, RUPTURE pl. RUPTURUS s. breaking (of skin) (ruptura, crepatura)
SAC s. pouch, bag, sachet (saccus, sacellus)
SACHELET s. small pouch, sachet (sacculus)
SACIER v.a. to sieve, strain (cribrare) SACIEZ imper.5
SAF see SAUF
SAFFRAN s. saffron (Crocus sativus L.) or bastard saffron (Carthamus tinctorius L.) (crocus)
SAGE s. sage (Salvia officinalis)
SAGEMENT adv. skilfully, carefully (provide)
SAGIT(T)ELLA s. surgical lancet (sagitella)
SAIM s. animal fat (sagimen)
SAIM SARAZIN s. error for 'savun sarazin' (I,37 sapo sarracenicus)
SAIN a. healthy, healed (sanus)
SAITE s. arrow (sagitta)
SALÉ a. salted, salt (salsus)
SALERNE s. Salerno
SALF see SAUF
SALGE DAMASCHE s. sage (Salvia officinalis L.) (salvia domestica)
SALGE SAVAGE s. wood sage, wood germander (Teucrium scorodonia L.) (salvia silvestris)
SALIVE s. saliva (saliva)
SANC DE DRAGUNT s. dragon's blood, juice or resin of the dragon tree (Dracaena draco L.)
    (sanguis draconis)
SANCE, SANTE prep. without
SANDALI s. red and white sandalwood (Santalum album L. / Pterocarpus santalinus L.) (san-
    dalus) S. BLANC E RUGE (III,9)
SANER v.a. and v.n. to heal (sanare, curare, procurare, curari)
SARAPINUM s. gum, resin from Ferula persica (sarapinum)
SARCOCOLLE s. sarcocol, gum sarcocolla
SAUF, SALF, SAF s. METTRE EN S. to store, set aside (usui reservare; servare)
SAUGE s. sage (Salvia officinalis L.)
SAUSE s. corrosive juice
SAUSEFLEME, SAUCEFLEME, SAUSEFLEUME, SAUSEFLEIME, SAUSEFLEGME s. sauce-
    flegm, swelling of the face (owing to salty humours) (flegma salsum)
SAVER v.a. to know SACHIEZ imper.5
SAVINE s. savin (Juniperus sabina L.) (savina)
SAVON, SAVUN, SAVAON s. soap (sapo) S. FRANCEIS, FRANCEAIS (sapo gallicus) soda-
    ash soap S. SARAZIN, SARAZIM (sapo sarracenicus) a mixture of soap-lye and olive oil S.
    SPARANTIC (sapo spatarentus, see notes to II,14)
SCABIOSA s. various plants incl. Knautia arvensis (L.) Coulter and Succisa pratensis Moench
SCIA, SCIE s. scia, hip (scia)

SCIATICHE s. sciatica (sciatica) a. sciatic (sciaticus)
SCROPHULARE s. figwort (Scrophularia nodosa L.) (scrofularia)
SCRUPLE s. unit of weight, 'scrupulum' (scrupulum)
SEANT pres.p. sitting, seated (sedens)
SEC(H) a. dry (siccus)
SECHE s. cuttlefish OS DE LA S. cuttlefish bone (os sepie)
SEC(C)HIER v.a. and v.n. to dry (exsiccare, desiccare, siccare, exsiccari) SEC(C)HIÉ p.p.
SEIGNÉ s. blood-letting, bleeding (minutio)
SEIGNIER v.a. and v.n. to bleed
SEIN a. healthy, cured (sanus)
SEINT sbj.pr.6 of ESTRE
SEL(E a. that
SELE s. ALER A S. to go to stool, evacuate the bowels (assellare)
SEMBLABLE a. similar (similis)
SEMBLANT a. ESTRE S. to seem, have the appearance
SEMBLAUNT s. appearance, manner
SEMENCE s. seed (semen)
SENATIONES s.pl. garden cress or watercress (Lepidium sativum L. / Nasturtium officinale
    R.Br.) (senationes)
SENESTRE a. left-hand (sinister)
SENEVÉ s. mustard (Sinapis L. spp.) S. SALVAGE charlock (Sinapis arvensis L.) (eruca agrestis)
SEON s. seton (seto, seton)
SERAPINUM, SERAPINO s. gum, resin from Ferula persica
SERPIGO s. scabious disease, tetter (serpigo)
SERVILE a. servile (servilis)
SETE s. arrow (sagitta)
SETISME a. seventh
SEU s. elder (Sambucus nigra L.) (sambucus)
SEUN s. seton (seton, seto)
SEUNT sbj.pr.6 of ESTRE
SEUR a. sure, certain (securus)
SEUREMENT adv. securely; without doubt, certainly (secure)
SEVRER v.a. to separate, detach (separare)
SIECE sbj.pr.3 of SEOIR to sit, be seated
SIENGNÉ p.p. of SEIGNER to show, indicate
SIL = SI LE and CIL dem.pr. m.pl.
SILOTRUM, SILOTRO s. depilatory (psilotrum)
SIMAINE s. week (ebdomada)
SINANCIE s. type of quinsy (II,16 scinantia, squinantia)
SIPHAC s. peritoneum (sifac)
SIRE see CIRE
SIRINGE s. syringe (siringa)
SIROP, SIRUP s. syrup S. ROSAT rose-hip syrup
SIS a. six
SISIMBRIO s. horsemint (Mentha sylvestris L.) (sisimbrium)
SISME a. sixth
SISUN s. ? aromatic umbelliferous plant
SIU s. animal fat S. DE MUTUN mutton fat (sepum arietinum)
SIUDEIN a. sudden (subitus)
SODURE s. mending, knitting (of bones) (consolidatio)
SOENT sbj.pr.6 of ESTRE
SOIE s. silk (sericum)
SOI s. thirst
SOIET sbj.pr.3 of ESTRE
SOL, SUL a. alone
SOLATRUM s. black nightshade (Solanum nigrum L.) or deadly nightshade (Atropa bella-
    donna L.)
SOLE s. sole (of shoe) (solea)

[SOLEIR] v.n. to be accustomed to SOT, SOUT, SOLET, SEULT ind.pr.3 SOLIUM ind.impf.4
SOLLURE s. blemish, stain
SOLUN prep. according to (secundum)
SOMET s. top, crown (of head) (summitas)
SORNOER v.n. to float to the top (supernatare)
SOUDURE s. healing (of wound) (consolidatio)
SOVEREIN a. upper
SOVIN, SUVIN a. supine, lying back face up (supinus)
SPADADRAPPUM s. sparadrap (spadadrapus, sparadrapus)
SPARAGI s. dove's-foot cranesbill / long-stalked cranesbill (Geranium molle / columbinum L.)
   (sparagus)
SPATULE FETIDE s. gladden, stinking iris (Iris foetidissima L.) (spatula fetida)
SPATUMINI s. surgical chisel (spatumen)
SPAUDE see ESPAUD(L)E
SQUILLE s. squill (Scilla L. esp. Scilla maritima Baker) (squilla)
SQUINANCIE s. quinsy (squinantia)
STAPHISAGRE s. stavesacre (Delphinium staphisagria L.) (staphisagria)
STORACUM CALAMITE, STORACIM, STORASCIS BLANC E RUGE s. styrax, resin from
   Liquidamber orientalis (storax)
STRANGURIA s. strangury, pain and difficulty in urination (stranguria)
STRICTORIE s. constringent, styptic (strictorium)
SUAGER v.a. to relieve, soothe
SU(B)STANCE s. substance, body (substancia)
SUCHER, SUCHIR v.a and v.refl. to suck (suggere)
SUE poss.a.fem. his
SUE(I)F adv. softly, gently (leniter, suaviter)
SUER v.n. to sweat (sudare)
SUFFLER v.n. to breathe in (insufflare)
SUFFRIR v.a. to permit, tolerate, support (permittere)
SU(L)FRE s. sulphur VIF S. (sulphur vivus) S. CHENELLIÉ (sulphur cannellatum, see notes to
   I,53)
SUI see SIU
SULUM prep. alongside (iuxta)
SUPERFLUITÉ s. superfluity, abundance (superfluitas)
SURAJUSTER v.a. to add (superaddere)
SURANÉ a. old, of long standing (inveteratus)
SURCRESTRE v.n. to grow (over) (excrescere, subcrescere) SURCRESSE sbj.pr.3
SURE adv. on top
SURIZ s. muscle (musculus)
SURMETTRE v.a. to place upon SURMIS p.p.
SURMUNTER v.a. to exceed (superare)
SURSANURE s. cicatrice, scab, scar
SURVENIR v.n. to occur (supervenire)
SUS adv. above, up (sursum) EN S. upwards (ad superiora)
SUSLEVER v.a. to lift up, raise (elevare)
SUSTANCE s. substance (substancia)
SUSTRAIANT p.p. raising, pulling upwards
SUSTRAIRE v.a. to remove (subtrahere)
SUTIL a. delicate (subtilis)
SUUR s. sweat (sudor)
SUVENIREMENT adv. see notes to I,34
SUZPALE a. palish (subalbidus)
SUZSEANT s. person sitting underneath (III,36 subsedens)
TABLE s. board, plank, plate (tabula)
TAILLIER v.a. to incise, cut open (incidere, truncare)
TAILL(I)URE s. incision (incisio)
TALENT s. desire, wish AVOIR T. DE to feel like, desire to
TALUN, TALON s. heel (calcaneum)

TANGNE see TEI(N)GNE
TANTET s. a little (1,16 tantillum)
TAPIR v.n. to lie concealed, hidden (latere)
TAPSIE s. deadly carrot (Thapsia garganica L.) (tapsia)
TAPSUS BARBASTUS, TAPSI BARBASTI s. mullein (Verbascum thapsus L.) (tapsus bar-
    bastus)
TARGE sbj.pr.3 of (SE) TARDER to take long (retardere)
TARTARUM s. tartar, wine lees
TASTER, TASTIR subst. vb. feeling, exploring by touch (digito temptare tactus)
TECHE s. infection (infectio)
TEI(E see TOIE
TEI(N)GNE, TEIGNEE, TEGNE s. tinea, disease of the scalp (tinea)
TEIL a. such
TEINGE sbj.pr.3 of TENIR
TEINT ind.pr.3 of TENIR
TEIRÇ, TEIRZ, TIRCE a. third
TEMPLUS s.pl. temples (tempora)
TENAILLES, TENEILLES s.pl. forceps (picicarioli, forcipes, tenaculum, forfices)
TENANT a. thick, sticky, viscous
TENDRE a. frail, ? squeamish (delicatus)
TENDRUM s. soft, tender part (II,18 of ear)
TENIR v.a. to hold SE T. A to adhere to, cling to (adherere, conherere) SE TENIR DE to ab-
    stain from SE TINGENT sbj.pr.6
TENS s. time
TENT(E s. tent (med.), pledget, seton (stuellus, tenta, tasta)
TENV(E a. viscous, sticky; light (of diet) AQUIS TENVE (II,17 parum liquidus)
TERDRE v.a. to wipe (abstergere, extergere) TERDE sbj.pr.3 TERDEZ imper.5
TEREBENTINE, TEREBENTINA s. terpentine (terebintina)
TERSZ a. third
TES see TEST
TEST s. cranium, skull (cranium)
TETTESURIZ s. common stonecrop (Sedum acre L.)
TIEDVE a. tepid, lukewarm
TINGE sbj.pr.3 of TENIR
TIRIASIS, TYRIASIS s. type of leprosy; ? psoriasis, pityriasis, scurf
TIRUS s. worm, venomous snake
TITIMALLE s. spurge (Euphorbia L. spp.) (titimallus)
TITLE s. title
TIULE, TEULE s. tile (tegula)
TOIE s. membrane (panniculus)
TORSUN DE FILS, T. DE FIL s. ball, hank of thread (globus filorum)
TORTEILUS a. winding, convoluted (tortuosus)
TOST adv. soon, quickly (cito)
TOSTÉ a. parched (tostus)
TOTESVEI(E)S adv. always (semper)
TRACHIE ARTERIE s. trachea (trachea arteria)
TRAIT p.p. struck (percussus)
TRAITABLE a. tractable (tractabilis)
TRAIT(I)É s. treatise, section (tractatus)
TRAITER v.a. to treat (tractare)
TRANSGLUTER v.a. to swallow (inglutire)
TRAVAIL s. ESTRE EN GRANT T. to be in great distress, discomfort
TRAVERS a. EN T. sideways (ex transverso)
TRAIRE, TREIRE v.a. to draw
TREMBLER v.n. to tremble, shudder
TRENCHER v.a. to cut (incidere)
TREPACIUM, TREPACIUN s. trephine, borer (trepanum, see notes to I,6)
TREPANUM s. trephine, trepan (trepanum)

TREPASSER v.a. to omit, pass over (praetermittere)

TRIBLER v.a. to grind, pound, crush (terere, pistare, contere)

TROCISSI s.pl. 'trocisci', lozenge-shaped medicaments (trociscus)

TUEL s. tube, funnel (embotum); passage (meatus) ; opening (III,30 orificium)

TUT adv. DE(L) T. EN T. completely, entirely

TUTDIS adv. always (semper)

UEL(E)MENT adv. equally, in equal measure (ana, equaliter)

UMBLIL s. navel (umbilicum)

UMB(I)LICUM VENERIS, UMBILICI V. s. pennywort (Umbilicus rupestris (Salisb.) Dandy) (umbilicum veneris)

UNCE s. ounce; a finger's breadth (uncia)

UNCE a. eleven

UNCHUS adv. ever; (with negative) never

UNCIME, UNZIME a. eleventh

UNCUS s. hooked surgical instrument (uncus)

UN(E)S indef. art. pl. some; pr. some people (III,45 quidam)

UNGEMENT s. ointment, unguent (unguentum)

UNI a. (of diet) easily digestible (I,47) (sorbilis)

UNNEZ imper.5 of UINDRE to anoint

UNT adv. where PAR U. through which

URE s. hour TEL U. sometimes

VAGIR v.n. to move (out of place) (vagari)

VALER subst.v. lowering (depositio)

VALOIR v.n. to be of value VALT, VAUT ind.pr.3

VARIEMENT s. variety (varietas)

VEEIR v.a. to see

VEINE pl. VEINUS s. vein (vena)

VEISIN a. neighbouring, adjacent (vicinus)

VEISSEL s. vessel V. ESTAINÉ tin vessel (vas stagnatum) D. DE TERRE earthenware vessel (vas fictile)

VE(I)SSIE, VEISIIE s. bladder (vesica)

VELLESZE s. old age (senectus)

VELU a. rough (rugosus)

VENGE sbj.pr.3 of VENIR

VENTOSITÉ s. flatulence, morbid wind in the body (ventositas)

VENTUSE s. cupping glass (cufa var. ventosa)

VER s. worm (vermis)

VER v.n. to see

VERM, VEIRM s. worm (vermis)

VERME(I)L, VERMAIL a. red (rubeus)

VERMICULARIS s. common stonecrop (Sedum acre L.) (vermicularis)

VERMINE s. worm (vermis)

VERNICE s. gum of Tetraclinis articulata (Vahl) Masters (vernex)

VERT s. V. D'AREIM, D'EREIM, DE L'AREINT, DE L'ARAIM, DE L'ARIM flowers of brass (viridis eris, flos eris)

VERTEBRUM s. hip-joint

VERVEINE s. vervain (Verbena officinalis L.) (verbena)

VESCU p.p. of VIVRE

VESPRE s. evening, vespers

VETONIE s. betony (Stachys officinalis (L.) Trev.)

VIER, A adv. truly, in truth

VIF s. TAILLIER AL V. to cut to the quick (ad vivum incidere)

VIN EGRE s. vinegar (acetum)

VIOLENTEMENT adv. violently (violenter)

VIS, A adv. scarcely (vix)

VIT s. penis (virile membrum)

VITICELLE s. red and white bryony (Bryonia cretica L. subsp. dioica (Jacq.) Tutin) (viticella)

VITREOLE, VITREOLUM s. (vitreolum)

VOIRE s. glass

VOLENTEIRS, VOLENTERES adv. carefully, attentively (diligenter)

VOLUBLE MAJORE s. bindweed (Convolvulus arvensis L.) or possibly honeysuckle (Lonicera periclymenum L.) (volubile maior)

VOMENTACION s. fomentation (fomentum)

YARI s. cuckoo-pint (Arum maculatum L.) (iarus)

YERALOGODION s. a purgative compound medicine containing aloes

YSOPHAGUS, YSOPHAGUM s. ysophagus (isofagus)

ZEMARINUM s. a type of cleansing lotion, possibly an error for 'alumen zucarinum' (see notes to I,44 and 45)

ZIMA s. boil, pustule (? oedema) (zimia)

ZUCRE s. sugar (zucara, zuccarum)

The Old French Translation of Roger Frugard's *Chirurgia* in MS
Cambridge, Trinity College 0.1.20 ff. 24va–30rb [= O]

[BOOK I]

[f. 24va] [1] *De tote manieres de froisseures*. Il avient ke li chief est naufrez en diverse
manieres. Kar il est a la fiez naufrez ovec la depesceure del tes, a la fiez sauns
depeceure del tes. La depeceure ovec la plaie est a la fiez grant [f. 24vb] e aperte, a
la fois petite e repuse. Mais quaunt la depeceure del tes ke om a* petite [est u
graunt], est a la fiez ovec large plaie e grande, a la fiez avec petite plaie e estreite.
En quelcunque maniere la depeceure del tes seit, il est a doter de la bleceure des
peaucellettes les queles envolupent le cervel, kar a la fiez la dure mere est blecee, a
la fiez la pieue mere. Quant la dure mere est blecié, ces sunt les signes: li naufrés ad
dolor el chief, rojor en la face, enbrasement es euz, il est tot devez, la langue est
tote noire. Mes quaunt la pieue mere est depecié, ces sunt les signes: il n'a point de
vertu ne vois, bocetes suelent lever en sa face tot au comencement, sanc e merde
sout decore de ses oreilles e de ses narines, il est tot serrés, [f. 25ra] il a freit .iii. fois
ou .iiii. le jor, e ce est certainement signe de mort. Iceus signes sorvenans, le
naufrés ne poet vivre au plus de cent jors.

[II] *Por depeceure*. Quaunt la depeceure del tes est graunt e aperte, sicom ele seit
faite d'espee ou de hache, si os ou autre chose deit estre estrait, tost seit estrait. Si
la plaie [ne] seine trop, donkes un delié drapel de lin seit mis entre la dure mere e
le tes en botaunt d'une penne en esclent. Drapeus de lin, ou de seie, ki meilor est,
sei[en]t mis en la depeceure del tes, si ke les chiefs des drapeles seient de totes pars
soz* le tes, ke ordure n'i pust venir a la dure mere e ke le cervel ne seit plus blessé.
Om poet faire iceste chose d'esponge de mer [f. 25rb] bien lavee e essuee, kar ele
beit la porriture. La plaie dehors se[i]t emplee de drapeles de lin moilez en aubun
de oef e un poi espressés* [e] un orilier seit mis desus e bien seit lié – .ii. fois en yver
e .iii. fiez en esté seit remué la plaie. Li malade gise sor sa plaie e si seit gardez desi
ke li tes seit gariz.

[III] Si morte char crest desur la dure mere devaunt ce ke li tes seit garis, esponge
marine bien* lavee e faite secche seit mise desi a ce ke la morte char seit ostee. Si
la morte char crest desur le repareillement del tes, poudre de ermodacles metés
sure. La plaie dehors seit garie de linge drap e de coton. Come la plaie seit garie,
apostolicum cirurgicum i seit [f. 25va] mis.

[V] Si la depeceure del tes est graunt e la plaie petite, si ke om ne puisse saver si la
depeceure est grant ou petite, botés i le dei e tastés amont e aval, kar nous ne

sentoms en nule manere si bien come del dei ke a ongle. Puis ke vous saverez de la depeceure del tes, si la plaie est estroite fendez le en crois e deseverez les quarters del tes d'un estrument ke om apele erugo. Et si sanc ou autre chose ne destorbe, si os ou autre chose deit estre trait, ostez le tost avec pissicalloris, c'est un estrument. Si la plaie seigne mult ou autre chose destorbe, n'i faites nient. Metés .i. drap entre la dure mere e le tes e faites totes les choses ke sont [f. 25vb] dites devant. Metés les quartiers ensemble, emplez tote la plaie de drapeles moillés en aubun de oef. Metés .i. oreillier de drapel desure e liés le e laissez le issi del matin treske au vespre ou del vespre treske au matin. Li malades gise sor la plaie. Quant vous revendrez al malade, si vous trovez les quartiers enflés e aoités, icest est bone signe. Si vous les trovez retraiés e amenuisés, mauveisse signe est. Faites iceste cure desi treske li tes seit garis. Amenuissé[s] donkes les drapeles e metés les quarters en lor propre liu. Garisez la plaie puis de drapeus e de coton. Nous metoms tant soulement drap en la plaie dont le tes est depeciez. Nous laissoms del tot en tot ointes choses. Apostolicom [f. 26ra] cirurgicum seit mis sor une coreie e la coreie seit mise sor la plaie sanee.

[VI] *Al tes depecié.* Il avient que li tes est depeciés en manere de crevache e isifaitement ke l'une partie del tes n'est plus basse ne plus haute de l'autre, mes om n'i set si tele depeceure va desi au tes. Donkes covient ke li malades tiegne sa bouche e ses narines closes e soffle durement. E si vent ist hors de la plaie, sachez ke le tes est depecés treske au cervel, al quel nous aidoms en tele manere. Si la plaie est estreite, faites le large e si sanc ou autre chose ne destorbe, faites creus dejoste le crevasce d'un estrument de fer ke om apele trepan. Tant de pertuis faites come vous volez. Aprés trenchez le tes de l'un pertus deske a l'au[f. 26rb]tre avec .i. estrument de fer ke om apele spatuminum. Jetez envoie la depeceure e ostez la porreture qui est sor le cervel de coton. Ou pernez .i. linge drap e botez le d'une penne en esclent entre le tes e la dure mere, ke le drap estraie la porreture. Ne faites autre chose en tes plaies que nous n'avoms dit devant.

[VII] *Por tes depecié.* Si le tes est depeciés en tele maniere ke l'une partie est plus basse de l'autre, si la froisseure ne poet pas estre de legier ostee, faites pertuis de cele part ou ele se tient. Aprés trenchez le tes de spatumino. Garisez la plaie sicome nous avoms dit devant.

[VIII] *A la plaie sanz froisse[ure] del [tes].* Si la plaie est sans froisseure del tes, emplez le teste de dra[f. 26va]peles moillez en aubun de oef e un poi esprient. Si il est yver, metez itele cure desi a ce ke la plaie merde, la quele cure est faite en tele maniere. Pernez braunche* ursine, mauve de cortil e autre mauve, parele, voluble le grande. De totes icés herbes pernez une poigne e taunt soulement des foilles, metés tot ce avec une livre de oint e .iii. onces de ferine de forment e deus onces de ferrine de semence de lin e .ii. onces de fenegru. Metez totes ces choses en un vassel de tere e mellés od blaunc vin. Metez le pot desor un lent feu e tant le laissez ilec en movaunt a l'espate* desi que il seit espés e quant vous en vodrez ovrer, si en pernez.

[IX] [X] [XI] *Por emflure**. [f. 26vb] Il avient ke li chief emfle de coup sans plaie, a la fiez est li tes sains, a la fiez depeciés. A la fiez conust om la depeceure del tes en tastant, a la fiez nient. Quant la depeceure est aperte, raez le chief e trenchiez l'emfle[u]re en crois e faites totes icés choses ke nous avoms dit devaunt.

[XII] Si la depeceure del tes est reclose, sicome ele seit faite en manere de crevace, vous le conustrez par les signes que vous verrez en le malade desc'a .v. jors ou a .vii. Si li malades n'a talent de mangier e il cuist malement sa viande e il dort mauveisement e mauveisement vait a chambre e mauveisement pisse e s'il a chalor come ce fust fievre, nous sumus certain de la froisseure del tes. Garissiez le issi. Fendez le quir [f. 27ra] en crois d'un rasoir e fetes totes les choses que nous avoms dit devaunt.

[XIII] *Por emfleure de coup.* Quant li chief est emflé de coup sauns plaie e sauns froissure del tes, par ces signes le conustrez desi a .v. jors ou a .vii. Si li malades a talent de mangier e ç'il cuist bien sa viande, si il dort bien e il va bien a chambre, si il pisse bien e il est sauns fievre, nous [sumus] certains ke li tes est entiers. Donc i deit om mettre itele chose ki oste l'emfleure. Fetes tele medecine. Pernez aloine, bibuef, rue, comin, sieu, chescune des herbes owellement. Pestelez bien ensemble e quisez en oile d'olive e metez le treis foiz ou quatre le jor sor l'enfleure au plus chaut ke li malades le por[f. 27rb]ra soffrir. E si ce n'oste l'emfleure, faites tele medecine. Pernez aloine, bibuef, mauve de cortil owellement .i. poignee, triblez icés .iii. herbes ovec .iii. onces de oint e metez .iii. onces de forment avec. Destemprez tot ice de vin e le metez al fu quire. Derechief metez i .iiii. onces de miel e movez de l'espate* deke il seit espés. Metez tele medecine a l'enfleure desi adonc ke il seit meurs. Après l'ovrez en cele partie ou il apent* plus d'un estrument de fer ke om apele sagitelle e après pressés tote la merde hors as mains e, si mestiers est, botez i le dei. Faites après sicome om enseignera en les cures des cleus.

[XIV] Si le quir est deseverez del chief [f. 27va] ovec la plaie e avec le tes sicom ce fust de coup de espeie ou de piere, fendez le quir parmi desi au tes froissié. Ostez la froisseure d'une estrument que om apele erugo, cosez le quir de l'une e l'autre partie. Comencez a la plus haute partie e faites un point de delié aguille quarree de fil de seye e noez le point ferm. Faites un point a la mesure de plain pauch entre .ii. Taunt i faites de poins com vous verrez ke mestiers est. Laissez la plus basse partie overt, par ou la porreture* istra. Metez rouge poudre desus. Iceste poudre est por resouder la plaie ki est faite issifaitement.

[XV] Pernez une once de grant consoude, de bol*, pois gregoise .iii. onces, mastic e encens owe[f. 27rb]lement demi once, sanc de dragon, mumie* owellement .ii. onces, c'est .v. deniers pesant. Triblez tot ensemble. Ovrez ent quant mestiers est. Ceste poudre restraint sanc e soude os e char, ele fait tost le quir revenir sor la plaie. Metez iceste poudre sor la costure e foille de plantain desore, botez l'entreit par desouz en l'overture. Metez .i. orreillier par desus qui espresse la porreture aval. Metez iceste poudre desi a .ix. jors sor la plaie .ii. [fois] le jor desi a ce ke vous

verrez la char crestre e souder. Deliez les poins e ostez le fil e garisez la plaie de drap
e de coton. En l'overture ke est faite enmi botés drap sec e aprés ovrez tot issi come
nous avoms dit devaunt.

[XVI] Si taunt poi de la tes est desevrés, ke il ne parviengne [f. 28ra] mie a la dure
miere, ostés cel tantelet* e faites issi com jo vous ai dit devaunt, fors ke vous ne
defendez pas le quir parmi, ke ordure ne pust avenir a la dure mere.   ·

[XVII] Si le quir est deseverez del tes, garisez le sicom nous avoms dit en la plus
proceine cure. Nous metoms oignement por saner la plaie, kar nous ne dotons pas
que il perce desi au cervel.

[XVIII] Si la plaie est el chief devaunt ou deriere e ele va desi al cervel, ele est
mortele. Mes si ele descent par les oreilles ou par les narines*, si ke le cervel ne seit
bleciez, ele n'est pas mortele. Garisez le come les autres devaunt.

[XIX] *Por plaie de niés e de lievre.* Si la plaie est en niés ou en levre ou en autre
partie noble del cors, [e] si ele de[i]t estre cosue, metez l'u[f. 28rb]ne partie a l'autre
e cosez le quir d'une delié aguille a fil de seye au plus belement que vous poez.
Laissez espace entre les poins, noez chescun point par sey. Si la levre ou le niés sont
fenduz d'entravers, metés chescun en son leu e cosez les sicom nous avoms dit
devant. Metez oreillier de drapel del .i. part del niés e de l'autre fetes sustenement
en manere de chavestre, ke li niés remaigne en son propre liu. Si mestiers est,
metés entrait es narines. En totes les costures laissez les plus basses parties overtes,
par ou om pust boter l'entrait si ce n'est en la verge ou el niés pou es oreilles. Metez
poudre rouge desi ke a .ix. jors sor la costure, la quele est dite devaunt e garisez
aprés sicom [f. 28va] nous avoms dit devant.

[XX] *Por coup en la face.* Si aucun est feru en la face ou es* narines ou delé l'oil, si
le fer est parfont e il ait entré par estreite veie, ja seit ce ke il ait travail au traire,
nekedent chescun travaille solonc son engin e pense longuement coment il pust
estre estrait. Si li fust est dedens le fer, botez une tente parmi la plaie desi au fer e si
vous sentez le fer aerdre durement al fust, eloschiez le [e] petit e petit estraez issi
fors, si vous poez. Si le fust n'est pas en le fer, demandez le malade* coment il estut
quaunt il fu ferru, ou sus ou jus, ou droit ou en esclent. Botez une tente parmi la
plaie e si vous trovés la veye del fer, traiez le hors, [f. 28vb] si vous poez. Si vous nel
poez oster sans graunt paine, mieuz vaut delaisser, kar maint home ke retient le fer
vit aprés ce longuement. Garissiez la plaie ensi. Quaunt li fer est ostez, fetes une
tente de lart e botez en la plaie. Si la plaie est si parfunde ke le lard ne poet avenir
au funs, faites une tente de drap e l'oignez de lart e botez laens e metez un oreillier
de drap desore. Liez le en tele maniere ke la bende seit sor la plaie. Si il i a .ii.
pertuis, le plus bas sereit derainement sanez; le pertuis qui est plus haut seit avant
gariz. Couchez le malade en tele manere que la porreture descende par defors. Si
vous volez fere porreture en la plaie solonc la diverseté del tens, metés les*

medicines qui sunt escrites [f. 29ra] devant. Aprés le garisez sicom nous avoms dit devaunt. N'obliez pas, puis que la plaie devient secche, amenuisez l'entrait solonc la soudeure de la plaie.

[XXI] Si la plaie est faite de sete barbee, nous l'ostoms issifaitement. Si fors pinches i poent entrer largement, nous pernoms les barbeus as tenailles, si les plujons* a la hanste en torjant. Si il vous greve a faire issi, faites une graille buhot de fer ou de areim e metez a l'un des barbeus. Ausi faites a l'autre barbel. Estraiez le hors issi par graunt estudie. Ausi poez vous faire de .ii. pennes d'owe. Garisez les autres plaies tot issi com nous avoms dit devaunt. [J]a seit ce que li somechon del chief ne seit pas sovent naufrés de sete, mais por [f. 29rb] ce ke la cure i est grief, nous ne trespasseroms mie. Si seete ou autre chose ad percié le tes de l'une partie e ele ist de l'autre apertement, faites icele cure. Si morteles signes n'aperent mie el malade, trenchiez le quir la ou la seete ist e deseverez le del tes d'une estrument ke om apele erugo e forés tost si vous poez delé le fer, mes mieuz vaut en reont, si ke la veie seit eslargie. Puis traiez le fer hors de cele partie e le fust de l'autre partie e bones signes aperent del malade desi a .v. ou a .vii. [jors]. Trenchez le quir delez le fust ou delé [le] fer sicome nous avoms dit devaunt e deseverez le del tes e faites pertuis de trepan delié e treez hors le fer. [f. 29va] Garisez tous les plaies sicom nous avoms dit en la premere cure de la froisseure del tes.

[XXII] *Por tes ploié par coup.* Il avient par coup ke le tes est plaiés vers le cervel sans plaie e sans froisseure, si ke le cervel ne se poet removir. Dont le malade se lieve en dormant e prent armes e combat e se demaine en dormant com home devez. Ceste est la cure. Fendez le quir en crois sor la ploieure d'une rasor e ostez le quir del tes e faites pertuis entor la plaieure d'un trepan e ostez la pece plaié. Garisez le aprés sicom nous avoms dit en la premere cure.

[XXVI] *Quant home chiet del fort mal.* Trenchiez le quir el somechon del chief en crois e fai[f. 29vb]tes pertuis en le tes, ke la matere s'en voist. Liez fermement le dervé. Garisez la plaie come devant.

[XXV] *A faire quiture.* Faites une quiture en la fontenele del col deriere.

[BOOK III]

[XXVII] *Si les bouele[s] issent.* Si les boueles issent hors par aucune plaie e les boueus seient trenchiés, mes ke la graindre partie remaine saine, aidez le issi. Si les boueus sont endurcis par froit, trenchez aucune vive beste parmi e metés sor les boweus desi a ce que il sevent rechaufés e amolliés. Apareilliés un buhot de seuch a la mesure de la plaie del bouel, si ke li buhot seit de chescune partie .i. pous plus long que la plaie. Faites le buhetel greille e botez en la plaie e cosez le de delié aguille e de fil de seye. [f. 30ra] Lavez esponge de mer en ewe chaude e tergiez hors totes les ordures des* boueles e quant il serront bien nettes, remetez les ens parmi la plaie e metez le malade sor une table sovin e roellez le amont e aval desi a ce ke les boueus seient revenuz en lor propre liu. Laissez la plaie overte desi a ce que les boueus seient resoudés. Cosez la plaie dehors e metez poudre rouge desore. Mais si la plaie est grant, metez un long drap de l'une partie desi en l'autre en la plaie e cosez la plaie desor le drapel e metez poudre rouge sor la costure del boel e traiez chescun jor le drapel hors* de la plaie devers le partie pendant. Quant vous verrez la plaie estre resoudee, traiez hors le drapel e garisez [f. 30rb] les deraines parties ki sont overtes. Lor diete seit digestive e tenve.

NOTES

1,1 la

O adds 'e repuse'. As in the AN translation, the opening is not entirely coherent and requires some emendation. O also adds the explanatory expansion 'les queles envolupent le cervel' to 'peaucellettes' and 'tot au comencement' when describing the eruption of pustules on the face (cf. the AN translation where 'e al commencement' is attached to the next set of symptoms).

1,2 sor   apres

O omits 'con amplo et largo vulnere' (132). O's 'hache' renders 'simili' (133). O simplifies this section, omitting a series of small details. The Latin describes the action of the sponge as follows: 'hec enim putredinem ab exterioribus derivantem velud bibula recipit' (141–2) which is followed by 'aliquantulum expressis' (143) the translation of which the scribe has botched. O's 'orilier' translates Latin 'plumaceolus' (144) which in MS M is glossed 'plumaceolus dicitur pulvinar de pluma' (Sudhoff p.159, n.8). The Latin specifies that it is to be adjusted 'pro varietate partis capitis' (144). The end of the final sentence in O diverges from the Latin 'con hec autem cura usque ad plenam cranei restaurationem est insistendum' (146–47).

1,3 ne mie bien

The second half of this chapter (ll.152–8) is abbreviated by O, which omits entirely the receipt for Apostolicon cirurgicum (= 1,4), as does Renzi's text of the *Chirurgia*.

1,5

For 'plaie petite' the Latin has 'vulnus autem in superficie strictum' (176). O's 'amont e aval' is an addition, as is 'ke a ongle'. O's 'erugo' renders the Latin 'con rugine' (181) and 'pissicalloris' is yet another variant of 'picicariolis' (183) with the addition 'c'est un estrument'. O's 'n'i faites nient' is followed in the Latin by 'quousque illa cessaverint, removenda vero statim [si] potes competenter removeas' (184–5). O omits 'infra craneum . . . constrictis' (188–89). Again (see 1,2 above) O omits 'pro varietate partis capitis' (190). 'Li malades gise sor la plaie' is an addition. O omits 'a secundo . . . hoc fac' (198–99).

1,6

'Hors de la plaie' is a surprisingly general rendering of 'per rimulam' (206). O's 'faites creus' renders Latin 'fora' (212). O is meticulous in reproducing the name of surgical instruments ('trepano' in 211, 'spatumine' in 212), but omits 'incidas, ita scilicet ut usque ad extremitates rimule talis veniat incisio' (213–14). O's 'Jetez envoie . . . sur le cervel de coton' at first seems to be a garbled rendering of 'ut putredinem derivaret, bombace vel subtilissimo panno lineo ex oblico intra cerebrum et craneum penna immisso, diligenter extrahere valeas' (214–16), with 'depeceure' apparently signifying fragments of bone rather than fracture ('fractura') as hitherto. But the next lines of O render the same Latin quite adequately. Either the garbled line in O represents a discarded first attempt at translation or, more likely, renders a reading in the translator's model which is not recorded in Sudhoff's text or apparatus.

1,7

O's 'cele part ou ele se tient' presupposes the reading '. . . segregari, illa parte ex qua tenet perforare incipias . . .' instead of Sudhoff's '. . . segregari ex illa parte, ex qua tenet, perforare incipias . . .' (220–21). O also omits 'et quot tibi competentia visa fuerint, foramina facias' (221). O's 'de spatumino' may be compared with MS M's 'spatumino' rather than the 'spatumine' of Sudhoff's text (222).

I,8 blaunche   espace

O's 'itele cure' corresponds rather inexactly with the Latin 'embroca talis' (226). The Latin has 'con libra semis axungie' (229).

I,9 om. O and partly om. Renzi

I,10 om. O and Renzi

I,11 emfluie

I,12

O's 'e il dort mauveisement' is an addition to the Latin of Sudhoff's text, but was doubtless in the source (cf. I,13), as it is in MS London, British Library, Royal 12 B III f.114v 'male dormiat'.

I,13 espace   apiert

In the first receipt for the 'medecine' (Latin 'embroca') O has 'oile d'olive', as in MS Royal B III f.115ra 'cum oleo olive', where Sudhoff's text has 'oleo communi' (285). In the second (the Latin again has 'embroca') the Latin has 'quatuor uncias de farina frumenti' (291). It is clear that O avoids the word 'embroca', which AN translates with 'embroche', 'embroke', 'embreke'.

I,14 porrreture

'Ovec la plaie' rather awkwardly renders 'ex vulnere' (300). O omits 'cutis ipsa dilaniata vel incisa dependeat' (301–02). As in I,5 above, 'erugo' corresponds to the Latin 'con rugine' (303) ('con erugine' in·MS M, Sudhoff p.164 n.10). 'A la mesure de plain pauch' renders 'sub mensura unius uncie' (306). O's 'Iceste poudre est por resouder la plaie' is an addition.

I,15 bos   mine

O agrees with MSS Fl. and J which read 'mummie uncias duas' (Sudhoff p.164 n.15) where Sudhoff prints 'scrupulos duos' (313). O's 'c'est .v. deniers pesant' is an addition, whilst 'botez l'entreit par desouz en l'overture' apparently renders Latin 'in extremitatibus stuellum inmittere' (318) and seems out of place (cf. the end of this section). In the Latin the 'pannus siccus' is 'in albugine ovi infusus' (325).

I,16 cancelet

O's 'la dure miere' renders Latin 'interiorem partem [cranei]' (329).

I,17

O's 'Nous metoms . . . au cervel' is an addition to the Latin.

I,18 marines

Neither translation renders Latin 'in contumacia capitis' (338), glossed in the Latin MSS by 'in summitate' and 'eminencia' (Sudhoff p.165 n.11).

I,19

After 'entrait es narines' O omits both 'ut per illos meatus sanies competencius educatur' (355) and 'et per illos meatus saniem effectam purgemus, nisi in cartillaginosis locis, in quibus meatus non est dimittendus, quia ipsi proprii meatus membrum expurgant'.

I,20 el   malade le maalade   les en m.

O omits 'vel maxillas vel in aliquo loco' (365) and 'subtiles' (365) and 'tortuosos' (366) applied to the 'meatus'. It also omits 'con cautela' (371) and 'unde putredo debet fluere' (381). Once again 'medicine' is substituted for 'embroca' (385). O omits 'hanc in estate . . . capitis' (385–6).

I,21 plunions

O omits 'ipsam barbulam in concavitatem canelli recipimus' (395) and 'ut si in anteriori parte percussus fuerit et per posteriorem exierit vel e converso' (404). Yet again (see I,5 and I,14 above) 'erugo' renders Latin 'con rugine' (406). The Latin 'in modum .c. [= crucis] perforamus' (407) seems to have been understood as 'circa'.

I,22

O's 'com home devez' departs from Latin 'velud vigilans' (419). Strikingly, O omits 'con rugine' (420).

I,26

O's 'fort mal' seems a strange rendering of 'maniam vel melancoliam' (516). The Latin specifies 'patiens autem in vinculis teneatur' (519).

I,25

O abbreviates, omitting the indications 'De cauteriis que fiunt ad epilensiam' (521), 'Ad epilempsiam fit ustio' (522) and 'hoc est in extremitate occipicii' (523).

III,27 del   bors

O omits 'in longum vel ex obliquo' (476) and 'Canellus quoque . . . valeat exibere' (494–96). O's 'roellez le amont e aval' renders Latin 'conquatiatur' (499). O omits 'Et si vulnus . . . quibus intromissus' (500–01; saut du même au même involving vulnus) and 'postquam vero vulnus . . . est superius' (503–04) and 'ut pannus . . . renovetur' (508–09).

THE
PRACTICA BREVIS
OF
PLATEARIUS

INTRODUCTION

The origin and history of the *Practica brevis* are wholly uncertain. Since Salvatore de Renzi collected them in print almost a century and a half ago little work has been done on the medical writings associated with Salerno[1] and his attempt to bring order to the Platearius family is optimistic, to say the least. In his history of the school of Salerno[2] he attributes the *Practica brevis* and the equally compilatory *De egritudinum curatione*[3] to Johannes Platearius II, that is the son of Johannes Platearius whose other son Matthaeus was also active as a medical writer. The family seems to have taken its name from the place Platea but its chronology is obscure. Renzi believed that the richest period of Johannes II's activity was 1120–50. It is from this period that the *Practica brevis*, with its Galenic doctrines only lightly touched by Arabic influence (via Constantine the African), most probably derives. Capparoni suggested[4] that Johannes Platearius II may have died in 1161. Whereas his brother Matthaeus may have been the author of the *Practica Archimatthaei*[5], his son of the same name is usually credited with the treatise *Circa instans* and with a set of glosses to the *Antidotarium Nicolai*.

The most accurate description of the *Practica brevis* is furnished by Paul Diepgen in his study of Walter Agilo:[6]

> Die folgende soganannte Practica brevis des Johannes Platearius II trägt einen erheblichen selbständigeren Charakter [sc. than Bartholomaeus's Introductiones et experimenta] und ist von scholastischer Form ganz frei. Nach der Einleitung ist sie auf Bitten von Freunden entstanden, denen der Autor mitteilen will, was sich ihm selbst in der Praxis am besten bewährt hat. Seine

---

[1] There is no reference to the Platearius family or to the *Practica brevis* in N.G. Siraisi, *Medieval and Early Renaissance Medicine: An Introduction to Knowledge and Practice* (Chicago / London 1990).

[2] S. de Renzi, *Storia documentata della scuola medica di Salerno*, secunda edizione (Napoli, 1857; repr. Milan, 1967), pp. 240–44.

[3] Cf. Fr. Hartmann, *Die Literatur von Früh- und HochSalerno und der Inhalt des Breslauer Codex Salernitanus* . . . diss. Borna-Leipzig, 1919 who says of the *Practica brevis* 'Die stellt ein Handbuch der inneren Medizin dar mit Ätiologie, Symptomatik und Therapie. Diese Practica bildet das Gerüst des II. Teiles der später zu erwähnenden anonymen Schrift "De egritudinum curatione" des Breslauer Codex'. There are certainly many passages common to both the *Practica* and the *De egritudinum curatione* some of which are utilised in another Anglo-Norman treatise, see T. Hunt, 'An Anglo-Norman Medical Treatise' in G. Runnalls & P.E. Bennett (eds.), *The Editor and the Text* (Edinburgh, 1991), pp.145–64.

[4] D. Capparoni, '*Magistri Salernitani nondum cogniti*'. A Contribution to the History of the Medical School of Salerno (London, 1923), p. 42.

[5] See de Renzi, *Collectio Salernitana* 5 (Napoli, 1859), pp. 350–76. The text has passages in common with the *Practica brevis*. There is a copy in MS London, B.L. Royal 12 E VIII (s.xiii) ff.160r–77r.

[6] P. Diepgen, *Gualteri Agilonis Summa medicinalis* (Leipzig, 1911) p.9.

praktischen Massnahmen sind freilich ganz und gar der Tradition entnommen. Was er angibt, findet man ausnahmslos bei den Vorgängen. Das individuelle repräsentiert nur die Auswahl, welche Platearius getroffen hat. Neben erprobten Verordnungen seines Vaters Johannes Platearius I und seines Vetters Matthaeus Platearius I, sowie anderer salernischen Meister, des Gariopontus, dessen Liber de dinamidiis er zitiert, des Bartholomaeus, Ferrarius, Petroncellus und Copho senior zählt er unter seinen Quellen das Viaticum, die Pantechne und den Liber de melancolica des Constantinus, ferner Hippokrates, Galen, Rufus, Alexander von Tralles, Solanus, den er als medicus Constantinopolitanus bezeichnet und Theophilus. Unter dem wiederholt zitierten Stephanonus ist nach Rose der Pisaner Stephanus (ca. 1127) zu verstehen. Unklar bleibt, von wem das fol. CCXIIv erwähnte Breviarium herrührt, welches dieselben Pillen wie das Viaticum gegen Husten angibt. Der jüngere Copho verfasste unter dem Titel Ars medendi, ein Kompendium der Medizin, welcher neben Hippokrates, Galen, dem Passionarius, Constantinus Africanus die Schriften seines Vaters Copho und der Zeitgenossen desselben, sowie einen unbekannten Sennonialis zitiert, welcher einen Pisaner von einer Genitalaffektion befreite.

The *Practica brevis*, which has not been edited, was first printed in Ferrara in 1488, but it is more usual to cite the Venice edition of 1497[7]. The following table shows the arrangement of contents in the 1497 print, the chapter numbers in MS London, B.L. Sloane 1124 which offers a good text of the *Practica*, and the location of the chapters in the Anglo-Norman translation (MS Cambridge, Trinity College O.1.20) where the text is disarranged.

1497 Venice edition	MS Sloane 1124	TCC O.1.20
	I. *De febribus*	
1. De effimera	i.	
2. De ethica	ii. cotidiana	
3. De flegmatica interpolata	iii. De febre interpolata	f. 55r
4. De colerica interpolata	iv. De febre tertiana	
5. De melancolica interpolata	v. De febre quartana	
6. De febribus erraticis	vi.	
7. De febre continua	vii. De sinocho	
8. De febribus emitriteis	viii. De cotidiana continua	ends f. 70r
	ix. De minori emitriteo	
	II. *De egritudinibus capitis*	
1. De frenesi	x.	f.105r
2. De litargia	xi.	
3. De catarro	xii.	
4. De apoplexia et epilepsia	xiii. De apoplexia	
5. De paralisi	xiv.	
6. De mania et melancolia	xv. De mania	
7. De dolore capitis	xvi.	
III. *De egritudinibus oculorum*	xvii. De oculorum passionibus	f.125r–130v

---

7   *Practica Jo. Serapionis dicta breviarium . . . Practica Platearii, expl. Impressum Venetus mandato et expensis nobilis viri domini Octaviani Scoti civis Modoetiensis per Bonetum Locatellum Bergomensem 17 kal. Januarias 1497.*

1497 Venice edition	MS Sloane 1124	TCC O.1.20
IV. *De egritudinibus aurium*	xviii. De passionibus aurium	ff.130v–134r

V.   *De egritudinibus narium*

1. De fluxu sanguinis	xix.	f.134r
2. De fetore narium	xx.	ends f.137r

VI.   *De egritudinibus oris*

1. De ulceribus et pustulis oris	xxi. De pustulis et ulcerationibus oris et gingive	f.137r
2. De fetore oris	xxii.	
3. De dolore dentium	xxiii.	
4. De vermibus in dentibus	(in above)	ends f.141v

VII.   *De egritudinibus spiritualium*

1. De relaxatione uvule	xxiv. Contra relaxationem uve	f.141v
2. De squinantia	xxv. De quinancia	
3. De raucedine vocis	xxvi. De raucedine	
4. De tussi et asmate	xxvii. De tussi	
	xxviii. De asmate	
5. De peripleumonia et pleuresi	xxix. De peripleumonia	
6. De empimate	xxx.	
7. De ptisi	xxxi.	
8. De emoptoica passione	xxxii.	ends f.159r

VIII.   *De egritudinibus stomachi*

1. De fastidio	xxxiii.	f.159r
2. De bolismo et appetitu corrupto	xxxiv. De bolismo	
3. De vomitu	xxxv.	
4. De singultu	xxxvi.	
5. De dolore stomachi	xxvii.	ends f.169v
	xxxviii. De dolore intestinorum	
6. De apostemate stomachi	xl.	ff. 83v–86r and 86r/171v–173v

IX.   *De egritudinibus intestinorum*

1. De dolore eorum	[see xxxviii]	ff.169v–171v
2. De lumbricis	xli.	f. 86r
3. De dissinteria	xlii.	
4. De lienteria	xliii.	
5. De diaria	xliv.	
6. De tenasmone	xlv. De tenasmon	
7. De emorroidibus	xlvi.	
8. De exitu ani	xlvii.	ends f. 99v

X.   *De egritudinibus epatis*

1. De apostemate eius	xlviii.	f. 99v
2. De ictericia	xlix.	ends f.104v
3. De idropisi	l.	ff. 75r–79v

XI. *De egritudinibus splenis*	li. De passione splenis	ff. 79v–83v

XII.   *De egritudinibus renum et vesice*

1. De diabetica passione	lii. De diabete	f.174r
2. De exitu sanguinis cum urina	liii. De minctu sanguinis	
3. De lapide in renibus et vesica	liv. De dolore renum et vesice	
4. De involuntaria emissione urine	lv. De diamne	ends f.179r

XIII.   *De egritudinibus virge et testiculorum*

1. De gonorea [De involuntaria emissione spermatis]	lvi.	f.179r

1497 Venice edition	MS Sloane 1124	TCC O.1.20
2. De immoderata erectione virge	lvii. De satiriasi	
3. De imperfectione coitus	lviii. De aproximeron	
4. De inflatione testiculorum	lix.	
5. De pustulis in virga nascentibus	lx. De virge passionibus	ends f.182v

XIV. *De egritudinibus matricis*

1. De retentione menstruorum	lxi.	f.182v
2. De fluxu menstruorum	lxii. De fluxu menstruorum nimio	
3. De suffocatione et precipitatione matricis	lxiii. De suffocatione matricis	
	lxiv. De precipitatione matricis	
4. De impedimento conceptionis	lxv.	ends f.189v
XV. *De artetica passione*	lxvi. De artetica passione	ff.189v–193r

XVI. *De egritudinibus cutaneis*

1. De lepra	lxvii.	f. 70r
2. De morfea	lxviii.	
3. De scabie	lxix.	ends f. 75r
4. De fistula	lxx.	ff.193r–194r

As can be seen, in MS London, B.L. Sloane 1124 the text of the *Practica* is divided into 68 rubricated chapters (incorrectly numbered 1–70 through accidental omission of the number 39; chapter 38 includes two chapters of the printed Latin).

The prologue of the *Practica brevis* runs as follows (text based on Sloane 1124):

> Amicum induit qui amicorum precibus condescendit. Justa igitur amicorum petitio effectui est celeriter mancipanda ne frigessere [var. fingere, frigere, fugere] videatur karitas ociosa. Unde ego Platearius, dilectissimi, vestris precibus condescendens breviter causas, signa et curas egritudinum scribere proposui, ut vestrum laborem optatus consequatur effectus et mihi vestra discretio [var. dilectio] gloriam pariat et honorem nec cuiuslibet egritudinis causas et signa et curas ad unguem prosequi me propono, tum quia verborum [var. membrorum] multiplicitas quorundam primitias perturbaret, tum quia in aliis aliorum operibus hec satis sufficienter sunt ostensa. Opus igitur propositum vobis socii morem gerens letus agredior nec de quacumque egritudine quelibet dicere sufficienter [var. sufficerem] dicturus, sed tamen ea que experimento meliora didici et quibus uti consuevi frequentius et in quibus in manu mea optatum Deus prebuit effectum.

The principal insular MSS of the *Practica brevis* are as follows:

London, B.L. Sloane 1124 (s.xiii ex) ff. 74ra–111rb ('Expliciunt cure magistri platearii') with table of chapters on f. 73vb–c. The text is divided into 68 chapters (70 in the table, but there is no no.39, and 38 conflates two chapters of the Latin print). There are red chapter headings and red initials (twice decorated in green, ff. 78ra, 84va), the opening initial and chapter heading being crudely executed by a later hand. There is some marginal annotation in a contemporary hand. The text is accurate, neatly written with frequent abbreviations. The MS represents an important collection of Salernitan texts: *Antidotarium Nicolai* (ff. 58va–71rb +

index on f. 5r); *Practica* of Bartholomaeus (ff.111va–146ra); *De passione stomachi* of
Petrus de Musaria (ff.147ra–171vb) which, despite its title, represents a comprehensive medical compendium of 77 chapters (table on f.146v); *Trotula* (ff.172ra–
178rb 'Incipiunt capitula trotule'). To these three texts, written in a single hand,
are joined a number of smaller treatises in different hands: a neat, glossed copy of
Johannitius on the *Ars parva* of Galen (ff. 5r–34r); Philaretus, *De pulsibus* (ff.
34v–36v); Hippocrates, *Aphorismi* (ff. 36v–45v) and *Prognostica* (ff. 45v–57v). At
the top of f. 4v is written 'Est medicinalis medicis data regula talis / ut dicant "da,
da" dum dicat languidus "ha, ha" ' (Walther *Proverbia* 7611) and at the bottom of
f. 71r is a note: 'Dat scrupulus [sic] numum [sic], scrupulos tres, dragma sed octo, /
uncia dat dragmas duodena dat uncia libram / Si solidum queris tres dragmas
dimidiabis, / Exagium solido differt in nomine solo' (Walther, *Initia* 4071).

London, B.L. Sloane 420 (s.xiii²) ff.126ra–144r ('Hic incipit practica magistri
Johannis platearii .s. amicum induit'). Red rubrics have been entered only on
ff.126r, 133v–135r and 142r–v. There are red initials marking each chapter. There
is very little annotation. The volume is a miscellany of various pieces mounted on
stubs. The *Practica brevis* consists of two quires of eight leaves + one leaf. Other
thirteenth-century manuscripts in the volume are Gerard of Cremona (or Montpellier), *Summa de modo medendi* (ff. 2ra–25va 'Explicit liber m. Geraldi de dandis
katarticis') and the *Modus medendi* of Archimathaeus (ff. 26ra–40rb) ('Explicit
modus medendi secundum magistrum Gerardum'). There is also a set of glosses to
the *Antidotarium Nicolai* (ff. 44ra–57va) and a text of the *De urinis* by Maurus or
Platearius ('Explicit summa platearii de urinis').

London, B.L. Sloane 371 (s.xiii²) ff. 73ra–130vb ('Explicit platearius'). An untidy,
unreliable text, the first page of which is so badly rubbed as to be largely illegible.
There are red and blue initials. A later thirteenth-century hand has provided some
of the rubrics and paragraph marks, some chapter numberings, and tables of
chapters. The vast compendium occupying ff.1*r–72v, acephalous and ending in
the seventh book, is identified in the Sloane catalogue as Constantine the
African's *De morborum cognitione et curatione*.

London, B.L. Sloane 2454 (s.xiii²) ff. 2r–25vb. There are red and green initials in
a neat and almost unannotated text. There are no rubrics or chapter numbers.
There follows (ff. 26ra–52vb) the *Practica* of Bartholomaeus ('Hic incipit Practica
magistri Bartholomei luculentissimi philosophi') and on ff. 53va–81vb ('Incipit
breviarius liber magistri Johannis Dama', 'Explicit hic breviarius') the *Breviarium*
of Johannes de Sancto Paulo, succeeded by the *De differentia animae et spiritus* by
Costa ben Luca in the translation by John of Spain (ff. 82ra–84va; 'In nomine dei
et eius auxilio incipit liber differencie inter animam et spiritum quam Constantinus Luce amico suo scriptori regis edidit et Johannes Hispaniensis ex arabico in
latinum Gumundo toletano archiepiscopo transtulit') and Constantine the African's *De natura humana* (ff. 84vb–86rb).

London, B.L. Sloane 3012 (s.xiii ex) ff. 3r–22v. The *Practica brevis* is acephalous
and lacks the ending (beginning at c.3 'De febre interpolata' and ending c.32 *De
dissinteria*). There are red rubrics, but no chapter numbers. Red and blue initials

separate the text, the sections headed 'cura' being introduced by a red initial. There is very little marginal annotation. The MS also includes an acephalous *Circa instans* (ff. 23r–68r ending with the verses 'Hactenus archanum Salerne diximus urbis / litera iam lasso pollice sistat opus'), the *Summa de modo medendi* of Gerard of Cremona (or Montpellier) (ff.107rb–122v, incomplete, see table of contents on ff.106va–107ra). At the bottom of f.102v there is a reference to 'Galterum in dosibus' i.e. Walter of Agilo.

London, B.L. Sloane 3557 (s.xiv in) ff. 5r–85v ('Explicit liber platearii'). The text begins with an extremely ornate initial A and much decoration. There are red and blue initials and paragraph marks, red rubrics (*not* provided between ff. 40v and 66v). There are chapter headings listed at the beginning of each book. The text is written in a single, large hand and there is no contemporary annotation.

London, B.L. Royal 12 B III (s.xiii[2]) ff. 67ra–88rb. This is a make-up volume, much of which dates from s.xiv. The text of the *Practica brevis* has red and blue initials, red paragraph marks and, rarely (ff. 79v–80r), green decoration (the opening green rubric is illegible). The other thirteenth-century copy in this volume is Arnald of Villanova's *Flores dietarum* (ff. 88rb–90vb), ending with a charm (f. 90vb): 'Ad restringendum sanguinem de naribus scribe istud supra frontem de sanguine: xpo. ✿ bella. ✿ poli. ✿.

London, B.L. Royal 12 B XII (s.xiii) ff. 80va–81ra. There is no opening initial or rubric. The fragment (c.1 and part of c.2) contains no rubrics, initials or decoration. It is discontinued and followed (ff. 81ra–83va) by an anatomy, sometimes attributed to Richard of Wendover, and a uroscopy '[U]rina est colamentum sanguinis ut dicit Ysaac in libro urinarum' (ff. 83vb–87rb).

Other Insular copies are:

Cambridge, University Library Dd. iii. 51 (s.xii) ff. 42ra–80ra. Red, green and ochre initials, no rubrics, coloured initials for each chapter and the sections headed *Cura*.

Cambridge, University Library Ii. vi. 39 (s.xiii[1]) ff. 5r–65r. There are alternating red and green initials and red rubrics (including each instance of *Cura*).

Cambridge, Corpus Christi College 511 (s.xiii[2]) ff.113v–134v. The text ends incomplete with *De lepra* (c.67 in the table of contents in Sloane 1124). The whole MS represents a medical compendium which includes receipts, Aegidius of Corbeil's *De urinis*, Galen's *Anatomia vivorum* and works of Ysaac Judaeus.

Cambridge, Gonville and Caius College 159 (s.xiii and xiv) pp. 51–90 (begun in a hand of s.xiii and continued by a hand of the following century). Other medical texts in the volume include the *Practica* of Bartholomaeus (pp.1–43) and the *Cirurgia* of Lanfranc (pp.111–443).

Cambridge, Gonville and Caius College 401 (s.xiii) ff. 63r–96r. A medical MS which also includes the *Circa instans*, the *Liber iste*, the *Practica* of Roger Baron and the 'Rogerina minor'.

Cambridge, Trinity College R. 14. 30 (s.xiii in) ff.119r–175v. As well as the *Practica brevis* the MS includes the *Circa instans* and the *Liber iste*.

Oxford, All Souls College 74 (s.xiii ex) ff.195r–220r.

Winchester College 26 (s.xiii/xiv) ff.181r–206v.

A continental (eastern France?) copy of the *Practica brevis* in England is:

London, Royal College of Physicians 223 [1928/223a] (s.xiii in) ff. 50va–68vb (incomplete). The opening introductory paragraph is set off. There are red rubrics and very little annotation. The text ends with *De artetica* (the last chapter of Bk XIV). It is preceded by the *Circa Instans* (ff.1r–26r) and the *Breviarium* of Johannes de Sancto Paulo (ff. 26v–50r).

There is a Middle English translation of the *Practica brevis* in MS Cambridge, University Library Dd. x. 44 (s.xv) ff.1r–100v. The prologue, written in red, runs as follows:

> Amicum induit qui justis amicorum precibus condescendit. I Plateary, for love of my dyre frendys, in þis treteys I am purposid forto shewyn the causes, cures and signes of sykenes, and not of alle sekenes, ffor why þe multitude and þe prolixite of wordys hathe distroblyd þe ferst froyte of whyse men herberfore and also al þese and many other ben openlyche inow schewid and expouned in other bokys save alone þe wyche I know best by experience and wyche I was wont most stedefastly to usyn and of wyche I hade most spede forto werk with. And ferst I begynne at the feverys.

There is a red rubric *Hic sequuntur capittula* and 68 chapters are then tabulated on ff.1ra–2vb. Each chapter begins with a red rubric *Capm. . . .* The initial letter of the text of each chapter is alternately red and blue. For each section on cures there is a red rubric *CURA*, and the same is often true for *SIGNES / SIGNA*, *CAUSE*, *DIETA*. There are some red marginal rubrics. Many initial letters in the text are splashed in red. There are some changes to the regular sequence of chapters of the Latin. The Middle English copy interverts VIII,6 and IX,1; IX,2 is displaced to f. 99r as c.67; and XVI,4 (c.58) follows XIII,5 and is followed by XVI,2 and XVI,3. The final chapter (c.68) is *Of wertis and þe cure þerof*.

Some idea of the translator's technique can be gained from the following passages:

> [f. 2v] *Capitulum primum de febre effimera*: Effimera is a fever that is gendrid of principall dystemperyng of the spiritys and it is causid of travyl or of wraythe and of meche usyng of hotte mette and drynk. And som tyme it comythe of coldnes of þe eyr and som tym of sorowe and many other. *SIGNA*. Effimera is most know[n] by (by) shewyng of the pacient and of this tempering of hette and wete that the hette of effimere in mannys body is lytill passyng kyndly hette. Noyther þer shewith no superfluitie in þe ury[n], neþer habundaunce of hym, nor of rotyng or putrefactoun and evermore þe fever is tormentyng in the begynnyng. *CURA*. 3yf the fever is causid of an hotte cause as hette of the ayre or of wraþe or of hotte mettis or drynkys and the pacient be fat, the

severall cure is þis. Take þeese herbys: malows and viol and sethe theyme in water. And then legge theym in a tobbe over wyche tobbe ley evyn treys above so þat the seke may lye nakyd above on the tubbe and receyve the breth of the water and herbys and doo lett hym swete. [f. 3r] And when he hath swete, let hym be wasche in the water and then let hym goo to reste and cover hym well with clothys. 3yf after þe bathe þe hete lest lenger, anoynte hym with oyle of violett or populeon and make hym an eyr cold be craft as by rennyng of water or cold herbys strowed in the payment of þe house. And his diete be colde. 3yf þat the pacient be [MS de] lene, than bath is not necessarye to hym save alone cold anoynting and cold diete and cold err suffysyth to hym. 3yf þat þe fever is caused of cold, as it is said afore, þan is þis þe best cure. CURA. Take the levys of laure and sepe hem in water, as it is said before, and lete þe seke receyve þe fume and let hym wasche in the water and let hym þenne goo in to a bed and rest and hele hym wele. And suche seke folk I was wont to refresche with flesche and wyne. And undyrstond þat þe fever ef-fimere, whanne it is caused of passioun or desese of þe spiritys or of what þe sowle, was wont forto be holpen with a contrarie medicine as in þis case. 3yf þe fever effimere be caused of wrathe, þan þe moost medicyne is joye and so of all oþer desese of þe soule. And take hede þe effimere be baythes mad of medycyne laxatif whole be delyverid and never over .iii. or .iiii. days it is wont forto abeyde. And 3yf it lest lenger, it wole turn in a rottyng fevere or ellis in the fever weche is callid ethica.

Capitulum secundum de ethica: Ethica is a fevere whyche is callid consuetudi-nalis, þat is, a wouyng fever, ffor why whan yt is comyng to þe body it is turnyd in habitum, þat is, in hanyng or in abydyng fever and þe *CAUSE* þerof comyth of principal schendyng of þe membris, as whan þe principal membris of þe body ben schent. And undyrstond þat þer been .3. spics after threfold humidites or mustnesse rotyd in þe body. 3yf the hete brennyng in þe membris consume or waste þe moost partie of þe fyrste humidite, þan þer is caused þe ferste spite of etik. And 3yf þe second þe second, 3yf pe thyrde þe thyrdde. SIGNA. Or þe tokyne of þe fever ethice. Summe be general and sume be special. Þe commune tokens are þese: a stedefast hete, now slow, now sharpe, and namly an hete in þe palme of the hande and at þe feete and an bryn lyke oyle in þe superfice and non resolucions. In þe seconde spice þer is a scharper hete þan in the fyrste spice, and namely more after mete þan before, and uryn oyl-lyke with manny smale resolucions.

The Latin corresponding to these passages occurs in MS Sloane 1124 as follows:

[f. 74ra] Effimera febris est illa que fit ex principali distemperantia [print = vicio] spirituum. Habet autem fieri quandoque ex calore aeris, ex labore, ex iracundia, ex calidis cibis et potibus assumptis. Fit etiam quandoque ex frigidi-tate aeris, ex tristicia et multis aliis modis ex quibus quomodo innascatur febris manifestum est. Et ideo ad presens pretermittimus ne nimia prolixitas fasti-dium pariat. Cognoscitur effimera maxime ex pacientis indicio .s. ex distem-perato calore non [f. 74rb] multum tamen naturalem excedente nec in urina aliqua indicia humoris superhabundantis vel putrefacti apparent et sine tipo semper nisi in principio affligit. CURA. Si fuerit effimera ex calida causa ut ex calore aeris vel ex ira vel ex calidis cibis et potibus et paciens sit plectoricus, generaliter curatur hoc modo: malva, herba violaria coqua[n]tur in aqua et cum aqua ponantur in tina super quam ligna sunt extensa, ut eger nudus super ea iacens superius cohopertus fumum ascendentem recipiat et sic sudet. Postquam sudaverit aquam intret, quando exierit in lecto bene cohopertus quiescat. Si adhuc post balneum calor perseveraverit, fiat inunctio per totam corporis superficiem ex oleo violarum vel populeon. Fiat etiam aer artificialiter frigidus ex [a]quarum discursione, ex frigidis herbis in pavimento domus stratis. Utatur frigida dieta et si paciens sit macilentus, non est balneum ei necessarium, sed sole frigide inunctiones et dieta frigida et aer frigidus sufficiunt. Si vero fuerit effimera ex frigida causa ut ex predictis [causis], sic utiliter curatur. Fiat balneum ex decoctione foliorum lauri et sicut prediximus eger prius recipiat fumum. Deinde descendat in aqua et exiens in lecto pannis cohoperiatur et quiescat. Huiusmodi effimeraceos carnibus et vino consuevi reficere et notandum quod effimera[m] ex anime passionibus innata contraria inducta solvere consuevi. Igitur contra tristiciam gaudium et e contrario et sic de ceteris anime passionibus. Item notandum quod effimera ex materia laxativa facta per balneum solvitur nec solet effimera ultra tercium vel quartum diem protendi quem sic transierit in ethicam vel putridam converti consuevit.

De etica [f. 74va] . . . Fit autem ethica ex principali vicio membrorum membris videlicet principaliter vicia(n)tis. Sunt autem ethice .iii. species secundum triplicem humiditatem in fontibus contentam. Si enim calor in membris accensus prime humiditatis maiorem partem consumat, fit prima species ethice, si secunde, secunda, si tercie, tercia. Febris autem ethice quedam signa sunt comunia, quedam spiritualia. Comunia hec sunt: calor continuus, modo lentus, modo acutus, calor in volis manuum et pedum, urina oleagina. Spiritualia hec sunt: in prima specie ethice calor continuus, maior ante prandium quam post, urina oleagina in superficie sine resolutionibus. In secunda specie calor est acutior quam in prima, post prandium maior quam ante, urina oleagina cum multis resolutionibus . . .

The following passage corresponds with the opening of the Anglo-Norman translation and may thus be compared (see notes for details of the Latin):

[f. 4v] *SIGNE* of a cotidian caused of a salte fleume is þe uryn aperyth ruff or subruff, meenly thyk or meenly thene, and nat blowesch, and þe mouth is saltysch and aboute nonee he entryth with a colde fevere before and after þe workyng folowith an hote. And a cotidian caused of a natural fleum or of an acetous fleum or of a vitre fleum neer hand þrei be curyd al an oon maner. *CURA.* Þe patient of þis fever, be he child or old man in a cold region and in þe wynter, þan ʒeve hym þe flech of smale byrddys and vinum limphatum, þat is wyn medlid with water, and namely at þe begynnyng be þe mater devoidid. Anf ʒyf þe patient suffre þe cotidian and be caused of a kyndeli fleum, þen ʒeve him oximel simplex and at þe mornyng with hoote water. And ʒyf þe cotidian commyth of an acetous fleume or of a vitre fleum, þan ʒeve þe patient oximel compositum [f. 5r] þat is componyd of þe rotys ffeniculi, petroselini, apii, or ells of þe rotys raphani or squilliticum. And yf þe mater be devoidid, þat shal be knowyn be þe anticipation in ferst takyng of þe tormenting of þe fever and be sesse of þe colde and augmentation of þe hete and yt be þe lesshed of þe thiknesse of þe urine. A[n]d in a cotidian caused of a naturall fleume þe digest mater shall be knowen be þe thykenesse of þe urine. In cotidian of an acetous fleum be þe moche thennesse of þe urin and in

cotidian of a vitre fleum be þe most quantite of þe urin. And in the resting
hores be he purged with benedicte scamonya put þer to or esule. Or clense
hem ellis, and þat is þe beste, with yeralog[odion] or with boylyng of fen-
kyllsede, polipodii, agarici, squinanti, interiorum coloquintide . . .

As is clear from this passage, the vernacular is still struggling to get to grips with
botanical terminology and medical terms, with the result that all but the com-
monest words are often simply left in the original Latin. The lexicological value of
the treatise is therefore limited. An incomplete copy of the Middle English translation of the *Practica brevis* is found in MS London, B.L. Sloane 14 (s.xvi) ff.1r–
24r which contains the superscript 'Liber Christopher Taylour'. It contains the
preface, albeit badly rubbed and hardly legible in places, Latin chapter titles,
boxed rubrics in the margins, decorated initials at the beginning of each chapter,
and much correction. There is no use of colour. The contents are arranged as
follows:

c.1–8 = I,1–8; c.9 = II,1; c.10 = II,2; c.11 = II,6; c.12 = II,4; c.13 = II,5;
c.14 = II,3; c.15 = II,6; c.16 = III.

The translation of the *Practica brevis* in MS Trinity College O.1.20 is written in a
writing block of 140/160mm x 90mm (19–26 lines per page), by three scribes: the
first is responsible for ff. 55r–98r, 102v–104v, 105r–194r; the second, an ugly hand
which gradually improves, ff. 98v–102r; a third hand has simply added on f.104v
(lines 11–21) a prayer to the Virgin. There are red and blue initials (not always
alternating) and sometimes red splashes on certain letters, like the *w* in *ewe* or the
abbreviation for *et* (ff. 58v–59v, 60v, 61r, 64v, 73v). The rubricator has occasionally failed to supply the initial indicated by a guide letter or the words *autre* or *cure*
(f. 78r ll.4, 8, 12; f. 81r ll.14 and 19; f. 87r l.1; f. 89v l.17; f. 93v l.8 *cure* entered by
rubricator in righthand margin; f. 99r l.9; f.130v l.4; f.136v l.22) and towards the
end (ff.183v, 184r) there are some initials that have remained uncoloured (there
are no coloured initials on ff. 88r–89r, 90r–92r). Given the extent of the text, the
scribes copied with remarkable accuracy, scribe 1 making a series of neat corrections. There are no annotations, save that a pointing finger appears in the right-
hand margins of ff. 63r, 63v, 79r, 80r, 182r, .N. [i.e. *Nota*] on ff. 95v, 97v, 99r, a red
cross at the top of f. 58v, red decoration in the righthand margin of f. 65v, and a
'signe de renvoi' in the lefthand margin of f. 72r. On ff. 80v and 98r the rubric has
been written by the scribe in the inner margin to aid the rubricator. There are
holes or tears in the parchment at ff. 70, 73, 74, 85, 86, 102, 118, 119, 120, 127,
137, 149, 172. Omission is prescribed by barring (in red f. 64v l.3 sanc *espes*; f.
122v l.5 over erasure between *vermaille* and *replecion*; f. 148r l.21 *l'asme* que *vient*,
in brown; f. 83v l.3 *queuque* chose *cause*; f. 96r l.4 *les sch seche*; f.153r l.5 *une corr
purrie*; f.160r l.17 *fesauce*; f.161v l.16 *ne soit*; f.167v l.14 *vient* qu *de soule*; f.176r
l.15 *queles* este *engendrent*; f.182r l.14 *nassent* a la fiez *goute festre*; f.188r l.10 *de de la
femme*) or by expunction (f. 60r l.6 *cele* ce qui; f. 80r l.14 *eles*; f. 81r l.7 *soient*; f.
82v l.16 *renovelen len*; f. 83r l.4 *nosi avons*; f. 83v l.14 *doitt len*; f. 90v *au soir cubau
cochier*; f. 92v l.1/2 *eepitimes*; f.104r l.6 *epithemens*; f.107r l.9 *contdescoloree*; f.108v
l.5 *cocarbons*; f.109v l.3 *face de vermaille*; f.116r l.18 *vient* sovent *grant*; f.119v l.12

contraire et *faire*; f.131v l.20 *overer*; f.133v l.1 *perre*; f.135v l.7 *mete len* en *sor*; f.153r l.6 *come* len *come len*; f.145r l.13 des *conduiz*; f.149r l.2 *ou* de *dragagant*; f.150v l.15 *apostume* vient *siet*; f.151v l.8 *doigne len* et *ou le face*; f.165v l.22 *estomac* et *leves*; f.175v l.16/17 *olibannum*; f.176v l.17 *fiez* e *aucune gravele*; f.178r l.1 *nescessaires*; f.178 l.3 *seneschons* de *philipendule*; f.181v l.16/17 *vascel* de de *voirre*; f.188r l.8 *la male* de *qualite*) or erasure (f. 61v l.8 *estu*(er)*uer*, f. 66r l.18 (bo)*les*, f. 73v ll.2–3 *in..piginem*; f. 76r l.10 *et . moistesce*; f. 77r l.20 *l.doit*; f. 93r l.20 *cause.ce conoist*; f. 97r l.9 *ydropisie . tisicle*; f.139v l.5 *pa. diz houres*; f.143r l.3 *.quinancia*; f.143r l.14 *si.ocist*; f.150v l.7 *mes.len*; f.150v l.18 *amt.dous*; f.169r l.16 *flux men* . . . . . . [*struel* erased though needed]; f.189v l.22 *tendus* et.. *et par la grant chalor*; f.190r l.17 a red rubric has been erased before *Cure si ce avient*). Insertions are indicated by super-script additions and insertion signs (f. 63v *unces .ii. de reubarbre*; f. 64r l.17 *de* la *porreture*; f. 67v l.6 *orine*; f. 68r l.21 *decoction*; f. 69v l.14 *de* written above ex-puncted *a* of *avant*; f. 75v l.5 *e* of *le* written above expuncted *a*; f. 84r l.17 *par* la *fevre*; f. 95v l.3 *corge*; f.102v l.20 *jaune*; f.103v l.5 *dogne* l'en *chescun*; f.110v l.16 *diaolibanum*; f.111v l.8 *superfluite* et de *destresse*; f.115r l.22 *sans jarse*; f.116r 18 *grant dissolucion*; f.117r l.4 *matere*; f.117v l.17 *par le devant*; f.119r l.19 *presque tot ades*; f.129r l.9 *purge*; f.134v l.8 *froidure demeine*; f.135r l.7 *seigner*; f.143r l.4 *parra*; f.149r l.9 *doigne* len *quatre*; f.148v l.18 *tant que*; f.152v l.6 *ovesques .i. dolor*; f.152v l.16 *parties*; f.155v l.8 *sont de ce*; f.159v l.13 *vient de* la *raison*; f.160r l.19 *quant abhominacion*; f.169v l.18 *bouel*; f.174v *violat* et [over expuncted *ou*] *rosat*; f.174v l.16 *grant engin*; f.177v l.6 *les doit* om *porueir*; f.179r l.3 *jus de mente*; f.184v l.11 *come* ce *avient*; f.192r l.15 *apres les gresses*) . A blank space was left after *cic* [*ruge* on f.104r l.7, but the word was never completed. There are also blank spaces on f.118r l.12 between *des* and *souse* and l.13 between *semence* and *del chou*, on f.118v l.13 between *et* and *si vienent*, and f.120r l.4 between *le* and *kar* and l.14 between *ce* and *lapidis*. There are a few cases of interversion marks (f. 67v l.7 *entense mult*; f.123v l.12 *deriere en la*); f.164v l.3 *choses ices*; f.168v l.22 *len le cire*; f.194r l.3 *une tente ovesques*). Close up signs (=) are found on f.129r l.23.

The *Practica brevis* is divided into 16 books, which the Anglo-Norman trans-lation refers to as *traitiés*, in turn subdivided into chapters, *chapitres / capitles*. Each chapter is systematically arranged according to a threefold division: *causa* (aetio-logy), *signa* (symptomatology), *cura* (therapy). This is reflected in the numerous cross-references contained in the text:

(71) Les causes, les signes, les cures quere l'en en lor propres chapitres.

(112) Les signes de dolor qui vient de apostume [et] par compassion de l'opila-tion del col de la vessie et les causes et les cures troverez vus en lor propres chapitles.

(180) Les signes, les causes, les cures de la retencion de flux de femme men-struel querez et encerchiez en lor propres chapitres.

A frequently found formula is 'Les causes sont a distincter par les signes'. The numbering of the text divisions in the edition below follows this threefold division of each chapter irrespective of the discrepancies in the length of each passage.

Apart from the displacement of folios in the exemplar which has produced a

considerable disruption of the ordering of the books and chapters and led to Book
VIII, c.6 (105–110) being copied twice (see Notes to 108–110), the translation
follows the original closely in all respects. The frequent cross-references, state-
ments in the first person (see 26, 32, 38, 42, 43, 49, 61, 67, 70, 75, 78, 79, 85, 86,
88, 99, 104, 113, 143, 165, 168, 179), anecdotes (37, 49, 67, 78, 85, 113, 143),
addresses to the reader (37, 78, 88, 130) and allusions to authorities (Galen 8, 20,
29, 30, 119; Hippocrates 30, 65, 79, 87, 91, 107, 124, 143, 154, 162; Constantine
35, [the 'Viatique'] 75, [the 'Panteigne'] 111, 119; Stephen [? Stephanus pisanus]
114, 116, 119, 162; Alexander [de Tralles] 8; 'les auctors' 18; 'li fous mire' 32; 'un
sage mire de Salerne' [Solanus constantinopolitanus medicus] 55; 'la doctrine de
alexandrinis' 155; 'les femmes de Salerne' 170, 173; 'ceus de Salerne' 173; the
'Four Masters' 185) all stem from the Latin and some of them may even derive
from Platearius's own sources. The constant copying and excerpting of medical
writings over centuries makes the identification of sources essential if we are to
avoid the blunder of seeing the reflection of contemporary conditions in passages
which are in fact verbatim repetitions of much earlier material.

The *Practica brevis* has therefore been accurately and comprehensively
translated, with only one original addition: the copying by a third scribe of a
prayer to the Virgin on f.104v. The Anglo-Norman character of the copy at this
point is unmistakable. The second scribe (ff. 98v–102r) displays a high density
of insular features:

velarisation of *ā*:	devaunt, blaunc, avaunt, dissaunttere. abundaunz, pesauntume, esculurgaunt etc.
widespread use of *u* for *o*:	retenciun, cumencement, umurs, culur, cotun, amentaciun etc.
use of *i* to represent 'mute *e*':	vainis, chosis, estupis, ovecis, curis, depecint, grevint, sustenint etc.
reduction of diphthongs:	plue
parasitic *-e*:	isire, porire, line, fenoile, del cele etc.
use of *w*:	wos wolés, womist, dewaunt
use of *-ʒ* for *ce*:	semenz, grevanz, sustanz
use of *h*:	heles [= eles], hof, he [= e], horge, jhaune, hi mette, athuche, esthancher, ethir
-er/ -ir for *-re*:	il demutir, autir, ethir, fever, fevir, metter, pudir, enplatir, cunutir cf. tribel for trible
use of *ai* for *ei*:	dait, sei, faie, fraide, trais

The sort of orthography exemplified in 'sce est asaveire de le ardur et de la
ebulliciun de sanc' (138) veils completely the linguistic properties of the scribe's
exemplar. However, the first scribe, who is responsible for the greater part of the
copy, exhibits a much lower density of Anglo-Norman features. For example,
there is only a handful of examples of velarised *ā* : saunz dolor, plaunteine, les
devaunt dites leus, and a fairly low incidence of *u* for *o*. The few examples of
unpalatalised *ca-* (capiau, capitles, caudere, cardons de mer, calemel, caus) would
not, of course, point unequivocally to Anglo-Norman. For much of the time the
text could easily represent a lightly modified Franco-Picard scripta. Thus the
origins of the translation are in doubt. There are no clear lexical pointers either to
England or (as with *bibuef* in the fragmentary translation of Roger Frugard's

Chirurgia) N.E. France. There is one noteworthy syntactical feature, namely the characteristically insular positioning of article and adjective involving *meime*:

en meime la maniere (12)
meime la cause (42)
de meime le comencement (42)
de meime l'ewe (70)
en meime le lit (78)
en trible meime l'erbe (149)
le color de meime le sanc (151) etc.

This is a consistent feature of the syntax, but it could, of course, be attributed simply to the scribe. It cannot, therefore, be asserted with confidence that the translation which survives in what is certainly an Anglo-Norman copy itself originated in England. The absence of the evidence furnished by rhymes coupled with the restricted and repetitious nature of the content deprives us of any convincing antidote to such agnosticism.

Readers of the text which follows may need to be reminded of some of the liberties taken by insular copyists with respect to the standard grammar of continental Old French:

1. Arbitrary observation of grammatical concord (complete breakdown of the two-case declension system, arbitrary use of -*s*):
   Le sanc qui en istra ert petit et troublees; tempre l'en psilium tant que ele soit gleuuse; de la decoctions elleborus; des choses resumptifs et confortatives; quant les boels sont estopees; li ventes est dures; oignemenz froides; veus plaies sursanees.

2. Uncertainty of gender owing in part to use of inorganic -*e* and -*s*:
   le inflation; li enfleure; aucune estrument; li foies; la membre; le bouche; la comencement; Galiene.

3. Frequent appearance of *que* for *qui* and *qui* for *que* (including: *fors qui, mes qui, aprés qui*).

4. Use of *le* for dative *li*:
   le doigne l'en la coleure; ja soit que le semble que la maladie li soit alegié.

5. Occasional use of spelling -*ant* / -*ont* for -*ent*:
   mordant (pres. 6 of mordre), tordont.

6. Use of *se* for *si* (< sic) and *ce* for *se* (< si).

A final linguistic point that needs to be made concerns the mixing of French and Latin (not English!). Unlike the translator of Frugard's *Chirurgia*, the translator of the *Practica brevis*, when maintaining Latin words (especially plant names) in his text, has sought to adapt them morphologically to the syntax. In some cases, notably in first declension feminine nouns when used in the genitive (e.g. *artemisie*), it is not always possible to determine whether the form is vernacular (and uninflected) or Latin (inflected). This must be borne in mind when using the glossary. The following examples will demonstrate the variety of bilingual constructions:

la poudre amidi et penidii; les somerones lentisci; la decoction ligni aloes ou de mastic; si loi doigne auream ou mitridate ou ygiam; del jus celsi; avec vin decoctionis olibani; semence bombacis; semence de bombacis; mirre, storacis calamite, galbani, castorei, piperis owel peis sis onces; la ferine fenugreci; la decoction de galles, de roses, simphiti; la poudre mummie, boli, simphiti; del fruit juniperii; des escorchis capparis; la racine rubee la menor.

At the beginning of a number of chapters (II,1; II,4; IX,3; IX,4) etymological explanations in Latin of key terms have been incorporated in the text.

The edition which follows aims, in the absence of any edition of the Latin original, to convey the sense of the text, not by restricting comparison to the early printed version of the Latin, but by drawing on the manuscript tradition, particularly the form of the text represented by MS London, B.L. Sloane 1124 which stands in a close relationship to the translation. In editions of scientific texts there is always the problem of whether to correct in the interests of scientific accuracy or in conformity with the source from which the text derives. The notes are designed to elucidate all such problematic instances as well as to record the translator's treatment of his sources.

TEXT

[BOOK I *De febribus*]

[f. 55r] [I,3 *De febribus interpolatis et primo de flegmatica*] [1] [. . . sunt] les signes iteles: l'urine [est] roge ou sorroge et si apiert moinement tenve ou moinement espoisse, et a om la boche salee, et asaut iceste fevre entor l'ore de none oveques une froidure avant et une chalor aprés. [2] *Cure. De cotidiane faite de fleume naturale ou de fleume acetouse ou de fleume* [f. 55v] *verrine, la cure de ces .iii. est tote une.* A touz caus qui ont tel maniere de fievre, come as juevenes et as viauz et as femes en froide region ou en yvernel tens, donons nos la char de petiz oisiaus et vin ovec la moitié de ewe, et defisons la materie des le comencement. Por cotidiane de fleume naturele donons nos oximel simple oveques ewe chaude au matin. En cotidiane de fleume verrine ou de fleume acetouse done om oximel composte, qui est [fait] de racines de fenoil, de perresil, d'ache; [ou] de raphe ou de squille. Et come la matire est defite, ce* quenoist om par anticipacion de [l']accés et par froidure remise et par l'aumentacion de la chalor de la fevre et par la remission de l'espoisce de l'orine. *En cotidiane de fleume naturale conoist om come la matire est defite par l'espoissece de l'orine. En la cotidiane de fleume acetouse conoist om co[me] la matire est defite par la grant extenuation de l'orine et par l'aumentacion de lui.* En cotidiane de fleume verrine donons nos al [f. 56r] huitime jor choses purgatives et les purjons communement as ores de repos aveques benoite aguisié d'escamonee ou d'eisle, qui miauz vaut, ou de ieralogodion ou de la decoction de semence de fenoil, polipodii, agarici, squinanti et interiorum coloquintide. Et si la fevre cotidiane est de fleume sause, por la melancolie bone choche est c'om mete oveques les devant dites choses sené, epithimi* [et] unce .i. de la poudre de mirobalans indes. Si la fevre ne cesse atant, si le resporgiez derechief .ii. foiz ou .iii., mais que vos metez* covenable espace entre dous. Et si fevre ne cesse pas oncore, si le purgiez en tiel maniere. Pernez le jus de la moiene escorce de seu et le jus des sumeçons des ebles autant com .i. unce, castorei cum .iii., et de poudre de esule unce .i., et les boilliez en une pome de coloquintida ou en ciclamine. Et metez ovec le jus de fenoil ou un poi d'ewe, s'il i a trop poi des devan[t] dites jus. Et esporgiez le malade de ceste* decoction. Et si fevre dure oncore, si li donez musam [f. 56v] eneam devant l'ore de l'accession oveques ewe chaude. Ou om li done musam ovec mitridato aprés le quarte accession. Mes a caus qui ont cotidiane de fleume douce ou de fleume sause si doit om doner tenve diete. Por defire la matire lor doingne om scirop acetouse en esté. Et a caus qui ont cotidiane de fleume douce doit on doner la decoction de violetes et de prunes. Et come la cotidiane vient de sause fleume, si done om scirop aceteus avec ewe chaude et en yver done om oximel. Et com la matere iert defite, la quel chose om conoist par les devant dites signes et par l'orine qui iert plus tenve que devant; en la cotidiane de* fleume douce, par la moiene espesseté de

l'orine. En la cotidiane de fleume sause le purjons nos comunement en l'ore de
repos de oximel, de benoite ou de electuaire froide. Caus qui ont cotidiane de
fleume douce porjons nos especiaument de ceste decoction: boille l'en violete,
prunes, polipodie en ewe et le [f. 57r] cole l'en et dessoille l'en cassiafistula en la
coleure .ii. unces, mauve .i. unce, de la poudre de mirobalans indes .i. unce ou de
kebles, et doigne* [l'en] au malade. A caus qui ont cotidiane de fleume sause si
faites ceste decoction: quisiez violete, prunes, polipodie en ewe et com ele ert
colee, si metez enz .i. unce de la poudre de mirobalans citrins et .i. autre de kebles
et donez au malade as ores de repos. Et si la fievre ne cesse en tel maniere, si li
donez devant l'ore de l'action rubeam trociscatam avec musa enea avec ewe
chaude. Notez que seignié siaut fere grant bien a caus qui ont cotidiane de chaude
chose et en chaude region et en chaut tens, et en home joene, non pas por la
cotidiane, mais por contregarder de chaoir en fievre continue.

[I,4 *De colerica interpolata*] [3] De tierceine entrepolaté faite de colre porrie dehors
les veines [qui] neporquant n'est pas coillie a apostume. Des tierceines l'une si est
[de] colre naturale et l'autre de colre innaturale, come de colre citrine ou de
vitelline. [4] De tierceine faite de colre [f. 57v] naturale si sont les signes iteles:
qu'ele asaut de tierz jor en tierz jor entor hore de tierce, primierement avec froit et
aprés avec chaut, et sent om une dolour ou front* et a om la boche amere et soif
grant et tonissement des oreilles et pert om le dormir, l'urine apert roge ou sorroge
et tenve, et si puet avoir .xxiiii. ores au plus en soverain travail et autres .xxiiii. en
verai repos. Mais notez que selonc la diverseté dou leu ou la matire siet si sont les
signes diverses. Car si la matire est en la boche de l'estomac, si est la dolour ou
front plus grant et la soif ensement avec une aspreté de la langue et une sechece en
la gorge et a om talent de vonchier et l'orine mains coloree. Mais come la matire
de la fievre est es boiaus, la dolor dou front n'est pas si grant ne la soif ne la volanté
de vonchier. Mais si la matire siet as soverains boiaus, la dolour iert entor le
numbril. Si la matire siet plus bas, la dolour iert plus bas et les egestions coleriques,
et [si plus haut], l'orine mains coloree. Mais come la matire siet ou foie ou el [f.
58r] fiel, si iert l'urine plus coloree ovec une espume jaune. Si la fevre tierceine
vient de colre citrine ou de vitelline, si assaut de tierz jor en tierz jor, primierement
oveques froidure et aprés oveques chalor lente, entre l'ore de colre et de fleume,
l'urine est citrine moinement tenve, mais plus se trait a tenveté que a espoisseté se
la fevre est de colre citrine. Mais si ele est de colre vitelline, l'urine si est subcitrine
moinement tenve. Et tex maniere de fievres ne gardent pas certaines hores de
l'accession, car a la fie si asaillent plus tost et a la fie si asaillent plus tart. Si sont o
totes les devant dites signes, sicome dolour dou front et des autres, mais plus sunt
remisses que de colre naturale. [5] Encore derechief de fievres terceines. L'une est
simple et l'autre composte. Le simple si est faite de une matire [porrie] en .i. leu
tant solement. La composte ou la doble tierceine si [est] faite de doble colre porrie
en divers leus. [6] De la quele les signes sont iteles: ele asaut chascun jor, primierement ovec froit et aprés ovec chaut, mais de tierz jor en tierz jor, si asaut [f. 58v]
plus grief et en divers hores, l'orine ert roge ou susroge, moinement tenve [ou]
espesse, par desus ombreuse*. [7] Cure a ceus qui travaillent de tierceine simple de

colre naturale et qui sont colerique et chauz et en esté tens et en chaude region. Si
doit om doner tenve diete. As enfanz et as vielles genz et as femes en ivernal tens
et en froide region done om la char de petiz oisiaus* et vin ovec la moitié d'ewe
[en jor interpolaté]. Mais ou jor de l'accion lor doigne om tenve diete. Et face om
fomentacions de l'ewe et de la decoction de mauves, de violete, de mirre, de roses
et li muelle om le front et les temples de ceste devant dite ewe ou de ewe chaude
solement. Por la soif doigne l'en l'ewe de la decoction de dragagant et li face l'en
tenir* le dragagant meimes tempré en ewe desus la langue. Et por defire la matire li
done l'en scirop acetous oveques ewe chaude ou zucre oveques ewe chaude et vin
egre ou* le jus de pomes grenates acetoses oveques ewe chaude. Et aprés la tierce
accession si doigne l'en trife sarrazine oveques l'ewe de la de[f. 59r]coction de
violetes et de prunes. Et come la matire est defite, la quel chose l'en conoist par
anticipation de l'accession et par la remisseté de froidure et par l'aumentacion de
la chalor et par l'afliction plus grant et par l'orine plus espesse qu'ele ne siaut, si le
purge l'en lors de oximel laxatif ou de oximel squillitique ou de electuaire froide ou
de ceste decoction de violete, de prunes, citruli, melon, cucumbre et cucurbite, et
les boille l'en en ewe et cole [l'en] et mette om [en] la coleure cassiafistula .ii.
unces et tamarind .ii. unces et .ii. unces de mirobalans citrins et si vaut plus se om
i met reubarber. Et si la tierceine est doble, si le face l'en en meisme la maniere fors
que om doit user plus tenve diete en la doble que en la simple et doit om seignier
plus soventes foiz. Et en la simple et en la doble si la matire est en la boche de
l'estomac et li malades ait mult talent de vonchier, si le face om vonchier d'ewe
froide ou d'ewe chaude et li doigne l'en ensemble oximel ou vomite scarpelle ou
patriarcie. Quant vos l'avroiz purgié .iii. foiz ou .iiii., [f. 59v] tant en la simple com
en la doble, si la matire est en la boche dou stomac et la fevre dure oncore, si donez
robeam trociscatam ovec ewe chaude devant l'ore de l'accession. La fievre qui
vient de colre citrine ou de vitelline doit om garir autresi come cotidiane de
sausefleme.

[I,5 *De melancolia interpolata extra vasa*] [8] De quartaine enterpolaté veraie qui
vient de melancolie porrie dehors les veines et qui n'est pas cuillie en apostume.
Des quartaines l'une est faite de melancolie naturale et l'autre de melancolie
innaturale et si vient de fleume acetouse et de fleume verrine et de fleume sause et
de sanc ars, sicome Galien le tesmoing et Alixandres. [9] Icés sont les signes de
quartaine qui est faite de melancolie naturale: qu'ele assaut de quart jor en quart, si
asaut primierement ovecques une froidure et aprés une lente chalor, et si a .xxiiii.
hores en soverain travail et .xlviii. en verai repos. Et si ele est de melancolie
naturale, si asaut de l'hore de none en aval et asaut en certaines hores et en certain
tens. L'orine apert le primier jor de l'[f. 60r]accion citrine ou sorruge. Es jorz
entrepolaté[s] si apiert l'urine palle ou sorpalle, jaune ou blanche, et tenve. Si la
matire est en l'estomac, si a om boce aigre. De quartaine bastarde: si est quartaine
bastarde cele qui est faite d'autres humors que de melancolie naturale, si asaillent
de quart jor en quart, mais ne gardent pas certaines hores ne certain tens de
assaillir, car ore asaillent plus tost et ore plus tart. En quartaine de fleume acetose
ou de verrine si apert l'urine autretele com en melancolie naturele, mais tant i a

qu'en l'urine de quartaine de fleume verrine apert .i. moncel d'umors oveques une muscillaginité. En la quartaine de melancolie innaturale, ou de fleume sause, ou de sanc ars, si apiert l'urine roge ou sorroge le jor aprés le accession. Mais es autres si apiert citrine ou subcitrine. [10] Quartaine de melancolie naturale* ou de fleume acetouse ou de fleume verrine. *Cure*. La quartaine si a tel cure que l'en li [f. 60v] done es jorz entrepolatés tel diete com il a acostumee et se gart de viandes melancolienes, come de chous et de char de buef et de chievre et de semblables choses. Mais le jor de l'action li doit l'en doner poi a mangier. Si l'en li done rien, si li doit om doner .iiii. hores ou [.v.] devant l'accession. Et des le comencement doit l'en defire la matire de oximel composte de racines de ache, de fenoil et de perresil, ou de oximel fait de racine de rafle ou de oximel squillitique que l'en fait en tel maniere. Trenche l'en squilla parmi et giete l'en hors ce qui est dedenz et ce qui est dehors, et ce qui est en mieleu mete l'en temprier en vin aigre par .ii. jorz et mete l'en o totes les racines diuretiques, si vaudra miauz. Et aprés les quise l'en tant que la moitié de l'aisil soit degastee et giete l'en hors la squille et face l'en oximel de .ii. parties de l'aisil et la tierce de miel et le quise om tant qu'il soit espés. Ou l'en face .i. oximel tel. Traie l'en hors de la terre .iii. racines ou .iiii. de raphano et face l'en enz ou plus basses parties de aux les racines de ellebro blanc [f. 61r] et fiche l'en derechief les racines en terre et les arouse l'en d'ewe, que les racines preignent de la terre lor acostumee norreture. Et les laisse l'en ensi en terre par .xii. jorz ou par .xiii. ou par plus. Et aprés les traie l'en hors et gite l'om ellebor hors et quise l'en les autres en aisil et mete l'en mel o tot et en face l'en oximel. Mais itel oximel ne doit l'en pas doner devant .vii. accions. Come la matire est defite, et ce puet om conoistre par les devant dites signes, si doit om purgier le malade de melancolie natural de diacené aguisié de scamonee le jor devant que il doit avoir son accion, ou de ceste decoction: preigne l'en la semence de fenoil, d'ache et de perresil, polipodie, thimi, epithimi et sené et les boille l'en en ewe et en la partie de la coleure mete l'en de la coleure de mirobalans indes .ii. unces et pierre lazule et pierre armenique selonc la doctrine que nos dirons aprés. Si la quartaine est de fleume acetouse, si le purge l'en de la medicine dont om purge fleume et melan-colie. Et si ele est de fleume verrine, si [f. 61v] le purge l'en oveques la decoction de semence de fenoil, polipodie, agarique, squinanci, interiorum coloquintide et sené. Si la fievre ne cesse atant, si le repurge l'en .iii. foiz ou .iiii. derechief, mais qu'il i ait raisnable espace entre les espurgacions. Et si la fievre dure oncore, si li doigne l'en devant l'ore de l'accés adrianum ou mitridatum ou tiriacam* oveques ewe chaude. Ou le face l'en estuver en tel maniere. Preigne l'en pulegium, ca-lamentum, origanum, folia lauri et les quise l'en en ewe et face l'en le malade seoir sor la cuve bien covert de dras et reçoivre la fumee. Et si fievre dure oncore aprés, si li donez* devant l'ore de l'accession oille pulegine ou oile juniperine unces* .iii. oveques mel. Ou l'en done la poudre de flame sechee et arse sor une tiule unce* .i. avec le jus [de] betonique ou la poudre [d']aristologie raonde avecques vin chaut. [11] Des signes de la quartaine bastarde; ja soit ice que la fievre soit de melancolie innaturale ou de sausefleume ou de sanc ars, [que] aient unes signes [f. 62r] co-munes oveques les devant dites fievres quartaines bastardes en* ce qu'il asaillent a la fie plus tost et a la fie plus tart, si ont il neporcant unes signes especiaus. Car si la quartaine est de melancolie [in]naturale, l'orine est coloree et tenve. Et si la quartaine est de sanc ars, si est plus coloree oncore et plus espesse et a l'en la boche douce. Et s'ele est de fleume sause, si est l'orine roge ou souzroge et moinement espesse, si a l'en la boche salee et li manjut trestot le cors. Et icaus quartaines avienent relement sanz eschaufement dou foie. [12] [Cure] Primierement le doit om ordener sa diete. En jors entrepolatés li porrez vos doner la char de petiz oisiaus et vin tempré, mais ou jor de l'accion lor doit om doner poi de viande ou nule. Et si om lor done nule, si lor doit om doner .iiii. hores ou .v. devant l'accession sanz vin et sanz char. Des le comoincement lor doigne l'en oximel simple a defire la matire ou scirop acetous oveques l'ewe de la decoction de semence de fenoil. Et com la matire est defite, laquel chose l'en [f. 62v] puet conoistre par les devant dites signes. Si purjons le malade de melancolie [in]naturale de ceste decoction: preigne l'en violete et prunes, sené, thimi, epithimi, et les semences des herbes diuretiques et les mete l'en boillir en ewe. Et en cele coleure fonde l'en .i. unce de mirobalans indes et .i. autre unce de mirobalans citrins et doigne l'en tant a ces com a caus qui travaillent de sanc ars. Pierre lazule et pierre armenique doit l'en afaitier en tel maniere. Trible l'en de pierre lazule .iii. unces soutilment et aprés mete l'en ewe sore et le move l'en bien et le laisse l'en raseoir. Et giete l'en hors cel ewe et mete l'en autre sore. Et ce face l'en bien .xx. foiz. Signe com ele est assez lavee: sicom l'ewe s'en ist clere, poi tainte ou noient, ensi le leve l'en por ce qu'ele ne blece par sa grant sechece les boiaus. [Preigne l'en] pierre armenique* .ii. drames et le leve l'en en meime la maniere .iii. foiz tant solement ou .iiii. et melle l'en icés .ii., mais ne les mete l'en pas en la decoction, mais aprés .iiii. seles les done l'en aveques une cuillier par soi ou oveques scirop ou oveques [f. 63r] mel, que li malades le puist miauz reçoivre. Mais com la quartaine est de sanc ars, si devez purgier le malade oveques la decoction de prunes, de violetes, de la semence citrol, de melons, de coccumbres et de cucurbite. Et mete l'en en la coleure .ii. unces de cassiafistula et .i. de manna et .i. de mirobalans citrins. Mais come la quartaine vient de fleume sause, [. . .] mais tant i a que l'en doit doner en ceste plus ague medicine. Et si la fievre ne cesse pas aprés iteus espurgemenz, restreez par covenable espace entre deus, si done om rubeam sole oveques ewe chaude et nules autres choses devant l'ore de l'accession. Mais come la quartaine est de melancolie [in]naturale ou de sausefleume ou de sanc adusté, si done l'en rubeam ovec musa enea oveques ewe chaude. Itel maniere de quartaine solaient oncore fere inflacion de l'esplene et opilacion et chaoir en ydropisie par les queaus signes nos conoissons come par les piez enfler et l'essplen. Nos contregardons com par doner lor scirop de diaquilon que [f. 63v] l'en fait en tel maniere: Preigne l'en le jus de fenoil, d'ache, de perresil, des racines speragi* et brusci et de scariolis et melle l'en ensemble. Et mete l'en zucre et face l'en scirop. En une partie de cestui scirop mete l'en reubarbre en tel maniere et tel proporcion: s'il i a une livre de scirop, triblez unces .ii. de reubarbre et le mete l'en temprer en ewe tot une nuit et melle l'en cele ewe oveques le scirop et donez icestui scirop por laschier; et de l'autre partie sanz reubarbre done l'en por ovrir, por dessoudre et por varier et por purgier totes eures come li estomac est voiz.

[I,6 *De febribus erraticis*] [13] Fievres erratique[s] si sont celes qui ne vienent ne ne departent en certain hore n'en certain tens. Si vienent iteus fievres de divers humors qui porrissent dehors les veines, sicome de colre, de fleume et de melancolie. Et por la multiplicacion des choses si avient la confusion des actions et des remissions. [14] *Cure a caus qui travaillent de fievre erratique*. Caus qui travaillent de fievre erratique devons nos dieter ausi come en quartaine, c'est asaver de choses digestives*. Mais tant i a que om [f. 64r] les doit purgier de medicine qui ait vertu de purgier de divers humors, c'est asaver de colre, de fleume, de melancolie, mais melancolie principalment. Doigne l'en en icés choses opiates compostes.

[I,7 *De febre continua*] [15] De fievre continue(e). Il avient a la fie que li sans porrist es veines et ameine une [fievre] continue que om apele sinoque. A la fie si ne porrist pas li sans, ainz sorabunde et eschaufe, et en issent unes fumositez chaudes et destemprees et destemprent l'espirit de vie ou cuer et engendrent une fievre qui est apelee sinocha inflative. A la fie colre porrist es soutilles veines de l'estomac et del poumon et dou foie et dou cuer et fait une fievre que om apele causon. Et a la fie colre porrist es* autres veines et fait une tierceine continue. A la fie li sans et la colre porrissent ensemble es veines et si la greignor partie de la porreture est de sanc, si fait une fievre c'om apele sinochides. Si la greignor partie est de colre, si est la fievre apelee causonides. [16] Selonc les diversetez des choses si sont les signes diverses. Les signes sinochi sont iteles: [f. 64v] l'en sent une dolor ou front et as temples mult tres ague et a soif grant et la boche douce, l'orine roge ou souzroge et espés. [. . .] sanz nule bleuissure, et autres comme les euz fors dou chief et roges et les veines pleines es iauz et par tot le cors et la face roge et trestot le cors, et les membres spirituels mult estroiz et pleines de la fumosité qui ist dou sanc. Mais en causon l'urine apiert roge ou souzroge et tenve et noire et umbrouse par desus et est la dolor ou front et es temples si grant qu'il semble c'om ait les temples et les iauz batuz de maçues, la color en la face et ou cors si est roges et .i. pou jaunes, et si est la soif grant, et si veille l'en tot adés, et si a l'en langue aspre et arse et compression grant ou ventrail de colre qui i habunde en la soe complexion, et a l'en menoison et vonche l'en choses coleriques a la fie. En la tierceine continue si est l'afliction continuele, mes plus est grant de tierz jor en tierz jor sanz froidure. En sinochide est [f. 65r] l'orine roge ou susroge et moinement espesse. En causonide si est l'orine roge ou susroge et moinement tenve. [17] *Cure a caus qui travaillent de sinoque ou de causon ou de terceine continue ou de sinoca ou de causonide ou de sinochide*. Si li malades est d'age et de force, le face l'en seignier dedenz le quart jor qu'il est acouriez ou qu'il a sentu la maladie*. En sinoque ou en sinoca le seigne l'en de l'un e de l'autre braz tant que il se pasme. Et come il est seigniez, si li arouse l'en sa chere d'ewe rose ou d'ewe froide et li doigne l'en maintenant a boivre sirop violat oveques ewe froide. Et si li face l'en l'air et la meson la ou il gist froiz par art de la decorse d'ewe et de roses et de foilles de sauz. Ou l'en preigne une escuele et le perce om menuement ou fonz et l'emple om d'ewe, si [que] l'ewe degote parmi les pertuis. Et mete l'en .i. autre veissel desus qui la reçoive, si que l'une ewe degote sor l'autre et refroide l'air en tel maniere. Ou l'en junche la maison de froides herbes, de roses, de foilles de sauz, [f. 65v] de mente, de mirte* et des autres froides herbes. La diete soit itele: mie de pain .iii. foiz lavé en ewe, prunes quites et crues, le jus d'orge quit et sa substance gieté, et portulaques quites. Et si l'en puet avoir citrueles*, si li done l'en la moele. Si cucurbites avez, si li done l'en le jus. Et choses froides li doigne l'en a boivre come la decoction de violetes et de prunes.

As eures de faus repos* [. . .]. Et lor doigne l'en des le comencement au matin sirop
acetous oveques l'ewe de la decoction de violetes et de prunes entor midi. Et au
soir et de nuiz neis li done l'en de cestui syrop: boille l'en en ewe violetes, prunes,
semence de citrol, melons, cucumbres, cucurbite, sandali albi et rubei, semence de
letues, berberis*, nenufar* et les cole l'en. Et mete zucre o tot et en face l'en syrop.
Ou envolupe [l'en] cucurbita en paste et le quise om en .i. for. Et aprés preigne
[l'en] hors l'ewe et en face om syrop, sicome en autre ewe. Por l'aspresce de la
langue mete l'en sillium en .i. drap linge et mete l'en .i. baston dedenz, si que l'un
chief pierge par dehors. Et le frote l'en fort [f. 66r] tant qu'ele rende une musculagi-
nité. Et de celui drap li moille l'en primierement la langue. Et aprés le rae l'en o .i.
cotel de fust et la frote l'en de aucunes foilles aprés. Et ce face l'en sovent. Et si vos
n'avez sillium, si face l'en ce meimes de la semence de pomes de[s] bos ou de la
semence de lin [. . .] en ewe tiede. Et li face l'en tenir sillium desuz la langue. Et
por estanchier la soif derechief mete [l'en] .i. unce de sillio en ewe et giete l'en ce
que noera et flotera par desore et boive l'en ce que asserra au fonz oveques meismes
l'eue, si refroidera merveilleusement et gardera le cors moiste. Et por la dolor si
moille l'en le front et les temples d'ewe tiede ou de l'ewe de la decoction de roses.
Et por dormir li face l'en fomentacion de l'ewe de la decoction cassillaginis,
jusquiami, mente, rose, herbe violete et lieve les piez tresc'au genouz et les braz et
les mains. Et boille l'en cassillaginem et li lie l'en sor le front et sor les temples. Et
li oigne l'en le front de oille violat et de oille rosat et de populeon et les temples et
les veines qui batent es mains [f. 66v] et es piez. Por fere dormir face l'en ceste
emplastre sor le front et sor les temples: preigne l'en la semence de laitues, de
papaver blanc et neir, jusquiami, cortex mandragore, et en face l'en poudre et les
destempre l'en d'oille rosat et de violat et de lait de femme et de .i. poi d'aisil et
d'aubun d'uef por miauz tenir. Et si puet l'en metre .i. poi de opie, s'il ne puet tant
ne quant dormir. Et se cil qui ont causon e tierceine continue ne terminent ou
setime jor, nos les purjons al huitime jor de la decoction de violetes et de prunes et
de semences. Et i metons .i. unce de tamarindes et .i. unce de cassiafistula et une
drame de mirobalans citrins et .ii. unces de reubarbe. Mais caus qui sont malades
de sinocho ou de sinoca purjons nos de la decoction de violetes et de prunes et de
la semence citruli, melons, cucumbres, cucurbite et mete om o tot .ii. unces
cassiafistula et .ii. unces manne. Mais ceaus qui travaillent de causonide ou de
sinochie si purjons nos de medicines compostes qui purgent autretant sanc come
colre et de choses mundifica[f. 67r]tives. Mais encontre sinochide metom nos plus
des choses qui mundefient sanc. Et encontre causonidem i metons plus des choses
qui mundefient colre. Et notez que com li malades est en peril, qu'il est biens que
l'en le face seignier par le niés, se om poet, de soies de porc botez es narines ou de
.i. bastonet ou de aucune herbe poignante ou de sansues mises entor le nes.

[I,8 *De febribus emitriceis*] [18] Fleume porrist a la fie es veines et fait une cotidiane
continue. A la fie melancolie si porrist dedenz les veines et fait une quartaine
continue. A la fie diverses humors porrissent, a la fie dedenz les veines et a la fie
dehors. Mais les auctors n'enseignent se .iii. diversetez non. Selonc les .iii. diversetez des humors qui porrissent enseignent .iii. diversetez de emitrices. Car a la fie
colre porrist dedenz les veines et fleume dehors, si font une fievre que om apele la

menor emitrite. Et a la fie avient le contraire, que fleume porrist par dedenz et colre par dehors et font une fievre que l'en apele la moiane [f. 67v] emitrite. A la fie melancolie porrist par dedenz et colre par dehors et font une fievre que l'en apele la greignor emitrite. [19] De la cotidiane continue icés sunt les signes: chalor continue et de nuiz plus grant es oures de fleume et sanz type nule, si est le chief pesant et l'orine poi coloree et tenve, [et si tient .xviii. hores en soverain travail et .vi. en faus repos], ne la chalor n'est pas mult entense mes lente. Et notez que l'enne conoist pas legierement cotidiane continue ne quartaine continue par l'orine. De la menor emitrite si sont les signes iteles: chalor continuele et plus grant de nuit, c'est asavoir as ores de fleume, et sent l'en une froidure au soir, si a l'en les extremitez froiz et le chief pesant et les pauperes, et dort om fausement, l'orine ert roge ou souzroge et moinement tenve ou moinement espesse et bleve*. La moiene emitrite conoist l'en par icés signes: chalor continuele sicom es autres, mais de tierz jor en tierz si est plus ague, oveques une froidure avant, si a soif grant et la dolor [f. 68r] ou chief, l'orine roge ou sozroge moinement tenve ou moinement espesse et bleve et a l'en .xxxvi. hores en soverain travail et .xii. en faus repos. En la greignor emitrite la chalor est plus grant, totes les accidenz en sont plus agues que es autres fievres devant dites, l'orine apiert a la fie noire et a la fie vert de la chalor dou foie, [a la fie] descoloree de la mortification, si a .xi. hores en soverain labor et .xiii. en faus repos. [20] *Cure de la menor emitrite ou de la moiene ou de cotidiane continue(e) ou de quartaine continue(e).* L'en doit seignier le malade dedenz le quart jor, por qu'il soit de l'aage et de la force, mes as juevenes genz et memement en esté tens doit l'en doner tenve diete come gruel et lait de amandes et scariolis et porcelane quite en ewe et prunes. Et lor doint om a boivre ewe d'orge. Et des le comoincement lor doigne l'en syrop acetous au matin oveques la decoction de prunes et de violete[s] oveques l'ewe de la decoction des semences. Et lor [f. 68v] face l'en usier de syrop fait de la decoction de violetes et de prunes et de semences et mete l'en zucre ovec. Et si li ventres est serrez, la quel chose nuit mult as emitrices, face om suppositories de lart ou de mel et de siel et oigne l'en le ventre de bure ou de oille violat. Si la soif est granz et la langue seche et le adustion grant, si li doigne l'en l'ewe de melons palestine[s], et envelope om melons et cucurbites* de paste* et les quise l'en en .i. for et preme [om] hors l'ewe sicom nos avons dit desus. Et mete l'en zucre dedenz et en face l'en syrop. Et come la matire est defite, la quel chose om conoist par la mendre espesseté de l'urine; en cotidiane continue [. . .] et [en quartaine continue] la conoist l'en ensint*: en la menor emitrite et en la moiene par la moiene espesseté de l'urine et lors devez vos purgier. Mais notez que nos ne faisom pas mencion de la greignor emitrite por ce que la cure de lui est solement en la main de Deu et non pas en main d'ome, sicome Galien meismes le tesmoingne. Et s'il torne a bien, on [f. 69r] amende dedenz l'uitime jor. Adonques caus qui travaillent de la menor emitrite ou de la moiene purjons nos de la decoction de violetes et de prunes et de semences, polipodie et fenoil [et] .i. unce de mirobolans citrins et .i. autre de kebles. Et caus qui travaillent de cotidiane continue purjons nos en meisme la maniere fors tant que om i mette .ii. unces de kebles et nule de citrine. Mais caus qui ont quartaine continue purjons nos de la decoction de sené et des semences et i mete l'en .i. unce ou .ii. de mirobolans indes. Et notez que cil qui ont emitrite ne sont ja delivre

si a poine non par une medicine dont on les doit soventes foiz purgier, mais non ja
devant le huitime jor. Et notez que en esté tens c'om doit atendre l'uitime jor e en
yver le disme ou le .xii. Et s'il n'est par tant delivre, si li doigne l'en medicine
aguisee de scamonee sicome oximel* squillitique [et] electuaire froide. [f. 69v] Et
s'il [n']est delivre en tel maniere, si signefie longue maladie, dont l'en doit doner
plus large diete. Quise l'en donques une geline en ewe et la trible l'en en .i. mortier
o toz les os et la destempre l'en oveques meimes l'ewe et le cole l'en parmi .i. drap
et doigne l'en au malade. Ou l'en le quise longuement oveques orge pilee et li
doigne l'en cel orge a mangier. Ou l'en li doigne les extremitez de menuz oiselez et
vin ovec et lor doigne l'en au matin icestui syrop: violetes, prunes, et les semences,
polipodie, fenoil, et les boille l'en en ewe. E mete [l'en] zucre et en face l'en syrop.
Et mete l'en reubarbre en tele porcion com nos avons dit devant. Iceu syrop a
delivré maint par la volanté de Deu. Et notez que maint, com il eschapent de fevre
emitrite, cheent en erratique ou en quartaine. Dont por contregarder si mete l'en
sené en la devant dite decoction. Mes enfanz qui ont emitrite porjons nos aprés .v.
anz ou .vi. de la decoction de prunes et de violete[s]. Et metons [f. 70r] o tot .v. ou
.vi. drames de reubarbre et la manere dou metre avons dit devant la ou nos feimes
mencion que les quartaines solement soloient chaoir en ydropisie des opilacions de
l'esplene et del foie. Et notez que as enfanz de .ii. anz ou de .iii. donons medicine
en tel maniere: nos metons la reubarbre trestote entiere en ewe et le laissons
temprer, et aprés en ostons la sustance et donons l'ewe. Mais aprés .v. anz ou .vii.
nos triblons la sustance et la temprons en ewe et engitom l'ewe et donons la
substance.

[f.105r]   [BOOK II *De egritudinibus capitis*]

[1 *De frenesi*] [21] *Por frenesie.* Frenesis si est une apostume qui naist en la premere
celle del chief. 'Et dicitur frenesis a frenibus, id est panniculis cerebrum involven-
tibus entor' les queles [crest] icest apostume, ou de frenon, ce est pensee ou raison,
por ce que la raison de l'home est mult blessee en ceste maladie. Si avient sovent a
home jovene colerique et en esté et en emitrite moine et en tierceine continue et
en causon* et en pleuresie* et ne n'avient ja fors en fevre ague. Des frenesies l'une
[est] veraye et l'autre non. Veroie est icele que est faite des humors coleriques,
coillie et confermé en apostume en la premere celle del chief. Kar i coile por sa
propre chalor et sa propre legierté, que por la chaline de la fevre si est ravie amont
as veines et as arteres et as ners del cervel. La non verraie frenesie vient de
fumosité que monte al chief et trouble le cervel. Et si vient frenesie de sanc qui
torne en abit de colere. [22] Les signes de verraie frenesie si sont iteles: decoloration et extenuation de l'urine avesques fevre et resver* et veillier tot adés, et torne
les euz hideusement et autremen que l'en ne seut, et porter les mains sa et la come
por porter aucune chose ou por prendre ou [f.105v] por pluchir aucone chose de la
pareie ou de sa robe. En la non verraie frenesie si sont meimes les signes fors que
l'urine n'est pas si descoloree ne si tenve. Kar en ceste solement la fumosité et non
pas l'umor est ravie amont ne l'alienation ne est pas continuele sicome ele est en la

verraie. [23] *Cure*. Cure: Si tost come on porra aparceivre les signes de frenesie se doit l'en traveilier quanque l'en porra, que la matere ne se coille [a] apostume, kar come l'apostume est confermee, la quele chose vient en trois jors, se garist hom a mult grant peine. Come on garist, se doit l'en donques coucher le malade en une maison oscure ou l'air soit froit, en un lit, que ne eschauve mie. Le tienge l'en en lit ou on li lie* et gart l'en que gens de diverses cheres ne ne viegnent devant lui. Et la maison ne soit pas painte et que sa robe [soit] tote de une color, qu'il ne soit plus fous por la diverseté del color. Et gart [l'en] que on ne parout entor lui por la devant dite cause. *Diete*. Sa diete soit tres tenve et li frote on tot sueef les plantes des piés et les plantes des mains d'ewe sause solement. Mes il i a uns fous que les frotent forment de vin egre et de sel, dont il eschaufent* trop les espiriz et destemprent, dont la co[f.106r]lere devient plus legiere et plus ague et est ravie plus tost amont. *Cure*. Et face l'en suppositoyres, de queles diversetés dirons nos el traitié de litargie. Et face l'en clistere len[i]tif et mordificatif ensemble de la decoction de mauves, d'orge, mercurialis et mete l'en o tot ole et sel et mel. Et quant l'en avera ce fait, se doit om user des choses locales. Raie om le chief et face om epithimites apocrastiques del jus de corrigiole, solatri, sempervive et mete om un peu de sel et de vert jus et face l'en itel epithime sor la premere celle del chief et desor la seconde et se soient froides en esté et en yver chaudes. Et face l'en epithime de la poudre de sandles blanches et rouges et le confise [l'en] de ewe rose et mete om un poi de vin egre et de oile rosat. Et face l'en sternutations de la poudre de caunfre sofflé es narines et non pas de elebore ne de autre chose qui soit mult dessollutif. Ou l'en moille une penne, se li boute l'en bien parfont el nes. Et ces choses doit l'en faire devant que l'apostume soit confermé. Mes come l'apostume est confermé, si covient autres aides. Fende l'en donques un caelet parmi le dos et le gete l'en fors les bowels et mete l'en sor le chief. Et se l'en poet avoir plusors caeles, si les re[f.106v]mue l'en sovent et mete l'en autre. Et ce meime poet l'en faire del poumon de chescune beste frescement trait fors et mis sore ou de un coc fendu parmi le dos. Et se doit hom travailler en tote maneres por faire le dormir. Face l'en donques les enonctions et les emplastres qui sont escrites par desus en causon. Et en ceste cause doit [l'en] meller opium avesques l'emplastre por faire dormir. Et ovre om la veine que est enmi le front. Ou mels vaut que l'en i mete sancsues es narines. Et si il ne volent soucher, si covient il oindre le leu de vin. Et come vus* averés fait icés aides covenablement et il dure encore en sa frenesie sanz dormir et l'urine soit descoloree au tiers jor, se poés desperer de sa vie. Mes si l'urine comence a colorer au tiers jor et les mauveis accidens a abesser, si porrés avoir esperance de sa vie et le devés porger de la decoction* de violes et de prunes et de semences et metre une once de cassiavistule et une once de thamarindes et trois onces de reubarbe.

[II,2 *De litargia*] [24] *Litargie*. Litargie si est une apostume en la deraine celle du chief. Si est dite litargia a lethes, quod est oblivio, por ce que ele fait tot oblier. Si vient de fleu[f.107r]me en* veus gens fleumatiques et en yver plus acoustimement en* fevre cotidiane et en* la menor emitrite et en p[er]ipleumo[n]ie. Et si n'est la maladie par soi, ains sorvient totes jors en aucune de ces maladies es queles fleume, come ele bout par la chalor de la fevre, est ravie desca au cervel et s'aune en la

deraine celle del chief et s'aferme en une apostume de la quele les signes sont
iteles: [25] fevre continue, l'urine descoloree et espesse, le chief pesant et les euz,
fausemen[t] dormir. Et kant om apele le malades, se respont a peines et se il
respont, ce sont estranges paroles et gist tot adés envers, si ad les extremithés
froides. [26] *Cure*. Cure: Al comencement le doit on aider de la soveraine et de la
principale cure, come de clistere. Face l'en donques la premere clistere mollitive
de* la decoction de mauves et d'orge. Et aprés face l'en une [clistere] mordificative
de ole et de sel et de mel et del jus de mercuriale et de un pou de saugemme. Et
face l'en esclistere neis de benoite aguisié de scamonie dous onces, de blanche
aguisié de scamonie ou de katartico* imperiale ou de teoder[ic]o[n] owellement. Et
destempre l'en la benoite ou* aucune de[s] devant [f.107v] dites choses de l'ewe de
la decoction de mauves, d'orge et la coule l'en et gete em ens la coleure. Et face
l'en suppositories de mel quit et de aisil et de sel tot si en tele manere. Quise l'en
mel sor une tieule ou en aucune autre vassel tant qu'il comence a ardre. Le signe
come il est quis [est] come il comence a estre citrins et nercir un poi. Lors si mete
l'en ens le sel triblé en pudre et le gete l'en sor un autre tieule ou sor une marbre et
enforme l'en les suppositoyres ains qu'il soit froides. *Cure*. Ou le face l'en suppositories* de fel de torel. Si [il] est sec, si enforme [l'en] le suppositorie*, si il est
mostes, si moilliez un poi de coton leins et en face om suppositorie* et mete om
ens. Ou l'en face une suppositoire de saugemme et le mete l'en ens et le* moillie
l'en avant en oile. *Cure*. Ou l'en frise mercuriale en oile et le mete l'en ens. Ou
l'en face suppositure de fiente de soris ou de mel. *Cure*. Ou l'en face tel suppositoire as enfans qui ont ceste maladie: boille l'en oile et aisil et zucre et mete l'en de
la poudre du sel et face l'en tel suppositure. Ou l'en face frications es paumes des
mains et es plantes des piés* et durement grant du [f.108r] sel et de vin egre. Et
leve l'en icés parties* avant de ewe sause. Et couche [l'en] le malade en un leu clier
de air et caus. Et li face [l'en] unes soufistries. *Cure*. Raie [l'en] le chief ou le haterel
soulement. Pregne l'en jus d'ape et oile rosat et vin aigre et eschauve l'en ensemble. Et face l'en une epithime sor le haterel. Mes quant l'apostume est confermé, la quele chose avient au secont jor ou au tiers, face* l'en itel epithime.
Cure. Boille l'en castorie en jus de rue et en aisil et face l'e[n] un epithime de ce et
enfrote l'en durement le haterel de jus de ache et de aisil et de l'humidité anacordorum. Et face l'en sinapisme de la pudre de sinapis, del jus de ache et de aisil et
mete l'en sor le chief. Notés que l'en doit boillir tot avant l'erbe del senevé et aprés
frire en oile et en vin aigre et metre sor le chief. Et face l'en sternutation de la
poudre castorei, alleboli, asboli et de neir poivre, euforbie, piretri et de semblables
choses. Et lie l'en iteu manere de pudres en une drap delié et mete l'en as narines.
Et s'il n'esternue mie, si li souffle l'en es narines de la pudre. Ou l'en la* [f.108v]
destempre de ole rosat et moille l'en une penne dedens et le bute l'en en parfont es
narines. Si il esternue, il est bons signes, se non, mauvais. Et li face l'en subfumigacions* es narines de asa fetida mise sor les carbons ou de sagapino, galbano,
oppoponac, armoniac ou de cor de cerf ou de chievre ou de mesches teintes* en lie
[ou] en oile et puis alumees et puis esteintes. Mes si la froidure des extremités est
grans, mete l'en asés de dras sor lui. L'en sout mult estreindre les dens en tel
maladie et baver mult. Dont l'en li doit overir la bouche de une quillier et froter
bien la langue de tiriaque ou de aurea ou de metridato ou de blanca. Et li face l'en

baissier le chief, que la salive puisse core fors. Et face l'en seignier de veine enmi le
front et li mete l'en les sancsues es narines. Et quant l'en avera fait icés remedies et
l'urine remaint descoloree aveque les autres accidens mauveises et les membres
comencent a trambler et il comence a movir le bras sodeinement et les extremités
des membres a refroydir, si est signe mortel. Mes si l'urine comence a colorer et les
accidens mauveis a alascher, si le purge l'en [de la] decoction de prunes et de
violettes et de semen[f.109r]ces, de polipode et de fenoil. Et mete l'en une once de
mirabolans kebles. Mes notés que li frenetiques est litargiques a mal. Mes litargiques devienent frenesiques, ce est bien. Dont mon pere aprés totes cures seut
metre li litargique en un bai[n]g fait des herbes chaudes por dessoudre la cause ou
por amener frenesie.

[II,3 *De catarrho*] [27] *Catarrus est une forte maladie*. Catarrus est flux de humors del
chief, c'est asavoir si vient de cause defors, sicome de chaline de air et de froide et
de moistece. Et de cause dedens si vient ele come de viandes et de boivres et des
qualités des humors des membres. [C]atarrus est fait en cinc maneres: [. . .] le
chalor qui dessout et fait cure, de froydure qui estreint et prent, de moistesse
escolorjante*, de liquide et la fluxibilité de meimes les humors, et de feblété de la
vertu contentive. La diverseté des causes conoist l'en par les propres signes, que
selonc la diverseté des causes soient les cures diverses. [28] Les signes de catarre
faites de habondance des humors qui corent si sont iteles: la* chiere est emflee et
rouge et les euz gros et fors de la teste, habundance de superfluiteez par la buche,
par le nes et par les oreilles et par les euz, le chief pesant et abitude de tot [f.109v]
le cors plectoriques. *Les signes de chalor dissolutive*. Les signes de chalor dissolutive
sont iteles: la chalor en la face vermaille, les veines ruges es euz et corent unes
lermes chaudes des euz et mordant le quir et le superfice et sent l'en une chalor en
parfont. Se poet l'en bien enquere del* malades s'il a mengé ne beu choses chaudes
trop ou s'il a esté en air chaut. Et quant ce avient de froidure constrictive et
exprimitive conoist l'en par iteles signes: la color ert pale en la face, si a l'en les
lermes froides sor la face et ensement a l'en une froidure en parfunt el cors. Se dira
le malades bien s'il mangie ou beive choses trop froides ou si il a demoree en air
froit. Et come ce avent de fluxibilité et de lubricité* de humors corans, ce conoist
l'en par la multitude* des superfluités que li issent par la bouche et par le nes et par
les oreilles et par [les euz et par] la liquidité de eux* qui* [ne] s'ahergent ensemble
et aprés si corent et degotent ignelement. Et quant la cartar[re] vient de feblece de
vertu retentive, ce conust l'en par le remocion de[s] devant dites choses et meimement par le* rebouchement des sens. [29] *Cure*. Cura. Catarre faite de habundance des humors [f.110r] garist l'en proprement et principaument par* le eduction
de superfluele humor. Donques se li sanc sorabonde, se le seigne l'en de la vein[e]
del chief se li cors est plectoriques et sanguins, s'il est de la force et de l'age, et
meimement se les humors courent as membres espirités. Mes si les humors corent
aillors que es membres espirités et il i ait de autres abundance, se li doigne l'en
medicine laxative en dure substance, sicome piles aurés, pilles de cinc maneres de
mirabolans. Aprés le tiers jor de la purgation done l'en rubeam. Et si le flux ne
cesse en tele manere, face l'en choses constrictives qui sont escrites en la cure de
catarre de froidure. Catarre qui vient de chalor si garist om en tele manere. Face

l'en air froit par art solonc doctrine assignee par desus. La diete soit froide. Et face l'en fomentacion au front d'ewe chaude ou d'ewe* de la decoction de roses. Et succe l'en* de cele [ewe] chaude meimes* parmi les narines. Et enoigne l'en le front et les temples de oile rosat ou de violat [. . .] sicome est requies ou* rubea. Catarre qui vient de froideure garist l'en en tele manere. Si l'en veit aucune humor surabunder, si purge l'en de covenable medicine, et meimement se li cors est plectoriques. Et [f.110v] face l'en l'air chaud par art et sa diete soit chaude. Et face l'en fomentation de ladane et de cendre de paille d'orge en tele manere: boille* l'en icés choses en ewe et li malades soit covert de dras et receive la fumee, si qui il sue tot*. Et aprés leve l'en ses piés desc'a[s] genules et les mains* desca as espaules. Et face l'en un estuel de ladane et le mete [l'en] es narines. Dessoille l'en aueram de oille musceline ou de commune et mette l'en de la pudre olibani, storace ca-lamite*. Et face l'en emplastre au chief ou res ou sans rere. Et aprés face l'en sacellation au chief de la pudre de baies de* lorier, de puliol et de origano. Eschauve l'en icés pudres en aucune vassel sans nule liquor et l'envolupe l'en en un linge drap et face l'en rubeam ovec vin chaut. Aprés li tiers jur li doigne [l'en] plus fort opiate, c'est asavoir aueram ou diaolibanum avec vin de la decoction de olibane*. *Cure.* Contre catarre de humidité escolorjante* se valent les devant dites remedies et icés choses especiaument: ladanum, olibanum, storax. Et les boille l'en en ewe de ploie ou de roses et covre l'en bien le pot que la fume[e] ne ne puisse issir. Et aprés descovre [l'en] le pot et covre l'en le chief au malade et le face [f.111r] l'en boivre la fumee par la bouche et par la niés. Iceste fumigation espessist les humors et estanche le flux. Et a ceus qui ont catarre de la defaute de la vertu retentive face l'en les devant dites aides et enoigne l'en le chief de oile masticine qui est faite de la decoction de mastic en oile. Iceste oile, sicome Galiene le tesmoine*, conforte mult le cervel. Experiment comune faite contre catarre de froidure ou de humidité escolorjante et de la feblece de la vertu retentive: Face [l'en] le malade transgluter trois grains de olibano pur a la quantité de une feve quant vus irrés coucher sans nule liquor. Et notés que l'en doit sovent faire ces aides si l'en ne garist a la premere fois.

[II,4 *De apoplexia et epilepsia*] [30] *Apoplexe si est une maladie que vient de la tousse.* Apoplexia* si est opilation de totes les ventraillies del cervel ovec la p[ri]vation [de raison] ou avec la diminution de sentir ou de movir. Epilencie si est opilation de[s] principaus ventrillies del cervel avec la diminu[ti]on de sentir et de movoir. Et est dite epilencia* ab epi, quod est supra, et lensis, quod est lesio. Et les ansiens apelent ceste maladie yerrameton, id est sacra passio, por ce que ele purprent les seinte[s] parties du cors, c'est asavoir le cervel que e[st] le secche de la [f.111v] alme. Et si l'apele l'en enfantile maladie por ce que enfans ont sovent ceste maladie. Et ceste maladie vient de superfluité de boivre et de manger et de viandes venimeuses et de boivres et de morsure de chien erragé et de vermine venimeuse* et de l'air corrumpu. Mes ele vient principaument de trois causes: de defaute de* chalor, de habundance de superfluité[s], et de destresse des conduis. De* la defaute de chalor, kar ja soit ice que la chalor soit febles, se soffist ele a dessoudre multes superfluitez, mais ele ne soffist pas a degaster les, les queles dessouses et non pas degastés aportent les devant dites maladies en estopant les ventrillies del cervel.

De habondance de superfluité[s] vient ele, kar ja soit ice que la chalor soit forte et degaste une grant partie des superfluités, se ne degaste ele mie totes por ce que eles sont mol[t]es. De la destresse des conduiz, kar ja soit ce que chalor soit petite et que les superfluités soient petites, se sufficent eles a estoper les conduiz qui sont estrois. [A]poplexia* si ad dous especes, une greignor et une menor. La greignor apoplexia* si est l'opilation de totes les ventrillies de[l] cervel avec la privation de movoir et de sentir. Dont ceus qui [f.112r] travaillent en ceste espece se ne movent ne ne sentent rien. Dont Ypocras dist que ce ne poet estre que l'en garise de la forte apoplexie, kar de la menor garist om a paine. La mendre apoplexie si est opilacion de* tous les ventrillies del cervel, non pas neporquant del tot. Dont cil qui travaillent de ceste espece se sentent bien et movent, mais ne poent pas parler. Epilencia ensement si a dous especes, une greignor et une menor. En la greignor si sont estopés les principaus ventrillies del cervel del tot*. Dont cil ki travaillent en ceste espece si chient soteiment et tordont la bouche et les jowes et lor tramble la teste et trestot le cors et estraingent* les dens et croissent et chient et se com-pissen[t] et foutent en meime l'action la ou il sont cheus et escument parmi le bouche. En la menor epilencie si sont estopés trestous les principaus ventrillies del cervel, mais non pas du tot. Donc cil qui travaillent en ceste espece si cheent a la fie, a la fie non, et com il cheent il relevent tost. Estre ice epilencie si a trois especes solonc la treble* variance des leus ou la cause* est contenue, c'est asavoir epilence, cathalensie, analensie. Epilensie si vient de la matere entor le cervel et ne vient pas [f.112v] ailurs*. Analensie* si vient de la matere qui est en la stomac, et non pas en la concavité de l'estomac sicome li uns dient, ains est es veines et es ners et es arteres* de l'estomac par les queles la matere, quant bout, si est ravie amont* au chief. Cathalensia si vient de la matere que [est es] extremités sicome es mains et es pees, les queles l'en conust par lor propres signes. Cathalentici s'aparceivent bien quant il doivent chair, kar il sentent bien la matere ramper contremont sicome formies li alassent entre quir et char et eschapent sovent de l'action par estraindre fort les extremités. Dont Galiens dit que cathalentici ont fevre, kar la matere ne porreit pas estre ravie amont au chief sans chalor de fevre. Analentici si travaillent de repletion de l'estomac et principaument de indigestion et de corruption de viandes et se aparceivent bien com il doivent chaier. Epilentici si travaillent de une continuele grevance [del chief] et ne sentent pas quant il doivent chair. Et si vient a la fiez de sanc et a la fies de fleume et a la fies de melancolie, la quele chose l'en conust par les signes de chascun humor.[31] Kar la sanguine habitude signefie que sanc est en cause, come collere vermalle, [f.113r] chalor, les euz boiant fors del chief et les veines des euz rouges et les veines emflees et pleines, l'aage, la diete, la region et le tens* que avienent et acordent en chalor et en moistece demostrant icel chose meime. Quant fleume est la cause, ce demostre l'abitude fleumatique sicome li abondance de superfluité par la bouche et par le nes et l'en a la bouche malsade et le chief pesant et la superficé del cors* sublanche. La diete, la region, le tens de l'an, si il acordent en ce meime, si* demostre fleume estre en cause. Mes come melancolie est en cause, ce mostre l'abitude del cors melancoliques come les euz reons et la superficé del cors noire ou cendrine. L'eage, la diete, la region, le tens de l'an, si il acordent en ce meimes, si demostre ice. [32] *Cure.* Cure: Aprés que nus averons demostré les causes et les

signes de apoplexie et de epilencie, si trovons cures dous. [M]es notés que la
greignor apoplexie est incurable. De la menor garist om a peine et se torne ele
sovent en pleuresie. Mes la meine* epilencie et cele qui vient de principal vice del
cervel en home* viel ou en juvene, si garist l'en a peine. Si doit l'en premerement
ordiner sa diete. Et aprés si demostrons coment l'en doit aider li devant l'accession
et dedens [f.113v] et aprés. Gardent soi generaument de feves, de chous, de
lentilles, de char de boef et de levre et de totes les choses que engendrent melancolie et colere adusté et fleume et gardent soi de moules et de cervele manger, de
choses frites, de choses salees, de totes airons, de poudre, de foutre trop, de
baignier, de presse de gent. Kar en iteles leus lor sout prendre lor action plus
sovent. Des chars si doit om manger gelines et autres oiseus fors iceus qui vivent*
en palus et manguent castriz de un an et de char de porc et de agnel et de chievre
et mangucent ces chars quites en ewe ou en rost et avec sauce faite des especes
chaudes aromatiques et les testes de bestes et le jus de cerres rouges et poires et
coiens quis aprés manger. Et mangucent assés au matin et al vespre peu. Des
poissons mangucent les plus escardeuses de ewe sause et de douce et les manguce
l'en en rost por lor humidité apeticier. Des herbes mangucent bourinches, spinaces,
peresin, fenoil, speragum;bruscer, por ce que ele desout les humors et les moet
amont, defent jo a manger*. Lor [pain] soit bien quis et bien levez et de forment, li
vins soit soutils et blans et succitrins aromatiques. Et ces choses suffisent de la
diete. Mais come le tens de l'action approce, la quele [f.114r] chose l'en conoist a
la fiez par le malede ou par ce que [quant] la lune est pleine ou defaucte sicom nus
avons dit devant, si sont teus ja plus malades, si les doit l'en tenir et lier en maison,
kar meint en cheent parmi la fenestre ou par autre leu perillieus et perissent ou
depecent aucon de lor membres. Icés chose[s] doit l'en faire en meme l'action. L'en
doit coverir sa chiere com il est cheus, por ce qu'il est horribles a veoir, et li doit
l'en terdre la bouche come il avera escumé, et drecier son chief et son col, s'il gist
malement, por avoir mels sa aleine. In analensia et in cathalensia del comencement de l'action se doit l'en faire sternutacions de castoree, de poivre, de euforbio.
Mais [in epilensia] ne doit l'en pas faire sternutacions au comencement, kar meint
en estengnent par les grans dissollucions des humors come li fous mire met sternutacions au comencement. Mes come li malades remaint fous long tens aprés et
resve*, lors li poet om faire sternutacions et li doit l'en froter les extremités
fortment. Et si l'alienation dure longement, face l'en clistere mult tres fort et
meimement cele que est faite de blanche* qui est escrite el traitié* de litargia. Por
les membres qui sont endormiz et meimement por contregarder de para[f.114v]lisie
face l'en un bai[n]g de la decoction des foilles de lorer, pulegii, origani et des autres
herbes chaudes quites en vin et en ewe et mete l'en spi[ca]nardi et face l'en le
malade entrer et issir trois fois el baing. Et lors face l'en moillier lor chiefs de l'ewe
del baing come il entre dedens. *Epilentiques*. Mais les epilentiques du principal vice
del cervel doit l'en purger. Mais devant ce que l'en les purge le doit om doner
pauline simple et potionem sancti Pauli. Et aprés le purge l'en de ieralogodion ou
de blancha ou de theoder[ic]o[n] owellement [ou] de piles aurés. Et quant il avera
espurgé et celebree les jors de la expurgation, si le face l'en seigner de la veine du chief,
si li cors est sanguins et plectoriques et il soit de l'age et de la force. Ou om li mete
ventouses entre les espaules a tot jarse. *Contre epilensie*. L'esperiment mon pere

contre epilensie. Traie l'en trois onces de sanc des espaules par jarser et li doigne l'en a boivre avec un oef de corbel en la fin de sa action, kar lors boiveroit il venin que li dorreit. Oes de corbel si valent mult a manger. Vin de la decoction de racine de pioné si vaut mult en ceste maladie. La pioné meime si est bon a porter entor le col*. Et li face l'en gargater en [f.115r] vin aigre et en vin dous et staphisagria, turbit, gingembre, peretro, roses, pillule* diacastoree avesques jus de mente agrestis ou de hermoise ou soveunon ovec vin chaut dessouses et getees es narines. Et mete l'en le malade dejoste le feu ou en air chaut et li doigne l'en diacené faite d'especes aromatiques. Et por ce le di jo que om trove diverses receptions de diacené. *Sirop.* Sirop que vaut mult a epilensie*. Ou l'en quise sené en jus des foilles de boraches* en teu proporcion que om i mete en une livre trois onces de sené. Et mete l'em zucre et face l'en sirop. Et se vus n'avés boraches, ice meime poés faire des foilles de pannasse et li doigne l'en de ceste sirop au matin et al soir. Mais si le epilense vient del vice del stomac, si li doit aider en tele manere. Estre icés devant dites choses li face l'en oximel simple ou squillitique ou de racines de peresin ou de ache. Le tiers jor com il avera beu oximel, se li doigne l'en choses salees et choses rosties et airon tot sen saul et li doigne hom ewe a boivre sen saul. Et aprés le face l'en voncher. Et ce est mult tres bon por espurgier l'estomac. Et mete l'en ventusses sor l'estomac aveques jarse ou sans jarse. Et enoigniés l'estomac de oignemens chaudes. Et li doigne l'en la coleure de vomitu patriarche [f.115v] ou de scarpelle. Et li doigne [l'en] ausi* diamargariton, pliris arconticon*, diarodon, julis, si l'en poet avoir. Cathalenticis si sont bones totes les devant dites choses fors solement tant que l'en doit purgier les* de dure medicine, kar la medicine que est donce en dure substance si atrait les humors de[s] longtaines parties. Et le face l'en seignier de saphena par dedens le pié et le jarse l'en es jaumbes. Et li oigne l'en les extremités de oignement ruptoire, que* l'en doit mener fors la matere. Et face l'en neis tel oignement. Coille l'en le fruit de concumbre agreste come il sont meur et laisse l'en purrir en vin ou en oile par quinse jors. Et aprés les quise l'en et coule et i mete l'en les poudres castorei, elibori nigri, euforbii* et roses et en face l'en oignement et enoigne om les extremités, et de ceus qui ont cathalensie ou analensie, et les dos a ceus qui ont epilensie. Et notés qui ceus qui travaillent de epilensie del vice del cervel sont coustomer* de chair si tost come sentent le fumee de corne de cerf.

[II,5 *De paralisi*] [33] *Paralisie* avient en membres soventefois. Paralisis si est une maladie qui avient a la fie en une des membres du cors, a la fiez en plusors, avec privation de sentir ou de movoir ou de l'un et de l'autre. Si vient a la fiez de froidure constric[f.116r]tive et a la fies des humors qui estupent les conduiz et [de]trenchent [les ners], par la quele chose les espiriz sont devees a passer as estrumens. Et si les ners sentibles ou movables sont del tot retrait ou estoupés ou coupés outre si que les esperis ne poent en nule manere venir as estrumens, si naist une paralisie avec privation de sentir et de movoir dont le cervel en devient stupides et non sensibles. Mes come la diminucion* de* sentir et de movoir est faite en une partie, mes que les esperis puissent passer par les ners que movent le membre, si governent le membre et le sustenen[t] totefois en une partie. Mes [come] ne soffissent pas a sustenir del tot, por ce que les espiriz [ne] poent venir en si grant quantité com il fust mester, si puisse le membre contreval et de icés dous mocions contraires si avient que li menbre tramble en aucun des paralitiques. Et si vient paralisie sovent par superfluités des mangers et des boivres, kar de trop boivre vient grant dissolucion des humors* [et de froydure de air] si vient l'opilacion des ners. Et si avient paralisie* de la menor apoplexie, kar la menor apoplexie ou ele occist maintenant la maladie ou ele termine en paralisie sicome nus avons dit devant. Item notés ke de[s] paralisies l'une est [f.116v] universale, l'autre est particulare. Universale est icele paralisie que porprent droit le moitié del cors, mes particulere est icele que porprent tant solement un des* membres, sicome la main ou le pié ou l'oil ou la langue ou aucun des autres membres. Item notés que la paralisie vient a la fiez de cause que est en meisme la na[i]ssance des ners et a la fies en meisme le membre paralitique*. Mes si la cause est en la na[i]ssance des ners, se ne sent l'en riens es membres soveraines sicome en la face n'entor* le pis ne es membres detriers. Mes se la cause est en meime le membre paralitique, si sent om mal en cele membre tant solement et non pas es autres. Et ce covient l'en distincter que solonc la diversité* des causes poissons diverser les cures. [34] *Cure.* Cure: A paralitiques doit om aider sicome nus avons dit solonc la diverseté des membres. Mes notés que la paralisie qui vient [de] couper, sicome de nerf quant il est coupés tot entravers, si est incurables, autresi com il ne poet estre que li ners soit resoudés. Et la paralisie de la quele le membre a perdu le sentir et le movoir si est incurables, dont ele est apelee cancerina. Et come home vieus est paralitiques [f.117r] a peines en garist om. Mes home jovene et enfant en garissent bien. Premerement donques par dedens et par dehors doit om overer des choses que amollissent les ners et les relaxent. Kar si la matere est encore espesse et dure et l'en done* au comencement choses desiccatives et consomptives, si devendroit la matere plus dure et plus compacte come les dures parties seroient remeses et les plus soutiles degastees. Et ceste rieule est generale en totes materes grosses et dures. Donques si la paralisie est universale, si doigne l'en icés choses des le comencement par bouce chascone semaine en vin chaut ou avec ewe, c'est asavoir piles de simple pauline sans opiate ou de benoite ou de gerapigre. Par defors li face l'en enonctions de diauté et de bure et de chaudes herbes quites et triblees et fait[es] emplastre par desore come de brancha ursina et de mauves ou de oignement qui est faite des moules de totes bestes et des oiseus. Et i mete l'en oile et icés choses face l'en un mois ou plus tant que la matere soit defite et relaschee. Et com vus averés ce fait, si purge l'en trestot le cors des choses laxatives que nus avons [dites] el traité de epilensie. Et li dongne l'en diacastoreum ou pillule [f.117v] diacastoree par la bouche et potionem sancti Pauli. Et quant vus l'averés purgé, si li dongne l'en auream ou opopire ou autres chaudes opiates et le face l'en seignier si li cors est plectoriques. Et au derein tot doit l'en overer des choses locales. Et enoigniés les membres malades de oignemens chaudes et de oiles, et de ceste chose meimement; pregne l'en une serpent rouge ou plusors et lor coupe l'en les chiefs et les coues quatre doies de chascone part et gete [l'en] for[s] les boieus et le remanant mete l'en en un pot percié par desus. Desuz soit mis uns autre pot qui soit appareillié en tele manere, c'est asavoir que le cul del pot percié soit joins en la bouche de l'autre pot et aprés seelee mult bien de croie ou de paste, que l'ewe n'i puisse entrer. Et estupe l'en mult bien la bouche del pot qui est desus et quant il seront ici appareilliés, si le mete l'en boillir en plein caudere d'ewe, si que la chalor quise les serpens et dessoillie la cresse, la quele colera par le devant dit pertuis en le pot desuz et ne se degastera pas por la humidité de l'ewe defors. Et en cel grese mete l'en la pudre ov le jus capparis et centauree [et] en oigne l'en les membres malades. Meime centoire quite en vin chaut et en oile si est bone a faire emplastre [et] a membres malades metre*. Ou l'en face emplastre de semence [f.118r] de senevié et de vin et de oile frite. Si est ausi bone a faire emplastre et metre soure. Et mete l'en une ventuse* sor le leu avesques garse ou sans jarse por atraire les humors et les espiriz au leu et por faire le membre revivre. Item pregne l'en castoreum, sauge et fenoil, primevoire, bethonicam, si fait grant bien as paralitiques quites en bon vin et boive l'en le vin. Sauge lor fait grant bien a manger ou en crespeux ou en pudre. Mais si la langue est malade de paralisie, estre les avant dites choses face l'en iceste esperiment por receivre la parole. Face l'en le malade tenir la pudre castoree desus sa langue tant que ce soit dessouse par soi ou degasté. Ou l'en pregne la semence del chou campestre ou de lappe everse et li face l'en tenir desuz la langue. Et face l'en gargarisme de castorie et de poivre et de gingembre, de vin et un poi de vin egre. Mes devant que li gargarisme soit fait enoigne l'en le col et le haterel et les parties detriés autre chose chaude dissollutive. Mes por la paralisie de la vessie moille l'en une drap en vin de decoction de castoire et mete [l'en] sor le penil et sor le vit et le remue om soventesfois. Et notés que bains chaus de soffre sont bons et [f.118v] mult profitables a gens paralitiques* ou a gens qui ont la paralisie secche.

[II,6 *De mania et melancholia*] [35] *Manie* est une espece de frenesie et de forsenerie et de malancolie.* Manie* si est une maladie que tient et maumet le premer celle del chief ovec privation de ymagination. Melancolia si est la infection de cele meine* celle oveques privation de raison sicome Costentin dit el livre de melancolie. Melancolie, fait il, si est une suspicion qui a seignurie sor l'ame qui tristesce et orguil ont engendree. Si a difference entre ces maladies selonc la diverseté et* la discretion des overaignes. Kar en mania pert l'en premerment ymagination de qui li seges est mués et maumis. En la melancolie est maumise la raison. Et si vienent icés maladies de unes choses generaus et d'une[s] autres especiaus: [de generaus] sicome de viandes melancoliques et meimement de boivre fort vin, dont les humors sont arses et ce vient bien* de fors pevrees et de aillies et des autres viandes qui engendront humors arses. Estre icé[s] si vienent icés maladies de* causes par defors et de causes par dedens: [par dedens] sicome de passions de l'alme, c'est asavoir de ire, de peour soudeine, de tristesce, de trop estre en estude, de perte de choses, de juner, de veillier. De choses defors si vient ceste maladie sicome de morsure de chien et de beste venimeuse et de corruption [f.119r] de l'air. Et si* vienent icés maladies especiaument de colere ou de melancolie ou de sanc. Et selonc la diverseté des causes sont les signes diverses. [36] Signes de colere: devereie, maniaca confidencia; [il] crient, saillent et corent et fierent aus et autres et veillient tot adés. Et cestes maladies vienent en esté seche et en home colleriques et sechc et en seque region et de user chaude et secche diete. Mes quant ce vient de melancolie, se crient et chantent et se pleignent mult et atapissent et se metent as angles des maisons et se habitent es sepultures des mors et ont fauses et diverses sospicions. Kar li uns quident qu'il n'ont point de chief, les autres quident qui uns angle* sustient tot le munde et ad peour qu'il le laisse chair com il en ert las. Les autres tienent le poi[n]g si fermement clos que nuls nel poet overir, si quident tenir uns grant tresor en sa main, les autres tot le munde et ces sont obedient. [Cestes maladies vienent] en aust, en home viel melancoliens et en froide region et secche et de secche diete. Mes quant ceste maladie vient de sanc, si rient presque tot adés, si sont liez mult et ont le color rouge et les euz [rouges] et les veines pleines et se vienent icés maladies de la retencion de sanc qui est acoustomé de coure par les narines ou par les emoroides ou par flux menstruel et meime[f.119v]ment en ver et en chaude region et en moiste et en home sanguin et qui ont prise chaude diete et moiste generative* de sanc. Et notés que icés maladies ne venent pas de fleume por ce que fleume est blanche et ne teint pas le cervel. [37] *Cure*. Cure: Generaument l'en doit aider en tele manere ceus qui sont maniaques et malancoliques. Por ce que tel manere des malades sont acoustomé de faire mal a aux et as autres, se les doit l'en lier et garder que ne facent mal [a] aux ne [a] autrui. Et solonc la diverseté des causes doit l'en varier l'air entor eux et lor diete. Se la na[i]ssance de tele manere* de maladies vient* des passions de l'aulme, se le* doit l'en del contraire faire, le* solacier s'il est* corocés* et tot autresi des autres choses. Et s'il a perdu sen tresor, se li doit aporter or et argent assés devant lui et faire li attendant qu'il soit trestot le soens. Jo vi uns qui devint malancoliques sicome il fu garis de fievre por ce qu'on li nu[n]cha qui sa bourse* estoit depecié et son avoir enporté tot. Lors par le conseil des sages mires et des amis si fist l'en venir plusors gens devant lui et li portent molt et disoient qui furent ses dettores et qu'il li rendront icel avoir, si en fu delivres en tele manere. Et si doit l'en chanter et harper et vieler et [faire] venir beles femmes devant lui et faire geuer [f.120r] ovec lui a la foie. Kar quant l'en* [croist] atemprément, si fait bien as esperis et oste fauses suspecions. Et si doit l'en oster fauses suspecions par douces paroles et par engin. En tele manere [fist] le [roux]*, kar ons hom quidoit* qu'il ne eust point de teste et il li fist uns capiau de plum et com li malades sentoit le pesantime de[l] capel, si crut bien qu'il avoit teste. Et ce qu'il quidoit* qu'il n'eust point de teste li fist humor chaude et legere qui li alegout le cervel. Mes come la melancolie est cause de ceste maladie, si doit l'en overer en tele manere especiaument. Face l'en par art l'air chaut et moiste et li dongne chaudes dietes et moistes. Et li dongne l'en piles faites de gerapigre et de aloe. Ou l'en le purge de ces piles qui sont especiales a ce. [Preigne l'en]* lapis* lazuli, lapis armenici* autretant de l'une come de l'autre et mete l'en trois itant de senee et pudre de mastic avec et bdellio* et enforme l'en les pilles aveques le jus de chou. Et lor dongne l'en diacené, theodoricon* anacardi et li face l'en sirop de senee et zucre ou* de jus de borages et de senee et de zucarro sicome il est escrist en la cure des epilentiques. Et si l'en li poet doner decoction, si dongne l'en itel: tymum, epithimum, polipode, semence de fenoil soient boillies bien* en ewe et en une partie de ceste coleure mete [f.120v] l'en une once de mirabolans indes et trois onces lapis lazuli et autretant lapidis armeneici lavés et apparillés sicome nus avons dit en la traité de quartoine. Et ne vus mervelliés mie si j'ai dit que l'en i mete trois onces de[s] devant dites peres, kar quant il seront lavés, si revendront a la quantité de trois escruples ou de quatre. Et notés que quant les devant dites pieres sont mises en decoction que l'en les doit laver sicome nus avons dit devant. Et notés que maniaci et malancolici doutent et heent tant a manger que il ne osent regarder sor la viande. Dont il i covient enging [por] eux pa[i]stre. Donques quant il [ne] vodroit boivre, si doit om doner a boivre parmi un calemel, si qu'il ne voient ja lor boivre. Et quant om lor vodra doner piles, si mete l'en une quiller entre les dens et li traie l'en fors la* langue et li bote l'en la viande en parfunt en la bouche et les piles ce l'en vodra. Kar quant l'en done les piles en tele manere, si ne sent l'en mie lor amertume. [E]t lor raie l'en le chief et lor mete l'en chaudes emplastres et moistes seuere et le oignés de oignemens chaudes et moistes. Si humor coleriques est cause, se li doit om aider en tele manere, kar cil sunt febles mult par coustume. Si lor doigne l'en chars froides et moites et meimement la char de [f.121r] petis oiselés qui vivent en ewe. Et le diete l'en de froide diete et de moiste et face om le air froyde et moiste et lor viandes meimement si soient laitues, kar eles re[n]ddent le cors froit et moiste et font dormir et lor sont mult necessaires sor totes choses. Et lor face l'en un sirop de jus de laittues et de zucre et les purge l'en avec la decoction de mirabolans citrins. Et lor raie om le chief et lor face l'en froides et moistes enonctions et ephithimis et emplastres. Et face l'en enonction de oile rosat et violat et de oile mandragorat. Et face l'en epithemes et emplastres de[s] devant dites choses ou del jus de laitues, sempervive ou des foilles mandragore. Neis memes icés herbes si sont mult bones a faire emplastre par soi ou par autres herbes et ovrent tres bien. Ou trible l'en le fruit de ma[n]dragore et face l'en emplastre[s], si valent assés. Ou l'en face emplastre de la semence de laitues triblees et les destempre l'en de oile mandragore. Ou l'en face itel qui est merveillusement boens. Face l'en boillier mauves et les foilles de violetes, laitues, sempervive et les foilles mandragore et i mette l'en oile violat et rosat. Et face l'en entrer le malade ens et de cele ewe meime li moillie l'en le chief. Et por faire [f.121v] le dormir si le doigne l'en requies. Et notés que mirabolans conduis sont bons, la quel que la cause soit, de colere ou de melancolie. Et si la cause vient par sanc, si face l'en l'air froit par art. Et li doigne l'en froide diete et l'enongniés. Et li face l'en froides eno[n]gtions et froides emplastres au chief. Et si ce avient de retencion de sanc qui est coustemé a cure par les nariles, se li face l'en seignier par froter les nariles de soie de porcel. Ou om trenche la feine que est enmi le front. Et si la maladie avient de la retencion de flux menstruel ou des emoroides, si le seigne l'en de saphena et l'espurge l'en de la decoction de prunes, de violettes, de cassiafistre et de mauve ou de piles de cinc maneres de mirabolans. La deereine cure de ces dous maladies si est que l'en ovre cyrugie, et si cointement, ou chief, que l'en ne trouble ne blesce les ners entor le cervel ne entor miri[n]gam, kar si l'en blesce les ou trouble, la dereine dolor ert plus grans de la premere. Après icés choses que nus avon dist ici, si dirons de la dolor del cheef.

[II,7 *De dolore capitis*] [38] *Dolor del chief*. Dolor del chief si vient a la fies des choses dehors, a la fies de choses dedens; defors, sicome de coup et de proprieté de l'air, [f.122r] et principaument de chalor dissolutive ou de froidure coartative; de cause par dedeins si deut le chief, a la fiez* de cause privee, a la fies de cause loi[n]gtaine. Cause privee apel jo come la cause est en meime le chief et ne vient pas de ailurs. Et cause loi[n]gtaine apel jo quant ele vient de ailliors sicome del stomac. Dolor de cause privee: ou ele vient soulement de vice de* une sole qualité et meimement de chaline ou* de froidure ou [ele vient] de vice des humors sicome de sanc, de colere, de fleume ou de melancolie, les queles choses l'en conoist par lor propres signes. [39] Kar si la dolor vient de coup ou de chaline ou de froidure de air, ce poet om savoir par le dit del malade qui dira bien si il a esté feru ou s'il avera esté en air chaut ou froit. Se la cause vient de cause privee ou dc la vice del chief, icés sont les signes: une dolor ague* et meimement en la partie del chief devant, la face rouge et les euz roges et le chief chaut et l'en sent une chaline en le cors parfunt. [. . .] Les chaudes choses profitent a li et les froides nuisent*. Si la dolor vient solement de froidure, icés [f.122v] sont les signes: la dolor del chief ert greveuse, la face pale et sent l'en une froidure en parfunt. Les chaudes choses li sont bones et les froides males. Et quant la dolor vient de sanc, iteles sont les signes: dolor extentive et la chiere vermaille et replecion de[s] veines del chief et les euz rouges et meimement la bouche douce. L'aage, la complexion, la region, la diete, le tens de l'an disposés en chaline et en moistesce se signefient que sanc est cause de la dolor. Si la dolor vient de colre, les signes sont iteles: une dolor ague est en le front et meimement en la destre partie, la face citrine* et les eus, la bouche amere. Et les signes particuleres devant dites quant il acordent en ce signefient colere. Mes quant la dolor del chief vient de fleume, la dolor est grevatif, habundance de superfluités par le niés et par la buche aveques un touse, et la face pale* ou subpale, cachie des eus, la bouche mal[s]ade. Et les devant dites particuleres s'il acordent en ce, totes icés choses sont signefié que fleume est matere et cause de la dolor. Et si la dolor vient de humor melancolique*, ce conoist l'en par iteles signes: une dolor grevuse et pesant el chief et meimement en la senestre partie, la face bleue et de terriene color, les euz parfunt, et si est [f.123r] mornes et pensifs et la bouche aigre et ce meime demostrent les devant dites particuleres com il sont froides et secches. Dolor del chief quant il vient de cause loi[n]teine faite del vice de l'estomac si depart de la dolor de cause privee en ce ke la dolor de cause privee est continuele devant manger et aprés. Mes solonc les diversetés de causes que nus dirons aprés si diversent les signes. La dolor del chief que vient del vice de l'estomac si vient a la fiez de colere et a la fiez de fleume et a la fie de melancolie. Et quant ele vient de colere, iteles sont les signes: unes mordications en l'estomac et la boche ert amere, la soif grans et vonche l'en unes choses coleriques. Et est la dolor plus grans devant manger que aprés. Mes come la dolor vient de fleume, si sent l'en une grevance en l'estomac, habondance de salive et la bouche mausade. Et si la dolor vient de melancolie, si sent l'en une dolor en l'estomac et sont les eructations aigres. Vice de scotomie [est] en ceste cause et en cele de fleume. Com au contraire de in[di]gestion si est l'affliction greignor aprés manger que devant. [40] *Cure de dolor que vient de coup*: Cure de dolor que vient de coup: si li doit l'en aider sicome l'e[n] enseigne en la cyrurgie. Mes si la [f.123v] dolor vient de chalor soule, soit dedens soit defors, si li doit om aider des choses qui sont dites en la dolor faite de colere, et mei[me]ment de frois oignemens. Et si la dolor [vient de] soule froidure*, soit dedens soit defors, si li doit om aider des choses que sont dites en la dolor faite de humors froides et meimement de ongnemens* chaudes. Mes notés que quant la dolor vient de sole qualité, que l'en n'a mester de purgation, si de soule alteration non. Dolor del chief fait de sanc garist om en tele manere. Face l'en seigner le malade de la veine del chief et meimement si la dolor est par tot le chief. Mes si la dolor est tant solement en la partie deriere, si face l'en seignier de la veine que est enmi le front. Et si la dolor est plus grans en la partie devant, si le face l'en seigner par le nes et mete l'en une ventuse sans garse en la fosse del col et dous entre les espaules. Et si colere est en cause, se li aide l'en en tele manere. Li ongne l'en le chief de oile rosat et violat et mandragorat. Et face l'en une decoction de semperviva et de oile commune et de vin egre et enongne l'en le chief. Et face l'en emplastre. Et ce est mult tres bone chose contre dolor del chief qui vient de cause chaude. Itel oile ou* oile mandragorat ou autre [f.124r] oile froide li degote l'en es orreilles. Et es narines le* oigne l'en dedens et defors. Et le purge l'en de piles aurees. Mes si la destemprance de l'air chaut est grans, si le purge l'en de mirabolans citrins. Mirabolans aforciés si sont bones contre dolor del chief de colere et de sanc a doner a manger. Et se li malades ne poet dormir por la dolor qui vient de chaude cause, si doit l'en mettre emplastres et oignemens pur faire le dormir des queles nus avons assés dit el traitié de fevres. Dolor del chief qui vient de humor froide garist l'en en tele manere. Face l'en premerement oindre le chief de oignemens moienement chaudes come de dialtea, marciaton, oile laurine. Et aprés oindre le chief de unguento aureo qui especiale est a ceste cause. Pregne l'en castoreum et poivre, mette l'en boilir en ewe corante et un poi de vin egre mellé ensemble. Et moille l'en ens une* esponge et enoigne le chief et face l'en epithime soure. Centaurea et brancha ursina soient quites en oile et en vin et en face l'en emplastre sor le chief. Pregne l'en castoreum et semence de rue agreste et quise l'en en oile et en vin et face l'en emplastre sor le chief. Et li doigne l'en piles diacastorea dous ou [f.124v] trois par les narines et purge l'en de brancha ursina ou de ieralogodion. Et face l'en les autres cures qui sunt escrites en epilensie. Et la dolor que vient de colere qui est en l'estomac, se li doit om aider en tele manere. Li doigne l'en par quatre jors sirop acetous et moiste diete et le purge l'en aprés de cestui vomitu meimement si colere est en la bouche de l'estomac. Et ce poet l'en conustre par les devant dites signes et par les mordicacions en la bouche de l'estomac. Trible l'en la semence atriblicis, radices, rape et les mullie l'en [en] l'ewe boillante et cole l'en l'ewe et doigne l'en la coleure a boivre avec sirop accetous. Mes si la dolor vient de colere qui soit el fons de l'estomac, ce poet l'en conustre par les egestions coleriques. Et le purge l'en lors de oximel ou de aucun autre colagogue* et enoigne l'en le ventre de frois oignemens. Si humors frois que soit en l'estomac fait le chief doloir, si li doit l'en aider en tele manere. Com il avera usé son oximel, se li doigne l'en la devant dite coleure et vomitus patriarche, si la matere est en la bouche de l'estomac. Mes [si] la matere est el fons de l'estomac, si li doigne l'en covenable medicine qui la meine fors par desuz. Et enoigne l'en l'estomac de chaudes [f.125r] oignemens. Et notés qui dolor del chief vient sovent de mult manger et de mult boivre. Et quant ce avient, la principale cure est itele. Dongne l'en au malade ewe chaude et boute l'en en la bouche une plume ou* li metés les dois en la bouche pur voncher. Item notés que dolor del chief si est a la fiez sinthome de fevre et lors si est la cure autretele come nus avons dit el traitié de fevres.

[BOOK III *De egritudinibus oculorum*]

[41] *De maladie des euz.* De maladie des euz: As euz si avienent diverses maladies sicome dolor, flux de lermes, defaute de veue. Dolor des euz si vient a la fies de cause dedens, a la fies de cause defors; de cause defors sicome de chaline ou de froidure de air, de coup, de fumee, de poudre, la quele chose l'en poet soventesfoies savoir par le dit del malade, qui tesmoinera s'il a esté feru ou il a esté en air chaut ou en froit de l'air; dedens, sicome de chaudes ou de froides humors, c'est asavoir de sanc fleumatique ou melancolique ou colerique, la quele chose om conoist par les propres signes de chescon humor. [42] Si la dolor est de sanc, la dolor est infixi[v]us rubor oculorum, les veines des eus emflees et pleines et aparans desfors. L'age, la region, le tens de l'an, la diete, la com[f.125v]plexion qui se acordent en ce meimes si demustrent qui sanc [est en cause]. Mes si fleume ou melancolie est en cause, la dolor est extensive ou agravativa et sont les pauperes emflees et pesans, les euz susblanches ou bleves. Es hores de f[l]eume ou de melancolie si est la infestation plus grant; autresi* come la dolor vient de sanc ou de colere, si est la infliction plus grant*. Come les parties s'acordent en ce meimes, si signefient meime la cause. Mes si la dolor vient de colere, si point et mort sicome pointure faite de aguille, si sont les euz rouges avesques une [color] citrine. Les parties devant dites, s'il acordent en ce meime, si signefient que colere est en cause de la dolor. Quant les euz courent et lerment, ce avient a la fiez de causes dedens et a la fiez de cause dehors; de cause defors sicome de calor de l'air qui dessout les humors ou de froidure estreignaunte qui prent fors les humors del chief et de fumee et de poudre et de odorer choses egres, les queles choses l'en conust par le dit del malade; de cause dedens sicome de chaudes et de froides humors et de habundance de humors corans par incontinence [f.126r] [et] de la feblece de la vertu retentive [el cervel]. Donc solonc la diverseté des causes se diversent les signes. Kar si chaudes humors sont en cause, les euz sont rouges et les lermes que courent eschaufent la face et ardent. Les froides choses profitent et les chaudes nuisent. Si humors froides* sont en cause, les euz sont susblanches ou bleves, si sent l'en les lermes que courent sor la face froide et ne mordent* pas la superficé de la face. Les froides choses nuisent et les chaudes profitent. Mes si habundance des humors est en cause, li flux de lermes ert grant plus que en la devant dite cause. La feblece de la vertu contentive conussons nus par la remocion des devant dites signes. Defaute de veue vient en plusors maneres, sicome por la defaute des espiriz visibiles, de viellesse, de longue maladie que l'en a eu devant, de geuner, de veillier, de croistre et que jo die brefment de totes les choses que muent et atenvisent le cors. Mes si la veue defaut de anathim[i]asi de l'estomac, la defaute de la veue n'est pas continuele, mes interpolaté et crest et menusse solonc la diverseté des viandes que l'en mangue. Mes si la defaute de veue vient de fumosité que lieve de meime le comencement, la [f.126v] defaute de la veue est continuele, ne croist ne amenusse devant manger ne aprés. Lors puet [l'en] bien conustre que verrai opilation est en cause si* la substance de [l']oil est cliere et pure et relusans. Mes les ca[ta]ractes qui

na[i]scent entre le cotele conjunctive et* cornine la* [cotele] uveine rendent* susblanche et la toie remaint defors et trait sa na[i]sse[ance] de memes la conjunctive cotele, si comence a la fiez desus et a la fies desuz et ce est la difference entre toie et maille, que la toie est plus soutive et plus tenve et la maille plus grosse. [43] *Cure*. Cure: Si la dolor vient de coup, la plus sovereine cure si est iceste. Face l'en emplastre sovent desoure de cire et de poudre de comin mellé ensemble et eschaufe [l'en] bien. Kar ele oste la dolor et la ble[ui]sseure et la dolor ensemble. *Autre*. Autre cure por ce meime. Pregne l'en* aloine et secche [l'en] sor une tieule. Et face l'en emplastre trestot chaut sor le leu. Et ce meime poet l'en faire de une drap linge escha[u]vé. Mes si ce est avesques plaie, si soit garie par cyrurgie. Mes si la dolor vient de chaline de l'air, si le doit om laver et froter de ew[e] commune teve, si que la teveté de l'ewe ateigne a la froidure, ou de ewe rosat. Ou l'en moille estoupes en oile violat et mete l'en sore. Et [f.127r] mauves triblees si valent a ce meimes. Mes si la dolor vient de froidure de air, boive li malades un poi de vin pur et quise l'en foilles de laurier en vin pur. Et face l'en le malade receivre la fumee es euz et leve l'en les euz de meime le vin. Et notés que de tele manere de dolor qui vient de froidure ou de chaline de l'air si garist om de legeres. Mes si humor chaut, c'est asavoir colerique ou sanguine, soit en cause, se li doit l'en aider en tele manere. Tot a premer le doit om seigner de la veine del chief e ventuser del col ou entre les espaules et garser, meimement se li cors est plectoriques et li malades soi[t] d'eage et de la force. Aprés le quart jor de l'expurgation si li doigne l'en rubeam trociscatam* avesques ewe chaude. Et mete l'en sor le leu emplastre ou desor le front et sor les temples de poudre de mastic et de aubon de oef. Et aprés lor doit l'en mettre sore choses locales. Mes notés que premerment doit l'e[n] mettre sore apocrastica [et] refroidans desc'a quinse jors. Mes come sanc est botés en l'oil, si doit l'en mettre choses dissolutives et atenuatives*. Si mette l'en del comencement donques verbenam triblee par soi ou avesques aubun de oef ou de oile rosat. Et dissoille l'en can[f.127v]foram en ewe rosat et muillie l'en coton ens et face l'en emplastre sor les euz. Et face l'en autre confection de saffran oriental et de moiel de oef et mete l'en canphoram et ewe rosat et mullie l'en coton dedens et mete l'en sor les euz sovent. Et notés qui dementers que om fait ces aides locales que l'en doit faire fo[men]tacions al front et as temples trois fois ou quatre le jor aveques l'ewe de la decoction de roses. Et boille l'en les roses et face l'en emplastre es euz. Et icés devant dites choses face l'en au comencement de la cause. Mes si li sanc est ja botés es euz, si doit om prendre moels de oef et la poudre de comin et melle l'en ensemble et ce face l'en boillir et moille* l'en coton dedens et face l'en emplastre es euz. Mes si la dolor vient de soule froidure sans apostume, si doit l'en user de chaudes choses alt[er]atives. Et moille l'en coton en oile comune et mette l'en sore. Ou l'en pregne rue et moille l'en en oile et mete l'en sore. Si la dolor est venue de humor froide, si purge l'en le malade de piles aurés ou de benoite ou de diacené scamoniaté. Et aprés li doigne l'en auream aveques vin chaut. Et aprés face l'en icés remedes locales. Pregne l'en rue et nepitam et les escaufe l'en sor une tieule et face l'en [f.128r] emplastre sor les euz. Et pregne l'en coton et moille l'en el jus de rue et de fenoil et mete l'en sore. Mes si la dolor des euz vient de poudre ou de fumee, se li doit om laver les euz de ewe tieve ou de ewe rose. *Contre flux de lermes*. Contre flux de lermes est la cure itele. Se li flux est de froide cause, si espurge l'en le malade de pile[s] aurees ou de ieralogodion ou de piles diacastorei getés ens par les narines. Et doigne l'en diaolibanum avesques vin de la decoction olibani que est mult bone en ceste cause. Et mete l'en ventuse el col avec garse ou entre les espaules. Et face l'en emplastre al front et es temples de la poudre de mastic, olibani, boli, sanc de dragon triblees ensemble sotillement* avec aubun de oef et oveques vin blanc tieve. Les confise l'en bien. Et boille [l'en] mastic et olibanum en vin blanc austeres et dur et auques stiptiques et covre l'en bien la bouche del pot de past ou de gleise, que la fumee ne puisse issir. Et quant il seront bien quites face l'en le malades baisser le chief et boivre la fumee. Et li lieve l'en les euz de meime le vin et li aroise l'en tote la chiere. Et ces meimes chose[s] valent mult encontre dolor des euz qui est venue de froide cause. Mes si li flux est [de] chaude* caus[e], si valent une par[f.128v]tie des devant dites choses sicome simple seignie. Rubea avec ewe rosat dogne [l'en] au soir et si sont bones a doner trois grains de olibano. Mes si la dolor ou le flux vient de fumee ou de poudre ou de manger airons, si est legier a dessoudre et a garir. Si doit l'en laver les euz de ewe tieve ou de ewe rosat. Et si ce avient de habundance de humors qui courent par incontinence, si* estreigne [l'en] le flux sicome il est escrit el flux de froide cause. Mes se le flux vient de febleté de la vertu contentive, se doit om conforter le cervel de quant que l'en poet et li doine l'en opiates covenables. Contre la defaute de veue si est la cure itele. Se la veue defaut par vice de l'estomac, si doit l'en espurgier l'estomac en tele manere. Done l'en au malade oximel squillitique quatre fois ou cinc et le diete l'en de tenve diete et de sorbile*. Et enoigne om sovent l'estomac et le pis de diauté. Et aprés li doigne l'en a manger sen saol des choses salees ou airons sicome formage, oignions, poraus et li doigne l'en a boivre vin fort a plenté. Et aprés dous hores si boive l'en ewe chaude tant come om plus pora. Et mete l'en aprés les dois en la bouche pur [f.129r] faire le voncher. Et s'il sent miels de ce, si est biens, si non, si li dogne [l'en] le colature vomitum* patriarche ou scarpelle. *Espurgement de l'estomac.* Et come l'estomac est espurgés, si li doine l'en la decoction olibani avesque le jus de la decoction d'aluigne et met[te] l'en zucre et doigne [l'en] et si l'en i met de tres bon aloen, si vaudra meuz. Si la defaute de veue [vient] de humor entor le cervel, si purge l'en le humor superfluele de covenable medicine. E jo meimes esprovai que sancsues sont bones a mettre as temples et as narines en ceste cause. Mes si la veue defaut de la defaute des espiris, se li doigne l'en mirabolans condit et li doigne l'en sirop ou mirre soit confite aveques mulse. Et li doigne l'en avec ewe tieve* pliris arconticon, diamargariton et quecunque choses repareillent les espiriz et confortent* le* cervel. Mes si la veue defaut de opilation de[s] ners, si est incurable. Les ca[ta]ractes des eus sont a la fiez curable, a la fiez nient curable. Les curables garist l'en de .i. estrument de cyrurgie, c'est asavoir de .i. aguille. Mes l'en seut rechair en ceste maladie, kar come [f.129v] [li] lius se deut, aprés si fait venir reume. Dont les humors corrent au liu que se deut et font revenir la maladie. Mes la maille en l'oil se est grosse et viels, si garist l'en a peine ou jamés*. Mes del toie qui est plus sottille* garist l'en sovent. Premerement donques doit l'en mettre choses auques legeres et non pas mult solutives, les queles choses se ele[s] ne profitent pas assés, si doit l'en lors metre plus fortes choses. Trible l'en sar[c]ocollam et licium en poudre sottille et destempre l'en les avec ewe rose. Et le mete l'en seccher sovent au solail et les mete l'en .iii. fois ou quatre

ariere en ewe rose. Et les mete l'en derechief secchir au soleil. Et apré[s] face l'en
pudre mult tres sottille et en mette l'en es euz ou par soi ou* avec ewe rose autresi
come collire. Autre. Pudre* est faite des os de mirabolans arses en .i. test et de
canphora et de tucia et le mete l'en es euz ou par soi ou aveques ewe rose. Et mete
l'en plus de la pudre de mirabolans que des autres dous. Autre. Traie l'en fors le jus
de l'escorce des racines de fenoil et le laisse l'en en un vassel de arain noef jors ou
par quinse jors. Et le mete l'en es euz, si esclarciera mult la veue. Autre. [Pregne
l'en] ozimum, racines de [f.130r] fenoil et les mete l'en en boillir en vin blanc desque
les .ii. parties soient degastee. Et mete l'en icel vin es euz. Et ce face l'en premerement. Et si ces choses ne suffisent pas, si mete l'en plus fortes. Pregne [l'en] poivre
noir et oste l'en l'escorce par defors, si que la moule soulement remaine, et mirre et
face l'en pudre et mete l'en as euz, ou par soi ou avec ewe rose. Autre. Pregne l'en
la fente del coufle et sarcocollam, canphoram et face l'en pudre et mete l'en es euz.
Et notés que le[s] uns metent es euz choses mult solutives ou mult corosives sicome
es ustum, fel avium qui vivent de ravine, la quele chose jo ne lo pas, kar la
substance de l'oil com* est tendre et soutille desoudroit* tost par teles choses
metre. Estre les devant dites maladies avienent autres maladies as euz sicome
mangisons et eminencia* oculorum. Pur mangison des euz pregne om la mellior
aloes que l'en pora trover et en face l'en poudre et le destempre l'en de vin blanc et
le laisce l'en issi tote nuit. Et le cole l'en le matin parmi .i. drap delié et enoigne
l'en les euz de cel vin. Autre. Pregne l'en les flors d'arenge* .i. cen[f.130v]trum
galli, gar[iofili] et aloes et mete l'en en une ventose avesque blanc vin et ewe rose.
Et en traie l'en fors l'ewe autresi come le fait le ewe rose et enoigne l'en les euz de
cele liquor. Esprové est. Autre pur mangisons et pur toie en l'oil. Pregne l'en
cendre de sarment et le confise l'en de l'urine de uns enfant et enforme l'en piles*
de tot et les secche l'en et quant il en ert mestier, si en face l'en poudre, si en mete
l'en as euz. Ou om destempre la de ewe rose et la mete om ens. Si le[s] euz aperent
defors contre nature, si mete l'en une ventose el haterel sovent, se li cors est
plectoriques, avesques garse, si non, sans garse. Et icés choses que nus avons dites
sofficent as* euz.

[BOOK IV *De egritudinibus aurium*]

[44] *Por maladie des oreilles.* De maladie des oreilles: Es oreilles si avienent diverses
maladies come dolor avec [a]postume ou sans apostume, plaie, vers, peres* qui
chient ens, ewe et autres petis corseles, sordesce et tinuissement des oreilles. Dolor
sans aposteime si vient a la fie es orilles par chalor dissolutive, a la fiez de froidure
constrictive. [45] Se ele est de chalor, icés sont les signes. Dolor ague, li leus ert
rouges et caus, chaudes choses i sont nusanz et froides bones. Si la dolor [f.131r]
vient de froidure, la dolor sera grieve, li leu ert bleves, les froides choses nuissent et
les chaudes profitent. Des aposteimes des oreilles les unes sont chaudes, les autres
froides, c'est asavoir l'une est de chaude matere et l'autre de froide. Si dolor
donques vient de chaude apostume, si sont les signes iteles: la dolor ague durement, la fevre grant, le leu rouge et chaut. Si la dolor est avec froide apostume, les

signes sont iteles: la dolor greveine mult et la fevre lente et remise. Car apostume de l'oreille n'est ja sans compaignie de fevre, si sent l'en a la fies les extremités des oreilles froydes et les particuleres come il courent ensemble si demustrent chalor ou froidure. Plaie avient soventefois as oreilles de apostume que l'en a eu devant, la quele chose l'en conust par dolor et par la titillation* et par lor porreture qui en est. Vers avienent es oreilles de humors viscoses [et] espessies par l'entreception de l'esperit vivificatif, de qui les signes sont pruritus* [et] titillation*. Et come l'en abandone l'oreille al soleil, si chient en l'oreille soventesfois peres*, eue et sam-blables choses. Et ce poet l'en savoir del malade et les poet l'en a la fies voir au soleil en l'oreille del malade. Sordesce si avient a la fies en tot, [f.131v] a la fiez en partie. Sordesce en tot vient de tote le opilacion des ners detriés, si est assés aperte. Sordesse en une partie vient a la fiez de la particulere opilation et a la fiez des devant dites causes sicome piere que est cheue en l'oreille. Et conust l'en la* par les devant dites signes. Les oreilles tinterunt. Tinissement* vient a la fiez de cause privee come de fumee qui vient de la matere qui est el chief et a la fiez si vient de cause lointeine sicome de vice de l'estomac et de foie. Si li tinisement des oreilles vient de cause privee, si est li tinniss(s)ement continuel. Mes neporquant plus ne meins ne crest ne descrest par maladie des membres plus bas. Mes si li tinnissement vient del vice de l'estomac, si est li tinnissement entrepollat et plus grant aprés manger que devant. Et itels soloient garir par voncher et estre plus seins. Et se ce avient de vice du foie, si sent l'en une dolor greveine entor la foie et apiert l'urine un poi coloree. [46] *Cure.* Si la dolor vien[t] de chalor sans apostume, si doit l'en ovrer et garir la dolor des froides choses alteratives. Oigne l'en l'oreile de oile rosat ou violat par soi. Ou mete l'en le jus strigni o tot et mete [l'en] es oriles itele manere de oiles tieves. Ou face l'en emplastre de co[f.132r]riandre triblé ou quite avec ewe rosat ou violat. Mes si la dolor vient de sole froidure sans apostume, si doit l'en user chaudes choses alteratives. Et moille l'en coton en oile comune et mete [l'en] sore tieve. Ou rue quite en oile degote* l'en en oile musceline tieve et enoigne l'en l'oreille par defors. Et notés que teles maneres des dolors qui sont faites de sole qualité* sont dessouses de legier. Mes si la dolor vient de chaude apostume, si li doit l'en aider de froides choses maturatives, les devant dites onctions froides que nus avons dites en la cure des oreilles que vient de sole chalor. Si vaut mult que l'e[n] seigne le malade de la veine du chief. *Por meurer.* Por meurer face l'en tel oignement. Pregne l'en greesce de veel et gresce de geline et les meules de totes bestes que vus porrés avoir et fundés tot et colés et metés i oile violat et rosat et cire et facés un ongnement et en ongnez l'oreille par defors. Et face l'en ongnement de bure et de mauves quites avec oile violat et face l'en emplastre sore. Ou pregne l'en moiels de oef et oile violat et confise l'en tot ensemble. Et face l'en une estuel delié et boute l'en en l'oreille. Mes si la dolor est de froide apostume, si doit l'en ovrer de ongnemens chaudes maturatives. Quise [f.132v] l'en la racine del liz en oile comune et face l'en emplastre sor l'oreille. Ou l'en quise les racines brance ursine et altee* en oile comune et face l'en emplastre sor l'oreille, si vaudra mult. Autre esprove a rumpre chescune aposteme: quise l'en un ongnon entier en oile et mete l'en la poudre de comin bien molu o tot et le face l'en fendre* parmi et en face l'en emplastre sor l'apostume. Et come l'aposteime sera rumpie, et ce porra om conustre par le flux de la purreture, si doit l'en

mundifier la plaie de la purreture et aprés saner la. Confise l'en donques la poudre
nitri de mel et moille l'en un limignon*, si le bote l'en ens. Autre. Pregne l'en
saugemme, euforbium et la confise l'en en oile [rosat] et aprés la cole l'en et mete*
l'en en[s] la coleure. Et come la plaie est nettié et purgié de ces devant dites
choses, si doit l'en soudre la plaie de la poudre de mastic et de encens sofflee
ens. Ou l'en la confise de oile rosat et moille l'en un limignon ens et mete l'en
sor la plaie. Et s'il a vers es oreilles, si les doit om tuer de verser es oreilles choses
ameres. Donques pregne l'en le jus de foile de peschier ou de aloigne ou de
[calament]. [. . .] amandes ameres [. . .] et li verse l'en es oreilles. Ou l'en trible icés
devant dites choses et les mete l'en quire entre dous foilles desus la cendre chaude.
Et preme [f.133r] l'en fors l'oile et la degote l'en es oreilles. Et notez que les choses
que l'en degote es oreilles doivent estre actuelment chaudes. Autre. Trible l'en
le[s] noiax de pesches et les destempre l'en del jus de persicarie et mete l'en de la
poudre aloes et le cole l'en aprés et degote la coleure es oreilles. Les vers tués en
tele manere s'en issent a la fies avesque la purreture. Si [ne] s'en issent en tele
manere par aux, si les doit l'en traire fors de un croc de fer. *Se ewe est cheue en
l'oreille.* Se ewe [est] cheue en l'oreille, si mete l'en ens laine pigne ou l'en mete
lens une leine que om trove en ces conches* de mer es queles l'en trove ces peres
precioses. Si est apelé par autre non melotida, la quele, s'en nel poet avoir ne
trovoir, si mete l'en ens coton. Autre a ce meme. Destempre l'en piper [et]
euforbium de aucone oile chaude et aprés la cole l'en et degote om tieve es oreilles.
Mes si grain ou perrette est cheue es oreilles, si doit om oigndre les oreilles dehors
de ognemens chaudes. Et aprés le face l'en sternuer et aprés li estopés la bouche et
estreigniez les narines, que de la force de l'esperit saille la piere fors. Si ce ne vaut,
si doit l'en prendre un greile baston bien poli* et l'enogne l'en de terrebentine ou
de glu [f.133v] et li boute l'en en l'oreille tant que il touch[e] a la pere. Et si ce ne
vaut, si mete l'en une ventuse sans garse sovent sor l'oreille pur traire fors la pere
en sucçant. Cure contre sordesce. Premerement doit l'en espurgier le cors ou le
chief de ieralogodion ou de piles aurees et meimement se ele est de cause privee
sicome de opilation del ners optique*. Et aprés la purgation si dogne l'en
auream et come l'en l'avera trois fois ou quatre espurgés et l'en l'avera doné
opiates, si doit l'en aler as adiutoires locales. Degoute l'en oile musceline tieve
et basme, qui est tres bon a ce, et pregne l'en lignum aloes, spicanardi, cassialignea et face l'en pudre et destemprés avec oile et gete l'en le coleure* es oreilles
tieve. Autre. Pregne l'en les someronnes de lorier et spicam nardi et les boille l'en
en bon vin roge en un pot bien covert, que la fumee n'en isse et li face l'en aprés
receivre la fumee parmi .i. calemel. Et itel subfumigacion ne est pas tant solement
a sordesce, ains vaut a tels ja des devant dites choses come pur ewe qui est cheue
en l'oreille et por espurger la purreture de l'oreille et pur tinnissement. Et notés
que sordesce de nativité est incurables et cele que ad duree par .ii. ans ou par trois
si est a paine curable. Si le tinnissement vient de cause privee, si face l'en iceste
[f.134r] cure. Boille l'en la poudre de comin avec le jus de foilles [de] porriaux en
squille cavee ou en .i. oignon cavé et le cole l'en et mete l'en la coleure tieve en
l'oreille. Me[s] si tinnissement vient del vice de l'estomac, si doit l'en purgier
l'estomac et conforter, [si del vice de la foie], si doit l'en curer le foie sicom nus
dirons aprés.

[BOOK V *De egritudinibus narium*]

[1 *De fluxu sanguinis*] [47] *Pur sanc qui ist par les narines.* Sanc* ist par les narines a la fiez par force de nature, a la fiez par force de accident. Par force de accident si cort il par mainte maneres; de habundance par incontinence, de la furiosité de meime le sanc, et de la froidure de l'air par expression, del vice de* l'esplen et del vice du foie et de l'habundance de multes superfluitez, les queles choses sont a distincter par lor propres signes. [48] Kar li sanc que cort par force de nature conoist l'en par ce qu'il cort en jor cretique endementers que la matere* avoié amont par force de nature desront des veines des narines, et s'en ist de* fevre continue et meimement et plus sovent de* sinoque et de l'alievance de la nature [et] de la defaute de la maladie. Flux de sanc par incontinence conoissons nus par les veines* que sont pleine[s] et par ce que l'en a mangé mult diete chaude et moiste* par devant qui* engendre [f.134v] mult sanc et de la sanguine habundance del cors [et] par ce qu'ele ist a grant quantité. Si conoist l'en flux de furiosité de sanc et de aguesse* par* la color del sanc jaune et par ce qu'il mort les narines et art et emflambe et par la diete chaude et secche que l'en avera usé par devant et de l'habitude del cors coleriques. Flux qui vient de froidure si conoist l'en par le froidure de meime l'air. Quant li sans cort par le vice de l'esplen conoissons nus par l'emfleure de l'esplen et par la grevance et par la compression del senestre coste et par ce que li sanc cort par la senestre narrine. Mes quant li flux vient del vice del foie, ce conust l'en par la dolor que om sent desus le* destre coste et par l'urine qui ert coloree et par le sanc qui corra plus de la destre narrine. [49] *Cure.* Cure: Li sanc qui ist par la force de nature ne doit l'en pas estancher. Mes notés que li sanc ne fine en .ii. jors ou en trois de corre en grant* quantité. Kar quant les veines sont overtes, se en est li sanc trais es narines por la voidesce et en ist en grant* quantité. Si torne li flux naturele en tele manere en mauveis accident dont nature se laist veintre sovent. Et ce se conoist par le flux qui est grans [f.135r] et par la febleté du malade le* quel, com il avient, doit l'en estancher, de quele chose nus dirons aprés. Mes si li flux de sanc vient de grant habundance par incontinence*, si traie l'en fors le sanc de la veine del chief, s'il est de la force et de l'age, et li mete om ventuses el col de le noveime an desca au quinzime et entre les espaules. Kar l'en ne doit pas seigner de veine devant que l'en soit de quinze ans ne ventuser ne doit l'en pas devant le novime an. Mes aprés le quinzime an poet l'en seiner et ventuser enseurement. Et si ces choses ne sufficent, si doit l'en metre choses locales sicome nus dirons aprés. Et si flux vient de la malice et de l'anguisse del sanc, si face l'en par art le air froit come de aroiser le pavement entor le malade de ewe froide et de juncher la maison de froides herbes. Et li doigne l'en froide diete come sont scarioles, portulaques, laitues et les garde l'en que il ne gostent de vin. Face l'en sirop de ewe mellonis palestini* et de zucre. Jo avoie en* cure a qui nules remedies locales ne valoient et en fu delivre par itele manere de sirop. Mes si ces choses ne valent, si doit l'en ovrir de choses locales. *Por ovrir de choses locales.* Pregne l'en .i. drap linge et le moille l'en en [f.135v] ewe tres froide [. . .] et l'oste l'en .ii. fois ou trois devant ce

qu'il eschaufe. Mes si l'en poet avoir [ewe rosat], mieuz vaut. La terre dont l'en fait
les poes ou croye sarazinoise destempre [l'en] avec jus de planteine et vin egre fort
et face l'en emplastre au front et a la gorge. Ou l'en face pudre de roses, de sandles
blanches et rouges et de sumac et les destempre l'en de ewe rose et moille l'en ens
coton ou estoupes et mete l'en sor le front et entor la gorge. Autre. Lapis ematiste
soit destempré sor .i. marbre del jus sanguinarie tant qu'il soit torné en color
sanguine et moille l'en ens estoupes et li mete l'en es narrines. Et face [l'en] al
malade succhier de tele manere les* resolution[s] pur restreindre et clore les
bouches des veines. Autre. Pregne l'en peus de levre et les ardez sor une vassel
chaut ou sor une tieule et l'arde l'en sans flaume avec gome arabic et jus de
planteine et en face l'en une estuel et li boute l'en es narrenes. Autre. Pregne l'en
la poudre antimonii et le suffle l'en es narines, si* restreindra merveillusement flux
de sanc en ardant le. Mes se li flux vient de froidure de air, si est leger a garir.
Couche l'en le mala[de] en .i. leu chaut et li face l'en fomentacions au front et a*
tot le chief de ewe chaude. Si le flux del sanc vient del vice del splen, si garise om
le splen sicome nus di[f.136r]rons aprés. Si ce avient del vice du foie, si garise l'en
la foie sicom nus dirons en la propre chapitre du foie. Mes tant i a que om mete
une ventuse sor le sumet du foie avesques garse ou sauns garse, si aidera mult.

[V,2 *De fetore narium*] [50] *Por puor de nes.* Puor de nes si vient des humors qui
descendent du chief et de une caroigne qui siet es narines, la quele porrist par
longe demorre [et] de la quele en ist une fumosité corrumpue et se melle avesque
l'air et fait le nes puir. Si na[i]scent unes quistures es narines des humors agues. Si
naist une char superfluele es narines des humors superflueles que [est] apelé polipum. Si doit l'en donques distincter les causes par lor propres signes por varier la
manere de l[a] curation solonc la diverseté des causes. [51] Puor de[s] narines qui*
vient des humors corrumpues conoist l'en par ce [que] l'une des narines ou ambuedous ert estopee et en ist une humor a la fiez corrumpue et puans. Les postules
conoist l'en par un ardor qui li malades sentira el nes. Polipus poe[t] l'en conoistre
tot a veue. [52] *Cure.* Puor de nes doit l'en garir en tele manere. Purge l'en le
malade de ieralogodion ou de theodoricon* anacardis ou de piles qui sont faite[s]
de ces choses. Enong[f.136v]ne l'en le chief de oile comune chaude. Mete l'en oile
musceline es narines et destempre l'en les piles diacastorei de jus de mente et de
vin tieve et le gete l'en ens par les narines. Et aprés le donés opopiram ou auream
[et] del jus decoctionis olibani o tot. La greine olibani vaut mult. Et face l'en le
malade succier sovent ewe chaude parmi le nes pur dessoudre les humors qui sont
englués* par dedens [et] a faire issir. Et se om ne les porra issi mener fors, faites .i.
estuel des racines mali terre et l'enongnez de oile et li metés es narines et le laissés
ileuc par .iii. houres et aprés le traez fors. Et come les humors sont dessoudes en
tele manere, si poent largement estre mis hors. Se doit om mettre une ventuse el
haterel deriere avesque garse. Et enoignés les quitures des narines de oignement
blanc ou de oile rosat. Ou face l'en tel ognement qui i soit tres bon. Prengnez les
somerones de ronces et le[s] extremités de seu et les triblés bien et les metés boillir
avec oile rosat et pressés hors le oile et metés o tot cire blanche fundue et poudre
de encens ou de mastic [et] faites ongnement et en oignés les quittures. *Polipum.*
[P]olipum garist l'en de choses courosives en tele manere. Espurgés avant le

malade et donés opia[f.137r]tes et faites une estuel de apostolicom et metés sore avec la poudre eris usti ou aristologie ou de hermodactilis et li metés es narines. Et se li polipus est petit, si vaudra ce mult. Mes se li polipus est grant, si le covient trencher et quire sicome l'en enseigne en cirurgie.

[BOOK VI *De egritudinibus oris*]

[1 *De ulceribus et pustulis oris*] [53] *Pustules.* Pustules, ulcerations et fendaches avienent sovent en la boche et es levres et es gencives et si avienent sovent unes inflations es gencives et es levres. [54] Come pustules et les quitures vienent de sanc, si sont rouges et quant eles sont de colere, si sont jaunes ou de amertume avesque chalor. Les ulcerations conoist om par veue et par la purreture qui en cort. Les fendaches des levres et les inflations des gencives conust l'en par veue. [55] *Cure.* [L]es pustules garist l'en en tele manere. Premerement si met om ventuse avec garse el col et le seigne om des veines qui sont desus la langue. Et face om gargarisme de mel rosat et de ewe tieve et enoigne l'en les pustules de diamoron. Contre ardor de pustules oigne l'en les pustules del jus de morele ou de semperviva tieve. Les pustules evanissent par les devant dites choses et a la fiez si depecent et devenent ulcerations*. Dont contre ulceration de bouche doit om premerment [f.137v] faire ice: mettre une ventuse el col deriere et destempre om dragagant avec ewe rose tant que ele soit tote glueuse et enoignez les ulcerations de tot. Ou l'en melle o tot la poudre amidi et penidii et enoigne om le[s] ulcerations et si vaut ce meismement a ceus qui comencent a garir de fevre. Cil soloient avoir ulceracions en la bouche de l'aguesce de fevre. *Autre.* Autre: Destempre l'en licium* de ewe rosat et mete l'en es ulceracions. Et ce est tres bone cure as enfans qui ont ulceracions en la bouche. Autre. Pregne l'en les somerones lentisci et les boille l'en en fort vin et lieve om de ce les ulceracions. Et ce vaut a la corosion des gencives. Autre contre purreture et corosion des gencives. Lieve om le leu de bon vin tieve avec aisil ou de ewe salee fort tant que le sanc* en isse. Et aprés si mete l'en une poudre sore qui soit fait des extremités des chancres de flueve et de cinamonie. Ou om face poudre de roses et de cinamonie, de girofle, de nois muscates en tele proporcion: de roses et de cinamome, de girofle et de nois muscates owellement, mes mete l'en des deus devant en duble plus que des deus deraines, et ceste poudre metés es leus qui sont mangiés. A[utre] mult tres bone. Chauz vive soit [f.138r] destempré avesques vin egre et le mete [l'en] seccher en un forn tant que l'en puisse faire poudre. Et mete l'en la quarte part de orpiment et aprés la poudre des especes aromatiques come de roses, de cinamone, de girofle, de espic, de nois muscates. Iceste soit mellé av-esques les devant dites choses en tele proporcion que les .ii. pars soient de cauz et de orpiment et la tierce des especes aromatiques. Iceste poudre mete l'en es leus qui sont mangés, si refait merveileusement les [gencives mangés par les] dens qui sont cheus. Et de ceste chose si usoit .i. sage mire de Salerne come le leu comence a achancrer. Nus garisons le inflation des gencives en tele manere. Premerement* doit l'en metre ventuses el col avesques garse. El quint jor aprés le mete l'en soz* le menton. Diz jors* ou quinze aprés mete l'en sancsues sor le leu de l'inflacion. Mes

contre fendaces des levres face l'en teu remede: le* enoigne l'en soulement de mel,
ou destempre l'en la poudre de muskes arses avesques mel et mete l'en sor le leu.
Autre. Face l'en poudre de racines de portulagues arses et les confise l'en de mel et
enoigne l'en les fendaces. Esprovee chose est.

[VI,2 *De fetore oris*] [56] *La puor de la bouche*. La puor de la bouche si vient a la fiez
de la purreture des gencives et de quitures qui na[i]ssent en la bouche. [f.138v] A la
fiez si vient* de la mauvesse habundance des membres esperitez, a la fiez del vice
de l'estomac, c'est asavoir des humors corrumpues el estomac. Puor de bouche si
vient a la fiez des quitures et de la purreture des gencives. Et la garise l'en en teu
manere come nus avons dit en la premere chapitre. Mes la puor de la bouche qui
vient de la male habundance des membres esperitez, si est continuele et dure
autresi bien aprés manger come devant. Et ceste poet [l'en] destorner, et garir non.
Mes la puor de la bouche qui vient del vice de l'estomac si est entrepollat grant
devant manger, aprés manger petite ou nule. Et en garist om bien de choses
extersives et confortatives. [57] Cure. Premerement li doigne l'en oximel divisif et
aprés li doigne l'en aucone chose qui li face voncher et li doigne l'en aprés manger
choses salees et acceteuses* et airons sicome nus avons dit en la cure de la defaute
de* veue del vice de l'estomac. Aprés la expurgation li doigne l'en auream ou
opopira[m] et le vin de la decoccion ligni aloes ou de mastic. Si vaudra mult. Face
l'en del poudre ligni aloes, piles macedoine, gariofile, nucis muscate et cardamome
et les confise l'en de vin aromatiques ou de ewe rosat ou dragagant avra esté
tempré lens pur faire les poudres meus aherdre ensem[f.139r]ble. Et en face l'en
piles de tot. Iteles maneres des piles sont bones a tenir desuz la langue por oster la
puor de la bouche qui vient des membres espiriteus. Diamargariton et laictuaires
confortatives et choses aromatiques si valent mult. Notez que les poudres nucis,
ambre et ligni aloes et des autres choses tenves suz la langue amende mult et oste la
puor de la bouche.

[VI,3 *De dolore dentium*] [58] *Dolor des dens*. Dolor des dens si vient a la fiez du vice
del cervel, a la fiez de vice de l'estomac; de vice del cervel sicom de chaudes
humors ou de froides qui degoutent et decourent de lui, qui mullient et temprent
les ners de[s] dens et les font dolir; del vice de l'estomac vient la dolor des dens
a la fiez de froides humors, a la fiez de chaudes, qui sont dedens lui, des queles
une fumosité sort et monte as ners des dens et les mort et les greve et en fait
une dolor, les queles l'en conust par lor propres signes. [59] Si la dolor vient des
chaudes humors qui degoutent del chief, la dolor est ague et poignante et la face
vermaille. Si la dolor vient de froidure, la dolor ert mendre et le chief pesant et la
chere pa[le] et enflee. Mes si la dolor vient de chaudes humors qui sont el estomac,
la dolor ert ague et la gorge ert aspre et secche avesques une soif et une amertume
de bou[f.139v]che. Et si la dolor vient de froides humors qui sont en l'estomac, ce
conustra l'en par la remotion* des devant dites signes, de l'acetouse eructacion et
de la bouche mal[s]ade. Et notez que la dolor de dens qui vient del vice de cervel
afflit et tient a la fiez pa[r] diz houres et a la fiez par tot le jor sanz interpolation.
Mes quant la dolor vient de vice de l'estomac, si afflit une houre ou dous et aprés si
entrelaist.

[VI,4 *De vermibus in dentibus*] [60] Vers si na[i]ssent es dens des humors qui porrissent es cros des dens et ce conust om par les mangisons et par les titilacions et de voir vers, kar come [om] leve les dens de ewe tieve, si porra om voir les vers qui noent en l'ewe. [61] Cure. Si la dolor vient de chaudes humors qui descendent del chief, si le face l'en seigner de la veine del [chief], s'il est de l'age et de la force. Ou l'en li mete ventouses el col sanz garse et li doigne l'en medecine que mundefie le sanc et qui purge colere sicome la decoction de violettes, de prunes, de cassiaf-istle, thamarindes, mauve et mete [l'en] .i. once de mirabolans citrins. Mes si la dolor vient de froides humors, si li doigne l'en blancham ou piles aurés. Mes si la dolor vient de chaudes humors qui sont en le estomac, si le purge l'en de oximel, si de froides humors, de benoite ou de autre medici[f.140r]ne covenable. Mes notez que le[s] humors qui sont en la bouche de l'estomac, soient chaudes, soient froides, que l'en doit mener hors par voncher si autre chose ne destorbe sicome anguoisse del piz ou* ptisicle et de semblables choses. Mes come les humors sunt en le funs de l'estomac, si les doit hom mener fors par desuz. Aprés ce qui il sera purgiés, si li doigne l'en aueam ou mitridate ou ygiam avesques la decoction olibani. Mes si li flux vient de foreines veines, face l'en emplastre al front et as temples de la poudre masticis, olibani, boli, sanguinis draconis destemprés de vin et de aubun de oef. Et aprés si doit l'en ovrer des choses locales. Et face l'en sacellacions au leu par defors de sel et de nitre ars sanz nule licor. Et li face om tenir aucone des devant dites opiates dessoudes aveques vin ou de jus de mente sor le dent malade. Et face l'en tenir vin egre de la decoction des racines titimalli si chaut com li malades porra suffrir. Les uns dient que le vin de la decoction(s) ellebori si vaut a ce meime, mes garde [l'en] bien que la force de lui ne entre dedens et dessoille les membres, kar eleborus si est fort et venimeuse. Mes jo croi neporquant qu'il profitera mult si l'en fait emplastre par defors de elleboro et de mente qui[f.140v]tes en vin. Et si ces choses ne sufficent pas, si doit om prendre une bouchete de fraine ou de ciprés qui soit a la mesure del pertuis del dent et le bote l'en tot ardant dedens tant que l'en sente l'ardor et la chalor en la racine del dent. Si est mult tres bone chose contre dolor de froide cause. Et ce meimes [face l'en] de une broche de fer – mes mieus vaut se ele est de argent ou de or – boté parmi .i. tuel de fer. Mes mieus vaut si li pertuis del dent est emplis de triacle tantdis com l'en mete en[s] la broche et l'en quist le dent. Autre. Overe l'e[n] une veine qui est en l'oreille et laisse l'en un poi de sanc issir fors. Et aprés la quise l'en un poi de un fer chaut. Si ces choses ne valent riens, la deraine ovre est que l'en traie hors le dent sagement o totes les racines de unes tenailles. Kar les racines remainent a la fiez, si est la deraine error peor que la premere. Si le doit l'en traire fors quant il* avra esté seignee et purgé et quant [l'air] est cliers et non pas reumatiques et meimement si le dent losche par soi et come l'en* n'a nule pour de suffocation. Et aprés face l'en gargatum [de] aisil, de la decoction de gales et des escorses de poume gernates et de roses. Les uns dient que l'en [f.141r] poet traire fors le dent legierement saunz dolor de la lie de olive ou del lait* titimalle confises de past et mises sore ou de gome de ere ou del jus celsi, mais c'est faus, kar jo l'ai esprovee. Les vers qui sont es dens tue l'en en tele manere. Verse l'en en le dent del jus centauree ou de aucone herbe amere et les tue l'en neis des pilles que nus avons dit contre les vers des oreilles. Autre. Mente et opium mellé ensemble mete l'en sore. Ou l'en face de ces choses meimes une estuel delié et le bote l'en en le pertuis del dent. Et a ce meime si vaut fumigation faite de la fumee de la semence cassilaginis* mise sor les carbons ou sor une tieule ardant. Et aprés la fumigation* si leve l'en la bouche de ewe et le gete l'en hors en un basin, si apariront les vers faus noant parmi le ewe. Mes si les dens sont relaschiés par aucune chose, si face l'en emplastre entre les gencives et les levres de la poudre olibani, masticis, ladani et storacis calamite et les confise l'en en tele manere. Ladanum et storax dessoudes ensemble soient et les frote l'en entre les mains et melle l'en o tot les dous devant dites choses. Si est mult bon contre corosion des gencives et por afermer les dens qui sont laschiés. Ou l'en pregne poivre, sel, piretru[m] [f.141v] owellement et en face l'en poudre et la destempre om de mel escumé et faites emplastre as gencives. Mes ains le faites bien gargater avesques ewe tieve et frote l'en le malade tant que le sanc en isse. Et si li malades soit plectoriques, si le purge l'en avant de covenable medecine*. Mes quan[t] l'en ad les dens endormis de froidure, si les garist l'en par manger aux et portulaques et formage.

[BOOK VII *De egritudinibus spiritualium*]

[1 *De relaxatione uvule*] [62] *De la luvete*. Sequitur de uva. Uva si est une char que pent el palais, si est grelle amont et grosse aval et est ausi en forme com .i. grape ou une mamele. Et si a dous pertuis, un amont, si est plus large, et .i. aval, si est plus estrois, que l'umor ne isse fors en trop grant quantité et soit caus[e] de nuissance*. Et l'office de ceste membre est de espurger* le chief de superfluele humidité. Dont ele est apelé uva por ce que ele tient en soi humidité, sicome fait la grape, ou por la forme de lui, kar ele est par amont grelle et par aval grosse autresi come grape. Iceste si lasce a la fies par l'umor fleumatique qui descent en lui, dont om touse, qui* enpece la vois et [sunt] mult autres accidens males. Et a la fiez si enfle par l'umor de sanc ou de fleume ou de melancolie ou de colere. Et le inflation et re[f.142r]laxation poet om aparceivre come om ovre la bouche et l'en abesse la langue aval. Mes come le inflation vient de aucun humor, cest poet l'en conustre par les* propres signes de chescun humor. [63] Kar si li sanc est en cause, li leus ert rouges et enflés et la bouche douce. Mes si li enfleure vient de fleume, li leus ert emflés et pallist et la bouche ert mal[s]ade et pleine de salive et la dolor petite. Mes se ele vient de colere, l'enflure ert petite et la dolor poignante et la bouche amere. [64] *Cure*. Cura contra relaxationem uve. Purgez le chief de piles aurés ou l'en li doigne rubeam ou di[a]olibanum ou auream avesques vin decoctionis olibani. Et face l'en premerment gargarisme confite de roses, de gome arabic, psidia, balaustia, galla quites en ewe de ploie et en aisil. Et face l'en gargater au matin et au soir. Et face le jur aprés gargarisme consumptif et deseccatif ou soient mises aucunes choses mollificatifs en tele manere: .ii. onces piper, piretrum, fiques secches, uve passes et boille l'en en vin douz et les colés et donés la coleure a gargater. Ou l'en gargate diamoron* avesques vin douz. Ou l'en leve en haut l'uve de la poudre cinnamonii. Mes avant le lieve l'en en haut del poucier ou de le meine doi*. Mes les uns la [f.142v] lievent en haut sotillement par art owelement et tyrent le malade parmi les chevols .iii. foiz ou quatre le jor par detriefs. Et ce vaut mult. Au comencement aurea avesque oile musceline tieve si est bone a metre sor la vertiz del chief res. Ou l'en quise l'uve de .i. dener d'or ardant ou de aucun estrument covenable a ce faire, si que le extremité de l'uve gise sor l'or. Mes si li inflation vient de sanc, si le face l'en seigner. Mes si ele vient de fleume ou de colere, si le purge l'en de covenable medicine. Et face l'en les devant dites gargarismes et li doigne l'en opiates et les devant dites aides. Et si totes ces choses ne sofficent, si le doit l'en couper au derein amont la ou ele est plus greile, kar, sicom nus avons dit devant, le pertuis amont est plus greile et aval plus large. Et si porra l'en avoir poor de suffocacion pur l'abundance du flux. Mes ce doit l'en faire avesques grant cautele come le malade est bien espurgés et quant l'en li avera doné les devant dites opiates et quant li tens est beaux et clers et non pas reumatiques, sicome l'en trove en pronostiques.

[VII,2 De squinantia] [65] Squinancie. Squinancie si est une aposteime qui avient en la gorge qui a .iii. especes. Kar a la fiez tote la [f.143r] matere est coillé dedens en ysmom en .i. foillet qui est entre ysophagum et tracheam arteriam, si est la prime* espece que l'en apele quinancia et la conust l'en par ce que l'en sent une dolor mult grant, se n'i parra point de enfleure par defors et neis come l'en ovre la bouche, si ne verra om nule enfleure par dedens. Et la conust l'en encore par ce que ele ne vendra ja sanz fevre ague et par le impediment de la vois et par ce que li malades ne poet avoir sa aleine. Et si seut le malades demostrer le leu de la maladie de son doi. Et ceste espece si est incurable. Dont Ypocras si dit que la quinancie que ne apiert pas en la gorge est mortele et memement come la dolor [est] tres ague. Iceste espece se ocist le premer jor ou le secund ou le tiers jor ou le quart jor. A la fiez si est la matere conquillie en mendre quantité* par dedens et en greignor quantité* par defors. Et ce est lors la secunde espece que est apelee sinancia et sil conoist l'en par la dolor [meins ague] et par un poi de inflacion qui apparra par defors et par la fevre que ert meins ague et par ce que l'en aleinera mieus en ceste espece que en l'autre. Et de ceste garist l'en a peine. A la fiez tote la matere est conquillie par defors et si est la [f.143v] tierce espece que l'en apele squinancia. Et la conoist l'en par la grant enfleure qui apara par defors et par la fevre qui serra lente ou nule et la dolor petite et se a om bien s'aleine sans nule grevance. Et ceste espece ne ocist pas se le enfleure ne torne par dedens. Et vienent iteles maladies principaument de fleume et secundaument de sanc. Mes relement avient de mel- ancolie ou de colere, la quele chose l'en conoist par les propres signes. [66] Kar come sanc est en cause de ceste maladie, ce conoist l'en par la fevre qui ert ague et par la dolor qui ert grant et la face rouge et la bouche douce et les veines pleines, l'urine coloree et espesse. Et si fleume est en cause, la face ert pale, la bouche malsade* et la dolor remise et la fevre lente et l'urine descoloree ou meinement* coloree et espesse. Mes si colere est cause de ceste maladie, la face ert vermaille et la dolor ague et la fevre tres ardante et la bouche amere et l'urine coloree et tenve et jaune pardesus. [67] Cure. Cure: Le premer jor le face l'en seigner de cephalica, mes ne traie l'en pas de sanc en grant quantité, me[s] sovent et petit. Et le secund [jor] si le fetes seigner de une veine que est desuz la langue et le face l'en ventouser en la fonteine del col ou entre les [f.144r] espaules. Et s'il a le ventre serré, si li face

l'en clistere mollitif*. Et s'il n'a pas le ventre serré, li face l'en clistere mordificatif
de ewe salee et de la decoction mercurialis et melle l'en o tot mel et oile ou
benoite ou autre medicine scamoniaté et la cole l'en et le gete l'en ens la coleure
por atraire la matere aval. Et aprés si face l'en aides locales. Mes notez que les uns
soleient mettre choses froides et durement apocrastiques, la quele chose nus defen-
dons a fere en ceste maladie et en aposteimes de membres espiritez. Kar a la fiez
iteles maneres de choses par lor grant constriction* si ameinent suffocation. Dont
l'en doit metre ens choses meinement* froides. Et encuntre l'ardor del leu si doit
l'en en oindre le leu de oile rosat ou de violat tieve. Et quise l'en mauves en oile
violat ou rosat et face l'en emplastre. Et aprés mete l'en choses dissolutives et
maturatives. Quise l'en bran en oile rosat et en ewe et face l'en emplastre sor le
leu. Tr[i]ble l'en alteam*, brancam ursinam, mauves avesques oint de pors fres. Et
face l'en emplastre sor le leu et le renovele on sovent*. Et moille l'en sovent
esponge en oile tieve et mete l'en sore. Et se li face l'en gargater choses mollitives
et consumptives que nus [f.144v] avons dit en la cure de uve. Et notez que en ceste
maladie ne en autres que soleient venir de reume ne doit l'en pas mettre es
gargarismes choses dissolutives mult come stafisagriam, kar nuisent plus que eles
ne aident. Mes com l'en voit que li malades doit esteindre*, si doit om [prendre]
aucune buschete ou aucune estrument bien poli, si li doit l'en ovrir la bouche et
ficher ens por depecer la pelete de l'aposteime. Mes il covient que l'en face mult
cointement et mut sagement. Jo nel fis unques, mes mon bon pere le fist, kar come
il jueit* .i. jor a un home de Salerne as escheks*, si li vit suspris de une squinancie
et estendre et li mostroit la maladie de son doi sicome celui qui ne pout parler. Et
quant mun pere aparceut la cause, se li ovri la bouche de une quiller et li bota
busche en la gorge et depessa la pel de l'apostume. Et en issi le sanc en grant
quantité et en fu li malades delivre en tele manere.

[VII,3 *De raucedine vocis*] [68] *Esroüre*. Esroüre et enpecement de la vois si avient
en maintes maneres et de* maintes causes. Mes de ces choses principaument: de
secchece et de mostece et de la defaute des esperiz et de la vertu. De secchece
vient ele en .ii. maneres. Et en une manere de secchece que fet .i. inequalité et de
.i. autre que restreint les conduis [f.145r] de l'air. Kar come la veine par ou la vois
s'en ist, que l'en apele tracheam arteriam, en devient aspre par secchece, si ensieut
une inequalité et de l'inequalité si vien[t] la enroüre de la vois et le impediment.
Item de secche[ce] qui restreint les arteres et les conduis del polmon si ensiut la
incontinence de ambesdous. De humidité si vient l'enflure en .ii.maneres. Ou ele
vien[t] de humidité contenue es vasseux sicome es veines et meimement de sanc
ou de fleume* qui degoute de[s] soveraines parties, kar li sanc qui sorhabunde si
moille et destent les veines. Dont les condiuz sont estrescez et la voiz est enpescé*.
Fleume ensement qui degoute del chief en tracheam arteriam et es conduiz del
polmon si ovre [et] meine la inconvenience des devant dites choses. De la deffaute
des esperiz et des vertus vient enpescement* de voiz, kar de la motion des e[s]periz
et de la force des vertus si seut la voiz estre enpescé. Les causes doit l'en deviser par
lor propres signes. [69] Come la enroüre ou le impediment de la vois vient de
secchesce, ce conoist l'en par la touse qui er[t] secche et poignture* es membres
espiritez autresi come l'en fust point d'espines, par la greillesce del col, et par la

megresce de tut le cors. Et come la enroüre vient de sanc, [f.145v] ce conoist l'en par la touse qui ert un poi moistes et par la chere vermaille et par la aparisansce des veines et par la douçor de la bouche et par ce qui li sanc qui soleit core par les narines et par la bouche cesse a coure et par la seignie entrelassié. Et come le enroüre vient de fleume degotante, ce conoist l'en par la tousse moiste et par la bouche que ert mausade et par l'abundancc de salive. Et [de] la defaute des vertus et des esperiz vient le enroüre a la fiez et ce conust l'en par la febleté et la megresce de tot le cors et par juner et par flux et, pur briefment dire, de totes les choses qui amegrissent et atenvissent le cors. [70] *Cure*. Cure: Premerement li doit l'en ordeiner sa diete. Mes notez quant le enroüre dure .i. an, a peines en garist l'en jammés. Come l'en trenche l'uve pur ceste cause et le enroüre dure encore aprés, si est la maladie incurable. Mes quant la enroüre vient de secchesce, si doit l'en garder de choses* salees et agues et frites. Doigne l'en ptisane et farine d'orge et amilum quit avesques ptisane, se li doigne l'en forment et li face l'en manger bure fres en* ses quisinages et oes mous quites en ewe. Et li doigne l'en a boivre de la decoction de dragagant et de gome arabic et de licorice et li face l'en tenir en la bouche chescune par soi ou totes ensemble. Et li doigne l'en [f.146r] a boyvre dragagant, amilum, gome arabic, semence cito[n]iorum, semence bombacis* et mauves et trible l'en et enforme l'en piles avesques l'ewe de dragagant et les doigne l'en a tenir desuz sa langue. Et lor doigne l'en letuaires moistes sicom [dia]dragagantum, diapen[i]dion et le lectuaire mon pere por restorer l'umidité. Et aprés face l'en choses locales et enoigne l'en le piz et tracheam arteriam de bure fres. Et face l'en emplastre de mauves quites en oile comune et face l'en baign de l'ewe de la decoction de mauves. Et si le enroüre vient de sanc, si le face l'en seigner. Et si ele vient de fleume qui degoute del chief, si li doigne l'en purgacions et les devant dites opiates et li dogne l'en o tot les choses que nus avons dit de catarre faite de fleume. Et estre ice face l'en fomentacions de paille de orge et de la cendre ladani, storax calamita et boille l'en en ewe et face l'en au malade receivre la fumee entor* les jambes* pur bien suer. Et li lieve l'en les pés et les jambes de meime l'ewe jusque au genous et les mains et les bras desca as espaules. Et puis les envolupe l'en bien de .i. beau drap linge. Et aprés li doigne l'en oes quit [ou] depeschiés desor les carbons [et] en la cendre* et fiques* secches emplis de la pudre de poivre. Et boille l'en [en] iteu manere des figues avesques [f.146v] poivre en vin dous et face l'en gargater le vin. Et doigne l'en crespeaux faits* de somerones de horties triblés et avesque moels des oes. Et enoigne l'en le piz et tracheam arteriam de diauté ou de marsiaton et de semblables choses. Et face l'en sacellacions de la pudre de comin [et de] pulegium* entor les membres esperitez. Diaciminum alexandrinum*, si est mult bone en ceste cause. Mes quant la esroüre vient de la febleté de la defaute de[s] vertus et des esperiz, si li doit l'en aider en tele manere des choses resumptifs et confortatives et des choses que nus avons dites en la cure de fevre ethique.

[VII,4 *De tussi et asmate*] [71] *Por le tousse.* Touse si est la offension des esperiz en tracheam arteriam. Si vient a la fiez par conpassion et a la fiez par passion. Par compassion come ele vient de autre maladie sicome de l'estomac et de emfleure del foie ou de l'esplen, sicom en icés qui sont ydropiques ou en pleuresie ou en periplemonie. Les causes, les signes, les cures quere l'en en lor propres chapitres. Par maladie si vient touse a la fiez de cause [privee] et non pas de ailliors sicome nus avons dit devant et si vient [de] .iii. causes; de secchesce, de froidure, et de humidité. [Si vient a la fie] de secchesce qui fait la gorge aspre et desyuele, dont touse est la desiuele allision de l'air et quant la chalor est forclos, [f.147r] a la fiez defors, si ameine une touse par l'effect de secchesce. Et si vient a la fiez le tousse de la froydure del polmon qui restreint tracheam arteriam. Dont les esperis corocent come il nen poent issir franchement, dont il font toussir. De humors vient la tousse en .ii. manere, kar a la fiez vient de humor qui degote del cervel ou d'umors qui sont es membres espiriteus, la quele chose l'en poet conoistre et distincter par les signes. [72] Tousse de secchesce conoist l'en de fumee ou poudre* que l'en a eu* devant ou par ce que l'en sentira unes pointures par dedens et par la tousse qui ert secche sans emissions de superfluités et par le megresse del cors. Tousse de froydure conoist l'en par la chere pale et par la froydure de l'air et par ce que chaudes choses li font bien et froydes mal. Tousse qui vient d'umor qui degote del cervel conoist l'en par la tousse moiste et par la muscilaginité* des narines et par l'abundance de salive et par la titillation de l'uve et del palat. Mes si ce avient de l'hum[i]dité entor les membres espiritels et qui ne cort pas del cervel, si est sans titillacion de l'uve et del palat et sans muscillaginité des narrienes, si est la tousse moiste sans rascacion et en issent les superflueles* choses par aval. [73] Asma. Disma* si est apelee une maladie que l'en aleine a grant peine et vient principaument de .ii. causes, [f.147v] c'est asavoir de secchesce et de moistesce. Kar de secchesce que restreint le poumon, qu'il ne poet ovrir ne clore, de ce si vient l'asme. Et si vient de moistesce que enpesce et destorbe le poumon a movoir. Et solonc les diverses positions des humors si sont les especes d'asma* diverses. Kar a la fiez humor superfluele sorhabunde defors en la superficé del poumon, de la quele pesantime le poumon est chargés, si qu'il ne poet pas overir* legierment. Et ceste espece de asme si est apelé sancsugium. A la fiez l'umor sorhabunde dedens es conduiz du poumon, dont li poumon ne poet pas clore franchement por la entreposicion de eux. Et si est lors la secunde espece que est dite ane[litus]. Kar cil qui travaillent en ceste espece travaillent* en hanelant. Et sovent sorhabunde l'umor par dedens et par defors. Dont le poumon ne poet pas delivrement ovrir ne clore. Et lors si est la terce espece que est apelé ortomia, id est spiritus rectitudinis. Kar cil qui travaillent de ceste espece travaillient tut owellement com il envoient hors lor aleine que quant il la reprenent. Et ensi sont il .iii. especes de asma solonc .iii. positions del leu de l'humor superfluele. [74] Asma de secchesce conoist om par la touse secche et par la megresce du cors et par la greilleté del col et par la soif [f.148r] et par l'aspreté de la langue et par la gorge et par la fevre et par le juner et par les autres choses que atenvisent le cors. Et si delitera li malades en atraire l'air moiste. Mes notés quant asma vient de secchesce, les devant dite[s] especes ne poent legerment estre distinctés ne devisees. Kar a la fiez il travaillient et en atraiant lor aleine a eus [. . .] et a la fiez en l'un et en l'autre. Mes quant l'asme vient de humidité, si vient mult sovent avesques reume et crache l'en mult et li malades se delite mult de atraire l'air chaut. Et si n'est pas la extenuacion del cors si grant com ele fust de secchesce. Nos traitons de tousce et de asmate tot ensemble por ce que l'en garist ambesdous par une meime diligence. [75] *Cure*.

Cure: Si la tousce est venue de froidure, oigne l'en le piz de oile laurine. Ou l'en moille une esponge en oile chaude, si li mete l'en sor le piz et li coverez bien, qu'il sue bien. Vin de la decoction cimini, calamenti li* doigne l'en a boyvre; l'ewe* decoctionis cimini, calamenti, pulegii face* l'en boillier avesques farrin[e] d'orge et doigne l'en au malade. Et de ceste garist l'en tost. Mes si la tousse ou l'asme vient de secchesce, doigne l'en dragagantum, dyapenidion, electuare a restorer l'umidité avesques ptisane et [f.148v], que jo die briefment, face l'en les devant dites remedes contre raucedinem de secchesce. Et notez que teu manere de maladie seut torner en arteticam* passionem, la quele, [si] est anciene*, est* incurable. *Por la tousse.* Tousce ou asme qui vient de humidité qui degote del cervel, si doit l'en garir des choses que nus avons dit en catarre. Et si la tousse dure encore ou se ele vient de humidité qui est entor les membres espiriteus, si li doigne l'en lectuare diacalamentum, dyayris, diapen[i]dion, dyaprassium, dyatrio[n] pipereon et enoigne l'en le pis de [di]alteia mellé avesques arrogon. Armoniacum pur et clier .iiii. onces doigne* l'en avesques vin ou avesques oes mous. Et doigne l'en crespiez fais de foilles centrigalli tribleez avesque moeux des oes avesques ferrine de orge et avesques saim comun. Autre mult tres bone. Mauves, racines de liz, bismauve, brancha ursina soient quites en vin et le garde l'en tant que l'en ait a fere et mete l'en figues secches, uves passes, alemandes, les noiax de pin. Et trible l'en et les quise l'en en vin et en face l'en boiller de ferine de orge. Et lor doigne unes piles que l'en trove en viatique qui sont bones et esprovés a ce. Recevez mirre, storacis calamite*, galbani, castorei, [f.149r] piperis owel peis sis onces, opii .iiii. onces et le confice l'en de ptisane ou dragagant avra esté tempré dedens et doigne l'en noef ou onze. Basmes i est mult bon a doner a ce meime. Aurea alexandrini si est mult bon a ce meimes en basme. Ou l'en doigne .iiii. once[s] de poudre genciane avesques vin ou avesques oes mous. Et ce doit l'en fere quant l'en est em peril. Pregne l'en .i. levre preins et traie l'e[n] hors le leverot del ventre et l'arde l'en en poudre et doigne l'en quatre once[s] as enfans ovec let de femme et dongne l'en ensement le sanc del leverot a boyvre au malade. Et dongne .iiii. onces de orpiment en .i. moel de oef. Et face l'en fumigation de l'orpiment mis sor les carbons. Et li face l'en receivre la fumee par la bouche. Et ce doit l'en fere ensement come l'en est en perril. Les uns font fumigations de suffre, la quele chose jo ne lo pas, perileuse chose est. Et notez que tousse et asme vienen[t] a la fiez de moistesce, et lors si sont bones chaudes choses et secches, a la fiez si vienent de humidité globose, lors si doit om user de chaudes choses et moistes. Et notés que teux maneres de maladies vienent a la fiez de repletion et ce puet [l'en] conustre par la chere vermaille et par les veines grosses et pleines et par le[s] autre[s] signes de habundance de sanc. Et lors doit l'en tant [f.149v] soulement fere seigner le malade tot premerement.

[VII,5 *De peripleumonia et pleuresi*] [76] *Por paralipomenie.* Perypleumonie si est une aposteime qui vient entor le poumon. Si est dite perypleumonia a pery, quod est circum, et pleumon, quod est polmo, quasi circa polmonem. Et pleuresis si est aposte[ime] qui vient es tendrons des costes, la ou diafragma se joint as costes. [77] Les signes de peripleumonie si sont icés: la difficulté* de aleiner ovesques tousse, fevre continuele, dolor greve et meimement entor la senestre mamele et derere en les espaules, les joes rouges et les euz jaunes*, l'urine ruffe ou suzruffe et espesse et bleve*. Les* signes de pleuresie si sont icés: aleiner a peine avesques une tousse menor que en perypleumonie, dolor el coste poignante et ague et meimement quant li malades toust, a la fiez au destre coste, a la fiez au senestre, a la fiez en l'un et en l'autre – kar pleuresis si vient a la fiez au destre coste, a la fiez au senestre, a la fiez en l'un et en l'autre – la fevre continue*, l'urine rouge ou suzrouge, espesse par tot et bleve par devises. Et si vienent icés apostemes et icés maladies de sanc, de colere, de fleume, de melancolie. Mes perypleumonie vient principa[u]ment de fleume, de sanc, secundaument de colere, [f.150r] me[s] relement de melancolie, la queu chose l'en conust par les propres signes de chescun humor. Mes s[i] colere est en cause, la dolor [ert] grans, la fevre ert plus entense et l'en a soif grant et la bouche amere et la salive chaune et l'urine teinte de color jaune ens en la superficé. Mes quant la maladie vient de sanc, dolor, fevre et* les accidens sont entenses*, mes mains neporquant que si la matere fust de colere. Estre ice l'en a la bouche douce et la face rouge, les veines apparanz et la salive mellé de sanc, l'urin[e] ert desus autresi com sanguine. Si fleume est en cause de la maladie, la dolor ert greve, la fevre lente, la bouche mal[s]ade et la salive suzblanche, l'urine ert meins coloree que es autres devant dites causes. Mes quant melancolie est en cause, la dolor ert gravatis et la salive jaune, la bouche secch, la fevre lente, l'urine remise et meins espesse. [78] *Cure.* Cura: Notés que les uns diversent la cure solonc la diverseté des humors qui sont en cause de la maladie. Mes mei est avis que ele n'est pas mult a diverser quant l'en doit aider au malade en l'un et en l'autre maladie en une meime manere de quele humor que ele soit, c'est a savoir l'en [f.150v] doit seigner le, oindre le et metre emplastre et dieter le. Neporquant si doit l'en noter avant unes choses generales ici, c'est asavoir que l'en ne doit pas mettre a teles maladies choses froides ne repercussives, sicom nus avons dit devant en la traitié de quinancie. Mes l'en doit ovrer de choses maturatives et de diaforeticis, mes* l'en ne doit doner nule chose que soit actuelement froide. Si matere chaude soit en cause de la maladie, se doit om doner choses meins chaudes et mettre ensement. Mes si la matere de la maladie est froide, si doit l'en metre et doner plus chaudes choses. Donques de la comencement de la maladie, si li malades est de l'age et de la force, se li doit l'en seigner per opposicion et meimement en pleuresie. Kar si l'apostume siet el destre partie, si le face l'en seigner del bras senestre et si ele siet au senestre, del destre. Si en l'une et en l'autre partie a apostume, si le seigne l'en de ambedous* les bras del veine du quer. Et ce poet l'en bien fere desque en la fin del quart jor et el comencement de la quint jor neis, si la vertu est fort, mes autrement non. Et face l'en l'air froit par art en tele manere: en yver et come bise vente [ou] en froide region, cloe l'en et estoupe l'en les fenestres de la [f.151r] maison et les huis, que froydure ne puisse entrer. Et face l'en fu de carbons sans fumee devant le malade. Enoigne l'en les costes au malade en pleuresie et le piz en peripleumonie cinc foiz ou set le jor et autretant de nuit; de diauté*, si la matere est froide, mes si la matere est chaude, si l'enoigne l'en de bure ou de oile violate. Si [l'enoigne l'en au feu]* ou, que miels vaut, en meime le lit et tiengne l'en par desuz lui .i. test ardant en air endementers que l'en le oint et envolupe l'en le liu ou il est enoint de leine. Et quise l'en mauves, brancham ursinam avesques oile violate et bure et face l'en emplastre et mete [l'en] chaut sor le leu et la renovele l'en sovent. Autre. Pregne l'en la ferine fenugreci et semence de lin et le boille l'en ovesque bure et avesques oile violate et face l'en emplastre. Ou trible l'en maves quites ovec freis oint de porc et mete l'en ovesques les devant dites choses et l'eschaufe l'en tot ensemble et le mette l'en tieve par desore et la renovele l'en sovent. Notez que flux de sanc que l'en fait venir par les narines et meimement quant l'en crient que la matere ne soit ravie amont au chief et face par illeuc frenesie. En a[i] gari mult de ceste maladie. Et ce doit l'en faire en jor cretique setime ou le novime. Et se lor [f.151v] doit l'en ordiner lor diete. Doigne l'en farrine de orge bien quit en ptisane ovec let de alemandes quites et faites de penidion et ovec lait de alemandes et lor doigne l'en a boivre ptisane ou l'ewe de la decoction dragaganti, goume arabic, regalice, les semences melonis, ci-trelis, cucumeris et cucurbite. Les trible l'en et les destempre l'en de la devant dite ewe. Et la cole l'en et la doigne l'en. Ou le face l'en soupes en cele ewe et doigne l'en. Destempre l'en alemandes triblees de ptisane et mete l'en ens [farine de orge] et le faite l'en de penidion et doigne l'en et les penides meimes* porra l'en bien doner. Autre, qui est viande et boyvre et medecine*. Pregne l'en canthabrum et destempre l'en de ptisane chaude et la cole l'en et doigne l'en la coleure. Autre, que l'en doit faire a home feble. Quise [l'en] une geline ovesques farine de orge tant que ele soit trestot dessoude et la cole l'en et le doigne l'en la coleure de dragagant neis si est bon a doner. [79] Et notez que meint sont deceu a conustre le[s] signes de ceste maladie. Kar a la fiez il se desespeirent des malades* et eschapent aprés. Et a la fiez ont esperance de bien et muerent aprés les malades. Dont nus avons porveu a bailer vus brieefment les signes que nos prometent mort ou vie [f.152r] en icés maladies. Quant l'en crache sanc au comencement de la maladie et l'en crache une purreture entor le setime* jor ou entor le noveime jor et le gete fors legerment, si est bone signe. Mes quant ce que l'en crache est noir ou bleve ou vert et la dolor dure o tot, si est mavais signe; urine noire et petite, male [signe]. L'urine grant, ja soit que ele soit noire, se ele resiet, si n'est pas male signe. L'urine tenve et blanche sans nule determinement cretique se signefie ravisement de matere et mort. Kar en pleuresie seut l'en devenir frenetiques, mes en perypleumonie seut l'en devenir litargiques. Feble pous si est mauveise signe. Fors pus, ja soit ice que soit desuwel, si est bone signe. Kar inequalité de pous n'est pas mult a doter en icés maladies, kar ce avient de la compression des membres espiriteus. Froydure* des extremitez [et] des oreilles ovesques une verdure des ungles [est male signe]. Come l'en desire vin a boy[v]re en perypleumonie et on ait la langue noire et aspre, si est male signe. Et ceste fu pronostique mon pere: flux du ventrail au comencement n'est pas a doter, mes li flux qui vient aprés* le setime [jor] est mauveis signe. Urine grant au comencement ou aprés le setime jor si est bone signe. Mes quant l'en dort mau[f.152v]veisement, si est male signe. Mes notez que une vessie ou une apostume sout a la fiez naistre el pié en ceste maladie, a la fiez a bien et a la fiez a mal. Dont Ypocras dist apostume ou vessie en perypleumonie si promet santé. Mes quant apostume ou enfleure i sorvient en jor non cretique ovesques .i. dolor en le destre pié, ja soit que le semble que la maladie li soit alegié, en le premere jor cretique aprés si sentira une dolor apres en le senestre coste et morra en meime le jor et en meime l'ore que la maladie leva premerement. Et m'en creez, que jo l'ai esprovee.

[VII,6 *De empimate*] [80] *Empima.* Empima si est une maladie come l'en crache une porreture. Dont empici sont apelé cil qui crachent itel purreture. Et si vient iceste maladie de catarro et de boivre trop ewe ou vin. Et si vient [de] pleuresie [et] de perypleumonie et si vient en tele manere. Kar come l'umor degoute des parties amont, si fiert le poumon et le foulle. Dont .i. purreture naist et devient l'abitude del membre plein de purreture por la quele la norreture qui vient a lui torne tot en purreture. Et si vient ceste maladie de pleuresie et de perypleumonie come la purreture n'est pas espurgés parfitement ou quant ele demeure trop a espurgier, dont li poumon est corrumpus. Dont, sicome nus avons dit devant, la viande et la norreture qui vi[f.153r]ent a lui en devient corrumpus. *Empicus qui crache sanc purri.* Et notez que empici sont dit a la fiez proprement, a la fiez non proprement: proprement come l'en crache sanc ovesques .i. corrupcion du poumon et ovesques une purrie disposicion de lui, non proprement sont il dit empici come l'en crache sanc sans les devant dites choses. Nus* ne apeluns pas empicum chescon qui crache sanc, kar en pleuresie et en perypleumonie si crache l'en porreture, si ne sont pas empici. [81] Les signes des empiques si sont icés: cracher .i. porreture, le cors megre, le col grelle, aleiner a peine, tossir, la face emflee, les euz reons, et ont a la fiez fevre et a la fiez non. La fevre poet l'en conustre par la chalor qui est es plantes des pes et es paumes des mains et neis par les signes de fevre. Et si doit l'en prendre garde ou li membres sont plus bleciés por faire li aides locales. Kar l'en sentira une dolor el leu maumis, a la fiez en la senestre partie, a la fiez enmi le piz, a la fiez detriés. A la fiez en tossant par evulsions si sent l'en une dolor al leu malade. [82] *Cure.* Cure: Al comencement doit l'en ordeiner sa diete et aprés dongne l'en autres medecines. Et si la maladie est avesque fevre, si le doit om dieter autre[f.153v]si com nus avons dit en pleuresie et en peripleumonie. Mes si la maladie est sans fevre, si lor doigne l'en pucins et la char de petis oiseus et qui ne vivent pas en ewe. Et lor donez vin tempré ovec ptisane et farrine d'orge quit aveques un poucin et lor doit l'en aider de tele manere de medicine. Et si la maladie vient de catarro, face l'en remedes que sont escrites en catarre. Trible l'en rubeam avesques ptisane et la destempre l'en et mete l'en .iiii. onces de la poudre de mirre et lor doigne l'en au soir .iii. onces de mirre. Si sont bones a doner par aus ou avesques ptisane ou avesques oes mols. Autre cure mult preciose et bone. Recevés spicenardi, mirre trocletem, cassialignea, piperis longi uwelment .iiii. onces et le quise l'en longement en dis livres de vin. Et estoupe l'en la bouche del pot de past ou de gleyse, que la fumee n'en puisse issir. Et aprés l'oste l'en del fu et face l'en le malade abesser le chief et receyvre la fumee par la bouche parmi .i. tuel. Et ce face l'en .ii. foiz ou .iii. la semaine. Et cole l'en neis iceste vin et doigne l'en .i. once au malade avesques ptisane tieve. Et face l'en piles de sola storace ca-lamite* molues entre les mains sans nule liquor et doigne l'en set ou noef .ii. fois en la semaine, kar [sunt] mult tres bone en ceste maladie. [. . .]

[VII,7 *De ptisi*] [f.154r] [. . .] [83] [natu]rele sentement, si se ne ose ovrir sicome il devroit. Dont il ne poet envoir au quer tant de air com il li fust mestiers. Et si alume* petit et petit la chalor, c'est asavoir une fevre ethique est tot adés com-paigne a ptisicle qui degaste la substantele humidité del cors. [84] Et teles sont les signes de ptisicle: la chalor est continuele, mes a la fiez plus et a la fiez meins, es paumes et es plantes des pes, la soif est ague et la langue aspre, et li col greille, trestot le cor megre et le ventre serrés et les extremités estrois et les euz parfons et reons. Et signe familier si est une dolor del senestre espaule desques al bras. [85] *Cure*. Cure: Si la ptisique vient de catarre, la quele chose l'en poet conoistre par la relaxation de l'uve et par la titillacion* del palais et par l'abundance des superfluitez qui istront par la bouche et par le nes et par le flux des narines, dogne l'en rubeam avesques ptisane. Ou, que miels vaut, la poudre [gumme] arabic et amili* melle l'en avesques rubea et en face l'en piles et ne les face l'en pas transglotir tantost, mes le face l'en tenir un poi en la bouche, que la fumee que en ist de eus puisse monter au cervel. Et estanche [l'en] le flux qui descent d'ileques et envoie l'en aucune chose de la substance de aux avesques la salive aval au pomon por purrer [f.154v] le et restreindre. Et face l'en quisinage de amido en ewe rose et arde l'en gumme arrabic sor .i. tieule chaude et le trible l'en en poudre et melle l'en la poudre avesques let de alemandes et face l'en amilum de ce et boille l'en en ewe goume arrabic et les semences* citrulis, melonis, cucumeris, concurbite, de ache, de anis et mete l'en zucre o tot et en face sirop et doigne [l'en] au malade avesques ptisane iteu manere de sirop. Si est mundificatif et humiditatif, les queles choses sont mult necessaires a ceus qui sont ptisiques. Et lor doigne l'en a boyvre lait de chievre ou de asne ou averont esté esteint dedens peres ardant de flueve ou une piece de ascer, si la fevre n'est mult entense, kar lait si est venim a home qui a fevre. Et li doigne l'en diadragagant et le lectuaire mon pere por restorer la substantele humidité perdue. Recevez succum liquiricie et regalice, dragagant et goume arrabic uwellement .i. once et semence papaveris albi, semence citoniorum, semence de mauves, semence de bombacis et de violetes uwellement .i. once, c'est asavoir sandles blanches et rouges, roses, cinamome, berberi, nenufar* uwellement .iii. onces, puis alemandes, sebesten* uwellement .i. once, des figues et confises de sirop de [f.155r] la decoction de goume arabic et de roses. Et lor face l'en bai[n]gs moistes teus com nus avons dit soventesfois devant. Estre ces face l'en les remedes que nus avons dit devant contre ethique et contre enroüre et contre asma de secchesce. Et notez que flux de ventre et quant les cheveus chient en ptisique, que ces sont signes que la mort li est proceine. Et notés que quant la ptisique est affermé, que l'en [a peine ou jamés] garist, kar jo ne me enmembre pas que jo en veisse onques nul garir. Et notez que ptisique que vient en home jovene de trente ans ou de quarante ans ne dure pas plus de un an qu'il ne garisse ou li covient morir, kar le premer an convient que om murge ou garisse. Mes es veus gens que ont passé quarante ans ou plus si ne ocist pas si tost et si il sont aidé de covenable medicine, si porront vivre longement tant come Deu lor avra destiné. Oncore notez que mult sont deceus de conustre* home ptisique, kar li uns dient de empicis qui il sont ptisicles come il ne sont pas, a la quele chose prover mon pere fist .i. esperiment. Il fist le malade alener, la bouche tote overte, et s'il sento[u]t qu'il avoit aleine mult puante et corrumpue autrement qu'il n'avoit eu devant, [f.155v] si le jugeit a ptisicle et a non garissable. Kar de la puor de l'aleine aparcevoit il la corruption de la substance del pomon. Mes quant il ne sentout pas l'aleine puïr, se ne desperout pas de la sancté.

[VII,8 *De emoptoica passione*] [86] Emoptici sont apelé cil qui crachent sanc et ce avient de veine que ovre ou depece par sailir, par haut crier ou par coup et de autres causes plusors. Mes come plusors autres causes particuleres sont de ce, jo croi icés estre les generales causes: l'aparcion des pores par diabrosim, par la multitude des humors et par la violence et la malice de eux et par la corruption des veines et par le excession de froidure. Kar a la fiez la chalor ovre les pores et en sue fors le sanc et ce apele l'en issir par diabrosim, ce est issir par resudation. A la fiez les humors qui sorhabundent destendent et desrumpent les veines. Dont come eles ne poent tenir le sanc, si le laissent issir. A la fiez si ne pecent pas les humors [en quantité, mes] en pecent en qualité, kar a la fiez eles font ulceracions es veines par lor grant aguesse et les depecent, dont li sanc s'encort. Item les humors porrissent et corrumpent le leu ou il sont, dont les veines corrumpues en laissent issir le sanc. A la fiez si depece la veine de froydure que la destreint, mes ce [n']avient pas [f.156r] fors en leu qui est abbandoné* sicome es narines et es leus en bas, sicome es emoroides. [87] Les causes doit l'en destincter par les signes. Kar li sanc qui en ist par dyabrosim come par resudacion si est clers et purs et si n'est pas mult en quantité et sans dolor et a l'en l'aleine chaude. Mes come li sanc en ist par superhabundance, si est la quantité grant, si est li cors pleins et la face vermaille et les veines aparans. Et quant li sanc s'en ist par la veine que est depecé, ce poet l'en conoistre par le sanc qui est chaut et par la malice des [humors] qui serront vert ou noyr et par la soif. La corruption de la veine conussons nus par le sanc porri qui en ist. Mes notés qui li sanc qui l'en gete par la bouche vient de divers membres ou a la na[i]ssance, a la fiez de[s] gencives, a la fiez de la gule, a la fiez del cervel, a la fiez del piz, a la fiez del pomon et a la fiez de diafragmate, a la fiez del bouche del stomac, a la fiez du fons de l'estomac, a la fiez du foie et a la fiez del splen, et de quilivena*, la quele chose l'en doit destincter par les signes. Quant li sanc vient des gencives, si en ist par la compassion et par la confrication des gencives et come li malades suche a la fiez. Et come li sanc s'en ist des jowes, si s'en ist ovesques .i. dolor des jowes sans touse. Et a la fiez s'en ist de la gule avesques un dolor [f.156v] de la gule et avesques une touse et est li sanc eveus*. A la fiez del cervel avesques une titillacion* de l'uve et del palais et la face ert vermaille et les veines dedens apparans et grosses, et refiert li sanc a la fies as narines de nuit et en ist par ileques. A la fiez si vient del piz avesques une touse et une dolor en la destre et en la senestre partie. A la fiez si vient del pomon avesques une touse et un dolor* desuz la senestre mamele et est li sanc espumeuz. Dont Ypocras dit quant om crache sanc espumeus, si poet om bien savoir qu'il vient del pomon. Et a la fiez s'en ist li sanc de diafragmate aveque une touse et si ert au malade avis que la dolor le ceint tot entor. Et a la fiez si ist de la bouche de l'estomac et vonche om o tot et sent om une dolor entor le setime esponle del dos et comence om a conter par devers le chief. Et a la fiez vient li sanc del fons de l'estomac et vonche om come il s'en ist et si est vert ou noir. A la fiez si vient del foie avesques une rougor en la chere et une dolor desuz le destre coste et s'en ist a la fiez par la destre narine. Et a la fiez si vient de l'esplen avesques .i. dolor del senestre coste et s'en ist par la senestre narine et si est li sanc autresi come de terriene color et les euz sont jaunes. A la fiez si vient de kili[f.157r]vena et sent om une dolor en la setime esponle* et comence l'en le conte par aval. Et notez qui li sanc qui degoute a la fiez del cervel el pomon, a la fiez en l'estomac, l'envoit om fors aprés et semble qu'il naisse del pomon ou de l'estomac come il ne naist point. Et quant il ist del pomon, si le poet l'en savoir en

tele manere. Quant il naist del pomon, et non pas del cervel, le sanc s'en istra
avesques .i. touse la quele estoit devant que le sanc s'en issoit et ert tandis come le
sanc s'en ist et qu'il ert issue. Mes quant li sanc vient del pomon et est deguté* del
cervel, si a l'en une touse come li sanc s'en ist qui n'i fu mie devant ni ne serra
aprés [et] sans dolor. Et quant li sanc vient de l'estomac del vice du cervel, si ert li
sanc puiant et corrumpus. Et notez que om envoit a la fiez le sanc fors parmi la
bouche et ne trait pas sa na[i]ssance de nule des devant dites membres, ains vient
de sanguisuga* qui ahert entor la gorge. Et ce conussons par la remocion des
devant dites signes et par la titillacion de l'uve* et del palais ou de la gorge, ou par
le dit del malade qui conustra qu'il avra beu ewe troble de nuiz ou ewe d'estanc ou
de palu. Et dira par aventure qu'il sentout une chose mole en sa bou[f.157v]che
come il bevoit. [88] *Cure.* Cure: Si li sanc s'en ist par superhabundance, qui il ne
poet estre tenus es veines, si face l'en seiner le malades. Mes l'en doit varier la
seigne[e] solonc la diverseté des membres malades. Kar si li sanc naist del cervel ou
des jowes ou de la gule, si doit om mettre une ventuse ovesques jarse ou l'en encise
les veines desuz la langue ou l'en le seigne del veine du chief. Et notez que jo ne fas
nule mencion des gencives, kar l'en les doit garir solonc la doctrine que nus avons
dit par desuz la ou nus traitames des gencives. Mes si li sanc vient des membres
espiritez, se doit estre seigné de veine du quer. Mes si li sanc [vient] de la bouche de
l'estomac ou du fons de l'estomac, si mete om une ventuse entre les espaules. Si li
sanc vient del foie, ovre om la veine del foie. Se li sanc vient de l'esplen, si le
seigne om de la veine que est entre le petit doi et l'autre qui est apelee salvatella et
mete l'en neis une ventuse sor l'esplen avesques garse. Et si le sanc vien[t] de
quilivena, si doit om seigner de la veine del* quivile du pié par dedens le pié. Et
notez en femmes se li flux de sanc vi[e]nt de la retencion des menstrueles humors,
que l'en les doit faire [coure]. Et en homes et en femmes, si la flux vient de la
retencion [f.158r] de sanc qui est acostumé a issir par les esmoroides ou par les
narines, si le doit l'en faire coure par ses acostumés regions. Mes si li flux i* est de
putrifaction des humors, si doit om doner decoctions mundificatives fetes de
dragagant, de goume arrabic, de prunes, de semences mellonis, citrulis, cucumeris
et concurbite et les boille l'en en ewe et les cole l'en et mete l'en en la coleure
cassiavistulam uwellement .ii. onces et doigne l'en au malade. Et si li flux de sanc
vien[t] de la furiosité* des humors, si li doigne [l'en] decoction qui atempre la
furiosité des humors et les espurge et la face l'en de violete, de prunes, nenufare*,
berberi, cassiavistule, tamarindes, mirabolani citrini owellement .i. once et mete
l'en reubarbe. Mes quant li sanc ist par resudacion, si ne covient pas doner
purgations. Si li flux ne cesse par ces devant dites choses, si doit l'en ovrer choses
constrictives. Et si li flux de sanc vient del cervel ou des jowes ou de la gule, face
l'en gargarismes de la decoction de galles, de roses, simphiti en ewe de pluie ou de
roses et ce face l'en sovent. Et le jor aprés doigne l'en icés piles. Prenés la poudre
mumm[i]e, goume arabic ars et les confise l'en de rubea et enforme l'en pilles et
doigne l'en a tenir suz sa langue. Et en mei[f.158v]me la manere face l'en les pilles
de atthanasia et les face l'en tenir ensement desuz la langue. Et si valent iteu
manere des pilles contre sanc qui ist des menbres espiritez. Doigne l'en les pilles
Galien qui sont formés de la poudre mummie* et de sanc de dragon et de semence
de planteine et les enforme l'en de jus de planteine, de la infusion de dragagant.

Mes notez que les choses constrictives que l'en dongne contre flux de sanc qui vient des membres espiritez ne estanchent pas le flux a la fiez, ains le croissent. Kar choses constrictives commovent la touse qui poet plus dessoudre qui les choses constrictives ne poent restreindre. Dont aprés le exibicion des choses constrictives doit l'en doner aucunes choses lenitives qui restreinent la tousse come dragagant ou ptisane ou goume arrabic. Et face l'en tele emplastre. Pregne la poudre de parchemin ars ou de peus de levre ars et la poudre mummie, boli, simphiti et les confise l'en ensemble de un poi de vin egre et de mult aubun de oef et mete l'en sor le leu malade. Si li sanc vient de la gorge, si le mete l'en sor la gorge et si il vient des jowes, si le mete l'en sor les jowes. Et si li sanc vient des membres espiritez, si le mete l'en sor les membres espiritez [f.159r] et ausi de totes les autres membres. Et si li flux vient des membres nutritives, si li doigne l'en athanasiam avesques le jus de planteine et doigne l'en la piere ematiste avesques le jus de planteine. Kar ja soit ice que ceste piere estanche autre flux, ele estanche especiaument flux de sanc. Et lor face l'en user en lor viandes les .ii. pars de la poudre ematistes, la tierce des roses, la quarte de canele et lor diete soit constrictive. Estre ice face l'en autres remedes que nus dirons aprés contre dissentere. Et se li flux de sanc vient de sancsue qui soit entor la gorge, si face om le malade a bouche overt receivre la fumee [de suffre] vif et arouse l'en les carbons de vin egre. Et aprés la fumigation li doigne l'en a boyvre vin egre avesques sel. Si l'envoiera [l'en] fors en tele manere ou par amont ou par aval. Et notez que ele ne porra* pas durer ne vivre en le estomac ne en les boeus por la grant ebullicion et por la grant chalor qui est naturele.

[BOOK VIII   *De egritudinibus stomachi*]

[1 De fastidio] [89] A *manger contre volenté*. Fastidium si est une abhomination de manger contre volenté et si vient de .iii. causes: par defaute des espiriz, et par opilation des ners sensibles, et de habondance de froides et de chaudes humors. Fastidium vient par [f.159v] defaute des esperiz, kar quant les espiris sont autresi come estrumens des vertus et les comovent a parfaire les actions de la defaute de eux, n'est pas destorbé tant solement l'effect de la vertu appeti[ti]ve, ains est destorbé chascune de lor overaignes. Kar l'appetite de l'estomac qui est apelé proprement appetite si vient de double vertu, c'est asavoir de vertu appeti[ti]ve naturele et de vertu sensible. Donques quant les ners sont estopés, si que la vertu sensible ne poet descendre en la bouche de l'estomac a parfaire l'appetite, donques defaut* encor l'appetite come l'autre [cause] de principal vertu defaut. Item de habundance de froides humors ou de chaudes defaut l'appetite, kar come l'appetite vient de la raison de voidesce, doit [il] bien defaillir de replecion des humors. [90] Les causes doit l'en conustre par les signes. De la defaute des espiris conoist l'en par la febleté de tot le cors et de la megreté de lui et de fevre que l'en a eu ou que l'en a oncore et de geuner et de veillier et del flux du ventrail et des autres causes qui amegrissent le cors de l'home. L'opilacion des ners conoissons nus de ce qui li malades ne trove nule savor en chose qui il prent. En ceste cause meimement si est la digestion des viandes petite ou nule. Kar notez que par absense des espiris refroide l'estomac [. . .] por la devant dite cause. Fasti[f.160r]dium qui vient de habundance de chaudes humors conust l'en par l'amertume de la bouche et par la secchesse de la langue et du palaiz et des chaudes fumosités qui montent amont et escorcent le palaiz de la bouche. Et vonche l'en a la fiez unes choses ja[u]nes. Quant fastidium vient de habundance de froides humors, ce* conust l'en par les egres eructacions et mausade[s] et de la indigestion de l'estomac. [91] Cure. Cure: Come l'appetite defaudra por la defaute des espiriz, si doit l'en attendre la cause de la quele les espiris defaillent et encontre ce doit l'en ovrer, si de fevre, contre fevre, si de geuner et de consumpcion de cors, si doit l'en restorrer les choses perdues de viandes et de lectuaires confortatives. Tot issi des autres choses face l'en icés remedes. Quise l'en oes en ewe et les traie l'en fors fresement et le fonde l'en en quatre parties et les laisse l'en .i. petit en sause faite de mente et de vin egre et doigne l'en. Kar merveilles restorent les espiris et meimement quant abhominacion de manger vient de flux du ventrail, si font mult grant bien et comovent les espiris. Autre. Pregne l'en pain de forment et le mete l'en toster tant qu'il soit .i. poi ars. Et le moille l'en en la devant dite sause et doigne l'en. Et face l'en emplastre de tot [f.160v] sor la bouche de l'estomac. Autre. Moille l'en le devant dite pain en aisil et le trible [l'en] avesques rore marino ou ovesques flors de rore marino, si l'en les porra avoir, et mete l'en de la poudre de cinnamome et .i. poi de nois muscate et les destempre l'e[n] od vin egre et boille l'en sor les carbons. Et doigne [l'en] par dis jors ou par quinze et en frote l'en les narines de ceste sause. Et arouse l'en la face de ewe rose et mete l'en as narines froides choses aromatiques sicome roses, mirre et canphora. Contre opilacion de foie le doigne l'en chaudes choses et divisives sicome oxcimel squillitique et chaudes lectuaires et confortatives come dyamargariton, pliris [arconticon], diacimi[n]um, dya[trion] pipereon et li doigne l'en opiates, auream, oppopira, diacastoreum, poudre de poivre et de senevé* et dongne l'e[n] avesques vin. Et destempre l'en la poudre sinapis de vin egre et en face l'en emplastre sor la bouche de l'estomac. Et si sunt bones enonctions faites de chaudes ongnemens sicome arrogon, marciaton, unguento aureo. Et face l'en les devant dites aides qui sont escrites en la traitié de paralisie, kar tele opilatio ovre* paralisie. Contre replecion de chaudes humors doigne l'en pre[f.161r]merement sirop accetous avesques ewe chaude por deffire la matere. Et com la matere est deffite,si le purge l'en de oxcimel laxatif ou de lectuaire de jus de roses ou de frigido* Cophonis. Et ameine l'en une partie fors par voncher et meimement si la matere est en la bouche de l'estomac en teu manere. Triblés la semence atriplicis, rape, radices et le destempre l'en de ewe chaude et la cole l'en et mete l'en en la coleure et syrop accetous doigne l'en. Traie l'en fors le jus de poumes egres et des poumes gernetes et de poumes citrins et metez zucre et en face sirop et doigne l'en au matin avesques ewe chaude ou avesques ewe salmacine*. Et melle l'en vin egre et ewe rose et moille l'en ens une esponge et mete l'en sor la bouche de l'estomac. Contre fastidium de habundance des humors froides doigne l'en premerement oxcimel. Si l'umor est fleumatique, le* purge l'en de benoite, si de melancolie, si le purge l'en de dyascené ou de autre covenable medicine. Et si la matere est en la bouche de l'estomac, si le purge l'en de la coleure vomitus patriarche ou scarpelle. Et li doigne l'en sause poitevine, qui est faite de peresil et de .i. poi de sauge et de poivre. Et destempre [l'en] de vin egre et li doigne l'en sause faite de la semence de senevé triblee avesques [f.161v] le mie du pain et destempre [l'en] avesques vin egre. Et li doigne l'en lectuaires chaudes et confortatives come diatrion pipereon, dyacimi[n]um, dyamargariton, dyacitoniton qui est plus especiale chose en ceste cause. Enoigne l'en le estomac de chaudes oignemens come de arrogon, de marciaton, unguento aureo, de oile laurine et de semblables choses. Et notés que om doit metre diverses viandes devant eux qui ont abhomination de manger por comovoir l'appetite de manger. Et face l'en manger devant eux unes gens qui manguent de grant talent por amovoir en eux en tele manere l'apetite de manger. Item notés que l'en lor doit doner a la fiez viandes contrarieuses et nuisantes si il le covoitent par grant talant. Dont Ypocras dit que une viande delitable est a la fiez plus a desirer, ja soit que ele soit peiore, que une meillior non delitable.

[VIII,2 De bolismo et appetitu corrupto] [92] *Appetit de chen*. Bolismus si est demesuré et desnaturele appetit de manger. Et l'apele l'en par autre non appetit de chien. Si vient de sole froidure qui a segnurie en la bouche de l'estomac ou de froidure ovesques humors. Kar* la froydure entense en la bouche de l'estomac bote aval par force de expression les viandes qui vienent a l'estomac et remeint l'estomac voide en te[f.162r]le manere et covoite a manger come il se sent voide. Si refroide a la fiez le bouche de l'estomac par fevre que l'en a eu avant por l'us de froyde diete. A la fiez si refroyde par boyvre mult ewe froyde et a la fiez par le vice de l'esplen et des autres causes refroydans. [93] Iteus sont les signes de bolisme communes: le malade covoite, plus que raison est et plus qu'il ne seut, manger et ne amende point de viande qu'il manjut, ains amegrist chescun jor et atenvist. Et si avient sovent de flux del ventrail et se doit om prendre garde [de] le quel ce avient, de sole froidure ou de froydure ovesques humor. Et quant ele vient de sole froydure, [ele est] sanz accetouses eructations et sans male savor de bouche et les egestions* ne demostrent pas nule superfluité de humor, mes come la froydure ovesques humor est cause de ce, si serront les devant dites signes. [94] *Cure*. Cure: Le quel que sole froydure ou froydure ovesques humor soit en cause, si doit l'en doner communement choses eschaufans. Mes si sole froydure est en cause, si doit l'en user choses eschaufans solement. Mes quant froydure ovesques humor est en cause, si doit l'en user des choses eschaufans et espurgans. [f.162v] [95] Premerement les doit l'en dieter et aprés lor doit l'en doner medecine. Doigne l'en lor donques viandes [qui engendrent] fastidium et abhominacion de manger sicome choses crasses sicome char crasse et viandes afaité de oile, que la cresse voit en la bouche de l'estomac et lor face* abhominacio[n] de manger. Et lor doigne [l'en] lectuaires chaudes come diatrion pipereon, dyacalamentum, dyaciminum, dyamargariton et semblables choses. Et lor doigne l'en la poudre castorei ovesques vin ou vin de la decoction de lui ou vin de la decoction de rue et de sauge et la poudre cassialignee ovesques vin. Ou l'en li doigne le vin de la decoction de eux. Et enoigne l'en l'estomac de oile laurine ou de oile musceline. Et en face l'en de ce enonction a la bouche de l'estomac ou d'oignons quis en oile et en vin et mete l'en o tot de la poudre de comin. Mes si froidure avesques humor soit en cause, si li doigne l'en estre les devant dites choses oximel squillitic et purge l'en l'umor superfluele de covenable medicine, meimement de medecine qui purge fleume. Kar ceste maladie vient sovent de fleume verringne. En aucun[s] avient a la fiez que l'appetite se mue et covoitent a manger carbons, croie, savon. Et ce avient d'umor [f.163r] melancoliques .i. partie et a la fiez de colere que teint la bouche de l'estomac et i ameine autresi come une mosse dont li estomac est corrumpus*, si coveite semblables choses ordes et a la fiez si coveite chaudes choses por le colere. Et itele appetite soloient avoir femme[s] grosses por les menstruele[s] humors que eles retenent. Maniaci* et malancolici soloient ensement avoir itel appetite. Contre ce lor doigne l'en chaudes choses et extercives*. Et lor doigne l'en oxcimel squillitic et les purge l'en de covenable medecine come de jus de aloigne, de aloen, de ierapigre G., pilles faites de ierapigre et de aloen. Chescone de ces si est bone et les devant dites lectuaires chaudes come diatrion pipereon, dyamargariton et semblables choses si sont mult bones. Et si valent mult enonctions faites de oilles chaudes et de oignemens. Face l'en poudre aromatique de ligno aloes, gariofilis, antofilis, nuce muscata, zinziberis, macis, cardamoni, cinnamomi et de semblables choses. Et en use l'en de ceste poudre en lor viandes et en lor boivres totefois qui il boivent.

[VIII,3 De vomitu] [96] *Maintes maneres i a de voncher.* L'en vonche de maintes maneres des causes, mes principaument de [f.163v] habundance de froydes et de chaudes humors par incontinence, de sole chalor par ebullicion sanz humor et ensement de sole froydure sanz humor par expression. Sicome froydure entens[e]* en la bouche de l'estomac par* la force de la expression boute les viandes aval et de ce vient li flux del ventrail, en meime la manere de la froydure entense en le fons de l'estomac avient que les viandes [par la force de l'expression] en issent par amont. Dont l'en vonche neis de habundance des superflueles viandes et boivres et de aguesse de viandes et de aguesse de medecine. [97] Et les causes doit l'en conustre par les signes. Mes si li voncher vient de [habundance de] soveraines humors, les eructacions sont insipides [et] egres, si verra l'en fleume mellé ovesques ce que om vonchera ueuse ou visquouse en grant quantité et grevance en l'estomac ovesques une viscosité et une froydure. Mes quant l'en vonche de sole froydure, si a une grevance* en l'estomac et sentira om [froydure] en le funs de l'estomac. Mes li vonchers ne demostre pas nule superhabundance d'umors. Et come l'en use froydes choses, si vonche l'en plus tost et come l'en use chaudes choses, si vonche l'en plus tart. Et come les humors chaudes sont en cause, ce conoissons nus par ce ke cole ert mellé ovesques ce qu'il vonchera et est teinte [f.164r] a la fiez de jaune color et a la fiez de vert solonc les diversetés des humors et sent om une amertume en la bouche. Mes quant la sole chalor est en cause sans humor, ce poet l'e[n] conustre par la chalor et par l'ardor de l'estomac et par le soif et par la secchesce de la bouche et par ce que colere n'iert pas mellé ovesques ce que om vonchera ne ne est teint de aucone de[s] devant dites colors*. Et les chaudes choses come l'en li doigne se commovent plus a voncher et les froides meins. De la super[habundance] des viandes et de l'aguesse de eux sumes nus certefiez par le dit du malade. Kar il reconustra bien qui il avra trop mangé choses salees ou agues ou airons. De l'aguesce de medecine sumes certefiés par la indic[ac]ion du malade ou du mire, kar li malades dira bien qu'il avra pris ague medecine et li mires si il li a doné. [98] *Cure.* Cure: L'en doit noter tot avant que si sole froydure est en cause, sans humor

[ou] ovesques humor la cure est une meime*, fors tant que l'en doit purger l'umor superfluele come ele est en cause. Et ce meimes di jo come ele vient de sole chalor ou ovesques* humor. Donckes si l'umor ou la chalor sorhabunde, si le doit om mener for[s] par covenable medicine et par covenable region [f.164v] sicome nus avons demostré en plusors leus. Et après si doit l'en mettre aides locales. Contre froydure face l'en icés choses. Enoigne l'en l'estomac de oile musceline tieve ou de laurine ou soveusnon de la decoction de puliole et poudre l'en par desus la poudre de comin, de baies de lorer, de mastic et de olibano. Et après le envolupe l'en de leine ou de estoupes eschaufés. Autre. Destempre l'en triacle et mete l'en de la poudre de nois muscate et de ligno aloes et mete l'en sore come emplastre. Autre. Destempre l'en la poudre aloes de aubon de oef et face l'en emplastre sor le bouche de l'estomac et doigne l'en neis lectuaires chaudes et confortatives et la decoction de mastic et de nois muscate. Contre chalor destempre l'en simila avesques aubun de oef et face l'en emplastre sor la bouche de l'estomac. Autre. Funde l'en le mastic sor une tieule chaude et face l'en emplastre sor .i. poi de quir ou sor .i. poi de parchemin et mete l'e[n] sor l'estomac. Autre. Face l'en boillir en vin egre roses, galles, mirte* et les escorces de chesne et moille l'en en cele decoction tieve une esponge marine et mete l'en sor l'estomac ou en la decoction de roses en vin egre. Autre. Destempre l'en bolum, mastic, sanc [f.165r] de dragon triblee en poudre de aubun de oef et mete l'en desore. Autre. Destempre l'en simila en ewe rose et mete l'e[n] la poudre de mastic et quise l'en et doigne l'en. Contre voncher de super-fluités des viandes la soveraine et la principale cure si est iceste. Que l'en boive en grant quantité et après mete l'en les dois ou* une penne en la bouche et se force [l'en] de voncher. Et après li doigne l'en aucun* electuaire confortatif come* dyacitoniton ou dyamargariton. Contre voncher qui vient de agues viandes si face l'en les choses qui sont dites en la cure come l'en vonche de chaude cause. Come l'en vonche de ague medicine prendre face l'en baign de ewe de ploye, de la decoction de roses, de galle, de mirte* et del fruit juniperii. Et come li malades est mis el bai[n]g, si li doigne [l'en] a boivre ewe rosat, la decoction de un poi de mastic, de nois muscate et de* la semence basiliconis. Et si valent icés remedes non pas solement contre voncher, ains valent neis contre flux du ventrail de l'aguesce de medecine. Et face l'en neis ceste cure: boille l'en roses, galles, tan en vin egre et moille l'en une esponge dedens et face l'en emplastre sor le fons de l'estomac et desor le penul por [f.165v] le flux du ventrail et desor la bouche de l'estomac por voncher. Et notés que unes gens ne poent en nule manere receivre la medecine, que il ne la vonchent fors. Donques devant ce que l'en doigne a teu gent medicine, si lor doit l'en lier fortment les extremités et lor verse l'en aisil et le jus de uves acerbes [es euz] et soit qu'eles corgent au leu blecié de l'estomac. Et en meime la volenté de voncher li gete l'en ewe froide en la chere soudeinement.

[VIII,4 De singultu] [99] *Sancglot*. Sancglot si est .i. son de la violente comocion de l'estomac qui vient de l'espaumeuse inanicion de lui ou de la position. Et ce vient principaument de .ii. causes, de replecion et de inanicion, et de froidure a la fiez, ja soit ce que ce avienge relement. Kar de ces choses si retraient les ners de l'estomac et come il sont retrait, si est levés le fons de l'estomac amont. Mes la vertu qui governe les membres s'afforce* de metre [le] aval et de tel assens et de descens si vient .i. son, sicome les unes dient, qui il appelent sancglot. Ou, sicome il m'est avis, endementers qu[e] li estomac est levés amont, l'air qui est en mileu de l'estomac s'en [f.166r] ist par la force de l'expression et sicome il s'en ist par les conduiz qui sont estroiz encontre l'autre air qui descent, si fait .i. son que l'en apele sancglot. [100] Les causes sont a destincter par les signes. Et quant li sancglot vient de replecion, ce poet l'en conustre par ce que l'en vonche mult sovent come l'e[n] vonche a la fiez por trop manger ou por trop boyvre. Si vient la replecion a la fie de mangers, a la fiez de boyvres. Et les eructuacions sont plusors et de diverse savor solonc la diverseté de l'abondance des humors, l'abitude du cors plectoriques, large diete que l'en a usé devant. Qua[nt] li sancglot vient de inanicion, ce poet l'en conustre par fevre que l'en a eu devant ou flux de ventrail ou flux de sanc ou de geuner et de totes les choses qui amegrissent le cors. Et quant li sangloz vient de froydure, ce conust l'en par la disposicion de l'air come si l'air est froiz et par le* dit du malade, qui dira bien si il a eu froit ou s'il a mangé ou beu froides choses. [101] *Cure.* Cure: Si li sangloz vient de replecion des viandes, la soveraine et la principale cure si est que l'en le face voncher sicome nus avons dit en le chapitre devant. Mes si ce vient de replecion [f.166v] de humors, si doit l'en purger de covenable medicine ou par aval ou par amont ou par l'un et l'autre. Et aprés doit l'en user choses qui eschaufent et secchent. Si doit l'en donques oindre l'estomac de oile laurine, de arrogon, de marciaton et de semblables choses. Et face l'en emplastre sor l'estomac de puliol quit en vin. Pregne l'en rue, calamentum, majoranam et les quise om en vin et en oile et face l'en emplastre sor l'estomac. Et li doigne l'en le jus de aloigne et zucre et mel ensemble, kar esprové l'ai. Aloe si est mult bon a doner par soi. Et li doigne l'en lectuaires chaudes et secches come diatrion pipereon, diaciminon, dyamargariton et semblables choses. Mes si sangloz vient de inanicion et ovesques fevre, si est periluse. Mes quant il est sans fevre, si est meins a doter. Contre sangloz de inanicion si doit l'en user des choses restauratives et de[s] choses humectatives. Doigne [l'en] lectuaires moistes, doigne l'en ptisane, fenugrec et semence de lin quit en oile et face l'en emplastre sor l'estomac. Et por briefment dire, face l'en cure dite contre ethique. De sangloz qui vient de froidure garist l'en en tele manere. Face l'en fomentacion a l'estomac de vin et de oile chaut, oig[f.167r]ne l'en l'estomac de oignemens chaudes et li doigne l'en lectuaires chaudes. Notés que esternuer fait mult grant bien contre sanglot de froidure et de replecion. Si vaut neis contre sanglot de ces .ii. causes une poor come li malades voit ou ot aucune chose espontable.

[VIII,5 De dolore stomachi] [102] *Dolor de l'estomac.* Dolor de l'estomac si vient de multes causes: de chalor qui dessout, de froydure qui restreint, de humor chaude [ou] de humor froyde, de ventosité qui destent et dessout et de aposteime qui opprent. [103] Quant la dolor vient de chalor, ce conust l'em par la dolor puignante, par le soif, par les eructuacions qui ardent le palaiz. Chaudes choses nuisent et les froydes font bien en ceste cause. Et les dures viandes defient bien et les tendres ardent. [Ne] li voncher ne les egestions ne demostrent pas nule habundance de humors. Humors chaudes conust l'en par les devant dites choses et estre ice de l'amertume de la bouche et par les egestions et par les vonchemenz coleriques et par l'urine teinte* de color [jaune] et si seut l'en avoir* fevre en ceste cause. Et quant la dolor vient de froyde cause, si est la dolor greve, ne li vonchers ne les egestions ne demostrent nule habundance de hu[f.167v]mors. Les froides choses font mal en ceste cause et les chaudes bien. Les dures viandes deffisent malement et les tendres mieus. Et si seut* l'en avoyr le ventre dur et serré en ceste cause. Mes quant la dolor vient de humor froyde, ce conust l'en par les devant dites signes de froydure et par les eructuacions accetouses et egre[s] et de ce que [en] les egestions et ce que l'en vonche apert une fleume eweuse ou viscose. Quant la dolor vient de ventosité, ce conoist om par le bruit del ventrail et par la multitude* des eructuacions qui ne demostrent nule habundance d'umor et de ce ke li malades se sent mieus aprés ce qui il sont issus. Les signes et les cures dirons nos de l'aposteime en lor propre capitre. [104] Cure. Dolor qui vient de soule chaline et dolor qui vient de chalor ovekes humor si garist l'en en une meime manere, fors ki l'en doit purger le malade quant la dolor vient de humor chaude. Ore donque come l'en avra usé avant sirop accetous ovesques ewe chaude, si doit l'en purgier l'umor chaude de covenable medicine, c'est asavoir de oximel squillitique ou de oximel laxatif ou ovesques la decoction de mirabolans citrins et meimement en esté, le cors* destempré en cha[f.168r]lor. Et aprés face l'en les remedes locales. Oigne l'en l'estomac de oile rosat ou de violat et face l'en emplastre de mauves, de roses, de violetes* quites. Autre. Trible l'en sempervivam, omblicum veneris et mete l'en oile violat et le eschaufe l'en .i. poi et enforme emplastre et mete l'en sor l'estomac. Autre. Confise l'en le poudre de sandles blanches et de rouges de oile rosat et de vin egre et face l'en emplastre. Et doigne l'en electuaires froides come triasandali et oximel simple, triffe sarrasin* ovekes rubeam et meimement come li ventres est dures et serrés. Trible l'en le[s] semences citruli, mellonis, cucumeris et concurbite et les destempre l'en de ewe chaude et mete l'en sirop accetous et violat et doigne l'en au matin et au soir. Autre. Quise l'en jus de planteine desc'a la consumpcion de la moine partie et mete l'en autretant de l'ewe et mete l'en zucre dedens et face l'en sirop et mete l'en .i. poi de reubarbe en la fin de la decoction. Un vil esperiment et tres bon. Boive l'en ewe froide en grant quantité et aprés le face l'en voncher. Mes si la dolor vient de sole froidure ou de humor froyde ou de ventosité, si est la cure une meime, fors que l'en doit user oximel avan[t] ovesques ewe chaude. Et purge l'en l'umor, si ele est en cause, [f.168v] de benoite ou de ierapigre ou des piles qui purgent fleume et meime[me]nt des piles de cinc maneres de mirabolans. Et aprés face l'en les aides locales come oindre l'estomac de oignemens chaudes et de oiles et face l'en sacellacions sor l'estomac de mel ou de sel rosti et de peritaria. Et mete l'en tieve sor l'estomac peritaria quit en vin oveke bran, si est bone autresi a mettre sore. Et renovele sovent l'en iteu manere de sacellacions et iteu manere de emplastres, les queles, ja soit ice qui il valent contre les devant dites choses, communement si sont* bones especiaument contre ventosité. Autre. Contre ventosité especiale mete l'en une ventuse sanz jarse sor l'estomac et si il est richez*, baume li feroit mult grant bien a boivre. Autre commune a trestote[s] les* devant dites causes. Doigne l'en goume de ere a la quantité de .iii. piles et mete l'en une emplastre fait de ciroine sor l'estomac. Face l'en poudre de mastic et de olibano et mete l'en cire et oile musceline ou commune et face l'en emplastre en petite quantité. Mete l'en de ligno aloe, de costo autretant come de tous les autres et les confise l'en en tele manere. Funde l'en le cire tot premere-

ment et aprés melle l'en oile o tot. Et aprés mete l'en la poudre de [f.169r] mastic et
de olibano et le move l'en bien. Et aprés mete l'en la poudre costi et melle l'en
totes icés devant dites choses sor le feu. Et quant li pot sera osté del feu, si mete
l'en ens les autres especes et face l'en emplastre sor l'estomac. Et li doigne l'en
lectuaires chaudes come diaciminon, dyamargariton. Et li doigne [l'en] triffe la
grant ovekes la decoction de giloffre en vin ou il n'i ait point de opium thebaicum
ne de tranense*, mes qui il i ait opium miconis. Kar come triffe la grant receit
opium qui est trop froide en grant* quantité, si n'est pas a doner contre froides
humors ne encontre vice del matrix en froide cause ne encontre chaudes causes ne
le doit om pas doner por les chaudes especes que i* entrent. Mes l'en poet bien
doner le contre flux du ventrail et por flux men[struel] qui vient par la feblefé de
vertu retentive. Mes jo fas triffe la grant ovekes opio miconis, sin[e] opio thebaico
et sine opio tranense*. [Et jo truve] grant efficace en lui contre froides causes et
contre ventosité. Et face l'en poudre de mace, de nois muscates, de ligno aloe et de
la semence basiliconis a la quantité de .iiii. onces et confise l'en la poudre de moel
de oef et le frise [f.169v] l'en en seim et li doigne l'en. Et lor face l'en user en lor
viandes de la poudre de canele, de comin et de coriandre. Et en use l'en neis de la
ewe de la decoction de mastic et de olibano et de la semence de fenoil et ewe tieve
neis a boivre. Lor fra mult grant bien. Notés que accetouses eructuacions font mult
grant moleste a plusors, contre les queles si sont mult bones a doner .iii. greins de
olibano prises par soi totes enteres sicome nus avons dit et enseigné el traitié de
catarre.

[f. 83v] [VIII,6 De apostemate stomachi] [105] Aposteme si vient a la fie en
l'estomac, a la fie es boiaus. A la fie si vient en la concavité de l'estomac et des boiaus,
et a la fie en lor superficé, et a la fie entre les peletes, et a la fie de chaude humor,
et a la fie de froide. [106] Si doit l'en donc distincter le leu* de la matire par les
signes. Car se la matire siet dedenz la concavité de l'estomac, ce puet l'en conoistre
par ce que l'en vonchera fors aucune chose de la matire des le comencement devant ce
qu'ele soit formé a aposteme. Et sentira l'en une grevance en l'estomac si tost come
l'aposteme est confermee. Mais si l'aposteme est dedenz la concavité des boiaus
devant [que] la matire soit confermee a aposteme, en istra [f. 84r] aucune chose de
la matire oveques les egestions. Mais quant l'aposteme est confermee et la digestion est celebree, si sent l'en une dolor es boiaus sicome les egestions i passent
parmi. Mais quant l'aposteme siet en la superficé de l'estomac ou des boiaus, une*
enfleure apiert tot entor ne riens de la matire n'en ist par desoz ne par desore. Mais
quant l'aposteme siet entre .ii. peletes, ce est grevos chose a conoistre. Mes om
conoist en tel maniere quant humor chaude est en cause et quant humor froit.
L'umor chaut quant il est en cause conoist om par la dolor ague et poignante et par
la fievre qui ert ardante et poignante et par la soif et par la sechece dou palat et de
semblables choses. La froide quant ele est en cause conoist [om] par la fevre qui ert
lente et la soif remisse et [la dolor] moins ague. [107] Si l'aposteme vient d'umor
chaude, si le face l'en seignier dedenz le quart jor s'il est de l'age et de la force.
Devant ce que l'aposteme soit confermee doit l'en metre par defors et doner par la
boche choses repercussives qui refroident, [f. 84v] qui referent enz la matire et la
botent* fors. Face l'en emplastre sor le leu de sandles blanches et roges [et] la

poudre de* roses seches et mete l'en oile rosat et vin egre. Et face [l'en] oncore epitimes dou jus [de] corrigiole ou de plantain ou de sempervive ou de morele. Ou om trible les herbes meimes et mete l'en sore. Et li doigne l'en a mangier laitues, scarioles, portulaques, morele. Et si la matire ne puet estre boté arriere d'icés choses, ainz vodra tendre a porreture, la queu chose l'en porra conoistre par les accidenz et par la chalor* de la fevre qui sera entense. Dont Ypocras dist 'Entor ce que la porreture est engendré avienent plus et plus dolors et fevres que* come la porreture est faite'. Et lors si doit l'en ovrer de choses maturatives. Destempre l'en farine d'orge oveques moieus de oes et face l'en emplastre sore. Ou om face emplastre de farine de fenugrec et de la semence de lin destemprez oveques moiaus de oes et de mauves triblees oveques oint de porc. Mais si l'aposteme vient [f. 85r] de froide humor, si ne le doit l'en pas fere seignier si li cors n'est plectoriques. Et lors le doit l'en seignier de la veine dou foie. Et notez que en ceste cause ne doit l'en pas metre apocrustica, ce sont choses repercussives, car eles en espoisseroient la matire et endurceroient. Mes l'en doit ovrer de choses diaforetiques et de extenuatiques. Boille l'en en vin cassiam ligneam, spicam nardi et mete l'en oile comune o tot et face l'en emplastre. Et face l'en sacellacions do comin tosti ou quit en vin. Et face l'en emplastre de satureia, aprotano tosti sanz nule liquor. Et si la matire n'atenvist par metre icés choses, ainz se tent a porreture, la quel chose l'en conoistra par les devant dites signes, si doit [l'en] metre lors choses maturatives. Quise l'en les racines de lis en oile et en vin oveques comin et face om emplastre, ce est tres bone chose a meurer. Autre, diaforetiques et maturatif tot ensemble: preigne l'en feves frasees que sont bien mondees de l'escorche defors et les quise l'en en vin et en oile et face [f. 85v] l'en emplastre sovent sor le leu. Et quant l'aposteme est depeciez – la quel chose om puet conoistre par la porreture qui en istra par desoz ou par desus, par desus* si la matire est dedenz la concavité de l'estomac ou en la superficé de lui, par desoz en istra la matire oveques les egestions si l'aposteme siet es boiaus ou dehors – s'en istra la purreture oveques l'urine si la matire siet entre les peletes autresi de l'estomac come des boiaus. Et lors doit om doner choses qui espurgent la purreture et essuent la plai[e]. Doigne l'en donques mulse et mete l'en de la poudre nitri ou de sel. Mulse* donee par soi [ou] oveques vin si est mult mundificatif. Si la matire se purge par l'urine, si doit l'en doner choses diuretiques, des queles nos dirons ou traitié de stranguiria. Et quant l'em avra espurgié fors la purreture, si doit l'en doner choses consolidatives, que la sorsaneure ne remaigne. Et doigne l'en ewe de pluie, decoctionis mirtille, galla-rum, sidie et mete l'en zucre. Et mete l'en emplastre par defors constrictive [f. 86r] la quele* nos deviserons ou traitié de dissenterie.

[f.171v] [VIII,6bis De apostemate stomachi] [108] *Apostume*. Apostume si vient a la fiez en l'estoma[f.172r]c, a la fiez es boueus et a la fiez si vient en la concavité de l'estomac et des boeus et a la fiez en lor superficé et a la fiez entre les pelectes et a la fiez de chaude humor et a la fiez de froide. [109] Se doit l'en donc destincter le leu* de la matere par les signes. Kar se la matere siet dedens la concavité de l'estomac, l'en conustra par ce que l'en vonchera fors aucune chose de la matere des* le comencement devant ce que ele [soit] formé a apostume. [Et] sentira l'en une grevance en le estomac si tost come l'apostume est confermé. Mes si l'apostume est

dedens la concavité des boueus devant que la matere soit confermé a apostume, en
istera aucune chose de la matere oveske les egestions. Mes come l'apostume est
confermé et la digestion est celebré, si sent l'en une dolor es boueus sicome les
egestions i passent parmi. Mes come l'apostume siet en la superficé de l'estomac ou
des boueus, une emfleure apert tot entor ne riens de la matere n'en ist par desuz ne
par desore. Mes quant l'apostume siet entre les .ii. pelectes, ce est greve chose a
conustre. Mes* l'en conust en tele* manere quant humor chaude est en cause et
quant humor froit. L'umor chaut come il est en cause conust l'en par la dolor ague
[f.172v] et poignante et par la fevre qui ert ardante et poignante et par la soif et par
la secchesce du palaiz et de semblables choses. La froyde come ele est en cause
conust l'en par la fevre que ert lente et la soif remisse* et [la dolor] meins ague.
[110] Cure. Si l'apostume vient de humor chaude, si le face l'en seigner dedens le
quart jor, si il est de l'age et de* la force. Devant ce que l'apostume seit confermé
doit l'en metre par defors et doner par la bouche choses repercussives qui refroy-
dent, ke referent ens la matere et la botent fors. Face l'en emplastre sor le leu de
sandles blanches et rouges, la poudre de roses secches et mete l'en oile rosat et vin
egre. Et face l'en oncore epithimes del jus [de] corrigiole ou de planteine ou de
sempervive ou de morele. Ou l'en trible les herbes meimes et mete l'en sore. Et li
doigne l'en a manger leitues, scarioles, portulagues, morele. Et si la matere ne poet
estre boté ariere de icés choses, ains vodra tendre a porreture, la queu chose l'en
porra conustre par les accidens et par la chalor de la fevre qui serra entense. Dont
Ypocras dit 'Entor ce que la purreture est engendré avenent plus et plus [f.173r]
dolors et fevres que* come la purreture est faite'. Et lors si doit l'en ovrer de choses
maturatives*. Destempre l'en ferrine de orge oveskes moeus de oes et face l'en
emplastre sore. Ou l'en face emplastre de ferrine de fenugrec et de la semence de
lin destempré oveskes moeus de oes et de mauves triblés ovesques oint de porc.
Mes si l'apostume vient de froide humor, si ne le doit l'e[n] pas fere seigner si li cors
n'est plectoriques. Et lors le doit l'en seigner de la veine du foie. Et notés que en
ceste cause ne doit l'en pas metre apocrastica, ces sont choses repercussives, kar
eles en essposseroient la matere et endurceroient. Mes l'en doit ovrer de choses
diaforetiques et de extenuatives. Boille l'en en vin cassiam ligneam, spicam nardi
et mete l'en oile commune o tot et face l'en emplastre. Et face l'en sacellacions de
comin tosti ou quit en vin. Et face l'en emplastre de satureia, abrotono tosti sans
nule liquor. Et si la matere n'atenvist par mettre icés choses, ains se tent a
purreture, la quele chose l'en poet conustre par les devant dites signes, si doit l'en
lors mettre choses maturatives. Quise l'en les racines de liz en oile et en vin oveske
comin et face l'en emplastre, ce est tres bone chose [f.173v] a meurer. Autre,
diaforetiques et maturatifs tot ensemble. Pregne l'en feves frasees qui soient bien
mundees de l'escorche defors et les quise l'en en vin ou en oile et face l'en
emplastre sor le leu sovent. Et come l'apostume est depescé, la quele chose l'en
poet conustre par la purreture qui en istra par desuz ou par desus, par desus* si la
matere est dedens la concavité de l'estomac ou en la superficé de lui; par desouz en
istra la matere oveskes les egestion[s] si l'apostume siet es boueus ou [dehors]; s'en
istra [la purreture] ovesques l'urine, si la matere siet entre les pelettes autresi de
l'estomac come des boueus. Et lors doit om doner choses qui espurgent la purreture
et essuent la plaie. Dogne l'en donques mulse et mete l'en de la poudre nitri ou de

sel. Mulse* par soi [ou] oveskes vin si est mult mundificatif. Si la matere se purge par l'urine, si doit l'en doner choses diuretiques des queles nus dirons en la traitié de stranguria. Et quant l'en avra espurgé fors la purreture, si doit l'en doner choses consolidatives, que la sorsanure ne remaine. Et doigne l'en ewe de ploie, decoctionis mirtiliorum, gallarum, psidie et mete l'en zucre. Et mete l'en emplastre par defors constrictive, la quele* nus deviserons en la traitié de dissentere.

[BOOK IX *De egritudinibus intestinorum*]

[f.169v] [1 De dolore eorum] [111] *Por dolor des boiaux.* Dolor es boeux si vient de plusors causes: de grosse ventosité entreclose [en] les boeux qui les* emfle et destent, et de h[u]mors chaudes ou* de froides sanz aposteime [ou] ovekes aposteime par la motion de ebullicion. Et si vient neis iceste dolor par compassion de l'opilation del col de la vessie. Kar come li col de la vessie est estopee, si est l'urine retenue et devient la vessie emflé, si estoupe le col del bouel qui vient a lui. Et quant les boels sont estopees, si ne poet la fente issir. Et quant la fente est retenue, si naist maintenant une ventosité qui destent les bouels et fet venir une dolor es boeus. Et la dolor des boeus solonc la diverseté des bouels et solonc la diverseté des leus ou il [f.170r] gisent si a divers nons. Kar dolor qui est es menus boueus desor le nomblil si est apelé st[r]ophicus dolor. Yliacus dolor si est .i. autre dolor qui est ensi dite de ylion, intestino, et n'est pas dite de grelles boueles. Dont Costentin dit en Panteigne 'Yleon si est .i. bouel gros et tor et envolupés el quel la fente durc areste et fet ileques venir qui est ape[lé] yliaca passio'. Et ceste dolor siet es costes del nomblil en aval. Dolor colicus si est un autre dolor, si vient de une cause qui est en .i. bouel que l'en apele colon. Et l'en sent ceste dolor en long del nomblil desques au penil devant et detriés*. [112] Les causes doit l'en destincter par les signes. Quant la dolor vient de ventosité, ce conust l'en come li ventre bruit et triboille et sone. Et quant la dolor vient de humor froyde, ce conoist l'en par le ventre qui est mult serré et dur et par l'urine descoloree et trouble et par les eructuacions aceteuses et mal[s]ades et la soif qui ert petite ou nule et par ce que ceste maladie seut avenir as veus homes en froide region et en tens froit et de user froide diete et moiste. Et quant ceste dolor vient de humor chaude, ce conust l'en par la dolor qui ert puignante et ague et par la soif grant ovesques fevre a la fiez, par [f.170v] l'urine coloree et tenve et par ce que ele seut avenir en home jovene coleriques en tens chaut, en chaude region, de user chaude et secche diete. Les signes de dolor qui vient de apostume [et] par compassion de* l'opilation del col de la vessie et les causes et les cures troverez vus en lor propres chapitles. [113] Cure. Dolor qui vient de ventosité et de froide humor garist l'en de une meime cure, mes solement de tant que encontre ventosité doit l'en doner choses plus dissolutives et plus extenuatives et, encontre l'umor, evacuatives. Enoigne l'en donques premerement le leu de dyaltea et aprés de aucun oignement chaut come de arrogon, marciaton ou de unguento aureo. Et face l'en suppositoires, la diverseté des queles nus avons enseigné en la traitié de litargie. Et lor face iteu bai[n]g. Pregne l'en mercurialem, mauves, senesçons, portulaques vers ou secches* et les boille l'en en ewe. Et mete l'en plenté de oile et face l'en le malade entrer. Et quant il istra del bai[n]g li face l'en clistere premerement mollificatif* de la decoction de mauves, de bran ou de orge et mete l'en mel et oile. Et aprés i melle l'en choses mollitives et mordificatives ensemble de l'ewe de [f.171r] la decoction mercurialis, de mauves et mete l'en sel et mel et funde l'en ens benoite et scamonee ou aucune autre medecine qui purge froides humors. Notez ke les uns usent de clistere mordificatif de[s] le comencement. Dont les egestions en sont plus secches et plus durs, dont li plusors en moerent. Dont jo comant ke nul ne soit tant fous qui il face clistere mordificatif en teu cause ne en nule autre si il n'a fet clistere mollificatif avant. Et come om avra bien espurgé le ventrail, si li doigne l'en benoite ovekes diamargariton ou l'en li doigne piles communes a artetique, les queles et les receites nus escriverons el traité de arte- thique. Le vin de la decoction de ciprés ou du fruit si est mult bon a boivre en ceste cause. Item pregne l'en file cru et boille l'en en ewe oveskes cendre. Et face l'en emplastre sor le ventre devant et detriés sovent. Et oigne l'en le ventrail [un- guento] Stephanonis, le quel l'en fet en tele manere: figues secches, uves passes, sebesten, branca ursina, squilla ou ongnions comunes et les mete l'en temprer en vin fort et en oile .iii. jors. Et aprés les quise l'en mult bien* et mete l'en en le coleure de la poudre de thamarinde, euforbii, [f.171v] castorei, de soffre vif et mete l'en cire et face l'en oignement et enoigne l'en le malade au soleil et au feu. Autre esprove. Pregne l'en le poudre de grisillions et de antimonio et doigne l'e[n] a boivre en vin en uwele quantité. Mes l'en doit juger de la quantité par veue et non pas par pois. Kar la petite quantité de antimonio poise mult. Dont la petite pois de lui ert plus que la grant quantité de la poudre de grissillons. Et de cest experiment .i. prevoire en garist en poi trestoz le[s] homes de sen pais en terre de labor. Et si la dolor vient de chaude humor, enoigne l'en le leu malade de oile violat et face l'en suppositoyres de lart solement et li doigne l'en a boivre l'ewe de la decoction de prunes [ou] de violete. Ou en face l'en sirop de cele ewe et i mete l'en ens les semences citrulis, mellonis, cucumeris, concurbite et li face l'en clistere lenitif et mollitif. Et come il comence a aler a chambre, si le purge l'en de oximel laxatif ou de electuares froides. Ce vi unes gens qui travoiloient de chaude matere as queles nules aides locales ne poe[n]t aider. Si lor dona* l'en ewe froyde et lor versa sor le chief et sor le ventre, si garrirent maintenant*.

[f. 86r] [IX,2 De lumbricis] [114] Lumbric si sont uns vers qui vienent de fleume, sicom Estevenon le tesmoi[n]g et le demostre par tele esprove, car chaudes choses et seches les ocient. Car il i a diverses e[s]pieces de teu maniere de vers selonc les diverses differences de la fleume. De sausefleume si vient uns vers lons et reonz, car fleume sause si est chaude et seche. Chalors s'estent toz jorz qu'ele regne, dont ele [le] fait esloignier, mais ne puet eslaisier por la sechesce qui se debat en centre*. Car sechece se tent toz jorz contreval, dont ele estrece et estreint et fait la chose reonde de quant qu'ele puet. Dont itel maniere de vers sont lons et reonz. Mais de fleume douce qui est chaude et moiste si vien[en]t uns vers qui sont lons et lez, car chalor esloigne et moistece eslaise. De fleume acetouse qui est froiz et sec si vienent uns vers courz [f. 86v] et reonz. Car l'une et l'autre, c'est asavoir froidure et sechece, muet contreval. Mais de fleume naturale si sont les vers petiz et lez, car fleume naturale si est froit et moiste. La froidure les fait petiz et la moistesce les fait lez. Et iteu maniere de vers sont apelé ascarides ou cucurbitini por ce qu'eles resemblent la semence de cocordes. Mais de fleume verrine ne puet riens vivre. Mes les vers lons et les reonz si sont engendrez sovent en grelles boiaus et meimement in orbo sacco. [115] Mes les signes des lumbriques si sont itex: l'en sent une dolor et unes torcions es boiaus et a l'en fevre, et enfanz meimement, si manjuent les narines por la colligance que les boiaux ont as narines et cil qui ont iteus vers ou ventre si crient en dormant et estreignent les denz et en issent les vers a la fie par amont et a la fie par aval. Et iteus genz si soloient avoir la boche puant et meimement [f. 87r] quant il sont jeun. [116] [Cure] Ameres choses si tuent les vers. Aloe donee par soi en piles ou la poudre de lui donee en vin si ocist les vers. Jus d'aloigne, persicarie et les foilles de persic[arie], cen[t]auree, la poudre de lupins ameres, la poudre centonice, la poudre de corne de cerf, totes icés choses si ocient vers. Mes notez que totes icés choses devant dites doit l'en doner oveques mel, car tant dementiers que les vers atraient le mel, la queu chose lor delite mult, si atraient o tot les choses ameres qui les tue[nt] et si sont deceuz en teu maniere a droit quant li hameçon est repost desoz la viande. Dont Estevenon si dist que quant nos volons bien ocirre lumbriques que l'en lor doit doner .iii. jorz lait de chevre, la quel chose il desirrent mult por* la douçor dou lait. Et aprés lor doigne l'en choses ameres quant l'estomac est voiz a geun, que les vers qui avoient apris ja la douçor dou lait devorent les choses ameres glotement, [f. 87v] qu'il les tuera, et ne porront ja aparçoivre l'amertume por la grant covoitise qu'il en ont. Estre ce le jus [de mente] romane ocist les vers. Et lor doigne l'en electuarie qui reçoit la poudre de lupins ameres et la poudre centonice, qui est apelee par autre non* herba babiloni[c]a, et corne de cerf ars une drame et les poudres des racines d'erbes .iii. unces et les confise l'en de mel et face l'en emplastre sor le ventre et meimement sor le ventre des enfanz qui ne puent reçoivre ameres choses. Ou preigne l'en la poudre de lupins ameres ou de fiel de tor et de aloe et les confise l'en ensemble oveques le jus persicarie et de aluigne, abrotani, paritarie* et aisil et doigne l'en a boivre por boter hors les vers. Et memement oveques l'ewe de la decoction agarici et de la moele coloquintide ou de benoite ou de catartico imperiali ou de yeralogodion ou de aucunes pilles laxatives et qui purgent fleume.

[IX,3 De dissinteria] [117] *Dissenteire*. Dissenterie si est flux del ventrail quant [f. 88r] les boiaus sont escorchiez ou oveques unes egestions plaines de sanc. Si est dite dissinteria a discendendo, car en ceste espece de menoison sont les boiaus escorchiez. Et si avient a la fie de colre naturale et a la fie de non naturale, sicome de colre prassine* ou de colre erugineuse ou de melancolie innaturale arse et a la fie de sausefleume et a la fie dou vice del foie*. Et si est apelee epatica dissinteria et si vient dou vice del foie, c'est asavoir come li foies est grevez par la feblece de la vertu retentive. Car quant li foie* est afebloiez, si ne poet retenir le sanc qui degote par unes veines es boiaus qui sont apelez vene meseraice et s'en ist par aval. Et a la fie si vient ceste maladie [de grand abundance de sanc] et meimement en ceaus qui ont les membres trenchiez, sicom l'en a copé pié ou poi[n]g. Car li sans qui soloit estre as voines a norrir icelui membre qui est copez, come il ne troeve son membre qu'il devroit norrir, si sorhabunde ou foie [f. 88v] et quant il ne puet estre tenuz, si l'envoit l'en fors et est apelé inproprement dissenteria. [118] Les causes donques doit l'en distincter par les signes. Car cum naturele colre est en cause, si sont les egestions sanguins et jaunes ou l'un et l'autre. Mais quant colre prassine est en cause, si sont les egestions partie sanguins et partie verz. Mais quant li flux vient de colre erugineuse, si sont les egestions une partie sanguins et une partie noirs, si resemblent roil d'arein en color. Et quant ele vient de melancolie innaturale arse, si sont les egestions une partie noires et une partie sanguins. Et quant li flux vient de sausefleume, si sont les egestions une partie sanguins et une partie sozblanche. En dissintere epatique si ist li sans a la fie mult purs et a la fie soutement et a la fie a monceaus. Car endementres que li sans decort dou membre chaut, c'est asavoir dou foie, as membres froiz, c'est as boiaus, si amoncele par la froidure d'aus et s'en ist tot betez et amoncelez. Dont .i. mires fous qui veoit le sanc amoncelé [f. 89r] et quidoit que ce soit de la sustance dou foie, la queu chose ne puet avenir come les venes que l'en apele meseraiques* [deliees sunt], car la sustance dou foie ne porroit passer par si deliees veines es boiaus por la soutilleté d'eles. Dont ne ci ne aillors ne porroit om pas assignier le trespassement de lui. Si vient itel flux oveques une dolor desoz la destre coste et si est la dolor petite ou nule es boiaus. Mes .iii. especes sont de dissintere quant ce avient dou vice des boiaus: la primiere, la seconde, la tierce. La primiere est en la quele si est dissous la ventosité des boiaus et aperent les egestions autreteles come laveure de char grasse. La seconde espiece si est en la quele les viles de l'estomac si sont reses et aperent en les egestions unes pelettes semblables a rasture de parchemin. En la tierce espece en issent les pieces des boiaus et en les egestions si apierent unes chars eschardouses et unes resolucions nerveuses et arterioses*. De la primer espece l'en garist bien, de la seconde a poine, de la tierce ne garist nul. [f. 89v] Derechief dissinterie qui vient do vice des boiaus si vient a la fie des sovrains boiaus et a la fie dou vice des basses, la queu chose l'en conoist par les signes. Car quant ce avient dou vice des boiaus en bas, si sent l'en une dolor desoz le nombril, c'est asavoir desor le penil et es rains, et n'i a pas grantment de sanc mellé oveques les egestions. Et ceste chose doit l'en entendre diligaument, car contre dissinterie qui vient des soverains boiaus si profitent miauz et valent miauz les choses c'om done parmi la boche. [119] Encontre dissinterie qui vient dou vice des boiaus en bas si valent miauz les aides et les medicines que l'en met par aval et les subfumigacion[s] et les bainz et les emplastres qui sont comunes a l'un et a l'autre que nos dirons ci aprés. [Cure] Ainz que l'en done choses constrictives contre* dissintere qui vient dou vice des boiaus, si doit l'en purger l'umor superflue de ceste sole especiale medicine contre [f. 90r] dissintere: .i. unce et demi ou .ii. de mirobalans citrins selonc ce que li malades est forz. Face l'en poudre et mette l'en temprer en ewe rose ou en ewe de pluie ou en lait cler de chievre et le cole l'en au matin et doigne l'en la coleure. Mais se sausefleume est en cause, mette l'en oveques li mirobalans citrins .i. unce de kebles*. Et si melancolie arse est en cause, mette l'en indes. Et quant la purgacion est faite, si doit l'en doner sa diete. Si li doigne l'en simila d'orge ou de forment oveques ewe de pluie ou oveques ewe de la decoction meisme de mastic. Ou l'en distempre la poudre d'un amatiste oveques jus de plantain ou oveques aucun autre liquor constrictive et melle l'en oveques simila en son quisinage, sicum nos avons dit devant. Et face l'en poudre de sanc de dragon, de sumac, de canele et li [f. 90v] poudre l'en desor ses viandes. Ou li doigne l'en a boivre ovec syrop et li doigne l'en pocins quiz en ewe et petiz oiselez et les extremitez de porc, poires quiz en ewe et pomes dé bois et coinz quites en ewe, sorbes et cornes et les autres fruiz constrictif[s] et les doigne l'en avant mangier et ne mie aprés. Et lor doigne l'en a boivre ewe de pluie ou ewe rose ou ewe de la decoction de mastic s'il i a fevre. Mais s'il n'i a point de fevre, si lor doigne l'en vin tempré o ces devant dites ewes. Preigne l'en gumme arrabic et mastic et arde [l'en] sor une teule et mete l'en la poudre oveques simila en quisinage sicom nos avons dit avant. Et doigne l'en lentilles quites ovecque vin aigre jusque l'aisil soit degasté et li doigne l'en .vii. jorz continuez, au matin a geon et au soir au cochier. .I. esperiment Galien et Costentin et Estevenon. Preigne l'en la semence de plantain triblee et mete l'en oveques aubun d'oef et la quise l'en sor une teule chaude et li [f. 91r] doigne l'en. Et preigne l'en fromage mult tres viez et le mince l'en menuement et le quise om oveques miel et doigne l'en. Ou .i. pocin quit en ewe rose ou en ewe de pluie oveques cire et doigne l'en. Autre. Pregne l'en .i. pocin et le rostisse l'en au feu et quant il sera quiz, si le degote l'en de cire ou l'en mette cire dedenz, si qu'ele funde de la chalor dou feu et li doigne l'en. Blanchisse l'en .i. pot d'argille et de bolo et d'ewe de pluie et en celi pot mette l'en une tortre vive o tote la plume et i mete l'en sanc de dragon et bolum, mummie .ii. unces et aprés estope l'en bien la boche dou pot, si que la fumee n'en puisse issir. Et le mete l'en tot enz en .i. four chaut et li laisse [l'en] tant qu'il soit tot ars. Et aprés le traie l'en et en face l'en poudre de ce qu'il i avra dedenz et doigne l'en la poudre en son mangier et en son boivre. Et li doigne l'en syrop mirtin ou miclete qui est especiale contre ceste cause. Et li doigne l'en diacodion et athanasiam* oveques le jus de [f. 91v] plantain. Mais si la dissintere vient dou vice des boiaus en bas, si est la cure itele. Estre les choses que nos avons dit devant quise l'en oes en vin egre, qu'il soient durs, et traie [l'en] fors les moiaus et les distempre l'en d'une partie de vin egre et mete l'en ewe d'orge et li giete l'en enz par desoz. Et face l'en eclisteire oncore des poudres constrictives oveques l'ewe de l'orge. Preigne l'en pin gummeuse et le quise l'en en ewe et le traie [l'en] fors et mete l'en sor les charbons ardanz et face l'en au malade reçoivre la fumee parmi .i. tuel ou fondement. Ou l'en face subfumigacions desoz de anguiles vives mises sor les charbons. Autre. Preigne l'en plantain o tote la semence et la trible l'en et le mete l'en sor une perre de mole chaude et poudre l'en cendre chaude par deseure. Et aprés les arose les en de vin aigre et face l'en le malade reçoivre la fumee parmi le fundement. Et face l'en bai[n]g qui est commune a l'une et a l'autre dissinterie. Preigne l'en les escorches de chaine, [f. 92r] galle, simphitum, cortex sorbi [et nespili], c'est esco[r]che de sorb et de nespler, de coi[n]g et de pome grenat et boille l'en en ewe de pluie et face l'en entrer le malade .ii. foiz le jor, au matin et au vespre. Face l'en emplastre de pomes macienes* quites en ewe de pluie ou de pomes citoines ou de sorbes ou des autres [fruits] constrictives ou des poudres des epices constrictives, sicome sanc de dragon, bolo, simphito et de la semence de plantain confiz oveques aubun d'uef et oveques aisil et mete [l'en] sor le leu malade. Contre dissenterie epatique doit l'en ovrier en teu maniere. Si ce avient de superhabundance de sanc, si le face l'en seignier de la veine dou foie. Mes si ce avient de la vertu contentive ou d'autre cause, si face l'en epithimes refroidanz de* jus de froides herbes et especiaument de sandles blanches et roges et de lacca autretant come des autres totes. Et en face l'en poudre et les confise l'en oveques ewe rose et [f. 92v] poi d'aisil et en face l'en epitime au foie. Et face l'en epitimes et emplastres contre eschaufement dou foie. Notez que si les egestions apperent verz ou erugineuses ou noirs en dissintere, ce est signe mortel. Derechief notez que se ceaus qui ont dissintere perdent l'apetit de mangier, si lor doit l'en aidier des choses que nos avom dit contre fastidium.

[IX,4 De lienteria] [120] *Lienterie*. Lienteria si est flux dou ventrail oveques une lenité de l'estomac et des boiaus quant li boivres et li mangiers s'en ist trestot desore et deffite. Dont lienteria si est dite de lienon, quod est lenire, et si vient ceste maladie de fleume porrie que s'ahert as fronces de l'estomac et des boiaus. Et si vient de dissinterie que l'en a eu devant et de aposteme de l'estomac ou de la plaie des boiaus. De fleume viscoseuse vient ele en tel maniere. Car endementers que teu fleume sorhabunde en l'estomac ou es boiaus, si oste les fronces, de la quele aspreté [f. 93r] la vertu retentive recevoit sa force. Dont quant ele ne puet pas retenir la viande, si le laisse issir fors trestote [non] deffite. De dissintere que l'en a eu devant vient ceste maladie en teu maniere. Car de la dissintere sont res les devant dites fronces [et] en les ulceracions ne naissent nules villositez. Dont les boiaus et l'estomac* remaignent polies et pleins et de ce en vient la lientere. De l'estomac et des boiaus vient la lientere, car quant les boiaus et l'estomac se sentent grevez des viandes, si les botent fors devant qu'il soient deffites. Et par l'asiduel cors des viandes qui ne sont pas desfites si naist une limosité et une lenité es boiaus, sicome l'en puet veoir en ces chanaz de molin par le cours assiduel de l'ewe, et devient escolorjant dou limon de la boue. Et de la lenité si vient la lientere. [121] Les causes sont a distincter par les signes. Come fleume viscoseuse est en cause, ce conoist l'en par une mus[f. 93v]cilaginité qui apiert as egestions et fleume globouse et espoisse en est mellé o tot. Lientere qui vient de dissintere conoist l'en par ce que l'en avra eu avant les egestions senglanz ou jaunes. Lientere qui vient de aposteme de l'estomac et des boiaus conoist l'en par les signes que nos avons dit ou traitié des apostemes. [122] *Cure*. Se fleume est en cause, si li aide l'en de ceste especiale decoction. Pernez agaricum, la sustance coloquintide, polipodie, semence de fenoil, squinance et les boille l'en en ewe et les cole l'en et en cele coleure mette l'en temprer une nuit .ii. unces de la poudre de mirobalans kebles. Et cole l'en au matin et doigne l'en cele ewe au malade. Et quant l'en avra purgié, si li doigne l'en electuaires chaudes et confortatives et consumptatives cum diaciminum, diatrion piper[e]on, diamargariton et semblables choses. Et li doigne l'en a boivre l'ewe de la decoction de mastic, cassialignee, macis. [f. 94r] Ou li doigne [l'en] vin tempré d'ewe. Ou l'en li doigne airons, oignons, auz, creissons, porriax, mostarde. Et quant il avra mangié a la fie choses salees, si le face l'en vonchier oveques ewe chaude beue* en grant quantité. Adrianum ou mitridatum soloit estre soveraine cure et la soveraine aide en ceste maladie. Et si icés choses profitent poi en ceste cause, si li doigne l'en choses constrictives que nos avons dit ou traitié de dissinterie. Lientere qui vient de dissintere que l'en a eu devant si jujons nos a incurable. Car sicom nos avons dit devant que ce est inpossible qu'en sorsaneure puisse naistre nule villositez par l'aspreté des queus si seut la vertu retentive avoir sa force. Mais si la dissintere vient de aposteme de l'estomac et des boiaus, si face l'en les cures qui sont escrites ou traitié des devant dites apostemes. Car quant l'aposteme est [f. 94v] garie, si gart l'en maintenant de la menoison.

[IX,5 De diaria] [123] *De diarria.* Dyarria si est flux simple dou* ventrail, c'est asavoir quant la viande s'en ist fors bien ovré et bien defite et sanz egestions senglantes. Et si vient icestui flux a la fie de trop mangier et de trop boivre et d'angoisse et de flux qui vient dou chief et de fleume escolorjante et de colre mordant meimement et de la febleté de la vertu retentive quant li estomacs ou les boiaus sont afebliz, si que il ne poent retenir ce que il devroient retenir. [124] Et quant li diarré vient de trop manger ou de trop boivre, ce puet l'en conoistre par le dit dou malade, qui dira bien s'il a trop mangié ou trop agues viandes eues. Le flux qui vient des humors qui descendent dou chief, ce conoist l'en par les egestions espumouses et ampuilleuses. Dont Ypocras dit 'Cil qui ont les egestions espu- meuses en diarré si puet l'en savoir que li flux vient d'umors qui descendent [f. 95r] dou chief'. Et quant fleume est en cause, ce conoist l'en par les egestions qui sont trop cleres et fleumatiques et blanches et ne sont pas crues, sicome en lientere. Et quant colre est en cause, ce conoist l'en par les egestions jaunes. Et quant li diarré vient de la febleté de la vertu retentive, ce conoist l'en par la remocion des autres signes et par ce que les egestions ne demostrent nule habundance des autres humors. [125] *De diarré.* Quant le diarré vient de la superfluité de mangier et de boivre, si li doigne l'en tenve diete. Et se li diarré vient d'angoisse de viandes, si li doigne [l'en] choses refroidanz et moistes sicome syrop violat et oximel simple et triasandali. Et si la menoison vient de flux d'umors qui descendent dou chief, si doigne l'en atanasiam ou rubeam et face l'en les remedies qui sont escrites contre catarre. Et si li diarré vient de fleume, si le purge l'en de [f. 95v] la decoction lien- teri[c]orum. Et si ce avient de colre, si le purge l'en de la decoction dissinteri[c]orum. Et si ce avient de la febleté de la vertu retentive, si doigne l'en les choses constrictives come nos avons [dit] ou traitié de dissintere ou primier chapitre devant. Et si vient a la fie de colre et a la fie de fleume froide et viscoseuse.

[IX,6 De tenasmone] [126] *Tenasmon.* Tenasmon si est une difficulté d'aler a chambre quant l'en s'aforce mult et a l'en volenté grant et l'en ne puet. Et si vient ceste maladie a la fie de fleume viscoseuse et froide, et a la fie de colre et en teu maniere. Car endementers que colre sorhabunde en le boiau*, si mort et point icelui boiau et de ce si vient une volanté grant de chier. Car quant les boiaus sentent la mordicacion et la fleume, si s'esmue[n]t naturelment a boter fors la superfluité des egestions. Et de ce si vient une volanté grant de chier. Et por ce que colre restreint tot adés par la sechece, si s'aforce l'en por ce [f. 95*r] durement et sent l'en une dolor. Et si vient ceste maladie de fleume froide et viscoseuse, car endementers que teu fleume sorhabunde en la devant dit boel, si la charge et la grieve. Dont li boel s'esmuet et travaille a delivrer soi de lui et a l'en de ce une volanté de chier. Mais quant fleume froide et viscouse est en cause, si constraint par la froidure et fait aerdre ensemble par la viscosité. Et quant li boiaus se sent grevé, si s'efforce de voider. [127] Et quant colre est en cause, ce conoist l'en par les pointures et par les arsures et par les egestions, a la fie jaunes et a la fie pleines de sanc, et par ce que li malades vait sovent a chambre et a la fie si fait .i. poi, et a la fie nient et a la fie une gote de sanc tant solement. Mais quant fleume est en cause, si sent l'en une grevance et une pesantume en bas et sont les egestions muscilagineuses et ont unes gotes de sanc mellees aveques aus par les vei[f. 95*v]nes qui rompent et depecent

com l'en s'aforce trop de chier. Dont come en l'un et en l'autre espece aperent
gotes de sanc, si est bien que l'en corge as autres signes. Car en cele ou om sent .i.
ardor et unes pointures verra l'en les egestions jaunes et n'ont pas nule muscilaginité mellé oveques aus. Mes en l'autre espiece si sont egestions sozblanches et si a
de la fleume viscouse mellé oveques soi. [128] *Cure*. De ceste maladie porra chaïr
en dissintere se l'en n'est plus tost gariz et a la fie si est muee de fleume en colre. Mais
quant colre est en cause, si le doit l'en purger de la medicine dont l'en purge les
dissinteriques. Et quant vos l'avroiz purgié, si li doit om aidier de choses locales.
Face l'en donques fomentacion de mauves quites en ewe ou de mauves [et] violette[s] ou de mauves et de branca ursina ou de ferine d'orge quite en ewe ou de la
farine de fenugrec et de la semence de lin quite en [f. 96r] ewe de pluie. Et en face
l'en fumigacions parmi .i. tuel* et de ferrume bien eschaufé et arosee desore de vin
egre, ou de une perre de molin et mete l'en par desore foilles de porriaus et les
arose l'en de vin egre. Et moille l'en cotoun en oile violat et mete l'en sor le
fondement. Autre. Preigne l'en seu de motoun ou de chievre et greisse de geline et
de ouwe et funde trestot ensemble et i mete l'en oile rosat ou violat et cire blanche
et face l'en oignement. Et moille l'en .i. limignon enz et li bote l'en ou fundement.
Mais si ce vient de fleume viscouse, si purge l'en le malade de la medicine des
lienteriques. Et aprés li face l'en locales remedes. Preigne l'en mirre et les foilles de
porriaus et .i. poi de castoreo et les boille l'en en tres bon vin blanc et face l'en de
ce subfumigacions par desoz et fomentacions. Autre. Preigne l'en puliol, ysope,
origanum, branche d'orse et les boille l'en en tres bon vin [f. 96v] blanc et face l'en
fumigacions et encatimes. Autre. Face l'en poudre de poliol, de ysope, de origanon
ou de lor flors qui miauz vaut et les seche l'en mult bien tant qu'eles soient mult
tres bien delié. Et lors s'aforce li malades de chier, si que li boiaus soit enversez. Et
mete l'en enz la devant dite poudre, la quele conforte merveilleusement et lasche
la dolor. Et face l'en fumigacion de colofonia ou de poiz* mise sor les charbons.
Autre esprove. Oigne l'en les rains et trestote l'eschine dou dos trestot contreval
de miel tieve. Et aprés poudre l'en par desore de la poudre colofonie, nasturcii,
pulegii, ysope, origanon et le lie om bien de une bende aprés.

[IX,7 De emorroidibus] [129] *Emoroides*. Emoroides si sont .v. veines qui sont ou
fondement es queles si vienent diverses maladies, inflacion, retencion et flux.
Notez donques que les superfluitez [f. 97r] en teus ja sont envoiez par force de
nature a celes veines et les depecent et en issent par ilueques, par la queu chose [le
cors] est gardé de diverses maladies. Mais quant eles corent trop, si engendrent
diverses maladies et quant eles retienent les superfluitez plus que reson et meimement en ceaus qui sont costumer a espu[r]ger par iluec, si engendrent diverses
maladies, sicome ydropisie, tisicle, manie et melancolie. Inflacion si vient en tel
maniere. A la fie avient que les superfluitez descendent as devant dites veines com
eles sont espoisses et puantes et estopent les boches des veines par lor espoissece, si
riens n'en porra issir, dont il covient qu'eles tendent et enflent. A la fie meimes la
substance des reins est espo[is]se et compacte, dont eles ne depiecent pas volen-
tiers. Et si avient a la fie de entense sechece qui [f. 97v] restreint meimes les
veines. Et si avient soventes foiz qui les cyrurgiens les quisent d'un chaut fer quant
eles corent trop. Et aprés si sont sorsanez et ne corent jamés, ou s'il corent, ce iert a

poine. La retencion des humors si vient de ceste cause et a la fie de la espoisseté dou sanc. Flux si vient a la fie de force de nature qui depece les veines et a la fie de la force de la maladie ou de l'aguesce des humors et a la fie de la grant aparcion des veines. [130] L'enfleure de ces veines puet l'en bien conoistre par le dit dou malade ou par veue, car les chiés des veines aperent enflees. Et quant eles retie-nent trop les superfluitez, ce puet l'en conoistre par le dit dou malade, car il dira bien s'il avoient piece a coru ou non, et par autres signes com par dolor do chief et par la face pale ou bleve et par les rains c'om avra pesanz et le penil et les quisses. Le flux dou ma[f. 98r]lade conoist l'en [par le] sanc qui en ist, a la fie pur et a la fie noir et a la fie jaune, selonc les diversetez des humors. Notez que plusor sont deceu que quident que cil qui travaillent de emoroides qui travaillent de dissinterie ou de tenasmon, ou la converse, car en icés maladies si seignent comunement par le fundement. Mais cil qui sont malades des emoroides seignent purement sanc sanz autres egestions et sanz aforcier et sanz avoir volanté d'aler a chambre. Et ce ne font pas cil qui ont tenasmon, dont l'en puet bien conoistre les uns des autres en tel maniere, et la converse, et par les autres signes que nos avons dit en lor propres chapitres. [131] *Cure contre emflure des emeroides.* Encise l'en la veine desoz le talon ou desoz la quiville dou pié par dehors le talon et face l'en subfumigacions de sale nitre, salgemme quiz en vin, car eles romperont en teu maniere [f. 98v] e si heles secherunt. Autre*. Prengne l'em .i. drap et le moile l'en en aubun de oef et face l'en en t[e]u manere enplastre. Et met[e] l'em sur les chefs des vainis et cum el seit seche sur, si l'ost l'em sutivement et a force, si ky les chefs des vainis depecint a l'oster. *Superfluité de sanc.* Pur fere isir la superfluité de sanc. Pur fer[e] oster la retenciun de superfluetez doit l'em trencher la devant dite vaine et le purge l'en de la decocciun de sené*, thimi, epetimi, mirabolans indes et la peire* lazuli et mete l'e[n] ventuses oveces garses sur le[s] reins en bas. Flux ky vent de vainis* par for[c]e de nature ne deit l'em pas esthancher. Mes cum li flux vent de la force de la maladie, la quele chose l'em poit ben cunutir par la febles[e] du malade, et lors dait l'en estancher. Et face l'en subfumigaciuns et fomentaciuns [f. 99r] de kalendula et de tapsie barbaste* quitis en vin blaunc u de foiles de porrel quitis en vin. *Oignement.* Oignem[e]nt Estevenon pur emeroidis restreindre. Recevez antimoni ars par sai et plum ars par sei et semenz de porieus ars par sei, litargiri. Tutis icés chosis soint* triblez en pudir et les confisez de oile fet de semenz de lin et mulez en cel oile cotun ou estupis et metez sur les emeroudis. Autir. Preng[e] l'em tendrunz de runcis et de seuz et les triblez mut ben ausi cum l'em vousit feire sause de tut et les temprez de oil feit de mueus de hof et moil[e] l'en un drapalet enz et metez desur. Si ceste[s] chosis ne sustenint, si face l'en les curis ky nus avuns dist avaunt [en] dissauntte[re].

[IX,8 De exitu ani] [132] Li fundement s'en ist a la fiez de deus causis: u par abundaunce de humuris ky li grevint he le funt isire, ou par la lubricité de aux. [133] Et cum ce avint de abundaunz de humuris, ce cunust l'em par [f. 99v] la grevanz et* la pesauntume de[s] membris basis. La lubricité des humurs cunust l'en par un viscosité esculurgaunt ky est en le fundement ovecis une froidure. [134] *Cure.* Cure si ce avent de habundaunz de umuris. Si l'espurge l'en tut primerment e aprés le seine l'en et aprés i mette l'em chosis localis. E le quel ky ce avene, de

habundaunce de umurs u de la lubricité de aux, face l'en fomentaciuns* et
subf[um]igaciuns de galla, psidia*, de balaustia, de tano, simfito quitis en eue de
plue et arose l'en le fundement cum il s'en ist de cele ewe, et pudir l'en par desur de
la pudre fait de bole et de sanc de* dragon et de galla, de simfito et de teu[s] chosis.

[BOOK X *De egritudinibus epatis*]

[1 De apostemate eius] *De un apostume.* [135] A la fiez avient un apostume au faie
de chaudis humuris et a la feiez de freidis et si aveint a la fiez en la buche du faie et
a la feiez ou cruce*. [136] E cum l'apostume vent de chau[f.100r]dis humurs, si
sunt les singnis itelis. Dolur desus le deter coste ague et punaunt, fever continue,
soif, les oiws rugis u te[i]ns d'une culur jaune, et a la fie si est trestuz le cors teins de
une tele colur, le urine ert ruge ou suzruge ou inopos, espés et jhaune et bleue par
en bas et jhaune et oscur amunt. Homur freide cum ele est en cause conust l'en en
tele manere: la fevir ert lente, la soif nule ou petite, et la dolur greve soz* la destre
coste, le urine descoluree et destempree et troblee et bleue par desuis, mes ne avera
pas le cors ne les eux teins. Mes cum l'apostume set en la part oscur dou faie, ce
poet l'em conutir en teu manere. L'en sent une dolure et une pesaunttime en
parfunde et sans glete l'en womist a la fiez de la conpressiun de l'estomac. E cum
l'en met sa maine sor le foie, si ne sent l'en pas la dolur plus graunt pur ce. Mes
cum l'aposteime siet en la buche du faie, si aleine l'en a peine* et tuse l'en par la
conpressiun des esperiz et a pain[e] [f.100v] suffre* li maladis ky l'em l'athuche rins
et apert li lius enf[l]és et en autel* furme cum une cresaunt ou cum* demi cercle
cum li maladis gist envers et estendu. Notez ky l'en a postume a la fie es coustes et
quidint teuis ja qu'el sait el faie cum el n'i est point, dunt maint sunt deceus. Mes
de ce poet l'em ethir cert en teu manere. Car l'apostaine des costes si a une furme
[bes]longe, a la fie de longe, a la fiez de traverse, sulunc la furme dou leu ou el sete.
Meis l'apostume dou faie si est ansi furmé cum la lune quant el est nuvel. [137]
Cure cuntre aposteime. Cure cuntir aposteime chaude pur que* il sait de la force et
de agee. Si le face l'em seiner de la vain[e] dou foie, de le senestre brace. Et aprés
des le cumencement dewaunt ce ky l'aposteime seit confermé, si met l'en chose[s]
froides et repercussives et oigne l'en le foie de oile rosate ou de vi[o]lat. Et face l'em
epitemes sur dou jus des herbis froidis cum de semperviva, de [f.101r] morele, de
portulagues, de scarioles et de sembla[b]lis chosis. Mes cum la matere tent a porire,
la quel chose l'en pot conoitre par la chalur de la fevere ky serra plus graunt et les
autres accidens, lors se doit l'em metter chosis maturativis. Pren l'en farin de horge
et la confise l'en leisseive forte menement, nent pas trop. Et face l'en emplastre et
met[e] l'en sur le lu. Ou l'en face emplastre de farine et de semence de line et la
confise l'en de la devaun dite leisive ou de braunca ursina et de autre chosis ky
sunt ditis cu[n]tre ch[a]ude aposteme de[s] boiaus. Mes cum freide humur est en
cause, si ne deit l'en pas seiner se le cors ne seit mut plectoriques. Et si le cors soit
plectoriqis, si le face l'en sainer de la devaunt dite vaine si il est de l'aeege et de la
force. Aprés hi mette l'en chosis extenuativis pur atenvir la matere. Tribel l'en
ysope, origanum, centauream et met[e] l'en tut chaut sore. Et doin[e] l'en neis
decoctiun de acun de ceus et face l'en les autre[s] chosis diaforetiqis ky sunt ditis
contre fraide apostome de[s] bouaus. Mes si la matere tent a pureture, la quel chose

l'em con[us]te par l'amentaciun de la fever et des autre[s] accidens, si doit l'en mettir chosis* maturativis. Face l'en emplastre froide encuntre teu maner de aposteme de racinis ef[f.101v]fodillorum, de uves passis, de fiques quites en lessive ou en vin ou en oiele. Auter levein confeit en oile si est bon a fair[e] emplatir ou sit* quite en vin ou en oile. E cum l'aposteme est depecé, la queu chose l'en purra cunistir par la purture ky en itera ouvec le urine ou oveke les egestiums, le* purge l'en et li doine l'en chosis mundificativis. Car si le tendir leus ne est pas espurgé de la pureture, la tendir sustanz de la foy en serait* tost corumpuz. Si umur fraide est purgés par le urine, si aidera mult a la nature. Si le doin[e] l'en la decoctiun de semenz de fenoile, de anis et de ache. Et si wos wolés purger chaudis humuris par le urine, si la donez le ewe de la decocciun citrolis, mellonis, cucumeris et cucurbite, ou par sei ou par le jus d'eskariolis. E si vus wolés ky la materi seit purgé par les egestiuns, si doit l'en aider a nature de la decocciun thimi, epitimi, polipodii, semen feniculi, agarici. Ou l'en face emplatir consolidative de speic nardine, aloe, mastic confiz de ewe de pluie ou de rosis. La dreine cure si est par incisiun*. Apostaine es costes garist l'en en memis le manere.

[f.102r] [X,2 De ictericia] [138] *Yterice.* Yctericia si est jhaunisce, se est asaver ordur de cuir dehors saunz ce ky el est entamé dehors et par autir nun est apellez morbus regius ou aurigeus ou arcuatus, pur ce ky il demutir la culur exteris ou culur de ros ou de or ou de arc del cele. Car trais especis sunt de jhauniz: jauniz de chos[e] natu[r]ele; agriaca pegazelontis de colur vert; melangiron de humur nairis, se est asaveir de colur adustus. E si vent ceste maladie de maintis causis, sce est asaveire de le ardur et de la ebulliciun de sanc ky pas[se] en coler. Et si vent de coler ky surhabunde et tent le sanc, e si vent de opilaciun de[s] poris* cisti[s] fellis*, ce est asaver de celi amounte ou* de li avale, [si] doit la coler redunder au foie* et tent et maumet le sanc. E si vent ensement de aposteme colerique dou foy ky tent le sanc. E si vent de fever continue, car li sancs com il est tiens de ces causis et il est envoiez a nurir les membris si les tent et mue en sa colour. [139] Dunt les causes sunt a destincter par les singnes. La jaunice ky vent de la forseneri de le saunc ou de ebolicion ou de coler si a les signis itelis, ce est a savo[i]r le cors trestut tent et la troeve* l'en* chaut mult cum l'en i tast[e] et memement entur le destre coste, soif mult et [f.102v] la boche amere, dolur el front et les oreilles cornanz, l'urine coloree ovesques une escume tot adés jaune et ce que il vonche et les egestions sunt jaunes en colur. Mes si l'ycterice vient de l'opilacion dou pertius dou fel amont, si ert le cors teint mult des le nunblil aval, mes des* le nunblil amont poi ou noiant et si sunt les egestions mult coleriques, ce que l'en vonchera n'iert pas teint et la soif ert petite ou nule, nule dolur el chef, ne* les oreilles ne corneront pas, l'urine est jaune. Mes si li pertuis d'aval est estopés del fel, si est li cors teint mult del numblil cuntremont et cuntreval poi ou nient, e les egestions ne sont pas coleriques et a l'en in[di]gestion et ce que l'en vonche ert jaune et meimement aprés manger et ad l'en soif grant et la boche amere et l'urine coloree et jaune. Mes si l'une et l'autre des pores est estupés, si pert l'en l'apetite de manger, ne les egestions ne les voncheures serront coleriques, et si ert li foyes pleins et tenduiz de la colere qui redunde dusc'a lui et l'urine est mult coloree et jaune. Et come ceste maladie vient de aposteme del foie, ce conoist l'en par les signes qui sont dites en traitié del foie. Yterice qui vient de fevre si vient a la fiez de force de nature et a la fiez de force de maladie. Mes cumme ce avient de force de maladie*, si vient [f.103r] devant le setime jor come la matere ist as parties defors ou pur le multitudine de soi ou pur la fumosité de soi ovesques l'aumentation de la fevre et de l'accident. Mes come ce avient de force de nature, si sout avenir aprés le setime jor et en autre* jur crettique* ovesques la diminution de la fevre et seront les autres accidens plus remisses et se sentira li malades autresi com tous alegiés. [140] *Cure.* Cure: Si la jaunice vient de ardor de sanc ou de superfluité de colere, si est la cure trestot une meime. Si est donques de l'aage et del force et nule autre accident n'est encontre, si le face l'en seigner des le comencement: si il ad fevre, de la veine del foie el destre bras dedens le [quart] jor de sa maladie, et le diete l'en de diete froyde come de laitues, de scarioles, de portulagues, de morele et lor dogne l'en icés herbes crues ou quites et lor dogne l'en a* buire l'eue de la decoction des froides semences sicome citrolis, cucumeris, cucurbito, melonis s'il ad fevre ovesques la maladie. Et s'il n'ad point de fevre, si lor dogne l'en vin blanc temperé ovesque la devant dite decoction et lor dogne l'en un puchin quit en ewe et les extremités des oiselez et poissons escardés quis en ewe. Et enoigne l'en le foie d'oile rosat ou de oile violat ou de oile froide Cophonis ou de oile ma[n]dragorat ou de populeon. Et face l'en epitimes del jus de herbes froydes come de sempervi[f.103v]va, de morele et de semblables choses. Ou l'en face epithemes de sandles blanches ou rouges et de roses triblees en pudre et de camphora et destemprés ovesques oile violat ou rosat et de vert jus et d'un poi de vin egre et la renovele l'en sovent. Et li dogne l'en chescun matin sirop acetous ovesques l'eue des devant dites semences. Et a l'utime jur ou au dime jor come l'urine comencera a espessir, se le purge l'en de la decoction de la semence citrulis, melonis, cucumeris, cucurbito, violettes, prunes, epatica, capillis veneris et mete l'en en l'eue unces .ii. de cassiavistula, de tamarindes unces .ii., mauve unce .i. et .ii. de mirabolans citrins. Et la tiers jor de la purgation dogne l'en reubarbe en tele manere. Pregne l'en unces .iii. de reubarbe et le mete l'en temprer en ewe par nuit et dogne l'en la coleure* de ce au matin ovesques sirop violat. Triffe sara[ci]nz ovesques reubarbe ou ovesques le jus de scarioles, cum* l'en le dogne sovent, si profite merveyllusement. Et lor dogne l'en a user de tel sirop: quise l'en en ewe epatica, capilli veneris ovesque le jus de scarioles et mete l'en zucre et en la fin de la decoction mete l'en reubarbe en tele proportion qu'a chescune livre de syrop mete l'en unce .i. de reubarbe. Mes notez que si li malades est deliez, l'en deit meller la coleure de la reubarbe et non pas la sustance. Mes si il est fors et rudes, l'en poet bien mettre la sustance. Si est bon li syrop en cest [f.104r] cas que nus avon dite contre jaunice de opilation, mes eschaufement de foie garist l'en de ces devant dites cures. *Ycterice.* Ycterice faite de opilacion dou pore amont ou dou pore aval ou de l'un et l'autre garist l'en des devant dites aides. Mes que l'en excepte les froydes oignemens et les epithemes ovesques les autres choses qui sont escrites aprés, c'est asaver cic[er] ruge soit quis ovesque le jus de fenoile, de ache et li dogne l'en sovent et doigne l'en le jus de aluigne et d'ache ovesque sirop au matin. Si l'opilation est grant, dogne l'en jus d'aloigne et le jus de planteine ana [demi] unce, c'est asaver ovesques zucre. Un grein de aloe, come l'en li dogne, si ovre merveilusement opilation. Ou un grein de euforbio* dogne l'en a la quantité d'une [drame] ovesques un oef mol. Et dogne l'en oxemel squillitiqu[e] a* beivre et aprés done l'en rachines raphani a manger. Et li doigne l'en ewe chaude a boyre en grant* quantité et puis le reface l'en voncher pur overir, pur mundefier, pur terdre. Et meine l'en le malade baigner pur suer. Et face l'en le bai[n]g en teu manere. Pregne l'en le[s] summerrones* de seu et les tendrons de l'eble et triffoille et boille l'en en ewe et emple l'en une cuve prés de cele ewe et mete l'en sure une table menuement percié ou l'en i mete busches sore de travers et face l'en seeir par desore le malade trestot nu pur suer. Et cum il comence a suer, si li dogne [f.104v] l'en le jus de planteine et d'aloigne ovesques zucre sicom nus avons dit avant. Une vielle empli un pot de jus de planteine et le quit tant que la moitié fu degasté et li dona chascun jor de ce au matin et le gari de cel sol esperiment qui fu pur poi aselitiques ou tympanites par la jaunice que tant avoit duree. Mes si l'ycterice vient d'aposteme, si deit l'en garir l'aposteme sicome nus avons dit eu traitié des apostemes. Et s'ele veint de fevre, se garise l'en la fevre et si la jaunice remaint encore, si le garisse l'en sicum nus avons dit devant. En quele maladie u prisun u anguisse u poverte ke l'en seit, face ceo ke ci est escrit, si avera cunfort denz l'an: 'Duce Dame virgine Marie, reine des angles, mere al seinur de cunseil, merci vus cri. Ausi verreiement cum le mund fu par Eve descunseilé e par vus recuncillé, issi verreiement requer vostre cher fiz ki est sire de cunseil, ke pur la vostre honur me conseilet de cest anguisse'. Si numét pus vostre dolur, si li facét un vu a tenir e si vus l'enfreinét, tut est a recumencer.

[f. 75r] [X,3 De idropisi] [141] *De ydropisie.* Ydropisie si vient de error de la vertu digestive del foie et engendre inflacions es membres, car si la vertu digestive est afebloié ou foie, si vienent et naissent de ce granz superfluitez d'umors, les queles la force de la vertu expulsive en[f. 75v]voit as membres et les font enfler. Et si vient ceste maladie de .iii. choses, principaument de la retencion des superfluitez* contre nature, et de la principal destemprance des qualitez de meisme le foie. Car quant les superfluitez sont retenues contre nature, sicome flux menstruel et le flux des emoroides et li sans qui est acostumez a issir par le nes, quant iceus flux sont retenues, si sont grevez les vertuz dou cors et afebliz et en naissent unes superfluitez qui font les membres enfler. Et par le flux de icés superfluitez contre nature s'en issent les esperiz et degastent et en afeblissent les vertuz et en espandent les superfluitez par le cors qui naissent de la indigestion des viandes et font les membres enfler. En la destemprance des qualitez foloie la vertu digestive ou foie en .iiii. manieres: de la destemprance de froidure et de moistesce ou de froidure et de sechesce [ou de chaline et de moistesce] ou de chaline et de sechesce. Selonc les .iiii. manieres des qualitez qui poent conjuindre ensemble si vienent [f. 76r] .iiii. espieces de ydropisie: leucoflemancia si vient de la destemprance de froidure et de moistesce et si est dite leucoflemancia por ce qu'ele est faite de blanche fleume – leucos et blanc si est trestot une chose; yposarca ou anasarca si vient de la destemprance de froidure et de sechesce; asclites si vient de la destemprance de chaline et de moistece; timpanistes si avienent de chaut et de sechesce. [142] Si avienent icés espieces en tel maniere. Car quant froidure et moistesce sont destemprez ou foie, si afeblist la vertu digestive et si ensordent unes superfluitez, laquele la vertu expulsive qui n'est pas afebloié en boté* fors as membres foraines, dont les membres en enflent forment. De la destemprance de froidure et de sechesce en afeblist forment ensement la vertu digestive et la vertu expulsive ensement, dont les superfluitez ne sont boté fors jusc'au cuir* et as membres foraines, ainz sont retenues entre cuir et char. Dont ceste espiece est dite yposarca ou anasarca, ce est joste la char. De la destemprance de chalor [f. 76v] et d'umor est destempree l'un et l'autre vertu, dont les superfluitez ne sont pas botez hors par trestot le cors sicom eles sont es autres devant dites especes, ainz sont retenues entre* le ventre et siphac tant solement, et ceste espiece est dite asclites, car lor ventre com om fiert sore si sone autresi com .i. bocel demi plain. Asclites si est dit li ventres*. De la destemprance de chaline et de sechesce en sont desouz les esperiz dont l'une et l'autre vertu est afebloié. Et les choses superfluele[s] qui levent de la indigestion* si remettent et fondent en grosses fumositez et en ventositez, les queles por la feblesce de la vertu expulsive ne s[on]t pas boté hors par tot le cors, ainz sont* retenue entor le ventre. Et ceste espece si est dite timpanistes, car com l'en fiert sor le ventre, si resone com .i. tabort. Mais en leucoflemancia si est l'inflacions granz par trestot le cors et la superficé blanche et mole. Et quant l'en prient le doi sore, si remaint en la char le signe* com en cyre ou en paste. Mes la char [f. 77r] releve aprés petit et petit. L'orine est descoloree, blanche et espesse. Mais en yposarca n'est pas l'inflacion si granz, et lor char si puit, lor orine est descoloree, a la fie tenve et a la fie moinement espesse. Mais en esclite si est li ventres tant solement enflé et come l'en fiert sore, [si sone] come .i. boscel demi plain, sicome nos avons dit, et l'orine [est] coloree roge ou susroge et espesse. En timpaniste si est li ventres ensement enflé, mais plus est tendu que en esclite et quant om i fiert sore, si resone com .i. timbre, sicom nos avons dit. L'orine [est] coloree roge ou susroge et le col graille et les narines agues et les euz reonz et enflez. Et notez que de leucofleumancia et de yposarca avant qu'il soient confermez puet om bien garir. Mais de asclite et de timpaniste aprés qu'il sont confermé garist om mult a peines. [143] *Cure de leucoflemancia et de yposarca garist om en une maniere.* I[l] doit estre chaut et moiste moinement [f. 77v] et choses seches lor puet om bien doner a la fie et lor doigne om vin ou il n'ait mie mult d'ewe et le tempre om de l'ewe de la decoction de fenoil et d'anis. Et lor doigne om l'ewe diuretique des esplenetiques, la quele nos dirons ou traitié de l'esplen. Et le purge l'en une foiz la semoine de benoite simple ou de hermodactile ou de esula ou de la decoction polipodii, de la semence de fenoil, agarique, squinanti, interiorum coloquintide et i mete om o tot .i. unce de mirobalans kebles. Et ceste decoction, s'ele est sanz mirobalans, si la puet om doner au soir, mes oveques mirobalans ne la doit om pas doner fors au matin. Et lor face l'en user chascun jor au matin oximel faite de racines d'ache, de perresil, de fenoil, speragi, brusci. Ou om doigne oximel de racines de rafle ou om doigne oximel squilletique oveques ewe chaude de la decoction de semence de fenoil et de mastic. Et lor face om user dou [f. 78r] jus fait des tendrons de seu et des sumerons des ebles et de fumiterre. Solement le jus des tendrons des ebles fera mult grant bien por doner au matin oveques zucre. [Autre] mult tres profitable as ydropiques et as splenetiques. Emple l'en .i. pot prés* plain de jus de plantain et coevre l'en bien la boche dou pot d'un drap linge et le lie l'en bien fermement, si que le jus n'i atoche point. Et mette l'en de la cendre sor le drapelet et face l'en le pot boillir sor les charbons tant que la moitié soit degasté. Et doigne l'en le remanant chascun matin au malade. La soverain cure que je sai en [ceste] cause: que om ameine le malade* as bainz salez, soffrines ou alumineuses, mais devant ce qu'il se lieve en l'ewe, si le face l'en bien suer et l'enoigne* l'en de caus oignemenz sicom de arragon, de marciaton et des semblables choses. Et es jors caniculers, si [f. 78v] le* doit l'en ensevelir en gravele chaude tant qu'il sue bien. Et l'enoigne l'en avant de fente de buef. Et li face l'en emplastres desiccatives et extenuatives. Face l'en poudre [de] camomille, de aloe, mel lavé, coste, aloe, spica nardi et face l'en boillir la poudre oveques fente de buef en tres fort aisil et mette l'en o tot farine d'orge et face l'en emplastre. Preigne l'en alun, suffre, bacce lauri, aspaltum, raiz de gramine, fente de colons et en face l'en poudre. Et boille l'en la poudre en vin egre fort et face l'en emplastre. Trible l'en fente de colon et figues seches et les quise l'en en aisil fort et en face l'en emplastre et renovele l'en sovent icés emplastres. Et icés emplastres ne sont pas tant solement bones en icés choses, ainz sont bones principaument contre ventosité. Et ja soit ice que om garist a poines de timpaniste et de asclite, la diete de aus soit atempré et les doit l'en asoier a garir. Et lor face l'en user d'ewe diuretique des semences citrolis, melons, cucumbres et cucur[f. 79r]bite, de fenoil, d'ache et de perresil. Et face om emplastre sor l'esplen que nos dirons ou traitié de l'esplen. Et lor face l'en user de mon syrop dont ge gari le neveu l'abé de Clerevaus. Prenez le jus de escarioles .ii. livres, dou jus d'ache et de perresil .i. livre et de esule en tele proporcion que en chascune livre dou jus dou syrop quis, ne di pas dou creu, soient mis .iii. unces de esule. Et boille l'en l'esule en les devant dit jus et mette om .i. poi de mastic et de semence d'ache et de fenoil et le cole l'en. Et en la coleure mete om zucre. En la fin de la decoction mette l'en reubarbe et doigne l'en au matin oveques l'ewe de la decoction de semence de fenoil .ii. foiz ou .iii. la semaine selonc la force dou malade. Car ce est laxatif tant com ce est. La darraine cure en leucoflemancie et en yposarca et en esclite si est que l'en trenche le malade .iii. doie desoz le nombril et mete l'en enz .i. doiel. Et face l'en issir fors petit et petit la superfluité de l'ewe. Fevre qui sorvient en ydropisie si est mauvais signe. Dont Ypocras dist 'Ydropiques s'il tousse, si soit desesperez [f. 79v] .i. poi. Si une tous li prent oveques la ydropisie et om l'ait eu longuement la ydropisie et om tousse aprés, si est signe mortel'.

[BOOK XI *De egritudinibus splenis*]

[De egritudinibus splenis] **[144]** De l'esplen. L'office de l'esplen si est d'epurer le foie de la superfluité de melancolie, car diverses maladies avienent en l'esplen, c'est asavoir enfleure grant oveques une extension, une dolor et oveques une grevance. Et ce avient a la fie d'umor et a la fie de grosse ventosité. Aposteme et enfleure avienent plus sovent d'umor melancolique, mes relement de colre. Mes la superfluité d'umor melancolique naist et est engendré dou foie de user longuement diete melancolieuses come char de vache, char de chievre et semblables choses, des queles come melancolie est engendré grant quantité, si emple et destent l'esplen come son receptacle. Colre ensement si sorhabunde a la fie tant qu'ele n'est pas envoié tant solement a l'amer [. . .], ainz qu'ele ne puet entrer en l'amer en voit a l'esplen. Dont une aposteme avient a la fie de la matire [f. 80r] qu'est espeissie ilueques par ebullicion et par chaline. Une grosse ventosité qui ist de froides humors si entre en l'esplen et a la fie le destent et enfle. [145] Si l'inflacion de l'esplen vient d'umor melancolique sanz eschaufement dou foie, les signes sont iteles: enfleure desouz le senestre coste oveques une grevance, devant mangier si sent li malades miauz, aprés mangier si se sent pis, et se muet perreceusement et a les quisses et les membres aval pesant mult et meimement com il voudra monter aucun degré, et si a indigestion grant et une tension dou ventre et des costez, l'urine descoloree et tenve mult et vergee, et le ventre serré et trestot le cors descoloré et les extremitez greilles, dolor a la senestre partie [del chief], et en ist li sans a la fie par la senestre narine. Mais si colre est en cause, l'urine est coloree et jaune, dolor ou senestre coste poignante et un soif grant et la boche amere. L'apostume de l'esplen conoist l'en par l'enfleure [entor] de lui, par la fevre lente, se ele est de froide humor, [f. 80v] et si ele est de chaude humor, si est la fevre ague. La ventosité conoist l'en par la dolor distentive qui ne parmaint pas tot adés en une maniere, ainz s'en depart, a la fie s'en remaint. [146] *Cure. Si la enflacion de le esplen vient de melancolie**, si est la cure itele. Primierement li doit l'en ordener sa diete. Face l'en le malade garder soi* de mangier viandes melancolieuses et de boivre ewe froide. Et les diete l'en de chaudes viandes et de moistes. Et lor boivre soit actuelement chaudes et eschaufe om lor vin d'une perre d'acier ardant ou de perres d'ewe eschaufees et esteinz dedenz. Et lor face om mangier et boivre de hanas et d'escueles fait de tamariz, et s'il est riches om, .i. tonel de meime le fust a metre son vin qu'il bevra. Et les face l'en travaillier meinement* devant mangier por conforter l'estomac. Et aprés mangier les face om reposer. Et quant om avra ordené lor dietes, si doit om metre cure a l'esplene garir. Mais notez que trestot primierement doit om metre sore choses mollitives et relaxatives. Et aprés mete om choses consumptives et extenuatives et desiccatives. Car se om meist* [f. 81r] [prime]rement choses desiccatives et consumptives, come les plus cleres parties* seroient degastees, si remaindroient les plus grosses parties et les plus dures, si mueroit tost l'enfleure en une duresce que om apele sclirosis, dont l'en ne puet garir. Derechief notez que om ne doit pas ovrer des choses diuretiques si la duresce de l'esplien ne soit relaschiez avant, car les choses diuretiques en amenroient primierement fors les plus sotilles parties, si remaindroient les grosses, si en ven-droit de ce sclirosis. Dont om doit primier[ement] ovrier de choses mollificatives et aprés de diuretiques et de consumptives. Oigne l'en donques l'esplen oveques diauté et oveques bure au solail ou dejoste le feu come li malades est jeuns. [Autre] Preigne om la farine d'orge et semence de lin et fenugrec et tailleures de vignes seches et raisins secs et le mete om temprer une nuit en vin egre. Et aprés les boille om et cole et mete om en la coleure cire et oille. Et face om oignement et enoigne om l'esplen. [Autre] [Pregne om] mauve, bismauve, branche d'ours, racines de lis, squille ou oignons quiz en vin et en oile et les cole [f. 81v] om et en la coleure mete om cire et face om oignement et enoigne om l'esplen. Et quant li esplen sera amoliz, si doigne l'en choses diuretiques. Doigne om donques l'ewe de la decoction de la semence et des racines d'ache, de perresin, ou par soi ou oveques vin et ewe. Autre ewe tres bone. Quise om en ewe les racines de fenoil, d'ache, de perresil, speragi, brusci, epatice, capilli veneris, pollitricum, adiantos, ceterac, scolopendria, filipendula, les escorces ou les sumerons de tamarit et doigne [om] cele ewe ovec

vin ou par soi. Et s'ele est abhominable au malade, si i mette om zucre et en face
om syrop. Et li doigne om autre ewe, c'est asavoir l'ewe de la decoction des
escorchis capparis, filipendule, et pentafilon. Emplastres consumptives et desiccatives et extenuatives doit om metre sor l'esplen quant il est amoliz. Preigne om
donques armoniacum, serapinum et les mette om temprer en vin egre fort .i. jor et
une nuit et les funde l'en sor le feu et les cole om. Et mette om en la coleure cire et
oille et [f. 82r] face om emplastre. Autre. Mette om porrir pomes de terre en vin et
en oile et après les quise om et cole. Et mette om en la coleure la poudre des
escorches des racines capparis, coste, absente*, artimesie, rue sauvage. Et mette om
cire et face om enplastre. Ou om face emplastre de apostolicon ou de diaceraseos*
ou de ceroneo* ou de diacené, diacapparis, diacostum, filoantropos et lor doigne
l'en itel maniere de syrop. Quise om en ewe les escorches des racines capparis et les
escorches et les semences de tamariz, filupendule et sené. Et mette om dou jus de
borrage et de zucre et en face l'en syrop. Et doigne l'en le* fruit capparis. Et quant
l'esplen est esmoliz avant, si l'enoigne l'en avant de agrippa. Et lor face l'en user de
ceu poudre. Face l'en poudre de ame[. . .], des escorches de capparis, de phil-
ipendula, de noiz muscaz et lor doigne l'en. Ou l'en preigne limaille de fer et le
trible l'en en poudre delié et la mete bolir en jus d'aloigne une nuit et .i. jor. Et
quant les licors [f. 82v] defaillent, si mette om de l'autre. Et après traie om fors
la poudre et la lie en .i. drapel linge et le mete om soz .i. cuissin trestote une
nuit por eschaufer. Et le melle om après oveques la devant dite poudre en tele
proporcion que les .ii. parz soient de la devant dite poudre et la tierce part de la
poudre de la limaille de fer. Et quant li esplen est amoliz, si la doit l'en purgier de
diacené scamoneaté ou des pilles de .v. manieres oveques cele decoction qui miauz
vaut. Face l'en bolir sené en la decoction de trestotes les herbes diuretiques c'om
porra avoir et boille om o tot thimum, epithimum et cuscute. Et mete om en la
coleure .ii. unces de mirobalans kebles [et] indes et lapis lazuli solonc la devant
dite doctrine et la renovele l'en sovent. Mais si li inflacion de l'esplen vient de
ventosité, si doit estre la cure de aider lui de choses extenuatives et de consumptives et de diuretiques. Mais si l'enfleure vient de colre, si doit l'en oindre
l'esplen d'oile violat [f. 83r] ou de burre. Et li doigne om l'ewe de la decoction de
la semence citrolis, melons, cucumbres et cucurbite, epatice, capillorum veneris.
Et face l'en autres remedies que nos avons dit contre ycterice*. Quise om plantain,
mauves, senechon, morele, mercurial, ou par soi ou oveques chars, et doigne l'en.
Mais si l'enfleure de l'esplen vient oveques eschaufement de foie, si est mestiers
c'om oevre par art. Si covient que la diete soit atempré, car froides choses nuisent
a l'esplen et chaudes au foie. Et notez que iceste chose covient trestot le plus ovrer
de choses locales plus* que des choses c'om reçoit par la boche, ou eles seront
chaudes ou eles seront froides ou eles seront atemprees. Les froides nuisent a
l'esplen et les chaudes au foie et les atemprees ne garissent ne l'un ne l'autre.
Enoigne l'en l'esplen de oignemenz [chauz] et meimement quant la maladie
vient de froide humor et mette l'en sore chaude emplastre. Mes le foie doit l'en
garir de oignemenz froides et de froides emplastres. [f. 83v] Et notez que encontre vice de l'esplen si vaut mult de seignier le malade entre le petit doit et
l'autre après, de queuque cause que la maladie soit. Si mete l'en ventouses ovec
garse sor l'esplen ou sansues, si feront mult grant bien. En iver le seigne l'en de

veine ou de ventouse ou de sansues. La darraine cure si est que l'en i mete seons.Aposteme d'esplen garist om si[com] aposteme de stomac ou de boiaus.

[BOOK XII *De egritudinibus renum et vesice*]

[f.174r] [1 De diabetica passione] [147] *Diabethes si est une maladie ke prent as reins.* Diabethes si est une desmesuré attraction de urine du foie as reins et si vient de la destemprance des rains en chaline et en secchesce dont la vertu attractive prent sa force. Dont les reins ne finent de attraire du foie ne le foie des membres foreines. Dont om a sovent soif et talent de pisser. Mes la destemprance des reins vient de plusors causes sicome de trop boivre et de trop foutre et de user trop chaudes dietes et de fevre et de chaudes unctions et de chaudes emplastres. [148] Les signes de diabethe si sont iteles: chalor entor les reins, soif et appetite de boyvre ewe froyde, et si tost come l'en a beu si a l'en tallant de pisser, et l'urine si est tenve et blanche et grant. Mes, ce semble contraire, de chaline viegne urine descoloree, mes non est, kar ains que l'urine puisse estre coloree ou foie si l'ont les reins ja traite a soi, dont ele est descoloree et tenve est ele pur la secchesce du foie qui [vient de] defaut de nurreture. [149] Cure. En ceste maladie est bien mester de aver aide hastivement, que om ne chiece en ydropisie par le error de la vertu digestive ou en ethique par le defaute de norreture. Et pur ce si doit l'en oindre les reins de oile violat et de rosat et de populion. Ou l'en face epithime sor les reins [f.174v] de jus sempervive. Ou l'en tribble meime l'erbe et face l'en emplastre sore. [A]utre. Quise l'en mauves et foilles de violette en oile violat et rosat et face l'en emplastre sor les reins. [A]utre. Pregne om balaustes, mastic, bolum, sandles blanche[s] et rouges et en face l'en poudre et la confise l'en de oile rosat ou de violat. Et en face l'en epithime sor les reins. Mes notez que om ne doit pas tot adés metre i moistes choses, kar la moistesce afebleroit trop la substance. Ne trop ne doit l'en pas mettre de secches choses, kar trop secchesce en aguse la chalor. Mes l'en doit metre lors de l'une et puis de l'autre por amoister la membre et refroydir par l'aposicion de mostes choses et por conforter le membre de l'aposicion de secches choses. Et mete l'en pieces de plum* pertusees menuement* sor les reins, qui la fumosité qui ist des reins en puisse issir. Et notez qui il covient grant art et grant engin a dieter iteus malades, kar la chaude diete nuist as reins et la froide au foie. Dont* l'en lor doit doner choses atemprees. Et por la soif qui il ont lor doit om doner aucune chose que esta[n]che la soif et atempre. Et lor face l'en user lec-tuaires compostes come diantos ovekes triasandali et diarrodon ovekes [dia]draga-gant.

[f.175r] [XII,2 De exitu sanguinis cum urina] [150] Li sanc qui ist ovekes l'urine si na[i]st a la fiez du foie, a la fiez de kylivena et a la fiez des flans et a la fiez des reins et a la fiez de la vessie. Et si avient a la fiez que l'en pisse sanc come la vein[e] depece par sailir ou come om est ferus. Si avient ce a la fiez de sorhabundance de sanc et a la fiez de aguesce* que depece les veines. Mes ce avient relement par resudacion. Mes quant ce avent de saillir ou de coup que l'en a eu, ce poet on savoir du malade, kar il dira bien si il avra sailli ou si il avra esté feru. [151] Et si ce avient de sorhabundance de sanc, ce poet om savoir par l'abitude du cors* plectoriques ou sanguines, et par les veines lees et grans et par le sanc que en istra oveskes grant quantité. Et si aguesce de sanc est en cause, ce conust l'en par le color de meime le sanc, qui ert un poi jaune, et de ce que ele point com ele ist et mort la verge et aporte un ardor. Et si doit l'en destincter par les signes le quel le sanc na[i]st du foie ou de autres devant dites membres. Kar kant li sanc vient du foie, si sent om une dolor et une pesantum[e] desouz la destre coste. Si ist li sanc purs et grans. Mes quant li sanc est de quilivena ou des reins, si sent l'en une dolor en celes parties, s'en ist le sanc en grant quantité, mes non pas en si grant com en cele [f.175v] que nus [avons] dit devant, et en est li sanc purs. Mes quant le sanc [qui] ist oveskes l'urine vient de la vessie, si sent l'en une dolor au penil et es parties entor et li sanc qui en istra ert petit et troublees. Mes notez que li sanc qui vient des autres membres chiet a la fiez en la vessie et s'amoncele ensemble par la froidure de[l] liu. Et a la fiez s'en ist ovesques l'urine a la manere de* sanc[sue] et a la fiez si est [si] gros qui il estoupe la vessie et fait une opilation ileuques et stranguiriam dont [mult] enperissent. [152] Cure. Si ce avient que on pisse sanc par superfluité du sanc du foie, si le face l'en seigner de la veine du foie del bras destre. Mes si li sanc que om pisse vient des reins ou de la vessie ou de kilivena, si le face l'en seiner de saphena qui est delez le talon desous la kiville du pé. Et aprés face l'en emplastre au malade leu et en tretotes les causes communes*. Pregne l'en mastic, olibanum et en face le poudre et le confise l'en de oile rosat et de aubon de oef. Et face l'en emplastre et le mete om sor le leu malade. Autre. Face l'en poudre de mummia, de sanc de dragon et de une pere que om apele amatiste et le confise l'en de oile rosat et de aubun de oef. Athanasia* done [l']e[n] oveskes jus de plaunteine ou mummia* ovesques meime [f.176r] le jus, si profite mult, ou le jus par soi et destempre [l'en] du jus de ematiste et doigne l'en. Et mete l'en emplastres constrictives que nus avons dist en la traitié de dissenteire. Et si li sanc est moncelés en la vessie, si face l'en icés remedes qui sont esprovees et assez bones. Pregne l'en chous* quites en oile et en vin et face l'en emplastre sor le penil. Autre. [De] rue quite en oile et en vin face l'en emplastre et mete l'en sore et face om renoveler sovent icés emplastres, kar eles son[t] esprovees et bone[s] contre stranguiriam qui vient neis de autre cause.

[XII,3 De lapide in renibus et vesica] [153] Pere et gravele et diverses superfluitez sont engendrees sovent en la vessie et es reins, mes principaument eles sont engendrees de boivre ewe limeuse* et de viandes melancoleuses come de char de boef, de chievre et de chous et de semblables viandes, les queles engendrent unes superfluités que estopent la vessie et les conduiz des reins. Et se muent a la fiez en semblance de substance de piere et de gravele par l'action de la chalor. Et de iteles maneres de opilacions si avienent mult grant maus sicome anguise de pisser et sent l'en une dolor es reins et es illiers. Kar quant les conduiz de l'urine sont estopees par aucune des devant dites causes, si ne poet issir, si covient que [f.176v] ele soit retenue en la vessie, si la destent et emple, la quele come ele est destendu et emplie si prent et fait presse au coilon qui est prés de lui, si que la fente ne poet issir et de la retencion* si vient une dolor qui l'en apele dolor yliacus. Mes trois especes sont de anguoise de pisser, c'est asavoir stranguria*, dissurria et scuria. Stranguria si est apelé une anguisse qui om a de pisser come aucune ne poet pisser fors une goutete aprés autre. Et si vient ceste espece de moine opilacion. Dissurria si est une anguoisse que om a de pisser sicome l'en a volenté de pisser et om ne poet tant ne quant par fiez et ce avient de la greignor opilacion. Scuria si est une anguoisse que om [a] de pisser et om ne poet tant ne quant et ce tot adés. Et ceste espece avient de la tres grant opilacion. [154] Si doit l'en diviser et juger le quel piere ou gravele ou humor est cause de ce. Kant piere est en cause, s'en issent a la fiez aucune gravele, mes non pas mult. Et en la grant anguoisse de pisser s'en ist a la fiez une piere autretele come une pois ou come une feve. Mes come gravele est en cause de ce quant om ne poet pisser, si en issent les graveles a grant quantité, a la fiez oveskes l'urine. Et come om les baillie, si les poet [f.177r] om sentir trestotes aprés. Et quant les humors sont en cause, ce conust om par [ce] qu'eles en issent oveskes l'urine et ont a la fiez une forme longue autretele come .i. peu. Et come om moet l'urine, si ne departent pas legerement. Et come les humors vienent des reins, si ont itele forme meimement. Mes come eles vienent de la vessie, si sont plus espesses et plus amoncelez. Et doit l'en destincter la quele cause est contenue et assis es reins ou en la vessie. Et come la cause est es reins, si sent l'en ileuc une dolor et les piés endormanz et les quisses, le destre pié si la cause est en la destre des reins, et du senestre si la cause est al senestre. Mes si la cause est en la vessie, si sent om une dolor entor le penil et entor le fundement. Et notez que les graveles* qui vienent des reins soloient estre rouges et celes qui vienent de la vessie si sunt blanches. Et notez que teles maneres de maladies qui vienent de humors sunt plus tost garis que celes que vienent de gravele. Mes de piere garist om a peine ou jamés. Mes enfans garist om par trencher les principaument et jovenes gens secundaument, mes [a] homes parcreus et homes vieus est ce [f.177v] perrileuse chose a trencher et ultre quarante ans n'en garist nuls. Dont Ypocras dist que nuls home nefretiques ne garist outre quarante anz. [155] Cure. Ja soit que les causes de icés maladies [soient] diverses, la matere de la cure si est tot une. Premerement donques les doit om porveir en diete et se gardent de totes groses viandes et in[di]gestibles et se gardent meimement de boivre ewe, et choses diuretiques lor sont necessaires. Pregne l'en fenoil, ache, peresin et lor doigne l'en cru ou quit oveskes char. Mercurialis, cretani marini, senationes doigne* l'en par soi ou ensemble, si f[e]ront pisser merveileusement bien. Et doigne om a boivre l'ewe de la decoction de fenoil, de ache, de peresil, sparagi, brusci ou l'en tempre le vin de cele ewe et li vin soit soutils et diuretiques sicome est calabrum. Ou l'en lor doigne cidre ou vin de la decoction de saxifrage, granorum solis, filipendule et lapis lincis. Et face l'en iteu manere de ewe sirop et mete l'en zucre. Benoite simple, liciotripon, justinon, philoantropon, electuarium ducis, dyamargariton, dyarrodon, julii et meimement as rois totes icés choses sunt bones a doner et les piles mestre Bertholomeu qui receit balsamum, muscum, ambram et multes autres choses. Opiates si sunt assés [f.178r] necessaires en ceste cause. Et sanc de buc solonc la doctrine de Alexandrinis apparellé oveskes aucun bevrage diuretique et donee oveskes piles en aucune autre manere si ovre merveileusement. Mes notez que teu manere de sanc est tost corrumpu si il n'est avant contregardés. I mete l'en donkes de la poudre de aloe, [mirre, sel] dedens come il est novelement tret en tele proporcion que .i. livre du sanc, .i. once de poudre de aloe, et de mirre demi once et de sel autretant et les melle om trestotes ensemble et en tele manere le poet l'en garder de corruption. Solement basme mis dedens le garde de corrupcion et le fait estre de plus grant efficace. Et li doit l'en aider de aides locales et enoigne l'en le leu malade de oignemens et de oiles chaudes sicome de oile laurine et musceline et oignement d'or que om apele unguentum aureum, arrogon, marciaton et de semblables choses. Et face l'en fomentacions a[l] leu malade de l'ewe de la decoction de mauves, de seneschons, de mercuriali en vin ou* en oile. Face l'en emplastre sor le leu qui deut. [A]utre. Triblés noiz et les boilliés en oile et les mete om en .i. vassel lonc fait a la forme de .i. vit et bote om en celui vassel le vit tant come il est tievet et ce atrait merveilleusement le [f.178v] piere des reins. Et face l'en le malade gesir a femme a la fiez. Et mete l'en ens oile par .i. estrument que om apele siringa et la decoction de seneschons, philipendule, lapis lincis et oile musceline ou baume ou petroleum et meimement en yver et se li malades n'est pas coleriques, kar ele ameneroit tost une fevre. Mes come le vodra boter ens siringam, si doit l'en amollir le verge avant de aucun oignement por eslarger les conduyz et li abeisse l'en le chief et li hauce om les reins et ne le boute l'en pas tot ens de droit, mes tot sueef et en torsant. Mes notés que les femmes ont piere es reins et* [relement] en la vessie por ce que eles unt le col de la vessie cort et large. Et s'il avient que eles ont piere, si face l'en les devant dites aides. Mes si dolor i avient des devant dites causes, si face om les devant dites cures et les choses que nus avons dit contre colicam et yliacam passionem.

[XII,4 De involuntaria emissione urine] [156] Diamné si est une maladie come li home ne poet tenir sa urine, ains pisse en son lit et par tot. Et ce avient de la intense froydure de la vessie et de la mordicacion de lui ou de la relaxacion des ners qui sont en la col de la vessie, dont l'en [ne] poet retenir sa urine. [f.179r] [157] Cure. Doigne l'e[n] au malade choses chaudes et confortatives et li doigne om castoreum par le bouche et rubeam, triacle a doner ovesques jus de mente*, si profite mult. Et li aide l'en de choses locales. Et face l'en boillir [triacle] en oile pullegine et face l'en emplastre as reins. Autre. Face l'en boillir castoreum et char de mer en oile muscelline et face l'em emplastre.

[BOOK XIII   *De egritudinibus virge et testiculis*]

[1 De gonorea / De involuntaria emissione spermatis] [158] Gonorrea si est une maladie come li home ne poet tenir s'esperme. Et si vient ceste maladie a la fie de superhabundance de sperme qui vient de multitude de sanc et a la fiez de la feblesce de vertu retentive et* des coillons. [159] Gonorrea ke vient de superhabundance de sperme et qui vient de multitudine de sanc conust l'en par les veines qui sont pleines et par le plectorique habitude del cors et par l'emission de sperme en grant quantité et oveskes aucune delectacion. Mes si ce avient de la febleté de la vertu retentive, si ne sont pas les devant dites signes de replecion ne l'esperme n'en ist pas en si grant quantité et en istra sans nul delit. [160] Cure. Si sanc est en cause, si garist l'en legerment de ceste maladie, c'est asavoir par seigner, par tenve diete doner. Face l'en donques seigner* [f.179v] li malade de la veine du foie ou de la veine desouz le quiville du pié et li apetice [l'en] sa diete. Lettues a doner si profitent mult, kar eles refroident et espoissent mult le sperme. La semence si aide mult*. Et si la maladie dure encore aprés ou si ele vient de la febleté de la vertu retentive, si le garise l'en en meime la manere. Face l'en poudre de mastic, de storace, de olibano et confise l'en la poudre de l'ewe ou psilum avra tempré enz, faite de ewe rose ou de pluie et le leisse l'en une nuit ou par treis houres. Et aprés face l'en emplastre as reins et as coillions. Autre. Face l'en emplastre de cassi-lagine* contrita ou de mirre et de sempervive quites en vin egre. Et mete l'en platines de plum sor les reins. Et face l'en les autres aides* que nus avons dit contre diabetem.

[XIII,2 De immoderata erectione virge / De satiriasi .i. involuntaria erectione virge] [161] Saturiasis si est une maladie come l'en est touzjors arest. Si vient ceste maladie de grant ventosité et de grant chaline. Et si ont enfans ceste maladie sans nule delectacion. Mes es grans homes vient ele oveskes une delectacion. [162] Cure. A ceste maladie garir si covient grant discrecion et grant sen, sicome Galiene tesmoigne et Estevenon. Del comencement donkes deskes au tiers [f.180r] jor doit l'en ovrer de choses diaforetiques et aprés de choses qui refroident. Le jus de rue champestre si est bon a doner au comencement ou le vin de la decoction de lui ou le vin de la decoction de comin. La semence de agno casto si est mul[t] bone a manger en ceste maladie ou [a] quire en vin et boivre le vin, et si est bone* a faire emplastre sor le vit. Et li face l'en son lit neis des foilles de agno casto, bacce lauri quites en vin. Et a fere emplastre sor le verge si sunt mult bones. Et si icés ne soffissent pas, si covient que l'en li aide de choses froydes et li doigne l'en campho-ram oveskes aucune liquor et si est bone a odorer en ceste maladie. Dont om trove 'camphora per nares castrat odore mares*'. Et sirop fait de nenufare* si est assés profitable. Et jonke om la meson de herbes froydes. Et le face om veiller et geuner et li aide om de choses locales. Tempre l'en psilium* tant que ele soit gleuuse. Et moille l'en une esponge ens et mete om sovent sor les reins et sor les coillions. Ou om i face epithime de vin egre solement et de jus des herbes froydes. Autre esprove. Face l'en muscillaginem de psilio mise en vin egre et destempre l'en opium de cele muscilaginité et enoigne l'en les coillions.

[f.180v] [XIII,3 De imperfectione coitus / De aproximeron .i. de imperfectione coitus] [163] Approximeron apele om une maladie come om a comencé a foutre et nel poet parfaire. Et si vient principaument de .ii. causes, c'est asavoir de froidure qui mortifie ou de la chalor dissolutive. [164] Come froidure est en cause, ce conust l'en par la froidure de meime les parties genitales et des autres qui sunt environ. Et si sentira le malades une froidure en parfont sans nule grevance et si est le vit arest*. Et froydes choses si nuissent. Et si sout ceste maladie venir de froyde diete et en tens froit et en froide region et meimement en home fleumatike et melancolique. Come ce avient de chalor qui dessout les espiriz, ce conoist l'en de une chalor que l'en sentira entor les membres honteuses, mes non pas grant neporquant por la defaute des espiriz. Et chaudes choses nuissent. Et la verge dresce a la fiez. Mes come s'esperme deit issir, si s'abesse et si seut ce avenir de chaude diete et de fevre que om a eu devant et de traveillier en tens chaut et en chaude region en home colerique. [165] Cure. Si froidure est en cause, si doit l'en doner choses qui eschavent. Et le face l'en ventuser a la fiez. Et li doigne l'en char de chastris a manger. Le crupe et les costes sont les meilliors a manger en ceste cause. Et si est bone a [f.181r] manger oignonee en ceste cause, por ce que ele engendre ventosité, et ciceres* et feves. Et li doigne l'en pins et alemandes, dathes, figues secches, pannaisses, festucas et cauketroppes et, que jo di brefment, le face l'en appareillier come por fere gingembre conduit. Et les quise l'en aprés oveskes mel ou oveskes sirop, si le poet avoyr, si vaudra meuz asez. En la fin de la decoction si mete om ens pins, alemandes, dathes, figues, festuce vel festuci. Et aprés mete om ens la poudre faite de cardamome, de poivre lonc, de girofle, de nois muscate, de nois de Ynde et stinccis*, si est mult puissante lectuaire en ceste cause. Et si vaut plus neis que triacle dyasaturion. Mes diasatirion si est .i. poi abhominable et extenuatif et afeblist le home et le font en suor. Item notez que .iiii. once de ce qui est dedens la nois de Ynde [. . .] Item notez que stinci* de mer ont petite vertu ou nule en ceste cause. Mes les escorces de noyz de Ynde si valent mult en ceste cause. Autre electua[i]re assez covenable et esprovee. Pregne l'en les coillions de gopil et les cervelx des passe[r]s et les trible om et en face om poudre de cardamome et de poivre lonc et de la semence erucarum et de le [f.181v] semence* de oignons et mete autretant de la poudre come des cerveles et les coillions et trible l'en alemandes et pins et les funde l'en sicome om fait en diapenidion. Et aprés mete om les cerveles et au derein la poudre des coillions. Neis come l'en mangue solement les* coillions ou les cerveles des passe[r]s [. . .] Oigne l'en les reins et les coillions et les parties environ de oignemens chaudes sicome de arrogon ou de marciaton, de oile muscelline, laurine et de semblables choses. Autre. Funde l'en mugue en grant quantité, si om le poet avoir, ovesques oile musceline et enoigne l'en les membres honteuses. Si est mugue bone a prendre par la bouche et* moille l'en coton ou estoupes en oile musceline ou en aucone autre chaude chose et se li boute l'en au fundement. Et face l'en itel oignement. Pregne l'en formies et lor oes o tot et les face l'en boillir en oile en .i. vascel de voirre ou en .i. pot ou for. Et aprés i mete om la poudre des oignons fait et de eruca et de euforbio et castoreo et mete l'en cire o tot. Et en face om oignement et enoigne les devaunt dites leus. Si la maladie vient de chalor, li doigne l'en diete atempree et face om epithimes as reins et as membres honteuses de vin egre solement*. Ou l'en face [f.182r] epithime de sandles blanches et rouges, de roses et de semblables choses froides aromatiques et de meimes les choses face l'en emplastres froides et constrictives.

[XIII,4 De inflatione testiculorum] [166] A la fiez si emflent les coillions de grosse ventosité sans humors et a la fiez oveskes humor. [167] Ce conust l'en par .i. inflacion ovesques une dolor et par la extencion dou leu. [168] *Cure.* Cure: Jo dirai poi, mes ce ert chose esprovee. Face om emplastre sor les coillions des feves frasees quites en ewe. Autre. Face l'en enplastre de figues secches, de uves passes, de cinnamome quites en vin douz. Autre. Pregne l'en peritariam, cantabrum et quise l'en en vin et face l'en emplastre sor le leu.

[XIII,5 De pustulis in virga nascentibus] [169] Pustulacions avienent a la fiez el membre*. Et come eles depecent si devienent ulceracions et i na[i]ssent goute-festre et cancre sovent. [170] Cure. Enoigne l'en le vit et le leve l'en de ewe chaude et de savon por atenirir et oster la superficé de pustulacions et por convert-ir la matere en purreture. Et mete om sore une foile de cholet. Et come la matere est porrie, et ce poet l'en conustre par les pustulacions que seront blanches, frote l'en tot sueef le vit et l'estende om sor le quisse et le preme l'en sotillement. Kar par tele compression si depecent sovent les pustulacions et les quitures. Ensi le soloient fere [f.182v] les femmes de Salerne. Et s'eles ne depesceient en tele manere, si le[s] creve l'en de une aguille ou de .i. alesne. Et quant la porreture* est issue, si doit l'en metre choses mundificatifs et consolidatifs. Et mete l'en par desore la poudre de mirre* et la poudre de aloe. Ou l'en mette desore icés .ii. ensemble. Ou l'en traie fors le jus solement de foilles de mirte. Ou l'en face emplasstre des fresches foilles de mirte et mete l'en sore. Ou l'en face poudre de foillies de mirta et des flors de roses que l'en apele antera*, de aloe, de mastic, de olibano, de colophonia et de mirre. Esprovee est.

[BOOK XIV *De egritudinibus matricis*]

[1 De retentione menstruorum] [171] Les superfluités des femmes sont menees fors acostomeement en .i. tens establi a ce par .i. flux ke om apele flux menstruel. Et come eles sont retenues contre nature, s'en avienent diverses et perileuses ma-ladies de la retencion d'eles. A la fiez eles sont retenues solunc nature sicome en veillesse, a la fiez eles sont retenues contre nature sicome de quinze anz tresque* au quarante. Mes flux menstruel est detenue en .iii. maneres contre nature: par humor viscouse qui estoupe* les bouches des veines, et de froydure que destreint et lie les bouches des veines, et de secchesce que [f.183r] degaste non pas solement les humors, ains degaste o tot les humors natureles. [172] L'umor viscouse qui estoupe le bouche des veines [conust om] de la gresse et de la plenere habitude du cors et par ce que om sent une grevance el chief et au penil et es reins et es parties [aval] et par ce que el tens menstruel en istra une glette et une gleyre. Et si avient plus sovent a celes qui sont fleumatiques. Et come li flux menstruel est detenue par froydure, si sent l'en une froydure en parfunt, neis hom com i[l] gist a li poet sentir une froidure el marris, et en le tens menstruel en istront petites mussillaginitez. Et ceste cause si sout avenir plus sovent en femmes melancolieuses. Et come la retencion vient de secchesce, ce conust l'en par la megresse du cors et par ce ke ele* avra eu fevre devant et par geuner et par veiller et par meneison que ele avra eue et par totes les choses qui attenvissent et amegrissent le cors de home. [173] Cure. Si li flux menstruel est retenue solonc nature, si [ne] doit l'en pas traveiller a faire le venir come il est retenus par reson de age. Mes come li flux menstruel st retenus contre nature, si doit l'en traveiller de faire le venir; le quel don[f.183v]ques que li flux soit retenus ou de froidure ou de humor, si est la cure trestot une meime. Doigne l'en donkes triffe le grant sans opio thebaico ou tranensi* ovesques vin de la decoction arthemesie. Et si est bons li devant dite vin a doner par soi. Emagogum si est bon a doner en ceste cure et si est bon a doner le vin de la deco[c]tion de savine et de diptani. Et le face l'en seiner de la veine du quiville du pié. Et apré[s] i doit l'en metre choses locales. Et li mete l'en enz par desouz* athanasiam quite en oile muscelline ou en commune. Ou pregne l'en les racines des mauves mundees des foreynes escorses et li boute l'en el con. Ou l'en enoigne la racine de mel et poudre l'en par desore de la poudre d[e] scamonee. Ou l'en li boute enz desouz la racine rubee la menor, si overa mervelleusement. Face l'en nastale tele. Pregne om la pudre de savine, aristologie longe* et reonde, diptani et les confise l'en de assa fetida sans aucune liquor et enforme l'en une suppositoire ausi lonc come vostre doi. Et le enoigne l'en de oile violat et le mete l'en enz ou la poudre des devant dites .iii. choses oveske le jus arthemesie. Autre nastale esprové. Pregne l'en la poudre de storace calamite*, [f.184r] ladano, ligni aloe et les confise l'en de galbano, serapino, asa fetida sans nule liquor et face l'en de ce .i. estuel autresi lonc come vostre doi. Et mete l'en enz. Autre. Pregne theodor[ic]um anacard[in]um oveskes oile musceline et mete om ens par desouz. Ou li face l'en fomentacions de l'ewe centrigalli ou de l'ewe de la decoction gallitrici, benoite simple et arthemesie. Autre. Basme beues* ou getés enz par desouz si vaut sor totes choses. Et notés que ces devant dites ovres doit l'en fere .ii. jors ou trois devant ce que l'ore ou la terme viengne ke la femme doive avoir ses flors. Si avront plus grant vertu come nature ovre ovec et aide la medicine et la medicine a nature. Notez ke totes icés choses que valent a flux menstruel fere venir valent a mener fors la secondine et l'enfant com il est mort dedens la mere et le frere a ceus de Salerne, ce est li crapout come il est norri dedens la femme. Et notez que les femmes de Salerne se travaillent de ocirre le devant dit crapout au comencement come la femme conceit ou come le enfant comence a vivre et amener le fors par doner lor jus de ache et de porriaux. Mes si secchesce est en cause de [f.184v] la retencion de flux menstruel, si doit l'en ovrer des resumptives choses et nutritives, kar la cause de secchesce [oste l'en] par contraires doner: come la secchesce vient de fevre, l'en doi[t] garir le malade*; si la secchesse vient de juner, si li doigne l'en large diete; et si ce avient de veiller, si le face l'en dormir mult; et si ce avient de meneison, si le estanche l'en et autresi des autres choses.

[XIV,2 De fluxu menstruorum / De nimia fluxu menstruorum] [174] *Flux menstruel.* Flux menstruel desmesurable si vient de .ii. causes, c'est asavoyr de superfluité de[s] humors et de aguesce des humors. [175] Et come ce avient de aguesce de[s] humors, ce conust om par une chalor que om sent en parfont et par le color jaune des humors qui en istront. Et come ce avient de habundance de humors, ce conust om par le cors plectoriques et par les veines grosses et par la large diete qui il avra eu devant et par le sanc qui en istra en grant quantité. Et ceste maladie come ele est vieuz, si est grevusse a garir. Kar come les bouches des veines ont esté lonc tens overtes, si sont greves a soudre et a clore et neporquant si doit om assair a garir. [176] *Cure.* Cure: Si li flux desmesurés vient de habundance des [f.185r] humors, si la face l'en seigner de la veine du foie. Et mete l'en ventusses ovec jarse desouz les mameles ou [sans jarse] desore et soit la ventose si grant que ele enclose trestote la mamele dedens soi. Mes si li flux vient de aguesse des humors, si doit l'en atemprer l'aguesce de aux par doner la decoction de prunes, de violettes, de casiavistula, de tamarindes, de reubarbe. Et aprés si doit l'en ovrer encontre l'une et l'autre en tele manere. La doigne l'en athanasiam* oveskes ewe rose ou oveskes le jus de planteine, si li vaudra mult. Neis jus de planteine si est bon a doner par soi ou oveskes la resolucion de .i. amatiste. Et si valent icés remedes que nus avons dite contre emopt[o]icam passionem, ce est come l'en crache sanc. Et aprés si mete l'en aides locales qui mieus soloient valoir en ceste cause, athanasia* teinte en jus de planteine. Et face l'en fomentacion de l'ewe de ploie et de la decoction de geneste. Et face l'en neis fomentacions des escorches de pomes grenades et de poumes de[s] bois, de poumes citonies, sorbarii, mespili et simphiti quites en ewe de ploie. Ou les face l'en boillir oveskes la poudre bistorte en ewe de ploie et face l'en fomentacions de ces [f.185v] devant dites choses. Ou pregne om .i. sacellet fait autresi come .i. doi et l'emple om de la poudre de aloigne, de roses, de simphito, de cinamomo, gariofilo et bistorte. Autre. Galle, tan, sumac, icés face l'en boillir en ewe* de pluie et face l'en fomentacions. Autre. Ce que* Esteveles loe sor totes choses. Face l'en poudre de cor* de cerf ars et de parchemin ars par soi et i mete om autretant de vin come des autres .ii. choses et i mete om o tot de la poudre fait des escorches de glan et i mete om autretant de cele poudre soule come des .ii. devant dites. La merde et l'ordure de fer triblee sotillement et puis boillé en vin egre et en ewe rose treske la liquor soit degastee ajoste* l'en oveskes les devant dites choses et en face om une substance de touz et face l'en une pesacion de une partie de ceste poudre et confise l'en une partie ovesques aisil et aubon de oef et face l'en emplastre sor le penil* et sor les reins. Autre emplastre. [Pregne l'en] mastic, olibanum, mummia, sanc de dragon et en face l'en poudre et la confise om ovesques vin egre et oveskes aubon de oef et face om emplastre sor le penil et sor les reins.

[XIV,3 De suffocatione et precipitatione matricis] [177] Soffocacion si est une maladie que les femmes ont en la matriz en la quele semblent [f.186r] por poi esteintes et mortes come la matrix monte et fait presse as membres espirités. Et si vient ceste maladie de la retencion du flux menstruel et de aucun humor venimeuse dedens la matriz et de corrompue et de venimeuse esperme qui est entor les coillions de la matriz, la quele chose avient sovent a ces puceles et en ces veilles femmes que sei tienent chastes*, par la quele chose le esperme en eles est corrumpue et muee en venimeuse substance. Et si vient ceste maladie en tele manere. Come les humors menstrueles sont retenues ou com humor venimeuse ou esperme corrumpue habunde en la matriz, si en ist de eux une fumosité que emple la voidesce de la matrix et destent. La matriz come ele est emplé et mené amont, comprent et charge les membres espiritez dont la feme ne poet avoir sa aleine, ainz esteint por poi. [178] Les signes de ceste maladie si sunt la retencion des humors menstrueles, une dolor et une grevance entor le penil et es reins et es quisses et par ce que la maladie vient par hores* et par hores s'en va. Et ce est la difference entre lui et les autres especes de sincopie. Et par ce que la affliction en ceste si est plus grant et la feblelé que en nule autre espece de [f.186v] scincopie et si est l'anguoisse si grant en ceste maladie que la femme ne se sent ne moet, einz semble meuz morte que vive. Et nel poet om aparceivre, si ele soit morte ou vive, fors par .i. flocon de leine mise devant ses narines et par le moevement de lui si conust om si ele est vive. Precipitation de la matriz vient come les ners se laschent et de superflueles humors qui descendent soz la matriz, dont ele decline, a la fiez a destre, a la fiez a senestre et en ist a la fie une partie de lui. Mes ce conust l'en de une dolor que om sent en la peniliere et es reins et es parties entor la matriz et de la dolor et des torcions que om sent entor le num[blil] de* la retencion des humors menstrueles. Et si li matriz s'en ist, ce poet l'en savoir par le jugement du malade. [179] *Cure.* Cure contre suffocacion: En meime l'accession doit om lier les quisses de la femme fortment et les estreigne l'en bien por fere la matriz descendre aval par la revocacion des espiriz. Et frote l'en fortment les extremitez des parties aval ovesques sel et li face l'en exsternuer de la poudre castorei, piperis, euforbii, piretri et de semblables choses. Et li mete om ventuses sans garse es quisses et li mete om puantes cho[f.187r]ses as narines sicome la fumee armoniaci, galbani, serapini, asse fetide, pissade versee sor les carbons et face om covrir tot entor la feme de dras por faire la fumee monter trestot droit as narines. Et li face l'en fumigacions desouz de choses aromatiques come de ladano, de storace, xilio aloe, de mirre* et de sem-blables choses. Et si ce avient de la retencion des humors menstrueles ou des humors venimeuses, si la face l'en seigner de la veine desouz la quiville du pié ou la doigne l'en choses qui facent issir les humors menstrueles sicome nus avons dit devant. Et li mete l'en ens par desouz ovesque oile muscelline benoite. Pregne l'en coton et moille l'en ens et li boute l'en au con et l'espurge om de benoite ovesques gerologodion ovesques theodor[ic]o[n] [eu]periston. Mes si ce avient de sperme corrumpue que la matriz est montee amont, si ele ad baron, si gise ovesque son baron. Si ele est pucele ou vedve, si li louns par conseil que ele se marie. Mes si ele a fait vou de tenir chastee, si face ceste cure. Pregne om saugemme, nitrum et en face om poudre et le destempre om ovesques vin egre et oveskes ewe sause et moille l'en ens coton et li bote l'en ens par [f.187v] desouz, kar de ce si vient une mordicacion que fait issir le sperme a la fiez, ou ele boute son doi en son con et le move amont et aval por fere issir le sperme. Cure come la matriz est avalee et ce avient de la retencion de flux menstruel. Si le face om issir, se li metez choses aromatiques as narines et face l'en subfumigacions par desouz de choses puantes et mete l'en ventouses sans garse entor le numblil ou desore. Et si li matriz en ist, face om les cures que nus avons [dit] come le fundement s'en ist.

[XIV,4 De impedimento conceptionis] [180] Si il pesche a la fiez en l'ome que femme n'a enfant et a la fiez en la femme, sicome par les retencions des humors menstrueles et a la fiez par trop flux menstruel et a la fiez de secchesce por la defaute de norreture. Et plus sovent si vient de grant humidité qui estoupe la bouche de la matriz et les bouches cotilidonum et ke fait le sperme escolorgier. Par la vice de l'home si avient ce a la fiez sicome par la male qualité de l'esperme ou par ce qui il avra le vit cort ou tort. Les signes, les causes, les cures de la retencion de flux de femme menstruel querez et encerchiez en lor propres chapitres. [181] Et come ce avient de secchesce, ce conust l'en par la secchesce de* [f.188r] la bouche de la matrix et par la petitesce du flux menstruel et de la megresse de la femme et par aucune cause que ele ait eu avant que ait le cors amegri. Mes come ce avient de superhabundance de humidité, ce conust l'en par la gresse et par la meine disposicion du cors et par flux menstruel qui istra ovesques une muscillaginité et ovesques une grevance et une froidure de la matriz et du con. La male qualité de l'esperme de l'home conust l'en par la remocion des devant dites signes et causes* de la femme et par ce que la femme sentira le esperme chaut mult come li home le getterra et autresi ardant come ewe chaude ou froide après l'action come .i. glachon par dedens* ou par ce que ele serra si escolorjante que ele en istra maintenant. Si li vit est tort ou cort, ce poet om veir a veue. [182] *Cure*. Cure. Si li vices vient de secchesce de la femme, si doit l'en ovrer encontre de choses restauratives et moistes. Face l'en baigner la femme de l'ewe de la decoction de herbe de violete, des mauves, de roses, brance ursine, foliorum citri, mirte*. Et boille l'en mauves et herbe de violete et en face l'en emplastres et subpositoires. [f.188v] Triblez la semence papaveris albi et la confises de oile violate et de lait de femme eschauvé en .i. test de oef. Et enoigne l'en la matriz et les reins et moillez ens un poi de coton et li faites subpositoire. Et donez electuaire a restorer l'umidité et li dognez diete froide et moiste. Et si ce vient [de] moistesce, por ce que ceste cause sout estre principale si doit l'en traveillier plus ententivement. Li face om donques user avant oximel et li purge l'en après de piles ovesque les .v. maneres de mirabolans ou ovesques benoite. Et après le tiers jor que ele sera purgee [. . .] si la face l'en seigner de saphena ou om la jarse es jambes. Et le tiers jor après la seignee li dogne l'en triffe la grant opiaté ovesques vin chaut. Et face l'en bai[n]g de l'ewe de la decoction de mauves, majorane, sisimbrii, melisse, camphoraté, rosarum*, mauve, brance ursine, mirte, pipernelle*, foliorum citri, foliis lauri et depece l'en en le bai[n]g une ampoile de oile de muscelline et de oile laurine et la face l'en entrer en teu bai[n]g .vii. jors continueles. Et quant el[e] irra dormir, si s'enoigne de cestui oignement. Recevez spic nardine, nois muscade, gariophili, galange, cardamomi, piperis longi, [f.189r] roses, storax calamite*, alipte uwellement, bistorte autretant come de touz les autres et les confisés de mel rosat. Et mete l'en musque. Au soir si mete l'en ens subpositoyre de triffe la grant et de la poudre olibani et de oile muscelline et la tiegne jesc'a la mie nuit. Et come ele avra cele traite, si mete om .i. petite faite de noiz muscate, de girofle, de ligno aloes, storace calamite*, musco et les confise l'en ensemble ovesques storace sanz nule liquor. Et come l'en avra ce fait, noef jors mai[n]tenant après que li flux menstruel est espurgez, si le face l'en jarser detriers es jambes et face l'en fomenta-cion de ewe de pluie ou de la decoction bistorte, pulegii. Et aprés maintenant face l'en subpositoire de ambra, de musque et des autres devant dites especes. Et come l'en avra ce fait .iii. jors, au quart jor face om le devant dite fomentacion au soir de puliol et de bistorte. Et lors premerement face om son seignur gisir ovesques li. Mes si le vice vient de la male qualité de l'esperme de l'home, si l'esperme est chaut, si li doigne l'en froides electuaires et sirop froit et li face om epithimes froydes sor les reins et sor les membres honteuses. Et si le esperme est froit ou mult* moistes, si li face om [f.189v] user electuaire[s] chaudes et espessissanz sicome diamargariton, diantos et de semblables choses. Et face l'en chaudes fomentacions et chauz oignemens. Mes le vice qui vient del vit qui est tort ou cort si est incurable.

[BOOK XV   *De artetica passione*]

[De artetica passione] [183] *Artetike*. Artetica si est une maladie qui vient es jointes et es dois des piés et des mains et es jointes de tot le cors ovesques une emfleure et ovesques une dolor, la quele come ele vient es jointes de la main, si est apelé cyragre, et come ele vient en les piés, podagre, et come ele vient en la hanche, si est apelé sciatica passio. Et si vient ceste maladie de sanc colerique et de humor fleumatique. Et si avient sovent de cause reumatique*. [184] Et come ceste maladie vient de sanc, ce conust l'en par la rougeour et par la chalor del leu et par la apparance des veines de la partie malade et de trestot le cors et de ce qui il avra usé diete chaude et moiste devant et par l'aage et par la region et de ce que ele moet plus en [i]veir que en nul autre tens. Et quant ceste maladie vient de humor colerique, ce poet l'en conustre par la dolor que ert tres grant et par les ners qui seront tendus et par la grant chalor et par la inflacion du [f.190r] leu et par la color roge mellé a une color jaune et par ce que ele se moet plus en esté que en autre tens et par ce qui il avra usé chaude et secche diete et par l'aage et par la region chaude et secche et par les egestions et par les choses qui il vonche qui sont coleriques et par ce qui chaudes choses li sont males et froides bones*. Mes come ce avient de fleume, ce conust l'en par la inflacio[n] du leu et par la dolor et par la chalor non pas grant, si ert la rogeor del leu petite ou nule, et par la disposicion du cors fleumatiques et par la region et par l'age froide et moiste et par la diete ensement. Les froides choses li sont males* et li chaudes bones*. Et quant ele vient de cause reumatique, ce conust l'en par la grevance du chief et par les mocions des humors et par les titillacions* et par le flux par le nouche* et par les espaules qui li malade sentira bien. [185] Cure si ce avient de matere sanguine: Si le seigne om desouz la quiville du pié devant l'accession de la maladie et de la veine du chief si la cause vient de reume. Si la cause vient de colere, si le purge l'en de lectuaire de jus de roses en tens froyt, en tens chaut ovesques la decoction de prunes, de [f.190v] violete, citrolis, melonis, cucumeris et concurbite, cassiavistule, tamarindes, mirabolans, citrins ou ovesques le syrop Cophonis. Et li aide l'en aprés de choses locales. Et pregne l'en .i. drap linge et face l'en epithime sor le leu quan[t] l'en avra bien moillié en ewe froide ou en rosat. Pregne l'en ferrine de orge et le jus sempervive et de planteine et de corrigiole, camphoram, accetum, ewe rose et oile rosat et les confise l'en ensemble et face l'en epithime. Et mete l'en psilium en ewe et en vin egre et ajoste l'en a tot la poudre de roses et camphoram et face l'en epithime. Et si la dolor est tres grans, si deffise om opium ovesques vin egre et face l'en emplastre ou l'en enoigne le leu. Autre. Pregne l'en le jus cassilaginis* en oile mandragorat et la poudre de roses, opium, acetum, camphoram et les confise l'en ensemble et face l'en emplastre. Autre. Pregne l'en .v. moiels des oes et vin egre et la poudre cassilaginis* et ferr[i]ne de orge et le confise l'en ensemble et face l'en epithime sor le leu. Autre. Pregne l'en escorches de racines d'orme et les trible l'en et les boille l'en en vin blanc et face [l'en] emplastre sor le leu. Et face l'en epithime de jus de morele. Mes por ce qui icés choses soleient amortefier [f.191r] le leu aprés qui la dolor avra cessé, si doit l'en doner maintenant choses meinement chaudes et vivificatives. Pregne l'en spic nardine, absinthium, brancam ursinam et la mie du pain et les quise l'en en ewe et i mete l'en o tot moiels des oes et face l'en emplastre. Et le face l'en seigner chescun mois, mes meimement iceus que travaillent de sanc. Mes ceus que travaillent de colere si se doivent garder de purgier et principaument de croistre et de vin egre et de user chaudes viandes. Mes si l'artetique vient de froides humors, si face l'en le malade user avant oximel squilletique et le purge l'en de benoite hermodactilaté ou de pilles artetiques ou de ieralogodion ou de benoite simple donee par espace et par reposees. Pilles artetiques communement compostés de meistre Feraire et de meistre Perroncaul et de meistre Plateaire si sont bones a doner .ii. fois ou .iii. la semaine au soir avesques les queles covient hermodactili, turbith, petrocillum owellement .iii. onces, cassie lignee, nardi, gariofili, xilobalsami, carpobalsami .ii. onces, masticis, seminis feniculi, semence de saxifrage, semen brusci, roses, grana solis, saugemme owel .i. once, [f.191v] aloes a la mesure de tot et confisies de semine feniculi. *Les pilles Cophonis.* Les pilles Cophonis si sunt bones a doner une fois la semaine por goute artetique. Et crespiex faites de orties et de ferrine si sont bones a doner. Et crespeux encore faites de la racine bardane et de ferrine si sont mult bones. La poudre Petroncel fait de .iiii. drames de esule et de .i. poi de cinamome et ovesque la semence feniculi et de mastic si est mult bon a doner por artetique. Ou l'en pregne le jus des somerones de* ebles .i. once, du* jus de la moine escorche du seu, et les boille l'en et les cole l'en et mete l'en en la coleure zucre et oxcimel et doigne l'en .ii. fois le mois au malade come il irra coucher. Aprés li doit l'en aider en tele manere* de choses locales. Come les ners sont secs* et tendus confise l'en cire ovesques la poudre de comin et le eschaufe l'en et face l'em emplastre sore. Et si l'artetique vient de humors chaudes, si est la cire bone a metre sore sans comin. Ortie vive triblee est mult bone a metre sor le leu contre artetiques froides. Et si la dolor est mult grant, si les mete om sore sans triblier. Boillie l'en les racines bardane en fort [f.192r] vin et face l'en le malade receivre avant la fumee entor le leu malade. Et aprés face l'en emplastre de tot. Autre. Fente de boef eschaufé ovesques vin egre si est bone a faire emplastre sor le leu malade. Ou face l'en emplastre de levein ovesques aubun de oef. Autre. Pregne l'en de la fente de colons et fente de boef et de chievre et mete o tot poudre de comin et les face l'en boillir en fort vin ou en vin egre et face l'en emplastre. Pregne l'en la merde [de] l'ors et le confise l'en ovesques la cendre de chief de gopil ars et enoignez le leu malade. Prenez les* meules de totes bestes que vus porrez avoyr et gresse de geline et de ors et de owe et fundez cire blanche o tot. Et mete om o tot oile rosat et violate et oile de seu. Premerement funde l'en la cire et aprés les gresses et les cole l'en et mete l'en ovec la cire et aprés les meules ovesques un poi de poudre de olibano et le[s] movés .i. poi et les ostés maintenant del feu. Et iceste oignement est mult profitable acontre goute froide et chaude et froide artetique. Oile le roi Williame esprovee a goute froyde. Pregne l'en tieules rouges en grant quantité et faite[s] en poudre et les arosés de petroleo et enfrotés les bien. Et aprés [f.192v] metez en .i. grant vassel percié au fons bien menuement et pregne l'e[n] .i. estrument de fer reont et croes et mete l'en sor les pertuis du vassel et ajoste l'en la bouche desouz de l'estrument de fer a la bouche de un autre poet mise desouz terre de deus coudes en parfunt et mete l'en terre par desus. Et face l'en grant feu pardesus [et] de jor et de nuit enoigne* l'en le leu malade de l'oile que l'en trovera pardesus. Kar mult est tres chaut icest oile petroleum par soi, si est bone a oigndre goute artetique froide. Et oile pullegine et unguentum aureum, arrogon, oleum laurinum, corubrum, ladanum, storax calamite*, terbentina, fente [de colons], confise l'en totes icés choses ensemble et face l'en emplastre sor le leu malade et baignier en ewe salee* ou en ewe suffrine, si est mult bon. Ou en teu bai[n]g: pregne l'en* cardons de mer et les somerones des ebles et de seu et les foilles de lorer, brancam ursinam, suffre vif, alum menuement minciez et les face l'en boillir en ewe de mer ou en ewe salee et mete l'en o tot oile laurine, musceline, pullegine, petroleum et face l'en li malade geun entrer en ite[l] baign. Quisçons faites si sunt bones. Trian[f.193r]gulus faite en scia si est bone. Come li podagre ou li cyragre est faite noueuse, si est non garissable. Et come li museles est dessouz en scia, si est incurable. Mes come il est laisciés solement, si est bien curable.

[BOOK XVI *De egritudinibus cutis*]

[f. 70r] [1 De lepra] [186] Lepre si est corruption des menbres fait d'umor aidables a porrir. Et si vient de viandes melancolienes, come de char de levre et d'asne et de semblables viandes, et de viandes coleriques, sicome de longuement user ailliés et pevrees et semblables choses, et de viandes corrumpues et obeissanz a corruption, sicome de char de porc mauveise et de vin porri et des semblables choses, et d'air corrumpu et de converser oveques [f. 70v] meseaus et de gesir a feme aprés mesel. Et a la fie si vient de generacion come quant aucuns est engendrez de sperme corrumpue et come il est norriz de lait corrumpu ou come l'en est conceu en tens menstruel. De totes icés choses, come les esperiz sont envenimez ou come les humors sont corrumpuz, si ensit maintenant la corruption des membres [et] aprés lepre. Et notez qu'il i a .iiii. espieces de lepre: elefancie, de melancolie naturale; leonine, de colre; allopice, de sanc; tyriasis, de fleume. [187] [Les signes] En elefancie devienent les iauz [reonz] et les paupers fronciez et les narines estroiz et la voiz esroé et le cors plain de buberons roges et dures et les superficés d'aucune des parties sont insensibles, les ongles grosses et desyuees. En leonine ensement sont les iauz raonz, si sont les veines aparanz et roges mellees d'une jaunesce et mov-ables mult, les narines sont grelles, si ont la voiz enroé et les gencives mangees, et a la fie en ist mult de sanc oveques l'orine, si ont [f. 71r] le cuir aspre et les sorciz .i. pou pelez et serpigines et inp[et]igines en naissent sovent de ceste espiece. Et l'une et l'autre espece corrumpist les extremitez. En la tierce espiece, qui est apelee allopice, si ont li malade les sorciz pelez et les cillerons enflez. De ce si est apelee ceste espiece allopice por ce que les malades poilent sicome font allopes, ce sont gopiz*, et si ont les iauz enflez et si sont roges mult et unes pustules roges en la chiere et a la fie si naissent par tot le cors des queles en cort li sans, a la fie oveques une porreture, et li nes engroissist et l'alaine [est] mauveise et puante et joes enflees et lor decort li sans des gingives et en ist grant quantité a la fie oveques l'orine. En la quarte espiece qui est apelee tyria si naissent unes glandres mouz et en amollissent le cuir et blanchist et come l'en arose le cuir d'ewe, si cole trestot outre et n'aert point. Et si naist en ceste espiece une maniere de roigne blanche qui est apelee morphea en latin: si ont les narines estopees et la voiz enroé. Et a la verité [f. 71v] dire, totes les espieces de lepre sont incurables, et meimement leonine et allopice. [188] Mes quant li hom est apareilliez d'avoir lepre, l'en le puet contregarder dou peril qui li est a avenir. Car quant li sans sorhabunde, si le face l'en seignier sovent, mais les autres humors, quant eles sorhabundent, doit l'en purgier de lor propres medicines: fleume, de yeralogodion, melancolie, de yera rufini. Et lor doigne l'en a la fie triacle. Preigne l'en serpenz roges au comoince-ment de ver* et giete [l'en] hors les boiaus et lor cope l'on la cowe et le chief a la mesure de .iii. doie et le giete l'en hors. Et le remaignant escorche l'en bien et le leve l'en bien et le mete l'en quire en vin oveques poivre ou en ewe. Et mete l'en au quire poriaus, perresil, poivre, comin, canele et .i. poudre de diptandre et doigne l'en au malade. Ou l'en apareille les serpenz sicom nos avom dit devant, mes qu'il ne soient pas quiz, et les mete l'en porrir en vin ou en most, que miauz vaut, et lor doigne l'en ce a boivre. Boille l'en seneschons [f. 72r] sovent en ewe en grant quantité et face l'en le malade baignier sovent en tel ewe. Et face l'en ite[les] pilles et doigne l'en parfiez: pernez semence de fenoil, d'ache, de perresil, de mastic, bdellii, thimi, epithimi, tant com .i. unce, ce qui est dedenz coloquintide, salgemme, elle[bo]ri nigri, agarici, polipodii tant come .iii. drames, mirobolans indes, sené, aloe epatique demi unce, et les confise l'en ovesques fumitere, the[o]d[oricum] anacardinum. Icés choses sont bones a doner par leus et pilles de yeralogodion sont bones a doner. Si est bon syrop qui est faiz de jus de borrages et de sené. Et face l'en teu syrop: preigne l'en le jus de fumiterre et face l'en boillir oveques la semence de fenoil et de mastic et mete l'en zucre et face l'en syrop. Et doigne l'en au malade au matin oveques ewe chaude. Autre. Cuillét encor les racines de rafle et de fenoil et les mette l'en temprer une nuit en vin egre ou en jus de fumiterre et les mette l'en [f. 72v] quire maintenant. Aprés le cole l'en et i mete [l'en] mel et face l'en oximel et doigne l'en au matin oveques ewe chaude. Et se gart li malades de choses frites et de salees et de choses agues et de fort vin et de croistre et de coper les coillons. Si sont plusors contregardé de lepre. Por oster quitures et por covrir les si mete l'en ventouses oveques garses detriés le col et entre les espaules. Et aprés tierz jor si mete l'en sansues sor les bocetes et aprés les oigne l'en d'aucun oignement. Autre cure mult tresbone a ce: preigne l'en les bocetes que l'en troeve es racines de lis sauvage qui portent une flor porprine et les* leve l'en bien et netoie et les trible l'en mult tres bien. Et preigne l'en les bericles de mer, coral blanc, antali, dentali, camphoram et en face l'en poudre et les confise l'en trestotes ensemble de oile de seu ou de rosat. Et aprés si mete om enz argent vif esteint et enoigne l'en les boces au malade de cest oignement. Et por la repression des pustules confise om creie ou terre de gleise et de vin egre et fac[e] om emplastre. Ou l'en confise acaciam, cretam sarracinoise, [f. 73r] litargirum, cathimiam auream, bolus armenicus et les confise l'en oveques vin egre et face l'en emplastre. A sechir l'umidité preigne l'en la poudre de baies de lorier, de* nitri, salgemme, et les confise [l'en] oveques terbentine et en oigne l'en le cors au solail et au feu. Ou l'en face oignement de anacardis et l'enoigne l'om au feu. Por les narines destoper au lepros doit om metre en lor narines auream alexandrinam oveques oille musceline ou .i. estuel fait de pomes de terre. Et l'enoigne l'en de oille et le bote l'en enz es narines ov oximel rosat [u] iaune. Les ulceracions des

gingives doit l'en garir sicome nos avons dit en lor propres capitles. Et mortifica-
tions des membres et insensibilitez doit om garir sicom nos avons dit ou traitié de
paralisie. Jarse l'en les sorciz et les frote l'en durement et face l'en poudre des aspres
et des espineuses foilles de chastaignes arses. Ou l'en mete la poudre fait de
musches et de guespes et de ees [f. 73v] arses et mete l'en sor les sorciz. *Contre
serpiginem et inp[et]iginem*: preigne l'en les flors de mores et les confise l'en de
salvie* et les mete l'en temprer en mult tres fort aisil tote une nuit. Et en frote l'en
le leu. *Cure contre inpetiginem*: confise l'en aspaltum oveques vin egre et en frote
l'en le leu bien, si est mult profitable. Preigne l'en la poudre de auripiment et la
confise l'en de savon françois et lieve l'en bien le leu de ewe chaude. Et aprés
enoigniez le leu. Et por ce qu'il quit trop, si le lieve l'en maintenant. Prenez
froment e metez entre .ii. fers chauz et le serrez bien ensemble a compresse* et
enoigniez les dertres de l'oile qui en istra.

[XVI,2 De morphea] [189] *A morphé*. Morphea est blanche, si est une maladie
come la naturale color dou cuir est muee en blanche color, et s'il i a peus ou leu, si
charront. Et quant l'en point le leu d'une aguille et il n'en ist point de sanc, si est
incurables. Mais si li sans en ist, si est bien curables. Et si a un autre morphé noire
[f. 74r] come la naturale color dou cuir est muee en noire color et cest si est plus
legiere a garir. [190] *Cure*. Jarse l'en bien le leu et le frote l'en bien de char de mer
arse et le confisez oveques aisil. *Autre*. Confisez la poudre elle[bo]ri nigri de savon
françois et de vin egre et en frotez bien le leu. *Autre*. Prenez la poudre de lupins
amers et les foilles de mirtelle et les confise l'en de vin egre. *Autre*. Alun, salgemme, voirre ars et .i. poi de orpiment et la flor de la meure soient bien conficés
de vin egre et en frote l'en bien le leu et les dertres. *Autre*. Pernez le jus de foilles
de sauge sauvage et domesche, yricii que l'en troeve en la mer, arde l'en ces choses
et confisez la poudre de oile et de vin egre et metez musque o tot, si frotez bien le
leu. Et li noir oignement as cyrurgiens i est mult bons et lor doigne l'en a la fie
medicine qui purge fleume et melancolie.

[XVI,3 De scabie] [191] *De roigne qui vient de superfluité d'umors*. De roigne qui
vient de superfluité d'umors les queles com il sont envoiez a la superficé [f. 74v]
dou cuir si manjuent le cuir et font ilueques une inequalité et unes quitures venir.
Et si avient itel roigne aprés longue maladie come la force de l'home est abaissié et
les superfluitez acreuez. Et si avient a maintes genz de la vice de l'esplen. [192]
Cure si la roigne vient de superfluité de sanc. Si face l'en seignier le malade et le
purgiez de oximel laxatif. Melancolie et fleume sause purgiez de yeralogodion ou
de yera ruffini. Mes por vielle roigne et anciane donez demi unce de la decoction
de sené et demi unce de polipodie et de la semence de fenoil .ii. foiz la semaine.
Mes as genz deliez donez syrop quant il seront purgié et aprés si lor done l'en aides
locales de itel oignement qui reçoit le jus de lappe ague .i. livre en oile, jus
d'aloigne .iiii. unces, oile de noiz demi unce, picle* .v. unces, nitre blanc, tartari,
et fulliginis .ii. unces, et les confisez en tel maniere. Quant les jus seront bien
builliz, si les colez et metez enz oile et poiz et les movez tant qu'il soient bien boliz.
Et lors le colez et premez bien parmi .i. drap. [f. 75r] Aprés prestez en cele coleure
primierement la poudre fuliginis, aprés la poudre tartari, et au darrain la poudre

nitri, et les movez sor .i. feu petit et lent. Et faites boillir membra ou picle oveques
.i. unce de fort aisil. Et aprés metez enz .i. unce de la poudre d'aloe et l'ostez
maintenant dou feu et [de] cest oignement enoigniez le leu roigneus au solail ou au
feu ou enz (ou) bai[n]g mes qu'il* ne sue. *Autre.* Destemprez .iii. unces de la poudre
litargiri oveques vin egre au feu et metez enz .i. unce de oile de noiz et de la poudre
elle[bo]ri .iii. drames et en oigniez le leu. Bai[n]g d'ewe sause si est bon a ce et
bai[n]g de soffre. Et metez sansues sor l'esplen et si ce avient [de melancolie], si
jarsez le leu dejoste les nages* et es musciaus des jambes et se gardent des choses
salees.

[f.193r] [XVI,4 De fistula] [193] Fistula si est une maladie que om apele goute-
festre. Si est une plaie parfont [et] estroit par desus en la superficé. Si vient
acostomément de veus plaies sorsanees. Come la bouche desouz est teint de venim,
dont tote la norreture qui i vient torne a corrupcion. Dont la superficé depece et
cort fors une porreture. Et come ele est une fiez resoudee ou .ii. fois, si depece
derechief. Et environ la plaie si naissent plusors bouches. Et si vient a la fiez de
cause reumatique sans plaie que l'en a eu devant. [194] Cure. Come li cors est bien
purgiés de pilles de benoite ou de pilles artetiques ou de meime la benoite, lor*
doigne l'en auream ou adrianum ou triaque, qui est plus fort de totes, et aprés
forme l'en une tente de malo terre a la mesure de la plaie. Et solonc ce que la plaie
enlargist, si doit om engrossir la tente et la renovele om la tente chascun jor. Et de
ce si alargira la plaie [f.193v] tant que s'il i a os depescé desouz, si le poet om bien
traire legerement hors. Et aprés le doit l'en garir come autres plaies. Autre. Confise
om* la poudre hermodactilorum, aristologie longe et conforme l'en une tente et la
moille om en cele confection et le bote om au plus parfunt qui om porra en la
plaie. Et si la pille li cuit et art, si pregne om estoupes, si les moille om en moel de
oef et en ewe ros[at] et mete om sore. Autre. Pregne om figues secches que soien[t]
bien secchies plus de un an et les rae om bien par dedens [. . .] et face om une tente
de ce. Et bote om au plus parfont que om* porra en la plaie. Autre. Pregne om la
poudre de grisilons secchiés et mete om ens ovesques mel et doigne l'en a boivre de
la poudre ovesques vin une fois la semaine. Autre mult tres bone. Tue l'en une
ranoile petite et vert que om i trovera en icés haies et en traie l'en fors le quer et le
leve l'en bien en vin et en jus de aloine et doigne l'en cointement [ou] deden[s] .i.
poi de mie du pain [ou] en le jor del derain joesdi del* descreissant de la lune.
Autre. Faites poudre en tele manere de cantaridis. Pregne l'en cantaridas vives et
les mete om en vin [f.194r] egre et en sel et au tierç jor les mete om secchier au
soleil. Et en face l'en poudre et mete l'en en goute festre ovesques une tente et face
l'en une quiture en la fonteine del col. Poudre precius a tuer cancre. Pregne l'en le
jus des racines affodillorum .vi. onces et chius .vi. onces et de orpiment .i. once et
les confise l'en en teu manere: les boille l'en en ewe et i mete om .i. once de
orpiment et les leisse l'en boillir .i. poi et les confise om et les mette om au solein
secchir. Et en face om trocisques et les estue l'en tant que om ait a fere por metre
sor cancre. Explicit Amicum Induit.

NOTES AND REJECTED READINGS

1.

A number of blank lines in the MS separate the section on urines in the 'Lettre d'Hippocrate' from the present translation of the *Practica*, which begins in the middle of Bk.1, ch.3. In S (= MS B.L. Sloane 1124) the rubric for this chapter is 'De febre interpolata cotidiana'. The *signa* with which the text begins relate to 'cotidiana flegmatis salsi facta'. The word 'froidure' translates 'tipus', a type of intermittent fever or ague with a characteristic cold stage. The passage on 'cotidiana ex flegmate vitreo facta' has not been reproduced.

2.   et ce   epither'   ne metez   coste   par la   doignes

'La moitié de ewe' renders 'vinum limphatum' i.e. wine diluted with water (cf. para.7). The sentence concerning 'cotidiane de fleume naturale' is not found in the print and 'donons nos . . . choses purgatives' seems to be an addition by the translator. The purgative beginning with the middle bark of elder omits the 'succi fumi terre' of the print, which is not however in S, and adds, with S, 'castorei . . . esule unce .i.'. Another addition is 'Aprés le quarte accession'. The lines that follow do not observe the order of the print. The latter has 'manne' for 'malve' in the penultimate decoction and in the final one 'rubea', to which AN has added 'trociscata'.

4.   froit

AN 'pert om le dormir' translates 'vigiliarum instantia'. The print describes the urine as 'rufa vel subrufa, rubea vel subrufea', cf. ME 'ruffe or subruffe, reed and subrubicund'. AN 'l'urine mains coloree' is based on the reading 'minus colorata' of several MSS rather than the 'nimis colorata' of the print. For 'soverains boiaus' both the print and S have simply 'in intestinis'. The sentence beginning 'Mais si ele est de colre vitelline . . .' is missing from the print, the text of which is deficient at this point, but is found in S which adds 'plus accedens ad tenuitatem'.

6.   et ombreuse

7.   oisiaus en jor interpolate   tenue   et

The print has 'iuvenibus etate calida et sica tenuis danda est dieta' where AN has 'qui sont colerique . . .' in accordance with the reading of S 'colericis iuvenibus estate regione calida et sicca'. For young and old (AN adds 'as femes') the Latin suggests 'vaporetur stomachus' (S = 'vaporetur frons'). The print specifies only 'trifera', but S has 'trifera sarracenica'. After 'electuaire froide' the print has 'vel electuario de succo rosarum'. The sentence beginning f. 59v is omitted in the print, which recommends purging 'bis vel ter', but S has 'facta purgatione tam in simplici quam in duplici, bis vel ter iteretur. Si febris adhuc perseveraverit, detur rubea cum calida ante horam accessionis'.

8.   The print has 'teste .H. et Alexandro', whilst S has simply 'teste .G.' ME agrees with AN.

9.   The print describes the first stage of the onset as 'primo orripilatione'. On the first day of the quartan fever caused by natural melancholy the urine is 'citrina vel subcitrina' (S = 'rufa vel subrufa') and on intervening days 'subpalida vel pallida, glauca vel etiam alba' (S = 'pallida vel karopos, glauca vel etiam alba'). As well as 'boce aigre' (oris acetositas) S specifies

scotomia as a symptom. In the case of quartan fever caused by vitreous phlegm 'apparet gleba humoris cum quibusdam muscillaginibus (ME 'a clod in þe urine of humours and sum resolution').

10. innaturale   ciriacam   d. apres d.   cum   cum

I have emended AN in accordance with the Latin 'Quartane ex melancolia naturali facte et ex flegmate acetoso et vitreo eodem modo curantur'. The pronoun 'li' refers to the patient whose presence is understood throughout. AN's reference to 'racines diuretiques' is not in the Latin. The print has 'in .iiii. vel .v. de radicibus rafani' and 'per .v. dies vel plus' (S = 'per .xv. dies') and 'tale oximel ante sextam (S = 'quintam') accessionem non detur' and 'iteretur purgatio bis vel ter intermisso spacio convenienti'. AN's 'la poudre aristologie . . .' agrees with S, but is not found in the print.

11. san

The Latin begins 'Febres ex melancolia innaturali vel ex flegmate salso vel sanguine adusto facte licet quedam signa cum predictis quartanis nothis habent communia ut in hoc quod modo anticipant modo suboccupant'.

12. darmenique   psperagi

AN 'vin tempré' renders 'vinum limphatum'. The Latin has 'In die accessionis vel nullus vel [saltem, S] tenuis dandus est cibus, longe ante horam accessionis absque vino et carnibus' and for the preparation of lapis lazuli 'dragmas .iii. lapidis lazuli subtiliter terantur et in vase argenteo [solido, S] cum aqua nocte [om. S] permittantur residere'. The Latin specifies 'lapidis armeni dragmas .iiii.' which are to be washed 'bis vel semel'. There is an omission in AN where the Latin reads 'Quartanarios ex flegmate salso purgabis sicut quotidianarios ex flegmate salso laborantes, hoc addito quod acutior debet esse medicina'. AN 'contregardons' translates 'preservamus' (see too paras. 20 and 32). In the final sentence the Latin has 'ad . . . purgandum per urinas et omni hora'.

13. The print has 'pre multitudine causarum', S 'pro multiplici varietate causarum'.

14. digestions

Once again (see para. 12) AN 'tant i a que' translates 'hoc addito quod'.

15. as

AN 'eschaufe' is a puzzling rendition of 'conculcatur': 'quantitate superabundans conculcatur: fumositates conculcate calefiunt et distemperantur [que, S] distemperate spiritum vitalem in corde distemperant'.

16. To the symptoms of sinocha the Latin prefixes 'febris continua'. In AN there is an omission where the Latin reads 'Sinoche inflative hec eadem sunt signa excepto quod urina est rubea vel subrubea et spissa, non livens distincte. Adsunt etiam alia [sc. signa] ut . . .'
Amongst the symptoms of causon are 'oculi et timpora clavis videntur obtundi' and facial and bodily colour is 'rubeus citrino admixtus'. AN 'si veille l'en tot adés' renders 'vigiliarum instantia', whilst 'compression' translates 'constipatio'. The Latin explains the symptoms of diarrhoea thus: 'constipatio ventris ex colera superabundante qualitative [et, S] ex eadem peccante quantitative ventris fluxus'.

17. maladie ne le seigne len pas   mutre   curueles   r. et en action sil ont soif   berbetis   venufar

AN 'dedenz le quart jor' translates 'usque ad tertium diem inclusive' and 'tant que il se pasme' renders 'usque ad lipotomiam'. AN 'seignier' corresponds to Latin 'sanguis per diaforesim detrahere' [S]. The use of 'roses et de foilles de sauz' in cooling the air is missing from the Latin, whereas AN misses out the detail concerning the perforated bowl 'quod quidam cum acu eneo vel vitreo fit melius'. The herbs scattered on the floor (*pavimentum*) of the house are 'foliis mirte, salicis, calamis, rosis, pampinis et similibus'. In the diet AN has telescoped the Latin: 'si affuerit citrulli, detur medulla; si cucurbita, detur assata; si mala granata, dentur acetosa dulcibus commixta'. In AN there is an omission where the scribe copied out the 'reficiantur' of his source, which reads 'In oris false quietis reficiantur', and provided no translation of the word. The reference to the 'baston' is based on a reading like that in S ('baculus etiam ponatur intus quo extra eminente possit [sc. pannus] teneri'). After 'semence de lin' the translator has omitted several lines of Latin through a *saut du même au même* ('semini lini') as follows: 'Hoc idem fiat de semine lini vel citoniorum. Nota si laborat constrictione pectoris [vel] ex apostemate, non fiat confricatio lingue cum psilio, quia nimia frigiditate nocet; sed bene potest fieri cum semine lini infuso in aqua tepida ita ut in frigida'. AN 'et por dormir' renders 'pro vigiliarum instantia', but there are some divergences in the rest of the sentence in the print. AN is based on a text like that of S: 'fiat fomentum ex aqua decoctionis cassilaginis, rose, mirte, herbe violarum. Laventur postea pedes in eadem aqua et crura usque ad jenua et etiam brachia et manus. Cassillago bullita et super frontem et timpora ligata sompnum inducit'. The seeds mentioned in the treatment where no crisis is achieved refer to the traditional 'cold' seeds: citrullus, melo, cucumer, cucurbita. The next sentence 'Et metons . . . reubarbe' is not in the print but corresponds to the text of S. The placing of leeches in the nostrils to provoke nosebleed is a detail not found in the Latin.

18. In the case of 'emitriteus maior' the print reverses the order of AN, 'colera intus et melancolia extra' (also = S).

19. b. et si tient .xviii. hores en soverain travail et .vi. en faus repos

Amongst symptoms of the 'quotidiana continua' the print offers 'oris insipiditas, urina parum et spissa colorata'. There is an omission in AN (after '.vi. en faus repos') where the Latin has 'In quartana continua hec sunt signa: calor quidem continuus sed de quarto in quartum diem acutior fit et sine tipo, capitis gravedo, urina parvum colorata et tenuis, calor intensus, sed lentus, et notatur quod continua cotidiana et quartana continua non facile per urinas discernitur'. In the last sentence the print has 'lx [xl, S] horas habet in summo labore, xii in falsa quiete'.

20. c. en ewe   pastre   e. el est defite e.   oximel et

AN 'dedenz le quart jor' again (see para. 17) renders 'usque ad diem tertium' [usque ad .iiii. diem, S]. In the diet 'gruel' translates 'farina ordei'. The Latin has 'vel cum aqua decoctionis seminum frigidorum' and specifies 'in mane' as the time of administration of both decoctions. AN 'le adustion' refers to a burning sensation in the tongue. The signs of digestion have been garbled by AN: 'Materia digesta que cognoscitur per maiorem attenuationem [S = spissitudinem] urine in quotidiana continua, per minorem tenuitatem in quartana continua, per mediocrem spissitudinem urine tam in medio [minori, S] quam in minori [medio, S] emitriteo et per cessationem tipi purgare debemus'. In place of Galen the print has '.H.' [i.e. Hippocrates]: the two are often substituted for each other (cf. para. 29). The prognosis in AN does not quite follow the Latin 'usque ad .vii. diem ad bonum vel ad malum terminatur'. In the composition of the first purgative 'semences' indicates the traditional four 'cold' seeds (see para. 17), whilst '.i. autre de kebles' agrees with S 'et alia sit kebulorum' against the print 'unciam .i. reub. vel ellebori scrupulum .i.' In the second the Latin has 'eadem addita tamen reub. unciam .i. et mirabolanorum kebulorum unciam .i.'. In the Latin the third purgative does not include the four cold seeds. 'Et en yver . . . xii' finds no correspondence in the print. AN 'orge pilee' renders 'farra ordei'. The last sentence in this section is missing in the print, but is found in S.

21. chascon   pleurerie

AN 'en la premere celle' renders 'in anteriori cellula'. The etymologies are taken directly from the Latin source. The print has 'frenos, quod est mens'. The true frenesis 'febrili [proprio, S] calore levigata et furiosa effecta rapitur superius . . .'

22. reiber

AN 'resver' translates Latin 'insania' (ME 'wodnesse') and 'veillier' renders 'vigiliarum instantia'. AN 'hideusement' is an addition to 'mobilitas [motus, S] oculorum preter solitum'.

23. lot   estopees   un   decoctions

The Latin specifies that the patient is to be placed in 'lecto non cancellante [cancellato, S] vel teneatur in lecto vel ligetur'. The sense, as understood by AN, seems to be that the patient be placed in a bed, not barred like a cot, but that he be bound or held in such a way that he cannot escape. Concerning his dress the Latin has 'vestes sint unius coloris, ne pro multiplicate et varietate colorum magis ad insaniam mutetur [incitetur, S]'. I have emended the AN MS reading 'estopees trop les espiriz' in accordance with the Latin 'spiritus vehementer calefiunt'. AN adds, with S, 'orge' to the ingredients of the clister and, at the end, 'mel'. AN 'des choses locales' renders 'localia adiutoria' i.e. local therapeutics. The 'epithimites apocrastiques' ('epithimata apocrustica') indicate repellent or astringent poultices (epithems) and show the translator inevitably resorting to the calque for rendering technical terminology, whilst also illustrating the scribe's unfamiliarity with the terms, leading to vowel distortion. To the ingredients AN adds 'un peu de sel', whilst 'vert jus' renders 'acresta' i.e. 'agresta' [agreste, S]. The translator does not adequately render the source 'fiant huiusmodi epithimata super anteriorem cellulam que principaliter patitur et etiam super mediam que anteriori compatitur'. According to the print sneezing should be produced 'cum eleboro albo vel alio dissolutivo et cum pulvere camphore', but AN clearly follows the reading of S 'non cum elleboro vel alio vehementer dissolutivo, sed cum pulvere . . .' AN's 'del poumon de chescune beste' conceals the Latin's specific reference to 'de pulmone porci' and 'trait fors' suggests that the translator read 'extracto' and not 'extincto', as found in the print [but see S 'Idem potest fieri de pulmone pectoris calido et recenti extracto']. After the administration of leeches AN adds 'Et si il ne volent soucher, si covient il oindre le leu de vin'.

24. et   et en   el

The etymology is given directly from the Latin source. AN 'Si n'est la maladie par soi' renders 'nunquam autem morbus est per se', but 'en la deraine celle del chief' simplifies the Latin 'in posteriori cellula ratione conformitatis'.

25.   Amongst the symptoms the Latin has 'oppressio oculorum et palpebrarum' which AN renders 'le chief pesant et les euz' (cf. para. 19 where 'le chief pesant et les pauperes' renders 'capitis gravedo, palpebrarum oppressio' and para. 154 where 'dormitatio coxe et pedis' is rendered by 'les piés endormanz et les quisses'). AN omits the detail 'si [sc. patiens] a medico in latus vertatur [ab alio super latus convertatur, S], iterum supinatur'.

26. en   katarticio   od   suppositiones   suppositione   supposition   les   et des pies et es plantes   p. aval de sel et de vin egre et leve len ices parties   et f.   la de d. neirs s.   esteintes

The Latin has 'Distempere(n)tur etiam ex benedicta scamoneata uncias .ii. vel blanca similiter scamoneata vel catartico imperiali vel theodoricon anacardium'. AN 'ewe sause' corresponds to 'aqua salmacina', whilst 'soufistries' presupposes the reading 'sophistriarum' (cf. 'sophisticarum' in S and 'sophistarum' in MS B.L. Sloane 420), where the print has 'Adsit simphoniarum importunitas' followed immediately by 'trahatur eger per barbam et capillos, proprio nomine sepe vocetur' (ME 'and be he drawe by thee here and by þe berde and ofte clepe hym by his name'). The physical cure is introduced by 'Deinde localia fiant adiutoria ante apostematis confirmationem. Fiat tale epithima toto capite raso vel solo occipitio . . .'

AN 'jus d'ape' for 'jus d'ache' is a lapse provoked by the Latin 'succus apii'. AN's 'alleboli, asboli' are almost certainly errors for 'ellebori albi vel nigri' with 'neir' now attached to 'poivre'. The passage 'Et s'il n'esternue mie . . . es narines' is not found in the print, but occurs in S. AN has 'sagapino' for the print's 'serapino', the two often being interchanged in medical texts. In place of AN 'quillier' the Latin has 'cuneo dentibus interposito' (cf. para. 37). The reading of AN 'comence a movir le bras' supposes a source like S ('brachii motione') and not the print ('minutione').

27. escoloriance

The Latin lists the five causes of catarrh as follows: 'Ex abundantia humorum per incontinen-tiam effluentium; ex calore dissoluente vel fluere [et fluxum, S] faciente; ex frigiditate con-stringente et exprimente; vel ex humiditate lubricante ex fluxibilitate et liquiditate ipsorum humorum; ex debilitate virtutis retentive'. The first of these has been omitted from the list in AN, but duly appears in the separate examination of each of the five causes.

28. et   de la   inbricite   les supertude   des euz   et q.   la

In the symptoms of the first cause 'les oreilles' is an addition to the Latin of the print. The last symptom is 'corporis habitudo plectorica'. In the second cause the first symptom appears in the print as 'color in facie rubeus', but S has 'calor', as in AN. In the third cause 'et ensement . . . el cors' is an addition to the Latin of the print, but corresponds to the text of S 'frigiditas sentitur in profundo'. The fourth cause is now given as 'fluxibilitatis vel liquiditatis humorum vel humiditatis lubricantis cognitio habetur per multitudinem superfluitatis [superfluitatum, S] secundum os, nares et oculos et per liquiditatem earundem [eorum, S] quia non coherent, sed quasi rare et liquide citissime defluunt [effluunt,S] et distillant'. Again, 'par les oreilles' is an addition to the Latin.

29. et p.   et en tel e.   et de succeners de   aneimes   en   et b.   si . . . tot follows
dras   et les mains follows pies   st. et calamine   et d.   olibanie   escoloriance
tesmoimoine

AN 'se li cors est plectoriques et sanguins' corresponds to 'corpore sanguineo existente'. The print has 'pillule de .v. generibus' (see *Antidotarium Nicolai* 84) erroneously omitting the 'mirabolanorum' of S. There is an omission in AN where the Latin reads 'oleo rosato vel violato vel aliquo alio frigido. Si sic non cessaverit catarrhus, detur frigidior medicina opiata que poterit inveniri cum aqua decoctionis violarum [et prunorum, S] et rosarum ut est requies vel rubea'. Clearly a *saut du même au même* has been occasioned by the word 'violato/viola-rum'. In the Latin print the plaster is applied 'raso vel pilato capiti', which is not accurately reflected in AN's 'res ou sans rere', which follows, rather, the reading of S: 'raso vel non raso capite'. After 'en un linge drap' AN omits Latin 'et fiat capitis sacellatio. Quod si catarrus his adhibitis non cessaverit dentur opiata'. As in para. 20 the print has 'teste .H.', where S has 'teste .G.' AN's 'experiment comune' also reflects the reading of S, the print having 'ex-perimentum conveniens'. In the final cure the change from third person 'le malade' to second person plural 'quant vus irrés coucher' seems odd but finds parallels in receipt collections.

30. apoplexio   apilencia   venimeuses   et de   et de   apoplexio   apoplexio
des   c. mais ne mie d. t.   estrangement   trouble   la cauc que e.   a la veue
epilensie   et es veines et es a.   au mont

The opening sentence is not in the Latin. I have emended AN in accordance with the Latin 'cum privatione rationis' (ME 'with þe privation of þe wit'). The etymology is taken directly from the Latin, which has 'lepsis'. AN's 'yerrameton' is an error for 'ieranexon' (yeranexion, S). The print omits the preliminary list of the three principal causes of apoplexia and associ-ated conditions. In the third cause the print has 'licet calor non sit defectus nec multa superfluorum copia', where S has 'quia licet calor sit debilis, superfluitates quidem multas sufficit dissolvere'. In the case of 'maior apoplexia' the Latin adds that sufferers 'suffocantur

258   THE PRACTICA BREVIS OF PLATEARIUS

cito et moriuntur et hec species incurabilis est' and in the case of 'minor apoplexia' that they
'quandoque enim apertis oculis nil vident, quandoque vident, sed loqui non possunt'. For AN's
'lor tramble la teste' the Latin has 'cum tremore cervicis' and the further symptoms of 'maior
epilepsia' are expressed as follows: 'quandoque urinam, egestionem, sperma involuntarie emit-
tunt, stertunt et spumant, spuma abstersa iterum spumant'. The symptoms of sufferers from
'minor epilepsia' include details omitted by AN: 'scotomiam patiuntur, spuma semel abstersa
non iterum subvenit'. Amongst symptoms of catalepsia the Latin has 'casum presentiunt quasi
reptionem formicarum [raptum quasi formicarum, S] vel motum cuiusdam aure ex [et, S]
materia sursum ascendente'. Once more (see paras. 20,29) the print has 'ut ait .H.', whilst AN
and S substitute Galen, but AN has not accurately translated the doctor's opinion: 'febriunt
[sc. cataleptici] sine febrilis caloris ebulitione, cum materia ab inferioribus vix rapi possit ad
superiora'. In the symptoms of 'analeptici' AN's 'corruption de viandes' reflects the 'ciborum
corruptione' of S, where the print has 'ciborum eructuatione et abhominatione'. In the
symptoms of the 'epileptici' AN omits 'nec adsunt signa ut in reliquis speciebus predictis'.

31. les dens   chief   sil

The Latin begins 'Ad cognoscendum sanguinem esse in causa hec sunt signa: habitudo corporis sanguinea, rubor faciei, totius corporis calor'. In the signs of flegma AN omits the Latin
'venarum repletio, dieta, etas, regio, temporis anni in frigiditate et humiditate convenientia'.
For AN's 'la superficié del cors noire ou cendrine' the print offers 'subnigri vel subcitrini
coloris', but S has 'occuli et corporis superficies sunt quasi subcinericii coloris vel subnigri' and
ME has 'subcinericum colorem'. These colours are applied in the Latin to both the eyes and
the surface of the skin. AN omits the final sentence of the Latin 'Et nota quod epilepsia ex
melancolia frigida [facta, S] in defectu lune magis infestat que autem [vero, S] fit ex sanguine
vel flegmate in plenilunio'.

32. greinor   homo   vienent   defent . . . manger follows humors   rebe   branche
es tranie   col et ausi bon est or a porter entor le col   pilluse   opilensie   j. de b. des
foilles   auser   arconticio   les epilentiques   ou   enforbii   coustonier

AN's 'torne . . . en pleuresie' renders the Latin 'in paralisim sepius converti consuevit'. I have
corrected AN's 'vienent en palus' to 'vivent' in accordance with the Latin 'degent in pa-
ludibus'(cf. para. 37 'oiseles qui vivent en ewe' = 'avium in aquis degentium'). ME has 'þat be
not fede in mareys'. After 'aromatiques' AN omits 'jus cellatas, capita etiam porcorum [porro-
rum, S] elixa, farinam ordei [om. S] speltam' and after 'jus de cerres rouges' ('cicerum rubeorum', S] 'et parum de granis'. In the reference to fish, 'escardeuses' reflects the 'scamosos' of S
(ME 'scalede fysch') and there is another divergence from the print, 'pisces in claris aquis vel
in fluminibus currentibus degentes,' where AN follows S 'in aquis salsis'. The roasting is
explained thus: 'et hos comedant assatos ut naturalis eorum humiditas reprimatur ex igne'. In
the list of herbs the Latin has 'brus [bruscos, S], apium fugiant quia. . .' In the symptoms of
epilepsia 'resve' translates 'aliena loquens'. The therapeutic bath is supposed to be taken 'ter
vel quater . . . in die'. AN does not translate 'Intrantes huiusmodi balneum caput eorum aqua
balnei aspergant'. The recommended treatment for epileptics is 'purgatione et minutione', but
AN makes no mention of bleeding at this point. In the list of purgatives 'owellement' is the
product of the misunderstanding of 'ana' = abbreviation of 'anacardorum' as 'ana' = 'in equal
amounts'. In the 'experimentum patris mei' the Latin specifies three scruples of blood and
explains that they should be given to the patient who is 'adhuc stupido' and would drink
poison if it were proffered. The directions for bearing peony round the neck are given 'teste
.H.', but this is not taken up in AN (S has 'teste .G.'). The Latin has 'ex staphisagria, turbit
purgetur', whilst AN's 'gingembre, peretro' are found in S but are additions to the text of the
print and of ME and 'mente agrestis' appears to be an error for 'rute agrestis'. In the receipt for
the epileptic suffering from the stomach the Latin has 'absque apio' whilst AN has 'ou de
ache'. 'Pliris arconticon' (see Antidotarium Nicolai 41; I have corrected 'arconticio' which is a
faulty expansion of the abbreviation 'arconticō') is not in the print. In the list of ingredients of
the astringent ointment AN omits Latin 'adarcis' and adds 'elibori nigri'.

33. palatiques   diminicion   des   h. et de ces humors   p. de froydure de air et de
d. des   paralatique   nen entor   diversites

The Latin begins 'Paralisis est lesio partis non tamen quelibet lesio, sed ea que fit cum diminutione vel privatione sensus vel motus vel diminutione utriusque'. In AN 'trenchent' seems to be the residue of Latin 'ex humore opilante vel etiam ex incisione nervi' and I have emended accordingly. AN's 'si puisse le membre contreval' renders the Latin 'gravatur inferius', 'grant dissolucion des humors' renders Latin 'nimia humiditatum dissolutio', and 'ne sent l'en riens' reproduces 'stupor et insensibilitas est'. The sentence 'mes se la cause est en meime le membre . . . es autres' is not found in the print, but appears in S 'si vero causa fuerit in ipso vero paralitico membro, ipsum tamen patitur et non superiora'.

34. donat   et metre   venture   parlatiques

The Latin has 'paralisis etiam de qua membrum ex toto privatur sensu et motu, unde ipsum dicitur cancrinum, incurabilis est', but AN has transferred the epithet to 'paralisie'. In the Latin desiccative and consumptive aids are not recommended for thick or hard matter, for 'liquidioribus partibus prius consumptis, reliquum magis inspissatur et sic compactius et dissolutioni et consumptioni inobedientius detur' [redetur, S]. This is not accurately translated in AN and 'remeses' seems to be an error (corr. *espeses?*). For 'chascone semaine' the Latin has 'bis in hebdomada'. AN omits 'blanca' in the list of ingredients and in the next list (after 'oiseus') does not reproduce the Latin 'quascumque poteris habere'. AN telescopes the Latin 'Fiat enim cataplasma ex semine sinapis cum vino et oleo. Ipsa etiam herba frixa in vino et oleo et superposita satis prodest', the last sentence being transferred to the preceding receipt including 'centaurea'. The application of the cupping-glass is directed differently in AN than in the Latin which has 'ventosa sine scarificatione et postea cum scarificatione'. In the following receipt 'et fenoil . . . bethonicam' is not found in the Latin. In the receipt for the restoration of the voice the Latin print has 'pulvis castorei . . . vel balsamum', whilst AN reflects the reading of S. Before the gargle the Latin has 'Fiat etiam minutio de venulis que sunt sub lingua', but this is omitted by AN. AN has misunderstood the Latin 'sed ante fiat gargarisma et postea fiat inunctio . . .', but note that S has 'Si antequam fiat gargarisma fiat inunctio colli . . .' The baths specified by the Latin are 'balnea salsa vel sulphurea'.

35. maine   maine   meime   det   bient   des   ce

As is frequently the case, the first sentence in AN is not found in the Latin. 'Premer celle' once again (see para. 21) renders 'anterior cellula'. I have corrected 'meime celle' to 'meine celle' in accordance with the Latin 'media cellula'. The reference to Constantine (the African) is to his translation *De melancholia*. Before 'tristesce et orguil' 'qui' stands for 'que' ('quam timor et tristicia generaverunt'). AN's 'la discretion' diverges from the Latin which has 'secundum diversitatem lesionis operationum'. The print has 'ex fortibus piperatis anatis', the last word being an error for 'alleatis' (=S). AN omits from the list of 'passiones animi' 'sollicitudo' and 'febre etiam precedente jejunio vigiliis'.

36. angte   generatives

Amongst the symptoms of those suffering from choler AN lacks 'tremunt se', which is also not in S, and incorporates the reflexive in the phrase 'alios percutiunt' following S 'se et alios percutiunt'. The Latin specifies that the symptoms afflict 'juvene colerico'. Amongst the symptoms of melancholy AN mistranslates 'timent' as 'se crient', adds 'chantent' and in 'se habitent' reproduces the reading 'inhabitant' of S rather than 'esitant' of the print. AN seems to have understood 'angulum' as 'angelum' and changes the sense of the Latin which has 'et ipsum fatigant velle dimittere' (see S 'quidam putant se angulum mundi sustinere et ipsis defatigatis velle dimittere'). In the symptoms of patients suffering from melancholia derived from the blood, 'sont liez mult' renders 'letantur' of S in contrast to 'saltant' of the print. Their eyes are 'rubei eminentes'. In the Latin the reference to phlegm reads 'cum sit album, albedinem cerebri non immutat'.

37. maneue   vienent   les   les   aste   corocees   bouche   lent   blank space
in MS   qui deist   qui dist   blank space in MS   lapidis   armoniaci   de dellio
theotoriciō   et   b. bien   lai

The treatment by contraries is described thus in the Latin: 'contrarie passiones inducantur, ut gaudium contra tristiciam, securitas contra timorem et sic de ceteris'. AN omits the following details in the case of the patient who became melancholic on hearing that his purse had been stolen: 'cum debitores suos et debita animo incessanter revolveret profectus est ad eos cum amentia melancolica, et etiam cum nihil debentibus pro debito est obiurgatus, unde consilio medicorum . . .' The therapeutic use of music is presented thus: 'Adsint soni musicorum instrumentorum cantilene iocunde, si his delectari consueverunt sani . . .' ['iocunde . . . sani', om. in S]. The reference in the Latin to 'sicut fecit rufus' ('sicut fecit .G. cuidam ruffo', S; ME 'and þus curid Ruffus') puzzled the translator or copyist and a blank space was left in the MS. In the treatment of those suffering from melancholy the Latin specifies 'pillule facte ex ierapigra aloetica'. In the receipt involving lapis lazuli and lapis armeni, following the reference to the chapter on quartan fever, the print has a number of lines which are not found in S or translated in AN: 'uncias .iii. subtiliter terantur et in vase argenteo vel aliquo alio cum aqua mote [corr. nocte] permittantur residere et illa aqua proiecta addatur alia et hoc vigesies fiat; vel sepius signum perfecte loture hoc est quod aqua supernatans parum vel nihil est infecta. Et autem talis lotura ne sua nimia siccitate vulneret intestina. Nec mireris . . .' AN again (see paras. 26 and 67) translates 'cuneo dentibus interposito' by 'quiller'. AN's 'Et face l'en enonction de oile rosat et violat et de oile mandragorat' is an addition to the Latin print but is attested by S. What in AN follows 'cyrugie' is omitted in S.

38. f. et a la fiez   v. ou d.   ou ele vient

39. d. de a.   n. et si la dolor vient de sanc ices sont les signes   curine   et en la face
pale follows buche   colerique

AN misinterprets the Latin 'calor sentitur in profundo oris dicendo' and reverses 'frigida prosunt, calida nocent'. As in para. 43 AN fails to find a translation for 'oculorum eminentia' (but see paras. 42 and 69). AN renders 'citrinitas faciei et oculorum' in the same syntactical manner that renders 'oppressio oculorum et palpebrarum' (see para. 25). When the cause is phlegm the Latin describes the face as 'pallida et subtumida' (AN has read 'subpallida'). In the case of melancholia, 'si est mornes et pensifs' is a gloss on Latin 'sollicitudo'. In distinguishing 'dolor ex causa privata'and 'ex remota' the Latin has 'dolor ex privata causa est continuus et ante prandium et post quandoque minus'.

40. s. de f.   ongnemesis   oiou   et le   cune   colagoque   et

AN omits the quotation from Hippocrates given in the section on treatment of headache caused by the blood; 'iuxta illud Hip. posteriora capitis dolentia incisa recta vena que est in media fronte iuvat'. In the receipt for headache produced from cold humours 'boilir en ewe corante' diverges from the Latin 'buliant in oleo communi'. The receipt comprising castoreum and rue ends in the Latin 'et penna [pecia, S] intincta fiat epithima'. In the following directions AN's 'brancha ursina' is an error for 'blanca' and the Latin adds at the end 'cum theodoricon ana'. In the Latin the emetic 'vomitus patriarche' is always accompanied by 'et scarpelle', here omitted by AN.

41. The gloss introduced by 'c'est asavoir' is an addition by AN.

42. autre [rubric] a.   g. et hors de sanc et de colere   chaudes   et ne mordent repeated
et   ou   ou cuveine   la r.

The word 'infixivus' appears in S, whilst the print has 'dolor est in oculis'. On this occasion (cf. para. 39) AN has found an adequate translation for 'eminentia', 'apparans desfors'. The section on pain caused by choler is displaced to a later position in AN than in the print. The phrase 'qui prent fors les humors del chief' is an explanatory gloss on 'frigiditate coartante'. Signs of an internal cause include 'debilitas virtutis retentive [contentive, S]', the last two words being omitted by AN. The word 'contentive' has the same meaning as the 'retentivus' of the print (cf.para. 43). In the causes of weak eyesight AN has telescoped the source, omitting 'ex anathimiasi stomachi .i. ex fumositate stomachi superius ascendente, ex fumositate ab ipso vel in ipso cerebro consurgente, ex opilatione optici nervi, ex cataractis, ex panno, ex macula. Distinguende sunt autem causae per propria signa. Solet deficere visibilis spiritus ex senectute . . .' The phrase 'de meime le comencement' is explained by the reading of S which has 'si ex fumositate ab ipso principio .i. cerebro consurgente' ('principio' apparently expuncted), where the print has 'ex ipso cerebro'.

43. ne len   triciscatam   atenuativatives   melle   sosotillement   froide   si ce sorbible   vomitum colature p.   t. et li doigne len   conforfortent   les   jaunes soitille   cou   pudre qui   qui   d. et mal metroit t.   eminenciam   en darenge piies   as. des euz

In 'si le doit om laver' the pronoun should refer to the eyes ('laventur oculi') and one might therefore correct to 'si li doit om laver les euz'. Here 'estoupes' renders Latin 'bombax' ('bombix', S). The directions for bleeding in the Latin provide alternatives: 'Fiat minutio de cephalica vena vel ventose in collo et inter spatulas apponantur cum scarificatione' which AN seems to have misinterpreted. As in para. 2 'trociscata' is an addition to the source. So also is 'desc'a quinse jors'. Amongst the astringent and cooling drugs the Latin adds 'vel corrigiola trita' after 'berbena'. For 'trois fois ou quatre le jor' the Latin has 'bis vel ter in die'. AN's 'au comencement de la cause' reflects the reading of S 'in principio cause', where the print has 'cure'. AN's 'Mes si la dolor vient de soule froidure . . . mette l'en sore' is an addition to the source. In the remedy for weeping eyes the print has 'fluxus ex tepida causa', but AN follows S 'ex frigida causa'. For the bleeding AN introduces an alternative where the Latin has 'collo et spatulis'. In the next remedy 'emplastre' replaces the more specific 'sinapisma' of the source. AN's 'come simple seigni[e]' diverges from the Latin 'ut detractio sanguinis [et] sinapisma'. For 'rubea avec ewe rosat' the Latin has 'tribus vel quattuor diebus'. The AN 'sorbi(b)le' reflects the reading 'sorbilis' of S, where the print has 'subtilis'. AN's '.iii. fois ou quatre anere' diverges from the Latin 'bis vel ter'. The phrase 'come collire' agrees with S ('in modum collirii') against the print which does not have it, and the same goes for the 'autre poudre' which follows. AN's 'fente del coufle' is not an accurate rendering of 'fimus passeris' (also in ME). The AN translator once again (see para. 39 but contrast paras. 41, 69) has difficulty with 'eminentia oculorum'. The 'flors d'arenge' represents a 'locus desperatus': S has 'flores andragie .i. citranguli', MS Sloane 420 'flores curzange .i. centrum galli' and the print 'flores yringe id est trianguli'. The two receipts immediately following 'esprové est' are not in the print, but the second is found in S, which adds a further receipt.

44. peus

45. tintillacion   purritus   titulatio   pecis   lor   sordesce

Amongst the symptoms for earache from a hot aposteme the print (but not S) includes 'extremitates aurium calidissime occurunt'. In the case of the cold aposteme the print reads 'dolor gravativus [et, S] lentus: febris remissior'. The reading in AN 'les particuleres come il courent ensemble' combines the reading of the print 'preterea propria concurrentia caliditatis sive frigiditatis sunt declarantia' with that of S 'particularia convenientia'. AN has 'titulatio' for 'titillatio', but the translator has misunderstood the Latin context: 'hec sunt signa: pruritus, titillatio, etiam aure soli exposita quandoque videntur', though he then proceeds to translate this correctly. There was probably an error in the source.

46. et degote   qualites   alree   f. fende len   et en ongne len un oingnon   le gete coutiches   polis   opitique   corole

The remedies 'Ou mete l'en le jus strigni . . .' and 'Ou face l'en emplastre de coriandre . . .' do not occur in the print but are found in S. The direction for bleeding concerns 'minutio facta de cephalica contrarii brachii'. In the making of the tent ('estuel') AN omits the ingredient 'farina ordei'. The AN MS has 'alree' for 'altee', 'mallow', which the translator apparently did not recognize. I have emended the AN text according to the Latin 'et licinium inde intinctum inmittatur' (ME has 'a tent of lynen cloth') and, in the next receipt, 'coletur et colatura inmittatur'. The administration of bitter drugs to the ears in AN telescopes the Latin: 'succus foliorum persici vel persicarie vel absinthii vel calamenti. Aliud: amigdale amare terantur et trite inter duo folia sub cineres ponantur et oleum quod postea ex eis elicietur auribus instilletur'. The sentence in AN beginning 'Notez . . .' is an addition to the Latin. The 'peres precioses' are 'margarite' in the Latin. In the remedy for deafness the Latin has 'yerapigra', not 'ieralogodion', and AN's 'cassalignea' derives from a text like S (it is not found in the print).

47. sanc qui   et de

S has 'ex furiositate et acumine ipsius sanguinis' in the second sentence.

48. nature   en   en   urines   et moiste follows par d.   et qui   si conoist . . .
aguesse precedes par ce quele   et p.   de le

In the last sentence 'l'urine qui ert coloree' is not the same as the Latin '[discernimus] ex colore urine . . .'

49. quant   quant   del   grant i.   mellon̄ pistin̄   une   de r.   si le   au

There is an omission where the Latin reads 'fronti et timporibus et gutturi aplicetur [et frequenter removetur . . .' AN's 'la terre dont l'en fait les poes' reflects the reading of S 'creta sarracenica vel terra figuli'. 'Sumac' is found in S, but not in the print. AN's 'sor le front et entor la gorge' for Latin 'in naribus' seems to be a repetition from the preceding treatment.

50. AN 'caroigne' translates Latin 'carunculus' ('carunculis narium inviscatis'). The Latin specifies that putrefaction takes place through 'diurnitate temporis et actione caloris' and that 'pustule' (AN 'quitures') arise 'ex acutis humoribus ipsos [ipsas, S] ulcerantibus'. With regard to the polyp AN's 'des humors superflueles' is an addition to the Latin of the print, but see S 'fit polipus ex superflua carne nascens in naribus ex superfluis humoribus generata'.

51. iqui

52. theodoro ou de   en e.

For 'jus de mente' the Latin has 'succo rute', whilst 'de jus decoctionis olibani' reflects the 'cum succo' of S (the print has 'cum vino'). Further, the Latin has 'dimittatur per .ii. vel .iii. horas'. In the treatment of the polyp the Latin makes no reference to corrosive agents, but begins 'Polipus [corrosivus, S] cum est corrosus curatur. . .'

53. –

54. The description of 'pustule' deriving from choler is found in S but not in the print.

55. quitures   lirium   lewe   autre p.   sor   fois   et le

The passage from 'de roses et de cinamone . . .' to 'qui sont mangies' is found in S but omitted from the print. AN's 'Si refait merveileusement . . .' is a misunderstanding of 'gingivas fere corosas dentibus iam cadentibus mirabiliter restaurat'. In the Latin the wise physician appears as 'Solanus Constantinopolitanus medicus' ['This experiment used Solanus Constantinus politanus medicus' in the ME translation]. AN now omits a whole series of cures found in both the print and in S. On the other hand, AN's 'diz jors ou quinze . . . leu de l'inflacion' is found in S but not in the print. AN's 'muskes arses' diverges from Latin 'apum ustarum'.

56. v. de purreture de la m.

AN's '[Puor de bouche] si vient a la fiez des quitures' finds no correspondence in the print, but is close to S 'gingivarum et ex pustulis in ore exortis'. AN consistently translates Latin 'mala habitudo' by 'mauvesse / male habundance'. On the first occurrence S has 'ex nimia habundancia vel mala habitudine membrorum spiritualium', and on the second 'proveniens ex mala habitudine membrorum spiritualium'.

57. accenteuses   d. te de

The 'choses salees' are the object of 'manger'. From 'ou de mastic' to 'piles macedoine' is omitted in the Latin which has 'macis'. AN has truncated the Latin 'In stomaco vero recepte fetorem ex eius vitio provenientem curant diamargariton . . .' The Latin has 'musci' ('masticis', S) for AN's 'nucis' in the last remedy.

58. The Latin has 'qui nervos dentium infundentes dolorem inferunt' which is not accurately rendered by AN's 'qui mullient et temprent les ners'.

59. retencion

In the case of toothache caused by cold humours the Latin print has nothing corresponding to AN's 'enflee', whilst it adds 'subcitrinitas faciei'. The reading is explained by S 'subtumiditate faciei'. AN's 'diz houres' also reflects the reading of S ('.X. horis vel 5'), where the print has 'quinque horis'.

60. The position of part of VI,4 from 'vers si na[i]ssent' to 'en l'ewe' appears to be quite anomalous by comparison with the print which continues para. 59 with 'Si dolor fiat ex calidis humoribus a capite descendentibus . . .', but the passage is found in S and MSS B.L. Sloane 420 and Royal 12 B III and so I have allowed it to stand.

61. ou de   le   et come len repeated   lar   f. cassialiginis mise de sa semence   funicacion   me m.

For 'ventouses . . . sans garse' the print has 'ventosa cum scarificatione'. In the following receipt the print has 'manne' for AN's 'malve'. AN 'ptisicle' does not correspond to the print's 'tussis', but rather to S's 'ptisis'. AN's 'ygia' agrees with the reading of some MSS, whilst others have 'yera[logodion]' and the print has 'v'gia' (expanded to 'virgia' in the 1525 edition). AN's 'Mes si li flux vient de foreines veines' is not in the Latin. AN's 'nitre ars' is not in the print, whilst S has 'vitreo'. The specifying of the wood twig as ash 'ou de ciprés' is an addition, as is 'si est mult tres bone chose . . .' and also 'mes mieus vaut se ele est de argent . . . de fer'. AN also adds 'kar les racines . . . premere', but see S 'His et aliis predictis parum aut nichil conferentibus, ultima cura est ut a perito artifice cum forficibus extrahatur cum radicibus suis. Remanent enim quandoque et tunc est error novissimus peior priore.' ME apparently read 'dolor' for 'error' ('þou þe ake is worse þan before'). AN's 'si est mult bon contre corosion . . .' is lacking in the print.

62. muissance   empeirer   qui on   lo

AN is fuller at the beginning than the print: 'Uva est quoddam membrum a palato descendens [dependens, S] in modum enim [uberum, S] mamillarum'. The Latin says the opposite of AN in the sentence 'Est enim superius lata, inferius angusta [acuta, S] quemadmodum uva'. The print has 'multa alia sinthomata'. AN understood 'mala sinthomata'. The Latin specifies in its account of the causes 'ex melancolico [colerico, S] [humore] raro vel nunquam'.

63. –

64. diamoratio   de meime le doi

AN 'rubea' is an addition to the source (S has 'detur aurea'). In the Latin the gargle is described as 'gargarisma constrictivum'. AN's 'psidia' reflects the reading of S where the print has 'psillio'. AN has misunderstood 'antere' as 'antius': 'Sublevetur uva cum pulvere cinamomi et antere, imposito pollice vel medio [longo, S] digito . . .' The Latin specifies that the patient's head be pulled back by the hair 'a posteriori parte inter occipitium et verticem'. If surgery is required the uvula is to be cut: 'Debet autem incidi in extremitate, non in sui origine, ubi [ut, S] videlicet palato inheret [adhereat, S]'. AN has not understood this and has again reversed the terms of the Latin: 'superius foramen, ut diximus, latum est et amplum', contradicting what was said in para. 62.

65. tierce   qualite   qualite

AN 'ne poet avoir sa aleine' renders 'spiritu orthomie'. The opinion of Hippocrates is given thus in the Latin: 'quinantia pessima est et mortifera cito'(ME 'and þerfor said Ypocras þat squinancy is þe wirste and most dedly and raþest sleyng . . .'). AN omits after 'que ne apiert pas en la gorge' the Latin 'nec extra [exeat, S] in cervice cum rubenti tumore, dolore tamen existente, acutissimo et spiritu orthomie' (ME 'noþer yt in þe pol with a red swellyng and within þe ake is schappste of al with þe spirit of ortomie .i. ry3t speche'). AN 'se ocist' renders Latin 'suffocat' (ME 'chokith'). AN has misread 'quantitas' of the source for 'qualitas' and reversed the terms of the print 'in maiore quantitate colligitur interius et in minori extra', a reversal which is shared with S and MSS B.L. Sloane 420 and Royal 12 B III. In describing all three types of quinsy the Latin states that they derive 'principaliter ex sanguine, secundario ex flegmate', which AN reverses, and 'raro ex colera, numquam ex melancolia'. In cases caused by choler the Latin states 'rubor faciei adest inmixtus croceo colori'.

66. ualade   meimement

67. mordificatif   constrinction   meimement   alteram   soueuent   estreindre
uuent   eschefs

AN's 'mes sovent et petit' bears no relation to the Latin 'propter sequentem flebotomiam' and the action on the second day does not accurately reflect the Latin 'ponatur in collo una ventosa cum scarificatione et due in scapulis [spatulis, S], sed reumatismo humorum cessante.' The Latin print is deficient on the subject of constipation, telescoping two cases into one: 'Si autem fuerit ventris constipatio, fiat clistere mollitivum ex aqua salmacina decoctionis mercurialis . . .' where S has 'Si autem fuerit constipatio ventris, fiat clistere mollitivum; si etiam multa sit constipatio, fiat postea morditivum . . .' The account of AN is surely erroneous. AN's 'Et quise l'en mauves . . .' is not found in the print but corresponds to the reading of S. Yet again (see paras. 26, 37) AN 'quilier' is used for Latin 'cuneum'. The Latin continues 'cuneo dentibus interposito clavam interius impulit' (ME 'set a sticke between the teith and within put a nayl'). AN 'busche' here has the sense of splinter or sharp piece of wood.

68. des   fleume ou de sanc   depesce   esipescement

In both S and the print 'incontinentia' is omitted. Similarly, there is no mention of 'l'enflure', the first causes of which are described in the Latin 'ex humiditate contenta in vasis, et maxime ex sanguine, aut ex flegmate a superioribus distillante'. 'Flegma' and 'sanguis' are reversed in the MS of AN. The phrase 'meine la inconvenience' has no correspondence in the Latin. AN omits a phrase from the Latin 'cum ex motu spirituum et fortitudine virtutum hec operatio soleat [solet, S] perfici [fieri, S] non immerito ex eorum defectu debet impediri'.

69. poignante

AN 'aparisansce' translates Latin 'eminentia' (cf. paras. 39, 41, 43). The AN departs slightly from the Latin 'ex eo quod sanguis consuetus fluere [per nares vel, S] aliunde cessavit [cessaverit, S] ex minutione consueta etiam in longum proiecta [protracta, S]'. In the final list of symptoms AN omits 'ex febre precedente'.

70. choseses   et e.   bonhacis   entre   jambees   en la cendre follows quit   et emplis de la fudre de f. s. et de poivre   faite   pulegium follows esperitez   alexandrim

AN modifies the Latin 'detur ei . . . frumentum cum ptisana et butiro non salso coquinatum'
and omits 'semina cocta dentur' and 'eidem sic in lecto collocato [dentur ova frixa . . .' The
remedies are presented in a different order in AN from that displayed in the print.

71. After 'idropicis' AN omits 'vel in flegmone splenis [vel inflatione splenis, S]'. It also departs from the Latin 'tussis hec ex calore fieri dicitur cum quandoque tussim inducit per effectum siccitatis'.

72. ou poudre follows devant   beu   muscilagonte   superfluiteles

There is an error in the print which has 'Tussis ex humore circa spiritualia existente' for 'tussis
ex humore distillante a cerebro'.

73. disnia   e. asmaus   o. ne clore   li t.

AN omits the explanation of why the lung needs to open: 'Ad hoc enim ut fiat inspiratio
oportet ipsum dilatari' and why this variety of asthma is called sansugium: 'quia laborans hac
specie laborat in attractione sanguinis' [in attractione aeris quemadmodum sanguissuga in
attractione sanguinis, S].

74. There is an omission in AN where the Latin reads '[modo est labor in inspirando], modo
in expirando . . .'

75. et li   avec lewe   et en f.   arteriacam   aneiene   si est   et doigne   calamenti

The pronoun 'li' refers, of course, to the patient. AN has 'artericiam passionem' for 'arteticam
passionem' of the print (S has 'arteriacas passiones'). For the '.iiii. unces' of amoniac the print
has ' Э .iiii.' (S = Э .iii.). AN 'viatique' is a reference to the *Viaticum* of Constantine the
African. The print and S add 'et etiam in breviario'. The AN 'opii .iiii. onces . . . noef ou onze'
is omitted in the print and follows the reading of S: 'opii uncias .iiii. conficiantur cum ptisana
infusione dragagant et dentur .ix. vel .xi.', which, however, has 'ana .vi. dragmas' in the
preceding phrase. After 'Э .iiii. dentur pueris cum lacte' the Latin has 'maioribus cum trifera
magna'. AN 'et dongne l'en ensement le sanc . . . malade' follows S 'Similiter sanguis lepusculi
recenter abstractus et in potum datus multum confert'. For '.iiii. onces de orpiment' the print
has 'auripigmenti Э .iii.', whilst S agrees with AN.

76. –

77. difficultas   there follows a falsely placed rubric which reads Ci parole il solonc les
urines et de lor colors   b. par   lurz   contenue   e. com   entonses

After 'derere en les espaules' the Latin has 'vel in sinistra spatula usque ad humeros'. AN's 'les
euz jaunes' translates 'cum glaucedine (vel gravedine oculorum)'. 'A la fiez au destre coste . . .
et en l'autre' corresponds to a passage in S which is omitted in the print. The print has
'peripleumonia ex sanguine et colera principaliter, secundario ex flegmate, raro ex melancolia'
where S reads 'peripleumonia ex sanguine et flegmate, secundario ex colera, raro ex melancolia'. When phlegm is a cause, one of the symptoms is 'febris remissior [remissa, S]' which AN
renders with 'fevre lente'. In the case of melancholy 'salive jaune' renders 'sputum subglaucum'
and 'la bouche secch' departs somewhat from 'oris acetositas'.

78. mesi   amb[?]dous with erasure after third letter   de diaute follows froide   MS has
si la matere est chaude   medicines   m. a boyvre

The phrase 'seigner per opposicion', not found in the print, renders S 'minutio per antipasim',
anti[s]pasis referring to the use of antispastics, or diverting medicines, but it looks as if AN

understood it in the light of the following observations. AN's 'cinc foiz ou set le jor' diverges from the Latin 'quinquies vel sexies in die'. There is some confusion in the AN text about anointing patients. The print, mispunctuated, has 'quinquies vel sexies in die et totiens in nocte ex [cum, S] dialtea. Si materia fuerit [fit, S] frigida [+ si autem calida cum butiro, S] ex butiro vel oleo violaceo, si materia sit calida [om. S] fiat etiam inunctio iuxta ignem . . .' It seems, therefore, that AN has followed the reading of the print, though the reading of S is surely superior. I have emended AN accordingly. AN's 'et envolupe l'en le liu ou il est enoint de leine' diverges from the print 'deinde lava loca inuncta', but follows S 'deinde lana involvantur loca dolentia inuncta'. The receipt 'Autre: pregne l'en la ferine fenugreci . . .' is found in S, but not the print. In the description of staunching nosebleed the Latin explains 'cum setis porci naribus inmissis provocetur', a detail omitted in AN. On the other hand, the Latin omits 'et face par illeuc frenesie'. AN's 'autre, que l'en doit faire a home . . . le doigne l'en' is omitted in the print owing to a *saut du même au même* ('colatura').

79. maladies   setine   kar f.   aspre

The text of this section differs widely in S and the print. AN's 'pronostique mon pere' is not an erroneous reading of 'pronosticum pessimum' (print) but follows S 'malum pronosticum est. Pater meus dicebat fluxum ventris . . .' The Latin reference to the death-rattle reads 'Oregmon [megmon, S] .i. sonus in gula superveniens, mortale [est]', but is replaced by 'mes quant l'en dort mauveisement, si est male signe'. The reference to Hippocrates corresponds with the text of S (the detail is not found in the print): 'Undeque Ypocras: "Apostema vel vesica in pede perypleumonicis salutem promittit" '. On the other hand AN fails to reproduce the detail that if a blister or boil occurs in the foot, 'quandoque ad malum et precipue si dilitescit .i. se de subito non appareat'. The final passage is garbled in the print and the MSS. In the print it begins: 'Si aliquis patiatur pleuresim in dextro latere et non in die cretico superveniat apostema et [vel, S] tumor cum dolore in dextro pede . . .' AN has omitted the sense of the opening words and modified the statement about the day of crisis so that the Latin 'sentiet dolorem in sinistro latere vel dextro' becomes simply, as in S, 'en le senestre coste'. In the Latin print the final autobiographical statement reads 'Experto credite. Iam enim pluries probavi hec vera esse et numquam deceptus sum in sinone comite. Hoc expertus sum ego et magister Matheus Platearius' where S has 'Iam enim pluries probavi esse verum et numquam deceptus fui'.

80. kar come n.

AN omits one of the common origins of empima, 'ab omnibus que reuma comovere solent'. Its 'devient l'abitude del membre plein[e] de purreture' renders the print's 'membri habitudo saniosa efficitur'. The text of AN seems to embody the residue of a rubric in 'Empicus qui crache sanc purri'.

81. AN's 'les euz reons' renders 'orbes oculorum tument'. The Latin has 'in loco enim infecto dolor sentitur quandoque in sinistra parte, quandoque retro secundum diversa loca infecta . . .' AN's 'par evulsions' reflects the reading of S 'propter motum evulsionis' as opposed to the reading 'infusionis' of the print.

82. calis

For '.iiii. onces de la poudre de mirre' the Latin has '.iiii. Ǝ' [.iii. Ǝ, S]. The Latin print does not have anything corresponding to the apparent repetition in AN 'et lor doigne l'en au soir .iii. onces de mirre' (S = 'et detur in sero Ǝ .iiii. mirre'). In the receipt cassialignea represents the reading of S as opposed to the cassiafistula of the print. In AN 'tuel' translates Latin 'embotum' (ME 'embotus is a stike holow within'; cf. 119, 128 below). Owing to the loss of a folio in AN the rest of this chapter and the beginning of the next are missing.

83. aloigne

In S the chapter begins as follows: '*De ptisi*: Ptisys est consumptio substantialis humiditatis corporis ex ulcere pulmonis proveniens. Fit autem quandoque ex catarro, dum humor a capite distillans in pulmone ipsum repercutit, repercutiendo cavat, cavando exulcerat, unde illud Cophonis: 'Gutta cavat lapidem non vi sed sepe cadendo' [Walther, *Prov.* 10508–9]. Si humor a capite descendens viciatque pulmonem fit etiam ex siccitate dum substantia pulmonis arefacta per motum facile rumpitur, quod est videri in pampino vitis, quod in fine autumpni iam desiccatus levi vento facile rumpitur. Fit preterea ex sanguine dum enim saltu vel clamore vel percussione vel aliis de causis vena rumpitur in pulmone sanguis prorumpens cum extra vasa locum non habet, vertitur in saniem et sanies inficit et ulcerat pulmonem. Unde Ypocras: 'In sanguinis sputo, saniei sputum, in saniei sputo ptisys et fluxus". The incomplete sentence in AN is part of the next sentence in S: 'Ex ulcere pulmonis fit consumptio corporis. Pulmo destinatus [est] ut per dilationem ab exterioribus suggat aerem, quem cordi ministret ad mitigationem innati caloris. Pulmo ulceratur sentiens lesionem naturali sensu motum suum cohibet et refrenat nec pro debito dilatatur'.

84. The Latin lists as a symptom 'unguinum et extremitatum constrictio' and 'familiare signum dolor sinistre spatule usque ad humeros'.

85. tintillacion   anuli et   senences   venufar   senestem   ce conustre

AN modifies further signs of 'ptisis ex catarro', namely 'per mucilaginem et sputorum abundantiam, per lacrimarum fluxum'. In the first receipt before the four 'cold' seeds the Latin includes 'dragagant'. The receipt beginning 'Et li doigne l'en diadragagant' shows some rearrangement from the Latin and a number of small differences. Most of it is omitted in ME. AN's 'c'est asavoir' results from a misreading of .i. as *id est.*

86. a. de froit

Amongst general causes of the bursting of a vein the Latin instances 'ex casu', and 'diabrosim' is glossed '.i. resudationem' on its first appearance. The bursting of a vein through excess of humours has as its result 'sanguinis . . . emissio per incontinentiam'.

87. quele veine   es veines   tintillacion   a. un dolor et une touse   espomle   qui est   depure   sanguifuga   vue

Here the Latin 'Quando sanguis per incontinentiam emittitur' is rendered by 'come li sanc en ist par superhabundance'. The Latin specifies that the black and green colour of the humours results from a vein burst 'ex acumine humorum', a detail omitted in AN. Blood emitted via the mouth derives from a variety of places amongst which the Latin includes 'ex faucibus' (not in AN) and AN 'del piz, a la fiez del pomon et a la fiez de diafragmate, a la fiez del bouche del stomac, a la fiez du fons de l'estomac, a la fiez du foie' is not found in the print but occurs in S. The print has 'arili vena' for S 'kilivena' (ME, þe veyn kili') which AN has clearly recognized later in this section where the print has once again 'arili vena'. AN 'eveus' is my emendation from the MS 'es veines' in accordance with the Latin 'aquaticus' (ME 'waterische'). AN's 'et comence om a conter par devers le chief' renders the Latin 'facta connumeratione a superiori' and a few lines later 'et comence l'en le conte par aval' renders 'facta connumeratione ab inferiori'.

88. dil   ni   fumosite   venufare   nnummie   porrra

Once more (see para. 87) 'superhabundance' is used to translate 'incontinentia'. AN 'veine du chief' renders 'cephalica', whilst 'salvatella' has been added to designate the vein 'inter medium et minorem digitum' [inter anularem et auricularem digitum, S]. The print consistently has 'arili vena' for 'kilivena / quilivena'. AN does not give the technical name ('vena saphena') for the vein 'dil quivile du pié'. In the case of menstrual humours AN's rather vague 'que l'en les doit faire' corresponds to 'menstrua sunt provocanda'. AN uses 'resudacion' again, where the Latin has simply 'diabrosim'. The sentence referring to 'pilles de athanasia' has no correspondence in the print but is found in S. Similarly, 'les pilles Galien' reflects the reading

of S where the print has simply 'pillule'. In the directions for constrictive medicines 'flux de
sanc qui vient des membres espiritez' reflects S 'sanguine a spiritualibus proveniente'. Again
AN's reference to blood from 'des membres espiritez' reflects the reading of S where the print
has 'a splene super splenem'. The final words of this chapter, 'et por la grant chalor qui est
naturele', are lacking in the print.

89. ne d.

The Latin begins 'Fastidium est involuntaria cibi abhominatio vel abstinentia'. The addition
of 'sensibles' to 'ners' is found in S but not in the print. The latter shortly afterwards has 'venis
sensibilibus opilatis', where AN follows the reading of S 'venis sensibilibus sint opilati', but
substitutes 'la vertu sensible' for Latin 'spiritus animalis'. AN 'parfaire l'appetite' renders S 'ad
appetitum perficiendum' (the print has 'confortandum vel perficiendum') followed by 'non
inmerito altera principali [principalium, S] causa deficiente, deficit appetitus' which AN
renders rather clumsily, obscuring through the repetition of 'appetite' the Latin 'Appetitus
enim stomachi qui proprie desiderium dicitur'.

90. p ce

AN's truncated sentence 'kar notez que par absense des espiris . . .' is the result of a *saut du
même au même* ('propter'): 'stomacho propter absentiam spirituum infrigidato, cibus etiam in
transitu sentitur frigidus propter dictam causam'. In the final sentence AN follows S 'ex
eructuationibus acidis sive insipidis' where the print has 'eructuationibus a cibis insipidis'.
Both S and the print have 'ex indigestione et gravedine stomachi'.

91. seueuse   dure   fron   salmaciue   et le

In the opening sentence the occurrences of 'contre' reflect the reading of S, where the print
has 'circa'. Following S 'ex jejunio et consumptione corporis predicta cibis et electuariis aliis
confortativis sunt recuperanda ut sic de ceteris' AN fully renders the source where the Latin
print has only 'si ex jejunio, corpus est reficiendum'. The phrase 'boille l'en sor les carbons' is a
misreading of 'buliatur et cum carnibus detur . . .' AN 'kar tele opilatio ovre paralisie' reflects
the reading of S 'talis enim oppilatio stomachi paralisim operatur' where the print has 'compi-
latio'. ME translates 'cum frigido Cophonis' by 'with a colde Cophonis'. AN misunderstands
frō [= frigido] as *fron*. The allusion is to the 'electuarium frigidum secundum Cophonem'
described in the *Antidotarium Nicolai* 43. In the Latin the emetic chosen is 'vomitus scarpelle',
not reproduced by AN. The reference to the 'sause poitevine' is omitted in the print, but S
includes 'salsa pictavensis' (a later hand has emended to 'salsamentum') with 'modico serpillo
et modica salvia'. In the print the quotation from Hippocrates runs 'Cibus parum deterior et
potus detestabilior melioribus delectabilis non magis apponendus' and in S 'Parum deterior
cibus et detestabilior quidem melioribus delectabilis vero magis appetendus' (continuing 'ex
quorum varietate appetitus varietur et excitetur nam idemptitas macri est sacietatis', which
AN omits).

92. kai

The Latin begins 'Bolismi hec sunt signa contraria'.

93. degestions

94. –

95. face len   c. et hors   mamiaci   excercives

In the list of things which the appetite develops a taste for the Latin includes 'tophos'. AN's
'autresi come une mosse' renders Latin 'quasi quandam lanuginem inducente'. The rejected
reading 'et hors' may be the residue of an attempt to translate Latin 'Unde stomachus infectus

ratione conformitatis appetit predicta . . .' The appearance of ginger in the last receipt reflects the reading of S and is absent from the print. The rejected reading 'et hors' may be the residue of an attempt to translate Latin 'unde stomachus infectus ratione conformitatis appetit predicta . . .'

96.   extens   kar

97.   froydure   choses

AN uses the familiar contrast 'tost . . . tart' to render 'Frigida exhibita magis incitant vomitum, calida vero reprimunt'. AN's 'solonc les diversetés des humors' follows S 'secundum diversas humorum differentias' rather than the print's 'secundum diversas colere differentias'. After 'certefiez par le dit du malade' the sentence 'Kar il reconustra bien . . .' corresponds to the reading of S and is omitted in the print.

98.   meine   de   mirre   ovec   aucune aucun   ou   mirre   del

In the second receipt the Latin has 'in oleo muscelino tepido resolvatur tiriaca'. In a later receipt the phrase 'sor .i. poi de quir' finds no correspondence in the Latin. AN's 'esponge marine' renders S 'spongia marina' where the print has 'spongia magna'. The sentence beginning 'Contre voncher qui vient de agues viandes' is not in the print, but is found in S. In the preparation of the bath 'ewe de ploye' is an addition to the print but occurs in S. In the final receipt 'tan' reflects the reading of S as against 'mirtus' of the print. In the Latin there the final section reads as follows: 'Hic non absque ratione interserendum [inserendum, S] arbitror quod quidam susceptas medicinas evomunt nullo modo retinere valentes antequam; igitur talibus exhibeatur medicina: ligentur [fortiter, S] extremitates, acetum vel sucus uve acerbe oculis infundatur, usquequo [ut, S] spiritus ad locum dolentem ab ore stomachi recurrat [recurrant, S]. In ipso etiam impetu vomendi aqua [frigida repente, S] in faciem proiiciatur'. S adds 'vel per xv dies ante fiat emplastrum constrictivum et stomachi confortativum ex bolo, olibano, mastice, et super stomacum ponatur'.

99.   sans force

AN's first 'inanition' is an innovation. ME 'disposition' in the same opening sentence reflects the reading of S which has 'dispositio' where the print, reflected here, has 'positio'. The section 'Ou, sicome il m'est avis . . . l'en apele sancglot' is omitted in the print through a *saut du même au même* involving 'singultus', but is found in S.

100.   la

AN diverges at the beginning from the Latin: 'singultus frequentius fit cum vomitu quandoque humorum, quandoque ciborum. Quandoque repletio est ex humoribus. Quando erit ex cibis eructuationes multe adsunt et diversi saporis [S adds et secundum humorum superhabundantium diversitates] plectorica est corporis habitudo, dieta precedens larga fuit'. In the symptoms of 'singultus ex inanitione' 'flux de sang' follows the reading of S (it is omitted in the print).

101.   AN's 'par aval ou par amont ou par l'un et l'autre' renders Latin 'vel per secessum vel per vomitum divisim vel mixtim'. In the Latin the section ends 'valet etiam contra singultum ex his duabus causis timor patientibus intensus [illatus, S] cum subito eis aliquid terribile nunciatur [t. subito videatur vel dicatur, S]. S adds 'Nota quod pillule de aloe cum aliquantulo mastice informate cum succo absinthii mirabiliter stomachum confortant ut dicit magister Petrus'.

102. –

103.   u. chaufe et t.   sent len avesques   sent   multudo

104. c. et en tens   violates   sarrum   sont el   fichez   les les   trauense   quant
il i   trauensi et citrinss

For AN's 'de oxcimel squillitique ou de oxcimel laxatif' the Latin has 'cum psillitico vel cum oxi laxativo'. The print has 'corpore distemperato in calore', but various MSS seem to have confused corpore (cp̄e) with tempore (tp̄e) (S has 'corpore et epate distemperatis in calore'). The receipt involving 'sandles blanches et rouges', whilst found in S, is not in the print. AN's 'rubea' appears to be a mistake for 'reubar.' AN's 'sacellacions . . . de mel' also involves an error, for the Latin has 'ex milio'. The receipt beginning 'Mete l'en de ligno aloe . . .' shows some small divergences from the Latin. For AN 'tranense' (i.e. from Trani) many MSS have 'turnense' through confusion of the abbreviation for 'ra' and that for 'ur'. The print has 'turnense'. AN's 'ne encontre vice del matrix en froide cause' follows the reading of S ('neque contra vitium matricis ex frigiditate') but is absent in the print. In the final receipt AN's '.iiii. onces' diverges from the Latin 'Ǝ .iii.' (S has 'Ǝ .iiii.'). AN 'fenoil' reflects S where the print has 'fenugreci'.

105. –

106. les signes   done

107. bochent   et de   color   que ne fait   desoz   mirre   les queles

AN 'dedenz le quart jor' renders 'ab ipso principio usque ad quartum diem' which is repeated in the next sentence, 'Similiter usque ad quartum diem antequam confirmetur ad apostema apponenda sunt . . . refrigerativa et apocrustica'. The phrase 'et extenuatiques' abbreviates the Latin 'que materiam in fumositatem extenuent'. AN's 'cassiam ligneam' follows S where the print has 'cassiafistulam' (see also para. 82 above). The sentence beginning 'Et face l'en sacellacions . . .' and the following one are found in S but not in the print. After 'les racines de lis' the Latin has 'branca ursina' and instead of cumin (= S) the print has 'cepula in vino'. The passage beginning 'Et quant l'aposteme est depeciez . . .' follows several readings of S against the print: 'Rupto apostemate quod cognoscitur per emissionem saniei per vomitum, materia existente in concavitate stomachi vel in superficie,vel per cessessum . . .' AN is less explicit and it is particularly unfortunate that the translator chose to employ such easily confusable expressions as 'desus' (above) and 'desuz' (below). In ME a note in red in the margin reads 'mulsa is a confection of wyne or water wyth hony'. AN's 'Que la sorsaneure ne remaigne' renders 'ne locus maneat ulceratus'.

109. les signes   del   m. come   telei   ce misse

110. del   que ne fait   naturatives   desouz   mirre   les quele

108–110. This is another copy of VIII,6 made from the same exemplar, repeating some of the errors (e.g. 'destincter les signes de la matere par les signes') of the earlier copy. On the other hand, in 107 it has 'extenuatiques' and in 110 'extenuatives', similarly also 'les queles' and 'les quele', 'maturatives' and 'naturatives', 'color' and 'chalor', 'apocrustica' and 'apocras-tica', 'mirre' and 'mulse'. In 110 'dehors' is omitted after 'siet es boueus ou' and 'la purreture' after 's'en istra'.

111. lesi   et   decries

The Latin has 'distenditur ergo vesica et repletur, unde colon in intestinum quod sibi adiacet comprimitur'. S has 'que distenta et repleta colon intestinum quod sibi adiacet conprimit'. AN's 'col' thus appears to be an error. The Latin asserts that 'yliacus dolor' does not derive its name from the small intestines 'ut quidam mentiuntur'. The following reference is to Con-stantine the African's *Pantegni* (a translation of Haly Abbas). The phrase 'ceste dolor siet es costes del nomblil' reflects the reading of S 'fit dolor yliacus in lateribus ab umbilico inferius' where the print has 'fit yliacus ab umbilico inferius'.

112. et de

The verbs 'bruit et triboille et sone' are the translator's attempts to render three nouns in the Latin: 'ex rugitu intestinorum et gurgulatione et multu sonitu'.

113. sefches   m. et mordificatif   b. et les quise len   doigne   si g. m. follows ewe froyde

The phrase 'encontre l'umor evacuatives' reflects the reading of S 'contra humorem evacuantia' which is missing from the print. AN's 'jo comant' introduces the first person where the Latin has 'Ideo etiam in tali causa et in similibus nullus presumat facere clistere mordificativum [morditivum, S] nisi pretendat [precedat, S] mollificativum [mollitivum, S]'. In the next sentence the Latin reads 'Cum igitur clisteris [clisteri, S] beneficio ventris officium fuerit procuratum . . .' The reference to 'diamarte' (= diamargariton) is followed by 'ita quod due partes sint de benedicta, tertia diamarte'. In the print 'sebesten' has been distorted to *sc^ube* (= scabe in 1525 print). AN's 'la poudre de thamarinde' appears to be a misreading of Latin 'pulvis cantaridarum'. The Latin also has the reference to the cure, 'quidam sacerdos curabat omnes fere in terra laboris' (ME 'And with þis experiment helid a prest almost al patients of þis syknes in þe lond of travayle').

114. en contre

In the opening AN diverges slightly from the Latin, which has 'Caliditas motum habet a centro, unde prolongat [elongat, S] cum repugnante siccitate non possit dilatare. Siccitas vero facit motum ad centrum, unde constringit, coartat et rotundat'. AN 'muet contreval' renders 'habet motum ad centrum'. AN's 'car fleume naturale . . . les fait lez' follows the reading of S but is absent from the print. The Latin MSS have simply 'orbo' to which AN has added 'sacco'.

115. –

116. par   non non   paruarie

AN 'la poudre centonice' renders the reading of S which is not in the print. The Latin has 'Stephanonus'. I have emended to 'herba babilonica', though 'babilonia' is sometimes found e.g. in ME. AN 'corne de cerf ars une drame' diverges from the Latin 'unciam .i.' AN 'fiel de tor' is an addition to the Latin, as is the rest of the same receipt from 'abrotani' to 'hors les vers'.

117. prassute   esplen   foief

Most of the Latin MSS give the etymology as 'a scindendo, quia in ea scinduntur intestina' (S has 'a dissindere quia in ea intestina dissinditur'). AN 'et a la fie de non naturale . . . innaturale arse' is missing from the print, but is found in S. AN 'et si est apelee epatica dissinteria' is similarly in S but not in the print. For 'come il ne troeve son membre' the print has 'cum non inveniat substantiam quam nutriat' in place of S's 'cum non inveniat subiectum quod nutriat'. AN does not render 'per incontinentiam emittitur' ('si l'envoit l'en fors').

118. meseraitiques   alterioses

AN 'ou l'un et l'autre' does not accurately render 'quoddammodo'. AN's 'si resemblent roil d'arein en color' reflects the reading 'erugini eris' of S which is not found in the print, which also omits the rest of the sentence. For 'un mires fous' the Latin has 'imperiti'. AN 'la queu chose ne puet avenir' renders the reading of S 'quod quidem impossibile est' rather than the print's 'quod falsum est'. AN's 'par la soutilleté d'eles' also reflects S, 'propter nimiam subtilitatem', absent from the print. In the description of the three types of dysentery caused by malfunctioning of the bowels 'ventosité' is an error, S and the print having 'unctuositas'. AN's 'unes chars eschardouses' only approximately reflects the Latin 'frustatim emittuntur intestina et in egestione apparent carnose et nervose et arteriose resolutiones'. AN omits the following description of the symptoms from the upper bowels: 'Cum enim sit vitio superiorum, dolor sentitur super umbilicum et videtur cingere patientem et sanguis egestionibus est valde permixtus'.

119. contres   k. .i. unce de citrins   artanisiam   marcienes   ou de

AN 'Ainz que l'en done choses constrictives' reflects S 'antequam dentur constrictiva' where the print has 'numquam dentur constrictiva'. Owing to a *saut du même au même* involving 'aqua pluvialis' AN's 'ou en lait cler de chievre . . . oveques simila . . . devant' renders S 'conmisceatur simile sicut prediximus coquinate', which is omitted from the print. In a similar passage a bit later the print has 'similiter' (sił) in error for 'simila'. In the 'experiment' Galen is omitted in the print which has a different receipt from that shared by AN and S. The 'blanchisse' of AN is not accounted for by the Latin. Once again (see paras. 82 and 128) 'tuel' translates Latin 'embotus'. AN 'lacca' reproduces the Latin (S has 'lacca').

120. lesfomac

The print gives the etymology as 'a lien, quod est lenire', S as 'a lenon, quod est lenire, vel lenositas'. AN 'en les ulceracions ne naissent nules villositez' telescopes the Latin of the print 'ulcera cicatrizantur, in cicatricibus villi non renascuntur' (S has 'ulcera cicatrizantur et inde lenitas sequitur et lienteria'). AN 'Dont les boiaus et l'estomac . . . la lientere' is not in the Latin and the beginning of the next sentence seems to be a redundancy. AN's 'chanaz de molin' embroiders the Latin 'in canalibus'.

121. –

122. boiue

For AN 'diamargariton' the print has 'diamuscum'. AN 'cassialignee' reflects the reading of S where the print has 'cassiafistula' (see para. 107 above). After 'mitridatum' the Latin adds 'cum aqua decoctionis olibani exhibitum'.

123. dou i

Through a *saut du même au même* involving 'flegmate' AN omits 'ex fluxu humorum a capite] ex flegmate, ex colera, quantitate peccante. Si enim qualitate peccaret dissinteriam potius induceret et ex debilitate virtutis retentive, ex multitudine ciborum et potuum aggravando similiter [ex flegmate lubricando . . .'

124. AN's 'espumouses' reflects the reading of S ('spumosis') which does not occur in the print. Instead of the reference to Hippocrates the print has simply 'iuxta illud' ('iuxta illud Ypocratis', S) and, within the quotation, 'egestiones mucilagines'.

125. The final sentence in AN is not in the Latin.

126. e. loniant

The AN MS has 'loniant' (cf. med. Lat. loinia, lonia) for 'longao', but then 'boiau' in the next line. AN's 'mort et point' renders Latin 'mordicatio' and 'titillatio'.

127. In the passage 'Mais quant fleume est en cause . . . signes' AN follows the order of S, whereas the print has a different arrangement which is deficient.

128. teule   de p. ou poiz

AN 'en colre' appears to be an error for 'in colicam'. In the fomentation the third reference to malva is malva viscosa. Once again (see paras. 82, 119) 'tuel' translates 'embotus'. AN 'Et moille l'en cotoun . . . fondement' is not found in the print. For 'fomentum' the Latin has 'encatisma' (= 'hip-bath'), which occurs in the next AN receipt, found in S but missing from the print. AN 'seche' compresses the Latin 'per pannum cribelletur ut fiat subtilissimus'.

129. AN 'espoissece' follows S 'spissitudine' where the print has 'feculente spissitudine'. In the last sentence the Latin reads 'quandoque vi sinthomatis, ut ex humorum acumine venas apertione [humorum acumine venarum nimia apertione, S]'.

130. AN 'car il dira bien s'il avoient piece a coru ou non' is apparently an attempt at rendering 'fatetur cessare purgationem [purgationes, S] sibi consuetudinariam [-as, S]' (ME 'for why he knowyth þat þe purgation whiche he is wont to have cessin'). AN 'le flux dou malade conoist l'en . . .' does not, as it stands, represent an accurate version of 'Fluxus etiam testimonio patientis cognoscitur et ex sanguine fluente . . .' In 'qui travaillent de emoroides qui travaillent de dissinterie' the second 'qui' = qu'il. AN 'et sanz aforcier . . . d'aler a chambre' follows S and is omitted in the print.

131. au dunc   senc   peirz   nainis   tapesie barbastie   soinit

In the first receipt the Latin adds 'pulegium'. AN 'car eles romperont en teu manere e si heles secherunt' follows S 'sic enim abrumpuntur vel desiccantur' where the print has 'abraduntur'. There is a change of scribe at 'e si heles secherunt' and the copy now exhibits sharper Anglo-Norman traits. The Latin has 'pannus lineus albumine ovi infusus vel carta . . .' 'Superfluité de sanc' seems part of a rubric, the Latin having 'Aliud contra retentionem'. AN 'ventuses' renders Latin '(s)cufe'. AN 'sur le[s] reins en bas' telescopes 'supra renes et inferius in carnositate natium'. After 'litargiri' the Latin has 'ana', 'in equal measure'. The Latin ends this section thus: 'Si parum profuerint, fiant remedia contra dissinteriam [+ scripta, S]'.

132. –

133. de

134. fomemtaciuns   spidia   et de

135. curuce

136. sor   perine   suffra   autrel   cum cum

The print has 'niopos', where the correct reading is that of S 'ynopos' 'wine-coloured'. In the case of cold humour the Latin lists as a symptom 'urina colorata'. 'La part oscur du foie' seems ironically named. The print has 'in luna epatis' which is an error for 'in sima epatis', referring to a hollow previously translated (see para. 135 above) by 'c(u)ruce'. AN 'sans glete' is an addition to the Latin. At 'coustes' there is an omission where the Latin has 'quandoque fit apostema in lacertis] sub diafragmate in longum [modo in, S] transversum extensis'. I have therefore emended AN in accordance with the Latin 'apostema lacertorum formam habet oblongam, modo in longum, modo in transversum'. In the Latin the 'apostema epatis' has 'semicirculi formam'.

137. quei   ch. lons m.   rit   ou le   sorait   neneisune

AN 'repercussives' renders the 'apocrustica' of S which is not in the print. In the Latin 'portulagues' and 'scarioles' are in a separate receipt: 'Interius recipiantur herbe frigide ut portulaca et scariole et similes'. AN reflects the reading of S 'cum lexiva [sic] non forti sed mediocriter confecta'. For 'chosis extenuativis' the Latin has 'diaforetica' which 'materiam extenuent in fumositatem'. AN 'ky sunt ditis contre fraide apostome de[s] bouaus' follows the reading of S, which is omitted in the print. AN 'et cucurbite . . . d'eskariolis' is found in S but is also missing from the print.

138. polis   follis   et   sanc

The print has 'auriginos [aurigeus, S] . . . eo quod colorem ycteris vel reguli vel auri vel arcus
celestis pretendit'. The three varieties are explained thus: 'crocea ex colera naturali; agria-
capega filontis [corr. agriaca pegasilontis = S] ex colera viridi; melanchilon ex humore nigro .i.
ex colera adusta'. AN 'ky pas[se] en coler' translates 'in coleram transeuntis' and '[si] doit la
coler redunder . . .' renders 'unde colera redundat ad epar et sanguinem inficit'.

139. troene   la   del   nel   maladies   auquen   crettilque

AN 'forseneri' is an usual choice to render 'fervor sanguinis', later (para. 140) translated by
'ardor de sanc'. AN 'les oreilles cornanz' translates 'aurium tinnitus'. AN 'dou pertius dou fel
amont' translates 'superius pori' and 'li pertuis d'aval . . . del fel' 'porus inferior'. Then AN
renders 'porus' with 'pore' (see para. 140). On the other hand, 'fumosité' is an error for
'furiosité'. I have emended MS 'auquen jor' in accordance with the Latin 'in alio die cretico
[critico, S]'.

140. od   coreure   et cum   e. et   od   quant   lesisonmerrones

The unexpressed subject of 'si est donques de l'aage' is, of course, the patient. The Latin has 'in
[a, S] principio si febris adest usque ad .iiii. diem fiat minutio', so I have emended AN
accordingly. In the recommended diet the print omits 'scarioles' (attested in S) and, like S,
adds 'cicorea', which AN omits. Where fever is absent the diet includes 'vinum arbustorum
[arbustratum, S] album'. AN 'vert jus' translates Latin 'agresta'. In the purgative AN includes
'mauve unce .i.' which is omitted in the print. The Latin has 'fiat balneum meum hoc modo'.
AN 'cuve' translates Latin 'tina'. The phrase 'c'est asaver' before 'cic[er] ruge' appears to be an
error. The passage 'Une vielle empli un pot . . . tant avoit duree' is omitted in the print, but is
found in S ('Quedam vetula liberavit . . .') where the patient is described 'fere aclites vel
timpanites factus'. The final prayer is, of course, unique to AN and replaces two receipts in the
Latin: 'Si yctericia cesset de corpore citrinitate in oculis manente, oculi laventur cum aceto et
coriandri succo vel aceto solo vel lacte mulieris. Sternutationes fiant cum succo sicidis vel cum
pulvere nigelle vel cum lacte mulieris, aceto vel oleo rosaceo et similibus'.

141. de retencion repeated after superfluitez

The Latin has 'ex fluxu humiditatum [humiditatis, S] preter naturam exsolvuntur spiritus'.

142. gote   cuer   contre   si dit li v. est   et les ch. qui levent de la superfluele i.
est   siege

AN curtails the Latin 'Ex distemperantia caliditatis et humiditatis per exsolutionem spirituum
utraque virtus, tam digestiva quam expulsiva, debilitatur'. AN's Greek is predictably worse
than that transmitted in the Latin which has 'aschis enim uter dicitur'. The sense 'wineskin'
was extended to 'belly, stomach', but, of course, the AN reading may simply have resulted
from a misreading, though it should be noted that S has 'asclites enim uter dicitur'. The Latin
has 'superflua . . . resolvuntur fumositatem [furiositatem, S] vel ventositatem que ex debilitate
virtutis expulsive non per totum corpus expelluntur, sed circa ventrem retinentur'. I have
emended AN accordingly. AN 'com en cire ou en paste' is an explanatory addition of a type
surprisingly rare in this translation.

143. pres de   les malades   lesi oigne   si si le

In the Latin the diet prescribed is 'calida et mediocriter humida' and (print only) 'levis et
digestibilis'. The wine is recommended 'non multum limphatum'. The form of oximel suggested for morning use follows the prescription of S, the print omitting the section 'de racines
de ache . . . u om doigne'. The 'soverain cure' is introduced in the Latin thus: 'Novi esse
summum remedium in hac causa, physica tamen est secreta', so it looks as if the phrase in AN
is incomplete. AN's 'mel lavé' is either a literal translation or a misunderstanding of the name

'mellilotum' ('melilot'). AN 'raiz de gramine' follows S 'radix graminis' where the print has 'radix gentiane'. AN '.iii. unces de esule' diverges from the Latin '.i. esule'. The reference to the abbot of Clairvaux runs 'Utantur sirupo meo quo curavi nepotem abbatis Clarevallensis'. AN's 'doiel' is apparently for 'stuel'. In the quotation from 'Hippocrates' the statement after 'desesperez .i. poi' is found in S, but not in the print.

144.   AN 'Et ce avient a la fie d'umor' follows S, but is not in the print. In AN, as in S, there is a *saut du même au même* (similium / similibus) where in the print the Latin 'dieta melancolica' continues after 'carnis caprina' 'caulis et similium, ex multo potu aque frigide, ex egritudine longa non bene discussa utpote quartana et ex similibus'. AN's 'a l'amer' for 'ad cistim fellis' seems to imply the omission of a noun. The print has 'Colera similiter adeo abundat quod non solum ad cistim fellis, sed etiam ad splenem per incontinentiam emittitur' (S, 'colericus humor quandoque adeo superhabundat quod non solum ad sistim fellis, sed etiam ad splenem fluit et transmutatur per incontinentiam').

145.   N reveals another *saut du même au même* involving 'croceo / -a': 'Si vero colera sit in causa, urina est colorata et crocea, ventris fluxus, totum corpus croceo colore affectum . . .'

146. humors   sol   meimement   mesist   percies   absence   diacerascos   ce-
rondo   et le   ydropisie   et plus

AN has corrupted the opening which runs 'splenis inflatio si sit ex melancolia et absque epatis calefactione'. I have emended accordingly. The passage beginning 'Et lor boivre soit actuelement chaudes . . .', which is garbled in the print, follows S: 'Potus actualiter calidus aut fervens aut calens vel saltem lapides extingantur in vino eorum. Ciphus eorum sit ligneus de tamarisco factus. Si fieri potest, dolium in quo vinum temperatur sit de eodem ligno'. The sentence beginning f. 81r runs in the Latin 'liquidioribus consumptis partibus remanentibus grossis et terrestribus, tumor in sclirosim incurabilem facile mutaretur'. In the receipt 'tailleures de vignes seches' has no correspondence in the Latin, which has 'ficus sicce, uve passe'. In AN 'vin et ewe' is used to render 'vinum limphetur', and 'pomes de terre' to translate 'malum terre' (Conopodium majus (Gouan) Loret or Cyclamen hederifolium Aiton). AN's 'diacostum, filoantropos et lor doigne l'en itel maniere de syrop' is not in the Latin and there are small divergences in the receipts, especially in the order of items. Where AN has 'poudre de ame[os]' the Latin print has 'pulvis dampneos' [S= utatur etiam hoc pulvere: ameos . . .]. In the Latin the 'ferrugo' ('limaille de fer') is to be ground 'in succo absinthii et aceto', the latter being omitted by AN. Where AN specifies that the resulting powder should be left to warm 'trestote une nuit' the Latin has 'per .viii. dies et noctes'. Where AN has 'lapis lazuli' the Latin has 'lapides lazuli et armeni'. In the case of swelling of the liver through wind AN adds 'diuretiques' which is not in the Latin and has 'En iver le seigne l'en de veine' where the Latin has simply 'in sero' and no reference to leeches. The end of this section diverges in the various versions. AN 'seons' may be the result of a misreading: the print is deficient with 'ultima cura est ut sepe apponantur'; S has 'ultima cura est si ignis apponatur'.

147.   In the causes of 'distemperantia renis' AN omits after 'ex multo coitu precedente' the explanatory phrase 'propter renum concussionem'.

148.   AN's 'ce semble contraire' comes from the Latin 'contrarium tamen videtur'.

149. plunc   meimement   d. dont

AN's 'la substance' renders Latin 'subiecta' [subiectum, S]: 'quia humiditas subiecta nimis debilitat'.

150. āguesce

151. c. si le cors   du

The print consistently has 'arili vena' for 'kilivena'. AN's 'Et si doit l'en destincter . . .' follows S 'Utrum habeat originem ab epate vel ab aliis predictis distinguendum est per signa'. AN's 'petit et troublees' reflects S 'paucus et turbulentus' where the print has 'purus et purulentus'.

152. commumes   anathasia   munnua   seuures

AN 'en tretotes les causes communes' reflects S, which has 'cais', an abbreviation which has evidently led to the incorrect resolution 'calidis' in the print.

153. limeuses   r. delez .iii. anguoises i ad de pisser   stranguriam

The dietary cause of stone includes, in the Latin, 'caulibus, lentibus', the latter omitted in AN. AN's 'semblance de substance' translates 'essentia' and 'l'action de la chalor' 'accessionem [actionem, S] naturalis caloris'. AN's 'dolor es reins et es illiers' renders 'dolor yliacus'.

154. gr. des reins et qui

AN's 'come une pois ou come une feve' renders 'in modum ciceris vel etiam fabe' and 'une forme longue autretele come .i. peu' 'oblonge forme [vel, S] in modum pilorum'. The reference to 'Hippocrates' appears in both the print and S as 'iuxta illud' followed by 'Quicumque nefretici sunt, si post .40. annos fuerint, non curantur'.

155. et doigne   et   et une char grosse   unente

AN's 'mercurialis, cretani marini, senationes' are in S but absent from the print. Similarly, 'sicum est calabrum' follows S 'ut est calabum vel silicum' but is missing in the print. Also absent from the print are 'liciotripon' ('licontripon', S) and 'et meimement as rois' (absent from S too). For 'solonc la doctrine de alexandrinis' the Latin has 'secundum doctrinam dumamidorum [dirmudiorum, S; 'after þe doctrin dmadimidiorum', ME] et Alexandri'. AN 'bevrage diuretique' translates 'apozimate diuretico'. After 'poudre de aloe' AN omits 'myrrha, salis' of the Latin which are subsequently referred to in the specification of quantities. 'Triblés noiz' is apparently a misreading of 'cimices . . . contrite'. AN 'a la forme de .i. vit' renders 'habente formam vitrei priapi' (S 'vel in alio vase vitreo oblongam formam habente ad modum priapi'). In the last sentence of this section the print has 'dolor yliacus' but omits 'et yliacam passionem' (found in S).

157. unente

158. et et

159. The print omits 'de replecion' (S, 'repletionis').

160. seiner seigner   m. a doner   cassialigine   aiides

In the Latin the instructions for bleeding include 'minutio de vena cephalica, epatica vel saphena' (S 'de vena epatica vel saphena').

161. –

162. b. a quire en vin et f. e.   utares   venufare   pusilium

For 'Galien' the print has '.H.', whilst S has 'Constantino'. AN omits one of the remedies in the Latin: 'Fiat etiam cataplasmata renibus et pudendis ex ruta vel cimino in vino cocto'. In the quotation concerning camphor the Latin has 'mares' for AN's 'utares'. AN's 'tant que ele soit gleuuse' translates 'quousque in mucillaginem convertatur'.

163. The Latin begins 'Aproximeron est partium genitalium inoperatio. Est autem passio quando coitus non potest perfici'.

164.   et . . . arest follows parfont

AN's 'sans nule grevance' reflects the 'gravedo nulla' of S where the print has 'cum gravedine'.
For 'home colerique' the Latin has 'juvene colerico'.

165.   cerices   strinctis   strinti   le semen s.   lesi   et et   et solement after reins

AN's 'le crupe et les costes' seems inexplicable except, perhaps, as a misreading of the Latin
'eruce cocte cum carnibus vel etiam crude et inter omnes herbas plus conferunt in hac causa'
which follows 'carnes arietis castrati'. AN's 'pannaisses' reflects the 'pastinace' of S where the
print has 'pistacee', and 'festucas' the reading 'festuce' where the print has 'fistici' [in S festuce
is corrected to fistici]. Some Latin is omitted by AN and there is some rearrangement of
material. AN's 'abhominable' reflects the 'abhominabile' of S where the print has 'insuave',
and 'extenuatif' apparently replaces 'diaforesim faciens'. There is an omission in AN where
the Latin reads 'Notandum quod .iii. [.iiii., S] scrupulos nucis indice vel stincorum transmari-
norum dati cum sirupo vel ovo sorbili multum conferunt. Cortex etiam nucis muscate [inte-
riorum indice nucis, S] multum valet. Stinci marini nihil vel parum valent'. A second
omission occurs where the Latin reads 'Soli etiam testiculi vulpini comesti vel cerebella
passerum libidinem excitant'. The remedy 'Funde l'en mugue . . . au fundement' is found in S
but is omitted in the print.

166.   At the end AN omits the Latin 'Nec in tussiendo dolor augmentatur et maior fit extensio. Hoc idem fit in ponderosis et per hoc discernitur inflatio a ruptura'.

167. –

168.   AN 'cinnamone' is a misreading of Latin 'cimino'.

169.   es membres

AN 'goutefestre et cancre' reflects the reading of S 'cancer vel fistula' where the print has
simply 'fistula'.

170.   porreture   mirte   ancera

The reference to Salernitan practices simply renders the equally laconic Latin 'sic consueverunt facere mulieres salernitane'. In the final remedy AN 'de mastic, de olibano' follows S and
is not found in the print.

171.   tresques   estoupent

AN's 'acostomeement en .i. tens establi' seems to combine the readings of S, 'tempore con-
sueto', and the print, 'tempore constituto'.

172.   il

Amongst the symptoms 'al chief' is an addition and 'au penil' is found in S but not in the
print. AN's 'une glette et une gleyre' renders Latin 'quedam mucillagines'.

173.   trauensi   enz follows par desouz   rouge   de calamento   beiues   m. de la fevre

AN's 'suppositoire' may be an error, for the Latin has 'stuellum' and AN itself later refers to '.i.
estuel autresi lonc come vostre doi', though the Latin continues 'vel pulvis predictorum trium
cum succo arthemisie pessarizetur [pulverizetur et pensarizatur, S]: solus etiam succus pessari-
zatus confert'. Later, AN 'benoite simple' appears to be a misreading of 'betonice, savine'. AN's
'.ii. jors ou trois' diverges from the Latin '.iiii. vel .v. diebus'. AN 'si avront plus grant vertu . . .
a nature' is inspired by the Latin 'Tunc enim citius suum consequunt effectum [suum officium,
S] medicine'. In the Latin the reference to Salerno is as follows: 'Item notandum quod ea que

valent ad menstrua provocanda educunt et secundinum [secundinam, S] et fetum mortuum et bufonem fratrem [m. et fratriculum, S] salernitanorum. Notandum etiam quod mulieres salernitane in principio conceptionis et maxime quando debet fetus vivificari predictum animal [fratriculum, S] nituntur occidere bibentes succum apii et pororum'.

174. –

175.   The Latin of the print reverses the order of 'fluxus ex humorum abundantia . . .' and 'ex eorum acumine'.

176.   arthanasiam   arthanasia   ewe ewe   a c. q.   quer   et lajoste   piz

In the treatment for 'fluxus . . . ex acumine humorum' the print ends with 'cum succo plantaginis', but this is in neither S nor AN. AN's 'oveskes la resolucion de .i. amatiste' clarifies the Latin 'cum lapide emathitis'. The receipt 'Ou les face l'en bouillir ovesques la poudre bistorte . . .' corresponds to the reading of S and is absent from the print. In the next receipt the print omits AN's 'aloigne', 'roses' and 'bistorte'. AN's 'la merde' is a reduplication of 'ordure' to render 'caca ferri' (S = 'scame ferri'). The expression 'merda ferri' is found in the Latin Dioscorides (6th C.), see for 'merde de fer' W. von Wartburg, *Französisches etymologisches Wörterbuch* 6, ii, 26a.

177.   chastees

For 'veilles femmes qui sei tienent chastees' the Latin has 'viduis et continentibus' and for 'venimeuse substance' 'venenosam habitudinem'.

178.   bores   et de

The Latin has 'nec in alio vita percipitur nisi in solo floculo lane naribus apposito vel ex ampulla vitrea [supra pectus posita, S] ut dicit .H. [.G., S]'. The passage 'Precipitation . . . jugement du malade' is not in S. The word 'jugement' has arisen from a misreading of 'indicio' as 'iudicio'.

179.   mirte

For 'la veine desouz la quivile du pié' the Latin has 'vena saphena'. The Latin has 'cum benedicta vel yeralogodion [vel cum, S] theodoricon eperiston [yperiton, S]'. AN's 'subfumigacions . . . de choses puantes' is the opposite of the Latin 'ex eisdem [= odorifera]' and one expects 'flairant', but it accords with S 'suffumigium fiat ex fetidis'.

180.   S has 'Tortuositas et curtitas virge satis solo usu [corr. visu] cognoscitur'.

181.   de de   les c.   dedesis

182.   mirre   rosorum   piperlelle   calamentum   calamento   meins

For the suppository made from mallow and violet the Latin specifies 'bulliantur in butyro'. There is an omission in AN where the Latin reads 'Post tertium diem purgationis ducatur ad balneum, secunda die fiat minutio de cephalica vena in tibiis [de vena saphena vel fiat scarifactio in tibiis, S]'. In the list of ingredients of the bath (the print has '.ix. diebus') AN's 'mauves . . . brance ursine' corresponds to S and is absent from the print. Similarly, in the next electuary 'galange, cardamom' are found in S but not the print and for 'bistorte' the latter has 'betonice'. AN's '.i. petite [suppositorie] faite de' reflects S's 'modicum suppositorium factum'. AN's 'noef jors' diverges from the Latin 'post .xx. diem'. The MS of AN has 'meins moistes' which illustrates a common misreading of 'nimis' as 'minus'.

183.   aromatique

184. sont bones et froides males   bones   males   tintillacions   et par le vonche

AN's 'par la chalor del leu' is a misreading of tbe Latin 'ex colore loci'. The Latin has 'fluxus per nucam et spatulas a patiente sentitur', so I have emended the AN MS reading from 'vonche' to 'nouche'!

185. cassialiginis   cassialiginis   et de   c'est asavoir du   manen   lees   des les
et enoigne   calamentum   saleo   ne len

The Latin begins with more specific references: 'de saphena . . . de cephalica'. AN omits a short receipt 'Sandali albi et rubei et rose pulverizata conficiantur cum aqua rosarum et aceto epithimetur'. AN's 'jus cassilaginis' reflects the reading of S and is absent from the print. In the second reference, where the AN scribe has written 'cassialiginis', the Latin has 'seminis cassilaginis'. In the Latin those suffering from choler are advised to abstain 'a forti vino', not AN's 'vin egre'. The reference to the Salernitan masters runs in the Latin: 'Pillule artetice comunes a magistro Ferrario et magistro Petricello [Petruncello, S] et magistro Plateario composite' (S = 'a me composite' reinforcing Platearius's authorship of the *Practica*). The receipt 'hermodactili . . . de semine feniculi' occurs in S but is missing from the print. Similarly, the section on 'les pilles Cophonis' is missing from the print, as is 'Et crespiex faites de orties et de ferrine si sont bones a doner'. In the 'poudre Petroncel' AN's '.iiii. drames' diverges from the Latin '.iiii. scrupulos'. AN's 'c'est asavoir du jus de la moine escorche' has evidently arisen from a misreading of abbreviations in the source e.g. 'succus summitatum ebuli in quantitate .i. [= unius] uncie cum uncia .i. et semis mediani corticis sambuci' where the numeral .i. has been misinterpreted as 'id est'. In the same receipt AN omits after 'boille l'en' 'bulliat] in pomo coloquintide et cum .ii. 3* hermodac- tilorum et cum pulvem masticis et seminis feniculi et aqua addita calida'. AN's 'merde [de] l'ors' misrenders 'fel ursinum'. The ointment said to be 'mult profitable' is in the Latin described as 'maxime anodinum' and the 'oile le roi Williame' appears in the print as simply 'oleum regium' [oleum regis Guillelmi, S]. AN's 'triangulus' survives from a variety of readings in the Latin MSS. S has 'Cauterie facte in fontibus conferunt. In scia triangu- lum zeuma [zema, Sl.420; scema, Sl.2454] fiat'. MS Sl.371 f.128v has 'In scia triangulum zeuma / .i. cauterium/'. MS Sl.3557 has 'Cauteria etiam facta in fontibus conferunt, in scia triangulum'.

186. The Latin begins 'Lepra est membrorum corruptio ex humoribus putrefactioni ha- bilibus effecta'. AN 'char de levre' is not found in S, which has 'ex lentibus', and the print has 'ex leonina [for leporina] carne'.

187. gorpiz

In the symptoms of 'lepra leonina' AN's 'si ont la voiz enroé' corresponds to the Latin 'cum vehementissima siccitate [acuitate, S]'.

188. diver   len   cest asavoir de n.   salive   colpresse

The scribe of AN wrote 'd'iver' but the Latin 'in initio veris' imposes the correction 'de ver'. For AN's 'a la mesure de .iii. doie' the Latin has 'mensura .iiii. digitorum'. AN 'ce qui est dedenz coloquintide' renders 'interiorum coloquintide' (gen. pl.). AN's 'cuillét encor les racines de rafle' seems to be an erroneous reading of 'squilla, cortex radicis raphani'. AN's 'et de coper les coillons, si sont plus contregardé de lepre' reflects the reading of S (missing from the print) 'per remotionem testiculorum multi preservantur'. Concerning 'antali' and 'dentali' S has 'qui sunt quidam lapides'. AN omits 'Similiter trita acacia cum aceto facta idem facit. Litargirum confectum cum oleo rosato et aceto illinitum idem operatur'. Before 'jarse l'en les sorciz' AN has omitted the indication 'Contra depilationem superciliorum'. In the receipt 'contra serpiginem et inpetiginem' the Latin print has 'gummi prunorum' where S has 'flos muri conficiatur cum salvia et inungatur' and then 'contra impetiginem: gummi prunorum in fortissimo aceto . . .', so the print telescopes two receipts.

189. The print omits reference to 'morphea nigra', whilst S has 'Est autem morphea nigra in qua cutis in nigrum colorem mutatur, et hec facilius curatur'.

190. For AN 'la flor de la meure' S has 'flos muri' which the print has corrupted to 'flos nitri'.

191. AN 'come la force de l'home est abaissié' is not found in the Latin which has 'unde unguium oppressio et superfluitatum incrementum fit'.

192. pilles   sil   narines

AN 'jus d'aloigne' is found in S but omitted from the print. AN has misread 'picl'e [= picule]' as 'pill'e [= pillule]' and 'membra' is a misreading of 'media' e.g. S [+ Sl. 2454] 'media libra picule' with *l* [= libra] misinterpreted as 'vel'.

193. –

194. et l.   com   que om que om   del la

In the receipt beginning 'confise om la poudre hermodactilorum . . .' the Latin print includes, at the beginning, 'capilli veneris' and S reads 'et licinium in ipsa confectione intinctum imponatur profundius quantum potest. Si autem ardor adest, superponatur vitellum ovi cum aqua rosacea'. There is an omission in AN where the Latin reads 'interius] ut tota carnositas cum arilis excludatur'. AN omits 'Aliud: ficus similiter coaptata in modum plagelle applicetur sic quod interior substancia ficus carni adhereat'. The section in AN from 'et face l'en une quiture' to the end is not in the Latin.

GLOSSARY

The glossary is intended to be as comprehensive as practicable but omits non-technical words which are familiar from modern French. Where possible the equivalents in the Latin source text are given in brackets at the end of each entry. Latin names incorporated in the text are normally given here in the nominative singular. It is sometimes difficult, especially in the case of first declension feminine nouns, to differentiate Latin and vernacular forms. Plant identifications conform to the nomenclature adopted in A.R. Clapham, T.G. Tutin & D.M. Moore, *Flora of the British Isles*, 3rd ed. (Cambridge, 1987). AN indicates a reference to the *Antidotarium Nicolai* in the edition and numbering of A.S. van der Berg, *Eene middelnederlandsche Vertaling van het Antidotarium Nicolai* (Leiden, 1917). I print in an appendix (see below pp. 316ff.) the relevant receipts with the exception of the compounds in *dia-*.

ABESS(I)ER v.a. and v.n. to lower (remittere, remitti, submittere)
ABHOMINABLE a. objectionable, disgusting (abhominabilis)
ABHOMINATION s. distaste, disgust, nausea (abhominacio)
ABIT s. manner, habit (habitudo)
ABROTANUM, ABROTONUM s. southernwood (Artemisia abrotanum L.)
ABSENTE s. wormwood (Artemisia absinthium L.)
ABSINTHIUM s. wormwood (Artemisia absinthium L.)
ACACIA s. gum from juice of green plums or sloes (Prunus spinosa L.)
ACCÉS s. bout, attack, onset (of illness) (accessio)
ACCESSION s. attack, onset, bout (of illness) (accessio)
AC(C)ETUM s. vinegar
ACCIDENT s.. symptom (sinthoma)
ACERBE a. bitter (acerbus)
ACETOUS, ACCETEUX a. sour, acid (acetosus, acidus)
ACHANCRER v.n. become cancerous, develop sores (cancerari)
ACHE s. smallage, wild celery (Apium graveolens L.) (apium)
ACOSTUMÉ, ACOUSTOMÉ p.p. accustomed, usual (consuetus)
ACOURIEZ p.p. afflicted
ACOUSTIMÉMENT, ACOSTOMEEMENT, ACOSTOMÉMENT adv. habitually
ACREU p.p. of ACREISTRE v.n. to increase (incrementum)
ACTION s. attack, onset (of illness) (accessio)
ACTUEL(E)MENT adv. (with effect) at the time, currently (actualiter)
ADÉS adv. all the time, continuously
ADIANTOS s. maidenhair-fern (Adiantum capillus-veneris L.) or black spleenwort (Asplenium
    adiantum-nigrum L.) or maidenhair spleenwort (Asplenium trichomanes L.)
ADIUTOIRE s. medical aid, cure, remedy (adiutorium)
ADONQUES adv. then, thereupon
ADRIANUM s. medicament associated with the emperor Hadrian AN2
ADUSTÉ p.p. burned (adustus)
ADUSTION s. heat, burning sensation; morbid process set off by excessive rise of temperature
    (adustio)
AFAITIER v.a. to arrange, prepare, fit (aptare, condere)
AFERMER v. refl. to harden, consolidate (consolidari) v.a. to make firm
AF(F)LICTION s. affliction, effects of an illness (afflictio)
AFFLIT ind. pr. 3 of AFFLIRE v.a. to afflict, assail (affligere)
AFFODILLUS s. ramsons (Allium ursinum L.) or sweet woodruff (Galium odoratum (L.) Scop.)
AFFORCER v. refl. to seek, strive (nitari, conari)
AFORCIÉ p.p. spiced, seasoned (conditus)
AGARICUS s. agaric, larch agaric (Polyporus officinalis L.)

AGARIQUE s. see AGARICUS
AGNEL s. lamb (agnellus)
AGNUS CASTUS s. chaste-tree (Vitex agnus-castus L.)
AGRAVATIVA a. gnawing (of pain), heavy ['fretyng'] (gravativus)
AGRIA PEGAZELONTIS s. type of jaundice
AGRIPPA s. 'unguentum Agrippa' AN132, allegedly used by Agrippa, King of the Jews
AGU a. acute, sharp; (of fever) having regular paroxysms, each proceeding through the stages of
   chill, fever and sweating
AGUESSE, ANGUISSE, AGUESCE s. sharpness, acuteness (acumen)
AGUILLE s. needle (acus)
AGUISIÉ p.p. sharpened, rendered more acute and pungent
AHERDRE v.n. and refl. to stick together S'AHERGENT ind. pr. 3 (coherent)
AIDABLE a. beneficial, favourable (habilis)
AIGRE, EGRE a. sour, bitter (acetosus)
AIL, AUX pl. s. garlic (Allium sativum L.)
AILLIÉ s. dish strongly flavoured with garlic (alleata)
AINZ, AINS adv. but, rather (antius)
AIRON s. any piquant herb (acrumen)
AISIL s. vinegar (acetum)
ALASCHER v.n. to lessen (remitti)
ALEGOUT ind. imp. 3 of ALEGIER v.a. to lighten, relieve (levigare)
ALEINE, ALAINE s. breath (anhelus)
ALEINER, ALENER v.n. to breathe (anhelare)
ALEMANDE s. almond LAIT / LET D'A. emollient solution of sweet almonds and water
ALESNE s. awl (subula)
ALIENATION s. delirium, delusions, wandering of the mind (alienatio)
ALIEVANCE s. alleviation, lightening, relief ['ly3tnesse'] (alleviatio)
ALIPTA s. ointment or salve, possibly associated with styrax (with para. 182 cf. Gilbertus Ang-
   licus, *Compendium medicine* [Lyons, 1510] f. 301v, col.2 [an electuary] 'storacis calamite alipte
   equali pondere'. The Latin print of the *Practica* has 'storacis calamite et alipte'). Cf. *Flos medici-*
   nae scholae salerni in Renzi, *Coll. Sal.* 1, p. 473 ll.846–9 and *ibid.* 5, p. 35 ll.1246–49
ALLEBOLUS s. see Notes para. 26
ALLISION s. violent movement (allisio)
ALLOPE s. wolf (alopes)
ALLOPICE s. alopecia, falling of hair (alopecia)
ALOE, ALOEN s. aloes (Aloe L. spp.) LIGNUM ALOES, LIGNI A., LIGNO A. XILIO A. (lig-
   naloes) aloe-wood (Aquilaria agallocha Roxb.) ALOE EPATIQUE a liver-coloured form of
   aloes, probably Socotrine aloes (aloe epaticus)
ALOINE, ALUIGNE, ALOIGNE s. wormwood (Artemisia absinthium L.)
ALTEA s. marshmallow (Althaea officinalis L.)
ALTERATION s. change of medicines ['chonchynge medicins'] (alteratio)
ALTERATIF a. alterative, productive of change ['chonchynge'] (alterativus)
ALUMINEUS a. BAIN A. aluminous bath (balnea aluminosa)
ALUN s. a variety of astringents esp. aluminium potassium sulphate
AMANDE s. almond (amigdalus)
AMATISTE s. haematite
AMBE(S)DOUS, AMBUEDOUS a. and pr. both
AMBRA s. amber, ambergris
AMEGRIR v.a. to make thin (attenuare, extenuare); v.n. (marcescere)
AMENDER v.a. and n. to improve; to recover, get better
AMENUSSE ind. pr. 3 of AMENUSER v.n. to diminish, lessen
AMEOS s. various umbelliferae incl. gout weed (Aegopodium podagraria L.) and bishopsweed
   (Ammi majus L.)
AMER s. gall
AMIDUM s. wheat starch
AMILUM s. fine flour, starch (amilum)
AMOISTER v.a. to moisten (humectare)
AMOL(L)IR v.a. to soften (mollescere)

AMONCELÉ p.p. condensed (conglobatus)

AMONT adv. up, above (superius)

AMORTEFIER v.a. to destroy, mortify (mortificationem inducere)

AMOVOIR v.a. to arouse (incitare)

AMPOILLE s. phial, small flask (ampulla)

AMPUILLEUS a. frothy (ampullosus)

ANA at the rate of, in an equal quantity

ANACORDORUM s. pl. anacard (Anacardium orientale L.) or marking nut (Semecarpus cassu-
vium Roxb.)

ANALENSIE, ANALENSIA s. analepsy, gastric epilepsy (analepsia)

ANALENTICI s. pl. patients suffering from analepsy

ANASARCA s. subcutaneous dropsy

ANATHIMASI s. anathymiasis, rising of vapours (fumositas stomachi superius ascendens)

ANE[LITUS] s. type of asthma (anhelitus)

ANGUILLE s. eel (anguilla)

ANGU(O)ISSE s. pain (angustia), difficulty (difficultas)

ANIS s. anise (Pimpinella anisum L.)

ANTALI s. (?) talc

ANTERA s. anther, stamens of the rose, confection of such

ANTICIPATION s. anticipation (anticipatio)

ANTIMONIUM s. stibnite, sulphide of antimony (antimonia)

ANTOFILUS s. cloves (Eugenia caryophyllata Thunb.)

APARANT pr. pt. standing out (of veins) (eminens)

APARCION s. opening (apertio)

APAREILLIÉ a. disposed (to) (dispositio)

APARISCANCE s. protruberance, prominence ['upbering'] (of veins) (eminentia)

APE (? error) s. smallage, wild celery (Apium graveolens L.) (apium)

APETIC(I)ER v.a. to diminish, reduce

APOCRASTICA s. pl. repellents, repercussives (apocrustica)

APOCRASTIQUE, APOCRASTICA a. repellent, repercusssive (apocrusticus)

APOCRUSTICA s. pl. repellents, repercussives (apocrustica)

APOPLEX(I)E, APOPLEXIO s. apoplexy

APOSICION s. placing next to (appositio)

APOSTOLICON s. 'ointment of the Apostles', cf. AN44 and see T. Hunt, *Popular Medicine in
Thirteenth-Century England* (Cambridge, 1990), pp. 268, 325f.

APOSTUME, APOSTE(I)ME, APOSTAINE, APOSTOME s. impostume, boil, ulcer (apostema)

APPARANCE s. prominence (eminentia)

APPAREILLIER v.a. to arrange, prepare, make ready APPARILLÉ p.p. (aptare, parare)

APPETIT(E s. appetite (desiderium) A. DE CHIEN bulimy, excessive appetite, 'canine hunger'
(appetitus caninus)

APPETITIF a. pertaining to, or provocative of, the appetite (appetitivus)

APPROXIMERON s. sexual impotence

APRE, ASPRE a. rough, harsh (asper)

APROTANUM s. southernwood (Artemisia abrotanum L.)

ARAIN, AREIN s. bronze, brass (eneum)

ARC DEL CELE s. rainbow (arcus celestis)

ARDOR s. burning sensation

ARDRE v.a. and n. to burn (ardere, exurere) ARS p.p.

AREST a. erect (of the penis)

ARGILLE s. clay (argilla)

ARISTOLOGIE s. birthwort, aristolochia (Aristolochia L. spp.) A. RAONDE, REONDE round-
rooted birthwort A. LONGE long-rooted birthwort

ARMONIAC, ARMONIACUM s. gum ammoniac (Dorema ammoniacum D. Don. and D. au-
cheri Boiss.); sal ammoniac (amoniacum)

AROMATIQUE a. aromatic

AROUSER, AROISER v.a. to water, splash with water (aspergo)

AROISE ind. pr. 3

ARRAGON, ARROGON s. 'unguentum Arragon' AN131

ARTER(I)E s. artery (arteria)
ARTERIOS a. composed of, rich in, veins (arteriosus)
ARTETICA s. gout causing inflammation of the joints; arthritis
ARTETICA PASSIO s. gout; arthritis
ARTETIQUE, ARTETHIQUE s. gout affecting the joints (artetica)
ARTIMESIE, ARTHEMESIE s. mugwort (Artemisia vulgaris L.)
ASA FETIDA, ASSA F., ASSE FETIDE s. var. umbelliferae esp. Ferula assa-foetida L. and the al-
    liaceous-smelling gum-resin produced therefrom
ASAVER adv. namely
ASBOLUS s. see Notes to para. 26
ASCARIDES s. pl. thread worms (ascarides)
ASCER, ACIER s. steel
ASCLITE(S s. ascites, abdominal dropsy (asclis enim uter dicitur)
ASELITIQUE a. afflicted with ascites ['askyte'] (aclites)
ASMA, ASME, ASMATE pl. ASMAUS s. asthma
ASNE s. ass
ASOIER v.n. to try, attempt (temptare)
ASPALTUM s. naturally occuring asphalt, bitumen (aspaltum)
ASPRESCE s. harshness (asperitas)
ASPRETÉ s. harshness (asperitas)
ASSAILLIR v.a. to attack, befall (affligere)
ASSAIR v.n. to try
ASSENS s. ascent (ascensus)
ASSERRA fut. 3 of ASSEER v.n. to settle
AS(S)IDUEL a. continual, persistent (assiduus)
ASSIGN(I)ER v.a. to indicate, specify, explain (assignare)
ATAPIR v.n. to hide (latitare)
ATEMPRÉMENT adv. moderately
ATEMPRER v.a. to temper (contemperare)
ATENIRIR v.a. to soften (attenuare)
ATENUATIF a. reducing ['slaking']
A(T)TENVIR v.a. to thin, extenuate, reduce (extenuare); v.n. to grow thin and weak
AT(T)(H)ANASIA s. tansy (Tanacetum vulgare L.); medicament AN4
ATRIBLEX s. orache (Atriplex L. spp.)
ATTRACTIF a. drawing, attractive
ATTRACTION s. attraction (attractio)
AUBUN D'UEF, AUBON s. egg white (albumen ovi)
AUCTOR s. author(ity)
AUMENTACION, AMENTACIUN s. increase (augmentatio)
AUNER v. refl. to gather, collect
AUREA s. an ointment A. ALEXANDRINI, AUREAM ALEXANDRINAM AN1
AURIPIMENT s. orpiment (arsenic trisulphide)
AUST s. autumn (autumnus)
AUSTER a. sour, bitter (austerus)
AUX s. pl. of AIL (q.v.); pron. = EUX
AVAL adv. EN A. downwards
AVOIÉ p.p. directed, propelled (transmissus)
BACCE LAURI see below
BAIES DE LAURIER / LORER s.pl. laurel berries (Laurus nobilis L.) (bacce lauri)
BAILER v.a. to present
BALAUSTIA, BALAUSTE s. pomegranate (Punica granatum L.)
BALSAMUM s. balsam, balm of Gilead (Commiphora opobalsamum (Kunth) Engler)
BARDANA s. burdock (Arctium lappa L.) or cleavers (Galium aparine L.)
BARDANE see BARDANA
BASILICON s. snake-root (Polygonum bistorta L.) or dragon arum (Dracunculus vulgaris Schott)
BASIN s. basin
BASME, BAUME s. balm (balsamum), balm of Gilead (Commiphora opobalsamum (Kunth) Eng-
    ler)

BASTON s. stick (baculus)
BASTONET s. small stick (baculus)
BAVER v.n. to dribble
BDELLIUM s. bdellium, pungent gum-resin (Commiphora roxburghii (Stocks) Engler)
BENOITE s. an electuary, 'confectio benedicta' AN9 (benedicta)
BERBERIS, BERBERI s. common barberry (Berberis vulgaris L.)
BERICLE DE MER s. shell of marine mollusc (Cochlea) (bellericus marinus)
BETÉ p.p. curdled, coagulated, condensed (conglobatus)
BISMAUVE s. marshmallow (Althaea officinalis L.)
BETHONICA s. betony (Stachys officinalis (L.) Trev.)
BETONIQUE see BETHONICA
BISE s. north-east wind (borea)
BISTORTA s. knotgrass (Polygonum aviculare L.), bistort (Polygonum bistorta L.)
BISTORTE see BISTORTA
BLANC(H)A s. medicament AN8
BLANCHE s. medicament AN8
BLEV a. livid (livens, lividus)
BLEUISS(E)URE s. bluish or livid colour (livor)
BOCEL, BOSCEL s. bottle, wineskin (uter)
BOCETE s. pustule, pimple; knob (tuber)
BOEL, BOUEL, BOIAU s. bowel, intestine (intestinum)
BOIAUS, BOWELS, BOUEUS s.pl. bowels, intestines (intestina) MENUS B. small intestine
    SOVERAINS B. upper intestine
BOJANT pres. p. bulging (eminens)
BOLUS s. fine earth (containing iron oxide) (bolus) BOLUS ARMENICUS bole armeniac, Armenian bole, copper ore combining the blue carbonate of copper (azurite) and the green carbonate (malachite)
BOLISME see BOLISMUS
BOLISMUS s. bulimy, excessive appetite
BOMBAX s. cotton
BORRAGE s. borage (Borago officinalis L.)
BORACHES, BOR(R)AGES s. pl. borage (Borago officinalis L.)
BOTER, BOUTER, BUTER v.a. to push, thrust (detrudere, expellere) BOTÉ (EN L'OIL) p.p. congealed, clotted (coagulatus)
BOUCHETE, BUSCHETE s. small stick, twig (subtile lignum)
BOURINCHES s. pl. borage (Borago officinalis L.) (boragines)
BOURSE s. purse (arca)
BOUT ind. pr. 3 of BOILLIR v.n. to boil
BRAN s. bran (cantabrum)
BRANC(H)A URSINA s. bear's breech (Acanthus mollis L.); possibly hogweed (Heracleum sphondylium L.)
BRANCHE D'ORSE, B. D'OURS s. bear's breech (Acanthus mollis L.)
BROCHE s. spike (stilus)
BRUSCER see BRUSCUS
BRUSCUS s. butcher's broom (Ruscus aculeatus L.) (bruscus)
BUBERON s. bubo (tuber)
BUC s. he-goat (hircus)
BURE s. butter (butirum)
BUSCHE s. stick
BUSCHETE s. twig (lignum)
CAELE s. whelp ['whelp that is sukkyng'] (catulus lactans)
CAELET s. see above
CALABRUM (VINUM) Calabrian wine
CALAMENTUM s. calamint (Calamintha Miller spp.)
CALEMEL s. reed, tube (calamus)
CAMOMILLE s. chamomile (Chamaemelum nobile (L.) All.)
CAMPHORA, CANPHORA s. camphor (Cinnamomum camphora (L.) Nees and Eberm.)
CAMPHORATÉ s. a camphoraceous plant such as Artemisia camphorata?

CANCERINA a. type of palsy
CANCRE s. tumour, cancer (cancer)
CANELE s. cinnamon (Cinnamomum zeylanicum Blume)
CANFORAM, CANPHORAM s. camphor
CANICULER a. JORS C. dog-days
CANTARIDIS s. pl. blister beetles (Cantharis vesicatoria)
CANTHABRUM s. bran (Triticum aestivum L.)
CAPEL s. cap, hat (pileus)
CAPIAU s. cap, hat (pileus)
CAPILLUS / CAPILLIS / CAPILLI VENERIS s. maidenhair fern (Adiantum capillus-veneris L.)
CAPPARIS s. honeysuckle (Lonicera caprifolium L. or periclymenum L.) or (see 146) caper (Capparis spinosa L.)
CARBONS s. pl. live coals (carbones, prunae ardentes)
CARDAMOME see CARDAMOMUM,
CARDAMOMUM, CARDAMONUM s. cardamom (Elettaria cardamomum (L.) Maton)
CARDON DE MER s. 'sea thistle' (? Eryngium maritimum L.) (tribulus marinus)
CAROIGNE s. fleshy protruberance (carunculus narium inviscatus)
CARPOBALSAMUM s. balsam fruit (Commiphora opobalsamum (Kunth) Engler)
CASSIAFISTRE, CASSIAFISTLE see CASSIAFISTULA
CASSIAFISTULA, CASSIAVISTULA s. a laxative pulp, purging cassia (Cassia fistula L.) (cassia fistula)
CASSIALIGNEA s. cassia (-bark) (Cinnamomum cassia (L.) Blume)
CASSILAGO s. henbane (Hyoscyamus niger L.)
CASTORIE, CASTOREE, CASTOIRE see CASTOREUM
CASTOREUM s. castoreum (secretion of the abdominal glands of the beaver)
CATARACTE s. cataract (cataracta)
CATARRE see CATARRUS
CATARRUS s. catarrh (catarrus)
CATARTICO IMPERIALI s. a cathartic, purgative medicament AN54
CATHALENSIE s. catalepsy (catalepsia)
CATHALENTICI s. pl. patients suffering from catalepsy
CATHIMIA AUREA s. ore containing gold, 'fex auri'
CAUDERE s. cooking-pot, cauldron (caldarium)
CAUKETROPPE s. (?) eryngo (Eryngium campestre L.) (yringi)
CAUNFRE s. camphor (camphor)
CAUSON s. burning fever (causon)
CAUSONIDE(S s. hectic fever resembling causon (causonides)
CAUTELE s. skill, care (cautela)
CAVÉ p.p. hollowed out, scooped out (cavatus)
CEINDRE v.a. to grip all the way round (cingere)
CELEBRER v.a. to perform, practise, engage in (celebrare)
CELLE s. cell (cellula)
CELSUS s. (?) common centaury (Centaurium erythraea Rafn) (celsus) or mulberry (Morus nigra L.)
CENDRIN a. ash-grey (cinericius)
CENTAUREA s. centaury (Centaurium erythraea Rafn)
CENTOIRE see CENTAUREA
CENTONICA s. sea wormwood (Artemisia maritima L.)
CENTRUM GALLI s. cockle or darnel (Agrostemma githago L., Lolium temulentum L.)
CEPHALICA s. cephalic vein (cephalica)
CERONEUM s. wax (-plaster)
CERRE s. chick-pea (cicer) (Cicer arietinum L.)
CERTEFIÉ p.p. assured, reliably informed
CERVEL(E s. brain (cerebellum)
CETERAC s. scale fern (Ceterach officinarum DC.)
CHAIER, CHAIR see CHAOIR
CHALINE s. heat (calor, caliditas)
CHALOR s. heat (calor, adustio)

CHAMBRE s. ALER A C. to go to stool, to evacuate the bowels (ire ad sellam, assellare)
CHANAZ s. pl. channels (canales)
CHANCRE s. crab (cancer)
CHAOIR v.n. to fall (cadere) CHEENT, CHIENT ind. pr. 6 CHIECE sbj. pr. 3 CHEU p.p.
CHAPITRE, CAPITRE s. chapter (capitulum)
CHAR s. flesh C. DE BUEF   C. DE CHIEVRE
CHAR DE MER s. salty efflorescence on water plants (caro marinus)
CHARGER v.a. to burden (onerare)
CHASTAIGNE s. chestnut (castanea)
CHASTEE s. chastity
CHASTRI(S) s. wether (aries castratus)
CHAUZ, CAUZ s. lime C. VIVE quicklime
CHIER v.a. to excrete (egerere, assellare)
CH(I)ERE s. face (facies)
CHIEVRE s. goat (capra)
CHOLET s. cabbage (Brassica oleracea L.) (caulis)
CHOU s. cabbage (caulis) C. CAMPESTRE wild cabbage (Brassica oleracea L.)
CIC[ER] (RUGE s. chickpea (cicer rubeum)
CICLAMINE s. earthnut (Conopodium majus (Gouan) Loret) or sowbread (Cyclamen hederifo-
    lium Aiton)
CILLERON s. eyelid (cilium)
CIMINUM s. cumin (Cuminum cyminum L.)
CINAMONIE, CINAMOME, CINAMONE, CINNAMONII, CINNAMOMI, CINNAMOME
    s. cinnamon (Cinnamomum zeylanicum Blume)
CIPRÉS s. cypress (cipressus)
CIRE s. wax (cera)
CIROINE s. wax (ceroneum)
CISTIS FELLIS s. gall-bladder
CITONIUS s. quince (Cydonia oblonga Miller)
CITRI s. lemon or orange
CITRIN a. yellow (of urines also indicates a variety of reddish colours) (citrinus) ESTRE C. (citri-
    nescere)
CITROL s. see CITRULUS
CITRUELE, CITREL s. see CITRULUS
CITRULUS s. water melon (Citrullus lanatus (Thunb.) Matsum and Nakai) and also conf. with
    white-flowered gourd (Lagenaria siceraria (Mol.) Standley)
CLISTERE, ESCLISTERE, ECLISTEIRE s. clyster, enema (clistera)
CLORE v.a. to close
COARTATIF a. binding, constricting ['byndyng'] (constringens, coartans)
COC s. cock (gallus)
COCORDE s. gourd (cucurbita)
COILLI, CUILLI p.p. of COILLIR v.a. to amass, gather, collect (colligere)
COILL(I)ON s. testicle (testiculus) COILLIONS DE LA MATRIZ ovary (testiculi matricis)
COILON s. colon
COIN, COING s. quince (Cydonia oblonga Miller) (coctanum)
COINTEMENT adv. skilfully, carefully (caute)
COLAGOGUE s. cholagogue (for drawing off bile) (colagogus)
COLATURE s. strained, sieved matter, filtrate (colatura)
COLE s. choler, bile
COLER v.a. to strain, sieve (colare)
CO(U)LER v.n. to flow (distillare)
COLERIQUE, COLLERIQUE a. made up of choler, afflicted with an excess of choler
COLEURE s. sieved, strained material (colatura)
COLICA PASSIO s. colic, various disorders of lower abdomen
COLLERE s. colour
COLLIGANCE s. connexion (coligantia)
COLLIRE s. eye salve (collirium)
COLON, COILON s. colon

COLON s. dove (columba)

COLOFONIA, COLOFONIE, COLOPHONIA s. colophony, Greek pitch (colofonia)

COLOQUINTIDA, COLOQUINTIDE, POMME DE C. colocynth (Citrullus colocynthis Schrader)

COLORER v.n. to become coloured (colorari)

COLRE, COLERE s. choler, bile (colera) C. ERUGINEUSE (c. eruginosa) bile tinged with verdi-gris C. INNATURALE pathological bile C. NATURALE C. CITRINE yellow bile C. PRASSINE (c. prassina) green bile C. VITELLINE bile the colour of egg yolk (deep yellow tinged with red)

COME conj. when

COMIN s. cumin (Cuminum cyminum L.)

COMOCION s. disturbance (commotio)

COMOINCEMENT s. beginning

COM(M)OVENT ind. pr. 6 of COMMOVEIR v.a. to arouse (incitare, excitare)

COM(M)UNEMENT adv. commonly, ordinarily (communiter)

COMPACT a. compacted (compactus)

COMPISSER v. refl. to urinate (urinam involuntarie emittere)

COMPLEXION s. complexion (complexio)

COMPOST a. compound (of medicament, and of 'double' tertian fever) (compositus)

COMPRENT ind. pr. 3 of COMPREENDRE v.a. to compress, press down on (conprimere)

COMPRESSE s. A COMPRESSE tightly

COMPRESSION s. compression ['stupping'] (constipatio); pressure (compressio)

CON s. vulva

CONCAVITÉ s. cavity (concavitas)

CONCHE s. shell of mollusc (conca)

CONDIT a. of mirabolans, like aforcié (q.v.) ['boylid'] (conditus)

CONDUIS, CONDUIT p.p. candied (165 'gingembre conduit') (conditus)

CONDUIT s. channel, passage (meatus, fistula)

CONFECTION s. medical preparation, compound

CONFERMER v.a. to harden, to consolidate, establish (consolidare)

CONFERMÉ p.p. hardened

CONFIRE v.a. to make, prepare, concoct CONFISE, CONFICE sbj. pr. 3 CONFIT, CONFIS, CONFIZ p.p.

CONFORTER v.a. to aid, be good for

CONFORTATIF a. soothing (confortativus)

CONFRICATION s. rubbing together (confricatio)

CONJUINDRE v.n. to unite

CONPASSION, COMPASSION s. sympathetic action (conpassio)

CONQUILLI(É p.p. of CONQUILLIR v.a. to gather together (colligere)

CONSOLIDATIF a. healing (consolidativus)

CONSOMPTIF, CONSUMPTIF a. 'consumptive', wasting ['wastyng'] (consumens, consump-tivus)

CONSTRICTIF a. constringent ['constrictive or stupping'] (constringens, coartans)

CONSTRICTION s. constriction (constrictio)

CONSUMPCION s. consumption (consumptio)

CONSUMPTATIF a. 'consumptive', wasting (consumens)

CONTENTIF a. retentive (contentivus, retentivus)

CONTRARIEUX a. contrary, adverse (contrarius)

CONTREGARDER v.a. to prevent, guard against, protect (preservare)

CONTREMONT adv. upward (superius)

CONTREVAL adv. downward (inferius)

CONVERSE s. converse (contrarium)

COR(NE DE CERF s. stag's horn C. DE CHIEVRE goat's horn

CORBEL s. crow

CORE, COUR(R)E v.n. to run, flow CORGE sbj. pr. 3 (have recourse to)

CORIANDRE s. coriander (Coriandrum sativum L.)

CORNER v.n. to buzz (of ears) (tinnitus) CORNANT pr. pt.

COROCER v.n. to be irritated

COROSIF, COROUSIF a. corrosive, consuming flesh (corrosivus)

COROSION s. corrosion ['fretyng'] (corrosio)

CORRIGIOLE s. bindweed ['wodbynde'] (Convolvulus arvensis L.)

CORRUMPU p.p. decaying, rotten, putrid, tainted (putridus, corruptus, infectus)

CORRUPTION s. taintedness (corruptio), infection (infectio)

CORS, COURS s. flow (discursus)

CORSELE s. little body, particle (corpusculus)

CORTEX MANDRAGORE s. rind of mandrake (Mandragora officinarum L.)

CORTEX SORBI s. skin of sorb-apple

CORUBRUM s. an aromatic gum-resin, a kind of incense (cozimbrum / cozumbrum)

COSTE s. side, rib (ypocundrium, costa, lacertus)

COSTUS s. costmary (Chrysanthemum balsamita (L.) Baillon)

COSTUMER a. accustomed (consuetus)

COTELE s. membrane of the eye (tunica) C. CONJUNCTIVE 42 (tunica conjunctiva) conjunctive membrane C. CORNINE (tunica cornea) cornea C. UVEINE (uvea tunica) choroid coat
/ membrane

COTIDIAN(E a. and s. quotidian (fever), characterized by daily paroxysms

COTILIDONUM s. pl. cotyledon, part of uterine membrane (cotilidonum)

COTON, COTOUN s. cotton

COUCHER v.a. to place, lay, put to bed v.refl. to go to bed

COUDE s. cubit (cubitus)

COUE s. tail (cauda)

COUFLE s. kite

COUSTEMÉ p.p. accustomed

COUSTOMER a. accustomed

COVENABLE a. appropriate (conveniens, competens)

CRACHER v.n. to spit (sputare, excreare, expuere)

CRAPOUT s. toad, foetus? (bufo)

CRAS a. fat, greasy (unctuosus, pinguis)

CREISSON s. cress

CRESAUNT s. crescent (luna novella)

CRESPEL (pl. CRESPIEZ, CRESPEUX) s. pancake (crispella)

CRESSE, GRESE s. fat, grease (pinguedo, unctuositas)

CRETA SARRACINOISE s. a type of clayey earth, (?) Lemnian earth

CRETANI MARINI s. sea holly (Eryngium maritimum L.) or rock samphire (Crithmum maritimum L.)

CRETIQUE, CRETTIQUE a. critical (creticus) JOR C. astrologically significant day of symptom's first appearance

CREVER v.a. to break open, burst (rumpere, crebare)

CRIENT ind. pr. 3 of CRIENDRE v.n. to fear

CROC s. hook

CROES a. hollow (concavus)

CROIE s. chalk, gypsum, marl (calx, creta)) CROYE SARAZINOISE 'creta sarracenica'

CROISSENT ind. pr. 6 of CROISSIR v.a. to grind, gnash (of teeth) and also of CROISTRE v.a.
to increase

CROISTRE v.n. to have sexual intercourse with C. ATEMPRÉMENT ['resonable swyning']
(moderatus coitus) CROIST ind. pr. 3

CROS s. hollow, cavity (concavitas)

CRU a. raw, uncooked (crudus)

CRUCE s. hollow (of liver) (sima)

CRUPE s. hindquarters

CUCUMBRE, COCCUMBRE, CONCUMBRE see CUCUMER

CUCUMER s. cucumber (Cucumis sativus L.); C. AGRESTE squirting cucumber (Ecballium
elaterium A.Richard)

CUCURBITA, CONCURBITE, CUCURBITO s. var. cucurbitaceae incl. Bryonia cretica L.
subsp. dioica (Jacq.) Tutin, Cucumis sativus L., Citrullus colocynthis (L.) Kuntze, Lagenaria
siceraria (Mol.) Standl, Lagenaria vulgaris Ser.

CUCURBITINUS s. type of short, broad worm

CUISSIN s. cushion
CUNUTIR v.a. to recognize
CURATION s. healing treatment (curatio)
CURE s. cure, remedy (cura)
CURE v.n. to flow
CUSCUTA s. dodder (Cuscuta epithymum (L.) L. etc)
CUSCUTE s. see CUSCUTA
CUVE s. basin, vat ['cophyn'] (cuva, cophinus)
CYRAGRE s. gout in *the* joints of the hand (ciragra)
CYRU(R)GIE s. surgery (chirurgia)
CYRURGIEN s. surgeon
DATHE s. date (Phoenix dactylifera L.)
DEBATRE v. refl. SE D. CONTRE to act against (repugnans)
DECEU p.p. deceived, mistaken
DECLINER v.n. to incline (declinare)
DECOCTION, DECOCTIONIS s. decoction, liquid (decoctio)
DECOLORATION s. discolouration (by darkening or diminution of colour) (discoloratio)
DECORSE s. flow (decursus)
DEFAUCTE s. lack, deficiency, diminishing (defectus, debilitas)
DEFAUT ind. pr. 3 of DEFAILLIR v.n to be lacking
DEFAUTE s. lack, deficiency, diminishing (defectus, deficientia, debilitas)
DEFENDRE v.a. to forbid
DEFIRE v.a. to dissolve, digest (digere) DEFISONS ind. pr. 4 DEFIT, DESFIT p.p.
DEGASTER v.a. to consume, disperse (consumere); to waste
DEGOTER v.a. and v.n. to drip
DEJOSTE prep. beside
DELECTACION s. pleasure (delectatio)
DELIÉ a. fine, delicate (delicatus)
DELIT s. pleasure (delectatio)
DELITABLE a. delectable (delectabilis)
DELITER v. refl. to take pleasure in (gaudere)
DEMENTERS QUE conj. loc. while (dum)
DEMOSTRER v.a. to reveal, show, demonstrate
DENER s. penny
DENTALI s. a type of stone
DEPARTIR v.n. to separate v. refl. to differ from (diferre)
DEPECER, v.a. to shatter, fracture DEPESCHIÉ p.p.
DERAIN, DEEREIN a. posterior (posterior)
DERECHIEF adv. again, a second time (iterum)
DERTRE s. tetter
DESCOLORÉ p.p. discoloured (darkened or else deprived of colour [parum coloratus])
DESCREISSANT s. waning
DESCUNSEILÉ p.p. abandoned
DESICCATIF a. desiccative, promoting a drying effect (desiccans, desiccativus)
DESMESURABLE a. excessive (immoderatus)
DESMESURÉ a. immoderate (immoderatus)
DESNATUREL a. unnatural (innaturalis)
DESRONT ind. pr. 3 of DESROMPRE v.a. to burst open (abrumpere)
DESSOILL(I)E sbj. pr. 3 of DISSOLDRE v.a. to dissolve (resolvere)
DESSOLLUTIF, DISSOLUTIF a. solvent, promoting dissolution or dissipation of a condition
    (dissolutivus)
DESSOUDRE v.a. to dissolve (dissolvere) DESSOUT ind. pr. 3 DESOUDROIT cond. 3 DES-
    SOUS, DESSOUDES p.p.
DESTEMPRANCE s. imbalance or disturbance of humours or qualities; the resulting morbid con-
    dition; excess; mixing (distemperantia)
DESTEMPRER v.a. to disturb; to mix DESTEMPRÉ p.p. disordered, unhealthy (distemperare)
DESTENDRE v.a. to distend
DESTOPER v.a. to unblock

DESTORNER v.n. to be diverted, eased (palliari)
DESTRESSE s. constriction, tightness (angustia)
DESYUEL, DESIUEL, DESUWEL pl. DESYUEES a. uneven (inequalis)
DETENIR v.a. to withhold
DETERMINEMENT s. determining sign D. CRETIQUE (determinatio) critical (astrologically
    significant) determining sign
DETRERS, DETRIE(F)S a. and adv. rear, behind
DETTOR s. debtor (debitor)
DEUT ind. pr. 3 of DOLEIR v.n. to ache, hurt, to be painful
DEVEER v.a. to prevent, hinder (denego)
DEVEREIE s. madness, delirium (furor)
DEVISE s. PAR DEVISES adv. distinctly, definitely (distincte)
DEVISER v.a. to distinguish
DIABETHE(S s. diabetes
DIABROSIM, DYABROSIM s. sweating through corrosion of the veins
DIACALAMENTUM s. medicament prepared with calamint AN29
DIACAPPARIS s. medicament prepared with capers
DIACASTOREUM, DIACASTOREA s. medicament prepared with beaver glands AN25
DIACENÉ, DYASCENÉ s. medicament prepared with senna (diasene) AN33
DIACERASEOS s. medicament prepared with cherries
DIACIMINUM (ALEXANDRINUM s. medicament prepared with cumin AN24
DIACODION s. medicament prepared with poppies AN31
DIACOSTUM s. medicament prepared with costmary AN26
DIAFORETIC a. diaphoretic, sudorific ['dissolvyng'] (diaforeticus)
DIAFRAGMA, DIAFRAGMATE s. diaphragm
DIALTE(I)A s. medicament prepared with marshmallow (dialtea) AN133
DIAMARGARITON s. medicament prepared with powdered pearls AN14
DIAMNE s. (complaint causing) involuntary urination (diampnes)
DIAMORON s. medicament prepared with mulberries AN16
DIANTOS s. medicament prepared with rosemary AN15
DIAOLIBANUM s. medicament prepared with frankincense AN21
DIAPENIDION, DYAPENIDION s. medicament prepared with barley-sugar AN23
DIAQUILON s. medicament prepared with litharge, oil and vegetable juices
DIAR(R)ODON s. medicament prepared with roses AN22
DIARRIA, DIARRÉ s. diarrhoea
DIASATURION s. medicament prepared with orchids
DIATRION PIPEREON s. medicament prepared with three types of pepper
DIAUTÉ s. dialtea, preparation of marshmallow (dialtea) AN133
DIETE s. diet, regimen
DIETER v.a. to put on a diet, treat with special diet
DIGESTIF a. digestive (digestivus)
DILIGENCE s. care, diligence
DIMINUCION s. diminution, reduction (diminutio)
DIPTANI s. dittany (Origanum dictamnus L. or Dictamnus albus L.)
DIPTANDRE s. as above (diptami)
DISCRETION s. disparity (discretio); discreteness
DISMA s. respiratory complaint, dyspnoea
DISPOSICION s. tendency (habitudo)
DISSINTE(I)RE, DISSINTERIE s. dysentery; (having origins in the liver) D. EPATIQUE /
    EPATICA DISSINTERIA
DISSINTERICORUM s. pl. patients suffering from dysentery
DISSINTERIQUE s. patient suffering from dysentery
DISSOLLUCION s. dissolution
DISSOLUTIF a. solvent, having property of dissolving or dissipating a condition (dissolutivus,
    dissolvens)
DISSURIA s. urinary complaint characterised by pain or difficulty in urinating; dysury
DISTENTIF a. spreading, extensive (of pain) (distensivus)
DISTINCTER, DESTINCTER v.a. to distinguish, differentiate

DIURETIQUE a. diuretic (diureticus)
DIVERSER v.a. to vary
DIVISER v.a. to distinguish (distinguere)
DIVISIF a.? solvent OXIMEL D. (oximel divisivum) Cf. 'oximel divisivum et dissolutivum' in
    'Compendium magistri Salerni' in Renzi, *Coll. Sal.* 3, p. 57.
DO(I)(G)NE sbj. pr. 3 of DONER v.a. to give
DOI(E, DOIT s. finger, finger's length (digitus) MEINE D. middle finger PETIT D. little finger
DOIEL s. tent (stuellum)
DOLIR v.n. to ache, be sore
DRAGAGANT, DRAGAGANTUM s. gum tragacanth (Astragulus gummifer Labill.)
DRAME s. dram, drachm (weight) (dragma)
DRAP s. cloth D. LINGE linen cloth
DRAPALET, DRAPELET s. cloth
DRECIER v.a. to raise, hold up
DREIT, A adv. truly (recte)
DUREMENT GRANT copiously
DYAIRIS s. medicament prepared with iris AN28
DYACITONITON s. medicament prepared with quince AN34
DYAPRASSIUM s. medicament prepared with white horehound (Marrubium vulgare L.) AN20
DYASATURION s. medicament prepared with orchids AN18
DYATRION PIPEREON s. medicament prepared with three types of pepper
EBLE s. danewort, dwarf elder (Sambucus ebulus L.)
EBULLICION s. turbulence, seething, fermentation-like change due to excessive heat (ebullitio)
EDUCTION s. drawing out (eductio)
EE s. bee (apis)
EFFICACE s. virtue, effectiveness
EFFODILLUS s. ramsons (Allium ursinum L.)
EGESTION s. excretion (egestio, secessum)
EGRE a. sour (acidus)
EISLE s. preparation of spurge (Euphorbia L. ssp.) (esul(e)ata)
ELECTUA(I)RE, ELECTUARIE s. electuary (electuarium)
ELECTUARIUM DUCIS s. electuary AN40
ELEFANCIE s. type of leprosy (elefancia)
EL(L)EBORE see ELLEBORUS
EL(L)EBORUS s. hellebore E. BLANC white hellebore (Veratrum album L.) ELIBORI NIGRI
    black hellebore (Helleborus niger L.)
EMAGOGUM s. haemagogue
EMATISTE(S s. haematite, native iron oxide
EMFLAMBER v.a. to inflame (inflammare)
EMFLÉ p.p. swollen (subtumidus)
EMFLEURE s. swelling (tumor)
EMINENCIA OCULORUM s. bulging, protruding eyes
EMISSION s. emission
EMITRICE, EMITRITE s. hemi-tercian fever LA MENOR E. (emitriteus minor) LA MOIANE /
    MOIENE E. (emitriteus medius) LA GREIGNOR E.
EMOPTICI s. pl. patients suffering from haemoptysis
EMOPTOICA PASSIONE s. haemoptysis, spitting of blood
EMOROIDES, E(S)MEROIDES s. pl. haemorrhoids; the five haemorrhoidal veins (emorroida)
EMPICUS s. patient suffering from empyema
EMPIMA s. empyema, collection of pus resulting from pleurisy
EMPIQUE a. and n. (patient) suffering from empyema
EMPLASTRE s. plaster (emplastrum, sinapisma, epithimetum, cataplasma)
EMPLIR v.a. to fill
ENCATIME s. hip bath (encathisma)
ENCENS s. incense
ENCISER s. to cut (incidere)
ENDEMENTERS QUE conj. loc. while
ENDORMI a. numb (stupor membrorum)

ENDURCIR v.a. to harden (compactiorem reddere)
ENFANTIL s. afflicting children (puerilis)
ENFLER v.a. and n. to swell
ENFORMER v.a. to make, form (formare, informare)
ENFROTER v.a. to rub
ENFREINDRE v.a. to break, violate, infringe
ENGIN, ENGING s. skill, contriving, artifice (artificium)
ENGITOM ind. pr. 5 of ENGETER v.a. to throw away
ENGLUÉ p.p. stuck (inviscatus)
ENMEMBRER v. refl. to recall
ENONCTION, ENONGTION s. application of ointment (inunctio)
ENPECE ind. pr. 3-of ENPECER v.a. to hinder, impede ENPESCÉ p.p.
ENPE(S)CEMENT s. hindrance, impediment (impedimentum)
ENPESSISSANT pr. pt. of ENPESSIR v.a. to thicken, inspissate (conspissans)
ENROÉ a. hoarse (raucus)
ENROÜRE s. hoarseness (raucedo)
ENSEMENT adv. likewise, similarly (similiter)
ENSEUREMENT adv. with confidence
ENSEVELIR v.a. to bury
ENSINT adv. thus
ENTAMÉ p.p. broken, damaged (of skin)
ENTENSE a. intense (intensivus, intensus)
ENTENTIVEMENT adv. diligently, assiduously (studiose)
ENTRAVERS adv. crosswise (ex transverso)
ENTRECEPTION s. interception (= stopping flow of a bodily fluid) ['undirfonging'] (interceptio)
ENTRECLOS p.p. enclosed, trapped (interclusus)
ENTRELA(I)SS(I)ER v.n. to remit, to cease temporarily (interpolare) ENTRELAIST ind. pr. 3
    ENTRELASSIÉ p.p. interrupted
ENTREPOLAT(É, ENTREPOLLAT a. intermittent (interpolatus) JORZ ENTREPOLATÉS non-
    consecutive days
ENTREPOSICION s. in-between position causing interference (interpositio)
ENVERS a. facing upwards, supine (supinus)
ENVERSER v.a. to invert (inversare)
ENVO(I)ER v.a. to send, transport
ENVOLUPER v.a. to wrap (involvere)
ENZ, ENS adv. inside, therein (intus)
EPATICA s.? liverwort (Anenome hepatica L. or Marchantia polymorpha L.)
EPILENC(I)E, EPILENSIE s. epilepsy (epilencia)
EPILENTICI s. pl. patients suffering from epilencia
EPILENTIQUE a. epileptic
EPITHIME, EPIT(H)EME see EPITHIMUM
EPITHIMUM s. common dodder (Cuscuta epithymum (L.) L.) (epithimum)
EPITHIME, EPITHEME, pl. EPITHIMITES s. epithem, moist poultice (epithimata)
EPURER v.a. to cleanse, purify (depurare)
ERRAGÉ p.p. mad, rabid (rabidus)
ERRATIQUE a. FIEVRE E. fever of no fixed pattern, irregular and intermittent
ERROR s. distress ['ake']
ERUCA s. garden rocket (Eruca sativa Miller) or skirret (Sium L. spp.)
ERUCTATION, ERUCTUACION s. belching, retching, vomiting ['bolkyng', 'rospyng'] (eructua-
    tio)
ERUGINEUS a. rust-coloured, tinged with verdigris
ES USTUM s. burnt brass, calcined copper, the crocus of copper
ESCAMONEE s. preparation of scammony (Convulvulus scammonia L.) (scamoneata)
ESCARDEUX, ESCHARDOUS a. scaly (scamosus)
ESCARDÉ p.p. scaly, spiny (aspratilis)
ESCARIOLE s. prickly lettuce (Lactuca serriola L.)
ESCHAUFER v.a. to heat v.n. to heat up, become hot (calefacere)
ESCHAVENT ind. pr. 6 of ESCHAUFER

ESCHAUFEMENT s. inflammation (calefactio)
ESCHEKS s. pl. chess (aleas)
ESCLARCIERA fut. 3 of ESCLARCIR v.a. to sharpen (vision)
ESCLISTERE s. see CLISTERE
ESCLITE s. type of dropsy
ESCOLORGIER v.n. to slide, slip
ESCOLORJANT, ESCULURGAUNT a. slippery, slimy ['sleder', 'sledery'] (lubricans)
ESCORCE, ESCORCHE, ESCORSE s. bark, rind MOIENE E. inner bark (cortex mediana)
ESCORCENT ind. pr. 6 of ESCORC(H)ER v.a. to scald, excoriate, scrape (excoriare)
ESCRUPLE s. scruple (measure) (scrupulus)
ESCUELLE s. bowl (lagena), dish (scutella)
ESCUMER v.n. to foam, froth (spumare); v.a. to skim
ESLAISIER v.a. to broaden (dilatare)
ESLOIGNIER v.a. to lengthen (prolongare)
ESMOLI p.p. of ESMOLIR v.a. to soften
ESPAUMEUS a. convulsive ['crampisch'] (spasmosus)
ESPECE s. spice (species)
ESPECIAL a. specific, special, particular (specialis)
ESPERIMENT, EXPERIMENT s. experiment, proof, test
ESPERME s. sperm (sperma)
ESPESSETÉ s. density, viscosity
ESPESSIR, v.a. and n. to thicken (inspissare) ESSPESSISSANT pr. pt.
ESPIC s. ? celtic spikenard (Valeriana celtica L.) or broom (Ulex europaeus L.) or eryngo (Eryngium campestre L.) (spica)
ESPINEUS a. thorny, prickly (spinosus)
ESPIRIT, ESPERIT s. spirit, humour E. DE VIE s. vital spirit, fluid believed to be source of movement and sensation ['lifly spiritis'] (spiritus vitalis) cf. the spiritus naturalis, vitalis and animalis of Antiquity
ESPIRITEL, ESPERITEL a. respiratory; pertaining to bodily fluids esp. the vital spirit (spiritualis)
ESPLEN(E s. spleen (splen)
ESPLENETIQUE s. patient suffering from disorder of the spleen
ESPOIS a. thick, turgid, viscous (spissus)
ESPOISCE s. density, viscosity (spissitudo, inspissatio)
ESPOISSECE s. density, viscosity (spissitudo, inspissatio)
ESPOISSETÉ s. density, viscosity (spissitudo, inspissatio)
ESPOISSIR v.a. to thicken, inspissate (condensare)
ESPONGE s. sponge (spongia) E. MARINE sea sponge (spongia marina)
ESPONLE s. spondil (spondile)
ESPONTABLE a. terrifying (terribile)
ESPORGIER v.a. see ESPURGER
ESPROVE s. test, experiment, proof
ESPROVÉ p.p. tried and tested (probatus)
ESPUME s. froth (spuma)
ESPUMEUZ, ESPUMOUS a. frothy (spumosus)
ESPURGACION s. purging (purgatio)
ESPURGEMENT s. purging (purgatio)
ESPURGER v.a. to purge (purgare)
ESROÉ a. hoarse (raucus)
ESROÜRE s. hoarseness (raucedo)
ESSUER v.a. to wipe dry (extergere)
EST ind. pr. 3 of EISSIR v.n. to issue, come out
ESTANCHER v.a. to stanch (blood), assuage (thirst) (cohibere, constringere, mitigare)
ESTE(I)NDRE v.n. to stifle, suffocate (suffocari)
ESTEINT p.p. extinguished, quenched (extinctus)
ESTENGNENT ind. pr. 6 of ESTEINDRE v.n. to suffocate, stifle
ESTERNUER, EXSTERNUER v.n. to sneeze (sternutare)
ESTOPER, ESTOUPER, ESTUPER v.a. to block, stop up (opilare, obturo)
ESTOUPE s. (fibres of) tow (stupa)

ESTRAINDRE see ESTREINDRE
ESTRE prep. besides, in addition to
ESTREIGNAUNT a. gripping, constricting (coartans)
ESTREINDRE v.a. to grind, gnash (of teeth) (dentium constrictio); to grip (constringere); to constrict (flow) ESTREIGNE sbj. pr. 3
ESTRESCEZ p.p. narrowed, constricted (coartare)
ESTRUMENT s. instrument (instrumentum)
ESTUDE s. thought, meditation (studium)
ESTUEL s. tent (stuellum, licinium)
ESTUER v.a. to store, reserve
ESTUVER v.a. to treat with vapour bath
ESULE, ESULA s.-spurge (Euphorbia L. ssp.)
ETHIQUE s. hectic fever (accompanying pulmonary tuberculosis)
ETHIQUE a. FEVRE E. hectic fever
EUFORBIE see EUFORBIUM
EUFORBIUM s. spurge (Euphorbia L. spp.)
EURE s. hour (hora)
EUZ s. pl. eyes
EVACUATIF a. laxative, emetic (evacuans)
EVULSION s. forcible extraction (evulsio)
EVEUS a. watery (aquaticus) cf. EWEUS, UEUS
EWE s. water E. D'ORGE barley water E. ROSE attar of roses, rose water E. SALMACINE salt water (aqua salmacina) E. SUFFRINE sulfurous water (balnea sulfurea)
EWEUS a. watery (aquosus)
EXCESSION s. excess (excessum)
EXIBICION s. administration (exhibitio, adhibitio)
EXPULSIF a. expulsive, expellent
EXPURGATION s. cleansing, purification (expurgatio)
EXPRESSION s. expression, expulsion (expressio)
EXPRIMITIF a. pressing (exprimens)
EXTENSIF a. characterised by swelling or distension ['priking'] (extensivus)
EXTENSION, EXTENCION s. distension (extensio)
EXTENUATIF a. rarefying, reducing (attenuans, extenuans)
EXTENUATION s. thinness, leanness ['thennesse'] (attenuatio, extenuatio)
EXTENUATIQUE a. reducing, thinning, lessening, extenuative
EXTENTIF a. inducing extension (extensivus)
EXTERIS s. yellow bird (icterus)
EXTERSIF, EXTERCIF a. cleansing, detergent ['quenching'] (abstergens, exstergens)
EXTREMITÉ, EXTREMITHÉ s. extremity (of limb)
FASTIDIUM s. lack of appetite, distaste for food
FEBLECE, FEBLETÉ s. weakness
FEINE see VEINE
FEL s. gall F. DE TOREL ox-gall
FENDAC(H)E s. crack, fissure (scissura)
FENDRE v.a. to split
FENOIL s. fennel (Foeniculum vulgare Miller)
FENUGREC s. fenugreek (Trigonella foenum-graecum L.)
FENUGRECUM see FENUGREC
FERRUME s. iron filings ['rost of iryn'] (ferrugo)
FERU p.p. of FERIR v.a. to strike
FESTUCA, FESTUCI s. fescue-grass (Festuca)
FEVE s. bean (Vicia faba L.) F. FRASEE crushed, ground bean (fabe fracte)
FEVRE, FIEVRE s. fever (febris) see under epithets
FICHER v.a. to fix, set, place (infigere)
FIE(S/Z, FOIE s. A LA FIE adv. sometimes (aliquando)
FIEL s. gall, gall bladder (cistis fellis) FEL AVIUM birds' gall
FIENTE, FENTE s. dung (fumus, egestio, stercus, feces)
FIERENT ind. pr. 6 of FERIR v.a. to strike

FILE s. yarn (filatum crudum .i. fila cruda)

FILIPENDULE, FILUPENDULE s. dropwort (Filipendula vulgaris Moench) or meadow-sweet (Filipendula ulmaria (L.) Maxim.)

FILOANTROPOS s. a medicament AN48

FIQUE, FIGUE s. fig (ficus)

FISTULA s. fistula (fistula)

FLAME s. yellow flag (Iris pseudacorus L.) (flamula)

FLAN s. side

FLEUMATIQUE, FLEUMATIK a. phlegmatic

FLEUME s. phlegm (flegma) F. ACETOUSE (f. acetosum) sour phlegm (i.e. mixed with melancholy) F. DOUCE (f. dulce) sweet phlegm (i.e. mixed with blood) F. NATURALE / NATURELE (f. naturale) uncorrupted phlegm F. SAUSE (f. acetosum) salt phlegm (i.e. mixed with melancholy) F. VERRINE, VERRINGNE (f. vitreum) congealed, glassy phlegm (i.e. mixed with melancholy)

FLOCON DE LEINE s. flock or tuft of wool (floculus lane)

FLORS s. pl. menses

FLORS D'ARENGE s. 'centrum galli', clary (Salvia pratensis L.)? (flores andragie .i. citranguli = Citrus aurantium L.) See Notes to para. 43

FLUEVE s. river

FLUX s. (pathological) flow (fluxus)

FLUXIBILITÉ s. liquidity, runniness (fluxibilitas)

FOIE s. liver (epatis)

FOILLET s. follicle (folliculus)

FOLIA LAURI, FOLIIS L. s. bay leaves (Laurus nobilis L.)

FOLOIE ind. pr. 3 of FOLOIER v.n. to wander, stray (errare)

FOMENTACION s. fomentation, application of cataplasm (fomentatio, fomentum)

FONDRE v.a. to melt, dissolve (resolvere)

FONTEINE s. fontanel, hollow between two muscles in nape of the neck (collum)

FONZ, FONS, FUNS s. bottom (fundum)

FOR(N, FOUR s. oven

FORCLOS p.p. excluded, shut out (excludere)

FOREIN, FORAIN, FOREYN a. outer, exterior (exterior)

FORMAGE s. cheese

FORMENT adv. vigorously, very much

FORMIE s. ant (formica)

FORS TANT QUE conj. except that

FORSENERIE s. madness, delirium caused by excess of certain humours in brain

FOSSE s. dimple, hollow (concavitas)

FOULLE ind. pr. 3 of FOULER v.a. to oppress (conculcare)

FOUTRE v.n. to have sexual intercourse

FRAINE s. ash (Fraxinus excelsior L.)

FRANCHEMENT adv. freely (libere)

FRENESIE, FRENESIS s. madness, delirium, frenzy (frenesis)

FRENESIQUE a. and s. (one) suffering from frenesis, mad

FRENETIQUE a. and s. (one) suffering from frenesis, mad

FRESEMENT adv. newly, recently (recenter)

FRICATION s. chafing, rubbing, massage (fricatio)

FRIGIDUM COPHONIS s. oil of Copho cf. AN43

FRISE sbj. pr. 3 of FRIRE v.a. to fry FRIT p.p.

FROIDURE s. cold, chill (frigor, frigiditas, oripilatio)

FRONCE s. lining, skin (villus)

FRONCI(É p.p. wrinkled (corrugatus)

FROTER v.a. to rub (malaxare)

FUL(L)IGO s. soot

FUMEE s. aromatic vapour, steam

FUMIGATION s. suffumigation, vapour bath, treatment with aromatic fumes (fumigatio)

FUMITERRE, FUMITERE s. fumitory (Fumaria officinalis L.)

FUMOSITÉ s. hot gas within the body, vapour, exhalation, fume (fumositas, fumus)

FUNDEMENT s. anus, rectum (anus, peritoneon)
FURIOSITÉ s. turbulence (furiositas) of blood
FUST s. wood (lignum)
GALANGE s. galingale (Cyperus longus L.)
GALBANUM s. gum resin, galbanum
GALLA, GALLARUM s. oak gall (esp. Quercus infectoria Olivier) (galla)
GALE see GALLA
GALLITRICUM s. clary (Salvia sclarea L.) or cockle (Agrostemma githago L.) or darnel (Lolium temulentum L.)
GARGARISME s. gargle (gargarisma)
GARGATER v.n. to gargle (gargarizare)
GARGATUM s. gargle (gargarisma)
GARIOFILUS s. cloves (Eugenia caryophyllata Thunb.), clove gilliflower (Dianthus caryophyllus L.)
GARSE s. scarification, incision (scarificatio)
GARSER v.a. to scarify
GELINE s. hen (gallina)
GENCIANE s. felwort (Gentiana amarella (L.) Börner)
GENERATIF a. productive, apt to engender (generativus)
GENESTA s. broom (Cytisus scoparius (L.) Link.)
GENITAL a. genital
GERAPIGRA, GERAPIGRE s. hiera picra, a purgative containing aloes AN143-45
GEUER v.n. to play (jocare)
GEUNER v.n. to fast (jejunare)
GINGEMBRE s. ginger
GI(E)TE sbj. pr. 3 of GETER v.a. to throw
GIROFLE s. cloves (Eugenia caryophyllata Thunb.), clove gilliflower (Dianthus caryophyllus L.)
GLACHON s. piece of ice (glacies)
GLAN s. acorn (glandis)
GLANDRE s. tumour (glandula)
GLEISE, GLEYSE s. clay (argilla)
GLET(T)E s. mucus, phlegm (mucillago)
GLEYRE s. runny emission resembling egg-white
GLOBO(U)S a. globulous ['glubby'] (globosus)
GLOTEMENT adv. greedily (gulose)
GLU s. birdlime (viscus)
GLUEUX, GLEUUS a. sticky (glutinosus)
GOME ARABIC, GOUME ARRABIC, GUMME ARRABIC s. gum arabic (Acacia Senegal)
GO(U)ME DE ERE s. gum ivy (Hedera helix L.) (gumma edere)
GONNOREA s. involuntary discharge of 'sperm' (actually mucus) from the urethra or vagina
GOPIL s. wolf (vulpis)
GOUTE ARTETIQUE s. gout (gutta artetica)
GOUTEFESTRE s. gouty swelling, fistulous sore (fistula)
GOUTETE s. droplet
GOVERNER v.a. to control
GRAIN, GREINE s. seed (granum)
GRAMEN s. couch-grass (Erymus repens (L.) Gould)
GRANUM SOLIS s. gromwell (Lithospermum officinale L.)
GRAPE s. grape (uva)
GRAVELE s. gravel, shingle (arena); gravel, urinary/vessicular calculus (medic.) (arenula)
GREIL, GREL a. slender, thin (subtilis)
GREILLESCE s. slenderness (gracilitas)
GREILLETÉ s. slenderness (gracilitas)
GRE(E)SCE, GREISSE s. grease, fat (pingues) G. DE CHIEVRE G. GELINE G. DE OUWE
GREVANCE, GREVANZ s. pain, discomfort, heaviness (gravedo)
GREVATIF, GRAVATIS a. painful, heavy, grievous (gravativus)
GREVEIN a. heavy, grievous (gravativus)
GREVEUX, GREVUS a. heavy, grievous (gravativus, difficile)

GRIEF, GRIEVE a. heavy, grievous GRIEF adv. severely
GRISILL(I)ON, GRISILON s. grasshopper (cicada)
GRUEL s. meal (farina ordei)
GUESPE s. wasp (vespa)
GULE s. upper part of throat (fauces)
GUMMEUS a. sticky, resinous (gummosus)
HABITUDE s. complexion, general disposition (of body)
HAMEÇON s. hook (hamus)
HANAS s. goblet (ciphus)
HANCHE s. hip (scia)
HANELER v.n. to breathe (anhelare)
HATEREL s. nape of neck (occipitium)
HERBA BABILONICA s. see CENTONICE
HERMODACTILATÉ p.p. medicated with ramsons or meadow saffron (hermodactilatus)
HERMODACTILE see HERMODACTILIS
HERMODACTILIS, HERMODACTILI s. ramsons (Allium ursinum L.) or meadow saffron (Colchicum autumnale L.) (hermodactilis)
HERMOISE s. mugwort (Artemisia vulgaris L.)
HONTEUS a. MEMBRES HONTEUSES genitals (partes genitales, genitalia, pudenda)
HORE s. hour (ora)
HORTIE s. nettle (urtica)
HUMECTATIF a. moistening (humectans)
HUMIDITATIF a. moistening
HUMIDITÉ s. moisture (humiditas, humectatio, humor)
HUMOR s. humour (humor)
IAUZ s. pl. eyes
IERALOGODION, YERALOGODION, GEROLOGODION s. a bitter medicine containing aloes AN141
IERAPIGRE s. a bitter, purgative medicine containing aloes   I. G[alieni] AN143
IGNELEMENT adv. speedily (citus)
ILLIERS s. pl. loins
IMPEDIMENT s. impediment (impedimentum)
IMPETIGINES s. pl. creeping skin diseases
INANICION s. morbid depletion of bodily humours ['ydelhed'] (inanitio)
INCISIUN s. cutting, incision (incisio)
INCONTINENCE s. incontinence (incontinentia)
INCONVENIENCE s. discomfort, disruption
INDICACION s. indication, information (indicium)
INEQUALITÉ s. unevenness, irregularity (inequalitas)
INFECTION s. infection (infectio)
INFESTATION s. encroachment (infestatio)
INFIXIVUS RUBOR OCULORUM ['drawing rednesse of the ey3en']
INFLACION, INFLATION s. swelling (inflatio)
INFLATIF a. SINOCHA INFLATIVE type of continued fever producing gases within the body (s. inflativa)
INFLICTION s. affliction (afflictio)
INFUSION s. infusion (infusio)
INOPOS a. wine-coloured
INPROPREMENT adv. incorrectly
INSENSIBILITÉ s. insensitivity, lack of sensation
INSENSIBLE a. deprived of sensation
INSIPIDE a. unpleasant tasting, unsavoury (insipidus)
INTERIOR COLOQUINTIDE s. pulp of the colocynth (Citrullus colocynthus Schrader)
INTERPOLATÉ a. interpolate, non-consecutive, interrupted; intermittent (fever) with attacks once, twice or three times daily (interpolatus)
INTERPOLATION s. interruption (interpolatio)
IRE s. chagrin (ira)
IST ind. pr. 3 of ISSIR v.n. to issue, come out, go out

IVERNAL a. winter (hiemalis)
JA SOIT CE QUE conj. loc. although
JARSE s. scarification, incision (scarificatio)
JARSER v.t. scarify
JAUNE, CHAUNE a. yellow (croceus, subglaucus, glaucus)
JAUNICE, JAUNIZ s. jaundice (yctericia)
JOWES s. pl. jaws (faux)
JUGEMENT s. opinion, indication (indicium)
JULIS, JULII s. a medicament
JUNCHER v.a. to strew (sternere)
JUNER v.n. to fast (jejunare)
JUNIPERII s. juniper (Juniperus communis L.)
JUSQUIAMUS s. henbane (Hyoscyamus niger L.)
JUSTINON s. an electuary AN53
KALENDULA s. pot marigold (Calendula officinalis L.)
KATARTICO IMPERIALE s. a cathartic medicament AN54 (catarticum imperiale)
KIVILLE s. ankle (cavilla)
KYLIVENA s. lacteal vein, chyliferous vessel
LACCA s. milk
LADANE see LADANUM
LADANUM s. ladanum, gum (Cistus creticus L. & C. ladanifer L.) (laudanum)
LAICTUAIRE s. electuary (electuarium)
LAINE PIGNÉ s. ['thu schalt fynde in conchis marinis in whiche be fondyn margarite .i. perlis']
    (lana pinnula concarum)
LAIT s. milk L. DE FEMME woman's milk L. DE AMANDES almond milk
LAPIS ARMENICI, LAPIDIS ARMENEICI s. copper sulphate
LAPIS EMATISTE s. haematite, native iron ore
LAPIS LAZULI s. lapis lazuli
LAPIS LINCIS s. fossil resin formed from the urine of the lynx (belemnite)
LAPPE AGUE s. dock (Rumex L. spp.)
LAPPE EVERSE s. burdock (Arctium lappa L. or Arctium minus Bernh.)
LARGEMENT adv. easily, freely (facilius)
LART s. lard, bacon
LASCHIER, LAISCIER v.n. to produce a laxative effect (laxare); v.a. to loosen
LAVEURE s. water in which something has been washed (lotura)
LAXATIF a. laxative (laxativus)
LÉ a. wide (latus)
LECTUA(I)RE s. electuary (electuarium)
LEINS adv. therein
LEIS(S)(E)IVE, LESSIVE s. lye (lixivia)
LENITÉ s. smoothness (lenitas)
LENITIF a. soothing, softening, lenitive (lenitivus)
LENTILLES s. pl. lentils (Lens esculenta Moench)
LENTISCUS s. mastic? (Pistacia lentiscus L.)
LEONINE s. type of leprosy, leontiasis
LEPRE s. leprosy
LEPROS s. leper
LEQUEL conj. whether
LERME s. tear
LERMER v.n. to weep
LETUE, LEITUE s. lettuce (lactuca)
LEUCOFLEMANCIE s. type of dropsy
LEVE ind. / sbj. pr. 3 of LAVER v.a. to wash
LEVEIN s. leaven ['sowr dow3'] (fermentum)
LEVEROT s. young hare, leveret (lepusculus)
LEVEZ p.p. risen (of bread)
LEVRE s. hare (lepus)
LICIOTRIPON s. a medicament, litontripon AN55

LICIUM s. (licium) in Antiquity applied to an astringent juice of the buckthorn (Rhamnus petio-
laris / lycioides) and occasionally of other medicinal plants e.g. Berberis; in medieval England
often used to refer to the dried leaves of honeysuckle (Lonicera spp.) as, probably, in para. 43.
See G. Ineichen in *ZfromPhil* 75 (1959), 456–8.
LICORICE s. liquorice
LIE s. lees (amurca)
LIÉ a. happy, glad
LIENTERIE, LIENTERIA, LIENTERE s. type of diarrhoea
LIENTERICUS s. patient suffering from lienteria
LIENTERIQUE s. patient suffering from lienteria (lientericus)
LIMAILLE DE FER s. iron filings (ferrugo)
LIMEUS a. muddy (limosus, lutiosus)
LIMIGNON s. wick forming a small tent ['a tent of lynen cloth'] (licinium)
LIMON s. slime (limo)
LIMOSITÉ s. sliminess (limositas)
LIN s. flax (Linum usitatissimum L.) SEMENCE DE L. linseed
LINGE s. linen L. DRAP linen cloth
LIQUIRICIE s. liquorice
LIQUOR, LICOR s. liquid (liquor)
LITARGIA, LITARGIE s. disease of brain from an aposteme in the rear ventricle causing le-
thargy and forgetfulness (litargia)
LITARGIRII, LITARGIRUM s. litharge, lead monoxide produced in the purification of gold and
silver (litargirium)
LITARGIQUE a. and s. (patient) suffering from litargia
LIZ, LIS s. lily
LO ind. pr. 1 of LOER v.a. to recommend, advise
LOCAL a. local (localis)
LORER s. bay (Laurus nobilis L.)
LOSCHE ind. pr. 3 of LOSCHER v.n. to be(come) loose (movere, removere)
LOUNS ind. pr. 5 of LOER v.a. to recommend, advise
LUMBRIC, LUMBRIQUE s. worm (lumbricus)
LUBRICITÉ s. sliminess (lubricitas)
LUPIN s. lupin (Lupinus L. spp.) LUPINS AMERS
LUVETE s. uvula (uvula)
MACIS, MACE s. mace, nutmeg (Myristica fragrans L.)
MAÇUE s. club ['nail'] (clavus)
MAILLE s. membrane of the eye (macula)
MAINS adv. less (minus)
MAINTENANT adv. at once, forthwith (statim)
MAJORANA s. marjoram (Origanum vulgare L.) or sweet marjoram (Majorana hortensis
Moench)
MAL s. A MAL to one's detriment (ad malum)
MALUM TERRE s. earthnut (Conopodium majus (Gouan) Loret) or sowbread (Cyclamen he-
derifolium Aiton)
MALICE s. malignancy (furiositas) of blood
MALSADE, MAUSADE a. unpleasant tasting, unsavoury (insipidus)
MAMELE s. nipple
MANDRAGORE s. mandrake (Mandragora officinarum L.)
MANGER s. meal
MANGER v.a. to eat MANGUE ind. pr. 3 MANGUENT ind. pr. 6 MANGUCE sbj. pr. 3 MAN-
GUCENT sbj. pr. 6
MANGISON / MANGISONS pl. s. itching, irritation (pruritus)
MANIACA CONFIDENCIA s. a type of mania ['presumpcioun or boldnesse of spekyng']
MANIACUS a. and s. (patient) afflicted with mania
MANIAQUE see MANIACUS
MANIE s. mania (mania)
MANJUT ind. pr. 3 of MANGER v.a. to irritate, cause to itch (pruritus)
MANNA, [MANNE] s. manna

MARBRE s. (piece of) marble (marmor)

MARCIATON, MARSIATON s. marciaton, a green ointment AN130 (marciaton)

MASTIC, MASTICIS s. mastic, resin of Pistacia lentiscus L.

MATERE s. matter, pus (sanies)

MATRIX, MARRIS, MATRIZ s. womb (matrix)

MATURATF a. ripening (maturativus)

MAUMETRE v.a. to damage, hurt, infect MAUMIS p.p. (infectio)

MAUVE s. marshmallow (Althaea officinalis L.), mallow (Malva L. spp.)

MEGRESCE s. leanness, thinness (macies, macilentia)

MEGRETÉ s. leanness, thinness (macilentia)

MEIN a. middle (medius)

MEINEMENT, MOINEMENT adv. moderately (mediocriter)

MEL s. honey M. ROSAT honey mixed with rose-hip

MELANCOLIE, MALANCOLIE s. black bile (melancolia) M. INNATURALE (m. innaturalis) M. NATURALE (m. naturalis)

MELANCOLIEN a. assisting production of black bile VIANDES M. (cibis melancolicis)

MELANCOLIEUS a. generative of black bile; prone to excess of black bile (melancolicus, melanconicus)

MELANCOLIQUE, MALANCOLIQUE, MALANCOLICI a. and s. melancholic, afflicted with black bile

MELANGIRON s. type of jaundice (melanchiron)

MELISSE s. balm (Melissa officinalis L.)

MELON s. melon (Cucumis melo L.) MELONS PALESTINES (melo palestinus)

MELOTIDA s. sheep's wool (lana melotida)

MELS, MIELS, MEUZ adv. better (melius)

MEMBRA s. see Notes to 192

MEMEMENT adv. particularly, especially (maxime, precipue)

MENDRE a. less(er) (minor)

MENOISON, MENEISON s. diarrhoea, discharge from bowels containing blood

MENSTRUEL a. menstrual FLUX M. menses

MENTE s. mint (mentha) M. AGRESTIS   M. ROMANE (Mentha spp.)

MENUEMENT adv. finely (minuter)

MENUSSE ind. pr. 3 of MENUSER v.n. to diminish, shrink

MERCURIAL(E see MERCURIALIS

MERCURIALIS s. dog's mercury or annual mercury (Mercurialis perennis L. / annua L.)

MERDE s. filth, excrement (caca, stercus) M. DE L'ORS (fel ursinum)

MESEL (pl. MESEAUS) s. leper (mesellus)

MESCHE s. wick (licinium)

MESERAIQUE a. VEINE M. mesaraic vein

MESPILUS s. medlar (Mespilus germanica L.)

MESTER s. need

METRIDATUM s. a medicament AN56 [see G. Watson, *Theriac and Mithridatium. A Study in Therapeutics* (London, 1966)]

MEURER v.a. to ripen, bring to a head (maturare)

MIAUZ adv. better (melius)

MICLETE s. an electuary AN58 (micleta)

MIE DE PAIN s. piece of bread (mica panis)

MIEL s. honey (mel)

MIELEU s. middle (medium)

MINCER v.a. to mince, chop into small pieces

MIRE s. physician (medicus)

MIRI[N]GAM s. cerebral membrane (miringa)

MIRABOLANI s. pl. myrobalans, fruit of varieties of Terminalia MIROBALANS s. pl. myrobalans, fruit of varieties of Terminalia M. INDES Indian myrobalan (Terminalia horrida Steudel), M. CITRINS citrine myrobalan (Terminalia citrina Roxb.), M. KEBLES chebule myrobalan (Terminalia chebula Retzius)

MIRRA, MIRRE s. myrrh (mirra) M. TROCLETEM myrrh from the area inhabited by the Trogodytae (see Dioscorides I,64 and Pliny Nat. Hist. XII, xxxv, 69; Aegidius Corboliensis, Carmina Medica ed. Choulant has *myrrhe trocleten* var. *troglytes*)

MIRTA, MIRTE s. sweet gale (Myrica gale L.)

MIRTILLE, MIRTELLE s. bilberry (Vaccinium myrtillus L.)

MITRIDATE see MITRIDATUM

MITRIDATUM s. see METRIDATUM

MOCION s. movement (motus)

MOELE s. marrow (medulla)

MO(I)EL (pl. MOIAUS, MOEUS) s. egg yolk (vitellum)

MOIEN, MOINE a. medium, moderate (mediocris)

MOILLER v.a. to moisten (humectare)

MOINEMENT adv. moderately ((mediocriter)

MOISTE, MOSTE, MOITE a. moist (humidus)

MOISTECE, MOISTESSE, MOSTECE s. moisture, dampness (humiditas)

MOL a. soft (mollis)

MOLE s. PERRE DE M., P. DE MOLIN mill-stone (lapis molinaris)

MOLESTE s. harm, damage

MOLLIFICATIF a. emollient (mollitivus)

MOLLITIF a. emollient (mollitivus)

MOLU p.p. kneaded (malaxatus)

MONCEL s. mass ['a clod'] (gleba)

MONCELER, AMONCELER v.a. and v. refl. to accumulate (conglobare)

MORBUS REGIUS, M. AURIGEUS, M. ARCUATUS s. type of jaundice

MORDICATION s. stinging irritation ['fretyng'] (mordicatio)

MORDIFICATIF a. caustic, corrosive ['fretyng'] (mordificativus, morditivus)

MORE, MEURE s. blackberry (Rubus fruticosus sens. lat.)

MORELE s. black nightshade (Solanum nigrum L.) or deadly nightshade (Atropa bella-donna L.)

MORPHÉ s. morphew, morbid eruption of the skin (morphea)

MORPHEA s. morphew, morbid eruption of the skin

MORSURE s. bite (morsura)

MORT ind. pr. 3 of MORDRE v.a. to bite (mordicare)

MORTIER s. mortar

MORTIFICATION s. mortification, necrosis (mortificatio)

MORTIFIER v.a. to kill ['fretyng'] (mortificare)

MOSSE s. moss (lanugo)

MOSTARDE s. mustard

MOTION s. movement (motus)

MOULE, MEULE s. marrow (medulla)

MOVABLE a. mobile (motivus, mobilis)

MOVOIR subst. infin. (capacity for) movement (motus)

MUELLE, MUILLIE, MULLIE sbj. pr. 3 of MUILLER v.a. to wet, moisten, wash

MUGUE, MUSQUE s. musk (muscus)

MULSE s. mead (mulsa)

MULTIPLICACION s. multiplicity (multitudo)

MULTITUDINE s. great quantity (multitudo)

MUMMIA, MUMMIE s. mummy (mummia)

MUNDEFIER, MUNDIFIER v.a. to cleanse (mundificare)

MUNDER v.a. to cleanse

MUNDIFICATIF a. cleansing (mundificus)

MURGE sbj. pr. 3 of MURIR v.n. to die

MU(S)CIL(L)AGINITÉ, MUSSILLAGINITÉ s. viscous substance having the property of mucilage (mu(s)cillago)

MUSA ENEA s. medicament AN57

MUSCHE, MUSKE s. fly (musca)

MUSCILAGINEUS a. mucilaginous, gelatinous

MUSCUM s. musk

MUSEL (pl. MUSCIAUS) s. muscle, fleshy part (musculus, pulpa)

NAGES s. pl. buttocks (nates)

NASTALE s. pessary, suppository (nastale)
NASTURCIUM s. garden cress (Lepidium sativum L.)
NATIVITÉ s. birth DE N. from birth
NEFRETIQUE a. nephritic, suffering from renal disorder (nefreticus)
NEIS adv. even, also (etiam)
NENUFAR(E s. water lily (Nymphaea L. spp. and Nuphar Sm. spp.)
NEPITA s. catmint (Nepeta cataria L.)
NER(F s. nerve, sinew (nervus, lacertus)
NERCIR v.n. to darken, become black (denigrari)
NESPLER s. medlar (Mespilus germanica L.) (nespilus)
NETTI p.p. of NETTIR v.a. to cleanse (mundificare)
NIÉS s. nose (nasus)
NITRE see NITRUM
NITRUM s. nitre (nitrum)
NOER v.n. to float (on the surface) (natare, supernatare)
NOIAL s. fruit-stone (nucleus)
NOIANT adv. not at all
NOIS, NUCIS s. (wal)nut N. MUSCATE, NUCIS M.
nutmeg (Myristica fragrans Houtt.) N. DE YNDE
NONE s. ORE DE N. nones (3.00 pm.)
NOUCHE s. neck (nuca)
NOUEUS a. knotty, twisted (nodosus)
NUISSANCE s. harm, detriment (nocumentum)
NU(I)SANT a. harmful (nocivus)
NUMBRIL, NOMBLIL, NOMBRIL, NUNBLIL s. navel (umbilicum)
NUNCHA pret. 3 of NUNCIER v.a. to inform, announce (nuntiare)
NUTRITIF a. nutritive (enutriens)
OCCIRE v.a. to kill, destroy (interficere)
ODORER v.a. to scent, breathe, smell
OFFENSION s. intrusion (offendiculum)
OFFICE s. function (officium)
OIGNE sbj. pr. 3 of OINDRE v.a. to anoint, smear (ungere, inungere)
OIGNEMENT s. ointment, unguent (unguentum); O. ESTEVENON (unguentum Stephanonis)
OIGNION, ONGNON s. onion
OIGNONEE s. onion dish (cepule)
OILLE s. oil O. FROIDE COPHONIS cf. AN43 O. PULEGINE oil made with penny royal O. JU-
    NIPERINE 10 oil made with juniper berries O. LAURINE oil of bays O. MANDRAGORAT
    oil of mandrake AN64 O. MASTICINE oil of mastic O. MUSCELINE oil of musk O. ROSAT
    oil of roses AN62 O. VIOLAT oil of violets AN64 O. LE ROI WILLIAME (oleum regis Guil-
    lelmi)
OINT s. animal fat (anxungia) O. DE PORC
OISELET s. small bird
OLIBANE see OLIBANUM
OLIBANUM s. frankincense (Boswellia thurifera L.)
OLIVE s. olive (oliva)
OMBLICUS VENERIS s. pennywort (Umbilicus rupestris (Salisb.) Dandy)
OMBREUX, UMBROUSE a. marked by shadowy patches (obumbratus, nigredine obfuscatus)
ONCTION s. application of ointment, unction (unctio)
OPIATE s. opiate (opiatum)
OPIATÉ p.p. medicated with opium (opiatus)
OPIE see OPIUM
OPILACION s. blockage, obstruction, stopping up (opilatio)
OPIUM, OPII s. opium O. MICONIS   O. THEBAICUM opium from Thebes in Egypt   O.
    TRANENSE opium from Trani in Apuleia
OPOPIRE, OPOPIRAM s. a medicament AN69 (opopira)
OPPOPANAC s. opopanax (Opopanax chironium (L.) Koch)
OPPOSICION s. opposite (contrarium) PAR O. per antipasim = antispasis

OPPRENT ind. pr. 3 of OPREINDRE v.a. to oppress, compress (conprimere) [a hapax at this date; oppreindre and opriembre are attested in 14th C.]
OPTIQUE a. optic (obticus)
ORBUS SACCUS s. part of the intestine (orbum)
ORD a. dirty, foul
ORDENER, ORDINER, ORDEINER v.a. to regulate, fix
ORDURE DE CUIR s. marking, disfiguring of the skin (fedatio cutis)
ORGE s. barley (ordeum) O. PILEE barley flour (farris ordei) FARINE D'O. barley flour PAILLE D'O. barley chaff
ORIGANUM, ORIGANON s. marjoram (Origanum vulgare L.)
ORME s. elm (ulmus)
ORPIMENT s. yellow arsenic trisulphide; also red arsenic sulphide, realgar (auripigmentum)
ORS, OURS s. bear (ursus)
ORTIE VIVE s. nettle (Lamium L. spp. / Urtica L. spp.) (urtica viva)
ORTOMIA s. a type of asthma, 'spiritus rectitudinis' ['the spirit of evenhed'] (ortomia)
OURE s. hour (ora)
OUWE s. goose (auca)
OVERAIGNE s. working, mode of operation (operatio)
OVERER, OVRIER v.n. work with, make use of; proceed (subvenire) OVRÉ p.p. processed (of food) (operatus)
OWELLEMENT adv. in equal measure (equaliter)
OXIMEL, OXCIMEL, OXEMEL s. oxymel, preparation of vinegar, herbs and honey (oximel) O. SIMPLE (o. simplex) O. COMPOSTE (o. compositum) O. DIVISIF (o. divisivum) O. SQUIL-LITIQUE (o. squilliticum)
OZIMUM s. mistletoe (Viscum album L.)
PALAIS, PALAIZ s. palate (palatum)
PALAT s. palate (palatum)
PALU(S s. marsh
PANNA(I)SSE s. parsnip (Pastinaca sativa L.) (pastinaca)
PAPAVER s. poppy (Papaver L. spp.) P. NEIR   P. BLANC   PAPAVERIS ALBI
PARALISIE see PARALISIS
PARALIPOMENIE s. aposteme in the lungs
PARALISIS s. palsy, paralysis (paralisis)
PARALITIQUE a. and s. (patient) suffering from the palsy (paraliticus)
PARCHEMIN s. parchment (carta, pergamenum)
PARCREU a. full-grown (in juventute)
PAREIE s. wall (paries)
PARFAIRE v.a. to complete, accomplish (perficere)
PARFUNT a. deep (profundus), sunken (of eyes) (concavus)
PAROUT sbj. pr. 3 of PARLER v.n. to speak
PARTICULAR, PARTICULER a. and s. particular, specific (detail) (particularis)
PASMER v. refl. to faint (lipotomia)
PASSER s. sparrow
PASTE s. dough (pasta)
PAULINE SIMPLE, SIMPLE P. s. medicament AN74 (paulinum simplex)
PAVEMENT s. floor
PEIS, POIS s. weight
PEL s. skin, hide PEUS DE LEVRE skin of a hare (filtrum pili leporis)
PELETE, PELECTE s. membrane, skin (pellicula)
PENIDE s. barley-sugar
PENIL, PENUL s. pubes, groin (pecten)
PENILIERE s. pubes, groin
PENNE s. feather (penna)
PENTAFILON s. creeping cinquefoil (Potentilla reptans L.)
PEOR a. worse (peior)
PEOUR s. fear (pavor)
PERETRUM s. pellitory (Anacyclus pyrethrum DC or Parietaria judaica L.)
PERILLIEUS a. perilous, dangerous (periculosus)

PERIPLEUMONIE, PERIPLEMONIE, PERYPLEUMONIS s. aposteme in the lungs, pneumonia (peripleumonia)

PERITARIA s. pellitory of the wall (Parietaria judaica L.)

PERRE DE MOLIN s. millstone

PERRECEUSEMENT adv. slowly, sluggishly

PERRESIL, PER(R)ESIN s. parsley (Petroselinum crispum (Miller) Nyman)

PERRETTE s. little stone

PERSICARIE s. persicaria, 'willow-weed' (Polygonum persicaria L.)

PERTUIS s. hole, opening, perforation (foramen)

PERTUSÉ p.p. perforated (perforatus)

PESACION s. pessary

PESANTIME, PESAUNTUME s. weight (mola, gravitas)

PESCHE ind. pr, 3 of PECHER v. impers. there is an impediment

PESCHIER s. peach tree

PETITESCE s. smallness, paucity (paucitas)

PETROCILLUM s. parsley (Petroselinum crispum (Miller) A.W. Hill)

PETROLEUM s. petroleum, mineral oil

PEU s. stake (pilus)

PEVREE s. peppered dish (piperata)

PHILIPENDULE s. dropwort (Filipendula vulgaris Moench), meadow-sweet (Filipendula ulmaria (L.) Maxim.)

PHILOANTROPON s. a medicament AN48

PICLE s. pitch (picula)

PIECE A adv. for some time

PIERE s. stone (medic.) (lapis)

PIERE EMATISTE s. haematite, native iron ore

PIERGE sbj. pr. 3 of PAREIR v.n. to appear

PIERRE ARMENIQUE s. copper sulphate (lapis armeniaci, lapis armenus)

PIERRE LAZULE, PEIRE LAZULI s. lapis lazuli

PIGLE s. greater stitchwort (Stellaria holostea L.)

PIL(L)E s. pill P. AURÉ(E)S AN79   P. DE CINC MANERES DE MIRABOLANS AN84   P. DE SIMPLE PAULINE   P. DIACASTOREA AN80   P. GALIEN   P. MACEDOINE (pille macis)   P. MESTRE BERTHOLOMEU   P. ARTETIQUE   P. COPHONIS

PILLULE s. pill

PIN s. pine, pine-cone (pinus, pinea)

PIONE s. peony (Paeonia L. spp.)

PIPER s. pepper PIPERIS LONGI

PIPERNELLE s. scarlet pimpernel (Anagallis arvensis L.), burnet saxifrage (Pimpinella saxifraga L.) or great burnet (Sanguisorba officinalis L.)

PIRETRUM s. pellitory (Anacyclus pyrethrum DC. or Parietaria judaica L.)

PIS, PIZ s. breast (pectus, thorax)

PISSADE s. urine (urina)

PISSER v.n. to urinate (mingere)

PLANTAIN, PLANTEINE, PLAUNTEINE s. great plantain (Plantago major L.)

PLATINE s. plate (lamina)

PLECTORIQUE a. plethoric, characterized by excess of blood or other humours (plectoricus)

PLENER a. plethoric

PLEURESIE, PLEURESIS s. pleurisy (pleuresis)

PLIRIS ARCONTICON s. an electuary AN41

PLOIE, PLUIE, PLOYE s. rain

PLUCHIR v.a. to pluck (decerpere)

PLUM s. lead

PODAGRA s. gout in the feet

POET s. see POT

POIGNANT, PUIGNANT, PUNAUNT a. pungent, sharp, pricking (pungens, pungitivus)

POI(G)NTURE s. pricking, stinging sensation (punctura)

POILER v.n. to lose hair (depilare)

POINT ind. pr. 3 and p.p. of POINDRE v.a. to prick, sting (pungere)

POIRE s. pear (pira)
POIS s. pea
POISSONS sbj. pr. 5 of POEIR v.n. to be able (punctura)
POIVRE s. pepper   NEIR P.   P. LONC
POIZ s. pitch (picula)
POLI p.p. made smooth (politus)
POLIPOD(I)E see POLIPODIUM
POLIPODIUM s. polypody (Polypodium vulgare L.) or oak fern (Gymnocarpium dryopteris (L.)
   Newman)
POLIPUS s. polyp
POLLITRICUM s. maidenhair-fern (Adiantum capillus-veneris L.) or maidenhair spleenwort
   (Asplenium trichomanes L.)
POME CITOINE, P. CITONIE s. quince (Cydonia oblonga Miller)
POME DÉ BOIS s. crab apple (Malus sylvestris L.)
POME GRENATE, POUME GERNATE, P. GRENADE s. pomegranate (Punica granatum L.)
   (granatum)
POME MACIENE s. crab apple (Malus sylvestris L.)
POMME DE TERRE s. earthnut (Conopodium majus (Gouan) Loret) or sowbread (Cyclamen he-
   derifolium Aiton)
POPULEON, POPULION s. ointment made with poplar buds
POR POI adv. almost (fere)
PORCELAINE s. purslane (Portulaca oleracea L.)
POR QUE conj. provided that, if only
POREL pl. PORAUS, PORRIAUX, PORIEUS s. leek (Allium porrum L.)
PORE s. pore (porus)
PORPRENDRE v.a. to seize, take hold of (occupare)
PORPRIN a. purple (purpureus)
PORRETURE s. pus, matter (putredo, sanies)
PORRI a. rotten, decaying, putrefied (putrefactus)
PORTULAQUE, PORTULAGUE s. purslane (Portulaca oleracea L.)
PORVEER v.n. to take care to, to arrange to (curare)
POSTULACION s. pustule, sore (pustula)
POSTULE s. sore, pustule (pustula)
POSTUME s. impostume, abscess
POT, POET s. pot POES s. pl.
POTIO SANCTI PAULI s. a medical beverage AN174
POUCIER s. thumb (pollex)
POUDRE s. pouder   P. PETRONCEL
POUME s. apple   P. CITRIN lemon
POUS, PUS s. pulse (of blood) (pulsus)
PRECIPITATION s. prolapse of the uterus (precipitatio)
PREME sbj. pr. 3 of PREENDRE v.a. to press
PREINS p.p. of PREENDRE v.a. to press
PRESSE DE GENT throng of people (conventus hominum)
PREVOIRE s. priest (sacerdos)
PRIMEVOIRE s. cowslip (Primula veris L.)
PRIVATION s. lack, absence, privation (privatio)
PRIVÉ a. close, local (privatus)
PROGNOSTIQUES s. pl. prognostica (title of Hippocrates' work)
PRONOSTIQUE s. prognosis (pronosticum)
PROPORCION s. proportion, measure
PROPRIETÉ s. particular quality
PRUNE s. sloe (Prunus spinosa L.), plum (Prunus domestica L.)
PRURITUS s. itching (pruritus)
PSIDIA, SIDIE s. bark of the pomegranate (psidia)
PSIL(I)UM s. fleawort (Plantago arenaria Waldst. and Kit.) (psilium)
PTISANE s. infusion, tisane (ptisana)
PTISICLE, PTISIQUE s. consumption, phthisis (ptisis)

PTISIQUE, PTISICLE a. suffering from phthisis
PUCELE s. virgin
PUCIN, POUCIN, POCIN, PUCHIN s. chicken
PUIR v.n. to stink PUIT ind. pr. 3 PUIANT pr. pt. (fetidus)
PUISSE ind. pr. 3 of POISER v.n. to weigh (gravatur)
PULEGIUM s. penny royal (Mentha pulegium L.), wild thyme (Thymus serpyllum L.)
PULIOL(E, POLIOL s. see PULEGIUM
PUOR s. stench (fetor)
PURGATIF a. purgative
PURGER, PURJER, PORGER v.a. to purge (purgare)
PURRER v.a. to cleanse (mundificare)
PURRETURE s. pus, matter (putredo, sanies)
PURRI p.p. rotten, containing decaying matter (saniosus)
PUSTULACION s. pustule, sore (pustula)
PUSTULE s. pustule, sore (pustula)
PUTRIFACTION s. decay, rotting (putredo)
QUARTAIN(E, QUARTOINE a. and s. quartan (fever) i.e. with paroxysms occurring every
    third day   Q. BASTARDE bastard quartan i.e. having a resemblance to a quartan fever (q.
    notha)
QUECUNQUE pr. whatever
QUILIVENA s. lacteal vein, chyliferous vessel (kili vena)
QUILLER s. spoon
QUINANCIA s. quinsy (quinancia)
QUIR s. skin, hide (cutis)
QUIRE v.a. to cauterize QUIST ind. pr. 3 QUISE sbj. pr. 3
QUISÇON s. cautery (cauterium)
QUISINAGE s. cooked food (coquinatum); cooking
QUI(S)TURE, QUITTURE s. suppurating sore, purulent matter, quitter (pustula, ulceratio)
QUITURE s. cauter, cauterization
QUIVILLE s. lacteal vein, chyliferous vessel (kili vena)
QUIVILLE s. ankle (cavilla)
RADICE s. radish (Raphanus sativus L.)
RAE, RAIE sbj. pr. 3 of RERE v.a. to shave
RAFLE s. (wild) radish (Raphanus raphanistrum / sativus L.) (rafa, raphanus)
RAINS s. pl. kidneys
RAISNABLE a. suitable, appropriate (conveniens)
RAISON s. reason (ratio)
RAMPER v.n. to creep (reptio)
RANOILE s. frog
RAPA s. turnip (Brassica rapa)
RAPHANUM s. see RAFLE
RAPHE s. see RAFLE
RASCACION s. hawking, scraping (in the throat) (rascatio)
RASEOIR v.n. to settle (residere)
RASTURE s. scrapings (rasura)
RAUCEDO s. hoarseness
RAVINE s. plunder, rapine (rapina)
RAVIR v.n. carry away, transport (rapere)
RAVISEMENT s. drawing up ['updrawyng'] (raptus)
REBOUCHEMENT s. dulling, blunting (of the senses) (hebetudo)
RECEITE s. medical receipt, recipe (receptio)
RECEPTACLE s. vessel, receptacle (receptaculum)
RECEPTION s. recipe, prescription (receptio)
REDUNDER v.n. to return (redundare)
REFERIR v.a. to strike, reach (repercutere)
REFROIDANS, REFROYDANS a. and s. pl. cooling agents (infrigidantia)
REFROIDIR v.a. to cool, refresh (infrigidare)
REGALICE s. liquorice (regalissa)

RELASCH(I)ER, RELAXER v.a. to relax; to soften; to loosen (relaxare)
RELAXATIF a. soothing (relaxativus)
RELAXATION s. loosening (relaxatio); morbid elongation of the uvula
RELEMENT adv. rarely, irregularly (raro)
RELEVER v.n. to get up
RELUSAN[T] a. bright, shining
REMEDIE s. remedy, cure (remedium)
REMÉS p.p. of REMAINDRE to remain
REMIS p.p. reduced, in remission, abated (remissus, remissior)
REMISSETÉ s. reduction, remission, reduction (remissio)
REMISSION s. remission, respite (remissio)
REMOCION s. removal ['remocion .i. puttyng away'] (remotio)
RENOVELER v.a. to renew
REON a. round (rotundus)
REPAREILLENT ind. pr. 3 of REPAREILLER v.a. to restore (reparare)
REPERCUSSIF a. designed to reduce swelling, expelling harmful matter, repercussive (repercussivus)
REPLETION s. repletion, fullness; morbid excess of humours; indigestion (repletio)
REPOSEE s. interval
REPOST p.p. of REPONDRE v.a. to hide
REPRESSION s. suppression (repressio)
REQUIES s. an opiate plant and medicament AN95
RES p.p. shaven, worn smooth
RESIET ind. pr. 3 of RESEEIR v.n. to settle (resideo)
RESOLUTION s. solution (resolutio)
RESOUDER v.a. to heal, knit together (consolidare)
RESPORGIER v.a. to purge again
RESTAURATIF a. restorative (restaurativus)
RESTOR(R)ER v.a. to restore (recuperare)
RESTREEZ p.p. repeated at intervals (iteratus)
RESTREINDRE v.a. to constrict (coartare)
RESUDATION s. sweating (out) (resudatio, diabrosim)
RESUMPTIF a. restorative (resumptivus)
RESVER v.n. to rave, become delirious (esp. in speech) (aliena loquor)
RESVER sbst. inf. raving, madness ['wodnesse'] (insania)
RETENCION s. retention; (of menstrual flow) amenorrhoe (retentio)
RETENTIF a. retentive ['holdyng', 'keping'] (retentivus)
RETRAIRE v.a. to withdraw, pull out   v. refl. to contract (contrahere)
RETRAIT p.p. shrunken, contracted (constrictus, contractus)
REUBARB(R)E, REUBARBER s. rhubarb (Rheum rhaponticum L.)
REUME s. rheum, mucus (reuma)
REUMATIQUE a. engendering or afflicted by rheum (reumaticus)
REVOCATION s. withdrawal (revocatio)
RIEULE s. rule, principle
ROIGNE s. scabies
ROIGNEUS a. scabious (scabiosus)
ROIL s. rust (erugo)
RONCE s. bramble, briar (rubus)
RORE MARINO s. rosemary (Rosmarinus officinalis L.)
ROS [= ROIS] s. wren (Troglodytes) (regulus)
ROSE s. rose
ROST s. great heat   EN R.
RUBEA, ROBEA s. an opiate confection AN94   R. TROCISCATAM made up into lozenge-shaped medicaments ('trocisci')   RUBEA LA MENOR cleavers (Galium aparine L.) (rubea minor)
RUDE a. robust (rusticus)
RUE s. rue (Ruta graveolens L.) R. AGRESTE,   R. SAUVAGE,   R. CHAMPESTRE meadow rue (Thalictrum flavum / minus L.) or 'wild rue' (Peganum harmala L.)

RUF a. red (rufus)
RUPTOIRE a. ruptory (of ointment)
SA ET LA adv. hither and thither
SACELLATION s. sachet ['pokett'] (sacellatio)
SACHELET s. sachet (sacculus)
SAFFRAN ORIENTAL s. saffron (crocus orientalis)
SAGAPINUM s. gum resin from Ferula persica L.
SAGEMENT adv. skilfully (artificiose) (forfex)
SAIM, SEIM s. animal fat (sagimen)
SALE a. salt (salsus) E. SALEE (aqua salmacina) BAIN S. salt bath
SALE NITRE s. saltpetre
SALIVE s. saliva (saliva, sputum)
SALVATELLA s. salvatella, vein between ring finger and little finger of the right hand ['the
    veyne epatica']
SAN(S s. blood (sanguis)
SANC ADUSTÉ, S. ARS s. burned blood ['adust bloode', 'brende bloode'] (sanguis adustus)
SANC DE DRAGON s. dragon's blood, red gum or resin of dragon tree, Dracaena draco L.
SANCGLOT, SANGLOZ, SANGLOT s. sob (singultus)
SANCSUGIUM (ASMA) s. type of asthma (sansugium aut sanguisuga)
SANCTÉ s. health (sanitas)
SANDALUS ALBUS ET RUBEUS s. white and red sandalwood (Santalum album L. / Ptero-
    carpus santalinus L.)
SANDLES BLANCHES ET ROUGES see above
SANER v.a. to heal, dress (sanare)
SANGUIN a. sanguine (sanguineus); blood red
SANGUINARIE s. shepherd's purse (Capsella bursa-pastoris (L.) Medic.) or knotgrass (Polygo-
    num aviculare L.)
SANGUIS DRACONIS s. dragon's blood, red gum or resin of dragon tree, Dracaena draco L.
SANSUE, SANCSUE see SANGUISUGA
SANGUISUGA s. leech (sanguissuga)
SAPHENA s. cephalic vein (saphena)
SARCOCOLLA s. sarcocol, gum sarcocolla
SARMENT s. twigs (sarmentum)
SATUREIA s. savory (Satureia L.)
SATURIASIS s. involuntary penile erection (satiriasis)
SAUGE s. sage (Salvia officinalis L. or Teucrium scorodonia L.) S. SAUVAGE (Teucrium scoro-
    donia L.) S. DOMESCHE (Salvia officinalis L.)
SAUGEMME, SALGEMME s. rock-salt (salgemma)
SAUL, SAOL a. full, replete   SON S. his fill (ad saturitatem)
SAUS a. salt (salsus)
SAUSE s. sauce (salsa) S. POITEVINE 'salsamentum pictavense' / 'salsa pictavensis' (see 91)
SAUSEFLEUME s. sauceflegm, 'salt phlegm', producing swelling, discoloration, pustules etc.
SAUZ s. willow (salix)
SAVINE s. savin (Juniperus sabina L.)
SAVON s. soap S. FRANÇOIS soda-ash soap (sapo gallicus)
SAXIFRAGE s. saxifrage (Saxifraga L. spp.), burnet saxifrage (Pimpinella saxifraga L.) or some of
    the spleenworts (Asplenium L. spp.)
SCAMONEE, SCAMONIE s. scammony (Convulvulus scammonia L.)
SCAMONIAT(É, SCAMONEATÉ a. medicated with scammony
SCARIOLE s. prickly lettuce (Lactuca serriola L.)
SCIA s. hip
SCIATICA PASSIO s. sciatica
SCIROP s. syrup S. ACETOUS(E
SCLIROSIS s. sclirosis
SCOLOPENDRIA s. hart's-tongue fern (Phyllitis scolopendrium (L.) Newman)
SCOTOMIE s. scotoma, dizziness accompanied by dimness of vision (scotomia)
SCURIA s. urinary complaint
SEBESTEN s. sebesten plum (Cordia myxa L.)

SEC, SECHC, SEQUE a. dry (siccus)
SECCHE s. seat, base (sedes)
SECHECE, SECCHESCE s. dryness (siccitas)
SECONDINE s. afterbirth, placenta (secundina) cf. G. Baader, 'Zur Terminologie des Constan-
    tinus Africanus', *Med. Hist. J.* 2 (1967), 45–7
SEELER v.a. to seal (sigillare)
SEGE s. seat, base (sedes)
SEIGNIE s. bleeding, blood-letting (detractio sanguinis, minutio)
SEIGNIER, SEINER v.a. to bleed (minutiare, flebotomare)
SEIGNURIE, SEGNURIE s. power, control
SELE s. stool (medic.) (sella)
SEMENCE s. seed (granum)
SEMPERVIVA s. houseleek (Sempervivum tectorum L.)
SENATIONES s. pl. garden cress (Lepidium sativum L.) or water cress (Nasturtium officinale
    R.Br.)
SENÉ, SENEE s. senna (sena)
SENESÇON, SENE(S)CHON s. groundsel (Senecio vulgaris L.) (senationes); 'holy thistle'
    (Cnicus benedictus L.); also cress, see SENATIONES
SENEV(I)É s. mustard (Sinapis L. spp.)
SENGLANT a. bloody
SENSIBLE a. sensitive, sensitory (sensibilis)
SENTEMENT s. feeling (sensus)
SENTIBLE a. sensitive (sensibilis)
SENTIR subst. infin. feeling (sensus)
SEON s. seton
SEPULTURE s. grave, tomb (sepultura, sepulcrum)
SERAPINUM s. gum resin from Ferula persica L.
SERPENT s. snake S. ROUGE (serpens)
SERPIGO s. creeping skin disease
SERRÉ p.p. constipated
SEU s. willow (Salix L. spp.); elder (Sambucus nigra L.) (sambucus)
SEU s. animal fat S. DE MOTOUN
SI A POINE NON only with difficulty
SIAUT ind. pr. 3 of SOLEIR v.n. to be accustomed (solere)
SIDIE see PSIDIA
SIEL s. salt
SIET sbj. pr. 3 of ESTRE v.n. to be
SILLIUM s. psillium, 'fleawort' (Plantago arenaria Waldst. and Kit.)
SIMILA s. flour S. D'ORGE barley flour
SIMPHITUM s. comfrey (Symphytum officinale L.)
SINANCIA s. type of quinsy (sinantia)
SINAPIS s. mustard (Sinapis L. spp.)
SINAPISME s. mustard compress (sinapismus)
SINCOPIE, SCINCOPIE s. syncope (sincopus)
SINOC(H)A, SINOCHI(E), SINOCHIDE(S, SINOCHO s. prolonged, continuous fever (sino-
    chus) S. INFLATIVE (sinocha inflativa)
SINOQUE see SINOC(H)A
SINTHOME s. symptom (sinthoma)
SIPHAC s. peritoneum (sifac)
SIRINGA s. syringe (see 155); a fistula or fester
S(C)IROP, SYROP s. syrup S. ACETOUS decoction of honey and vinegar S. MIRTIN myrtle
    syrop S. VIOLAT S. COPHONIS (frigidum C.) cf. AN43
SISIMBRIUM s. horsemint (Mentha spicata L.) or watermint (Mentha aquatica L.)
SOFFLER v.a. to blow, puff (sufflare, insufflare)
SOFFOCACION, SUFFOCACION s. stifling
SOFFRE, SUFFRE s. sulphur
SOFFRIN a. sulphurous BAIN S. sulphur bath (balnea sulphurea) EWE SUFFRINE
SOIE s. hair S. DE PORC(EL hog's bristle (seta porcina)

SOLACIER v.a. to comfort, console, cheer up

SOLATRUM s. black nightshade (Solanum nigrum L.)

SOLEIR v.n. to be accustomed SIAUT, SEUT, SOUT ind. pr. 3 SOLAIENT imp. 6

SOLUTIF a. solvent (dissolvens, dissolutivus)

SOMERON, SUMMERRON, SUMERON s. tip, top (summitas)

SORABUNDER v.n. to be present in large quantities, to abound (superhabundare)

SORBARIUS s. sorb-apple tree (sorbae)

SORB(E s. sorb-apple, fruit of service tree (sorbum) (Pyrus domestica L.)

SORBILE a. easily absorbed (of diet) (sorbilis)

SORCIL s. eyebrow (supercilium)

SORDESCE, SORDESSE s. deafness (surditas)

SORE, SOURE, SEUERE adv. above, on top (supra)

SORIS s. mouse

SORPAL(L)E a. palish (subpallidus)

SORROGE a. reddish (subrufus, subrubeus)

SORSANÉ p.p. cicatrized

SORSAN(E)URE s. scar (cicatrix)

SORVENIR v.n. to happen, occur

SOTEIMENT, SOUTEMENT, SUTIVEMENT adv. suddenly (subito, repentinus)

SOUCHER v.n. to suck (sugere)

SOUDRE v.a. to heal, knit together (consolidare)

SOUFISTRIE s. sophistry (sophistria)

SOUPE s. sop (offa)

SOUTIF a. fine, delicate (subtilis)

SOUTIL, SOTTIL a. fine, slender, delicate (subtilis)

SOUTILLETÉ s. fineness, delicacy

SOUZROGE a. reddish ['subrubicund', 'subruff'] (subrufus, subrubicundus)

SOVENTESFOIS adv. often, frequently

SOVEU(S)NON adv. at least (saltem)

SOVERAIN a. supreme, most intense, peak EN S. TRAVAIL at the peak of the attack, crisis (in summo labore)

SPARAGUS, SPERAGUS s. asparagus (Asparagus officinalis L.)

SPERME s. sperm (sperma)

SPICANARDI, SPEIC NARDINE, SPIC NARDINE s. spikenard (Nardostachys jatamansi L.)

SPINACES s. spinach (Spinacea oleracea L.)

SPLEN s. spleen (splen)

SPLENETIQUE s. patient suffering from disorder of the spleen

SQUILLA s. squill (Scilla esp. Scilla maritima Baker) (squilla)

SQUILLITIQUE, SQUILLITIC, SQUILLETIQUE a. made with squill, see OXIMEL

SQUINANCIA s. quinsy (squinantia)

SQUINANTI, SQUINANCE s. camel's hay, squinant (Andropogon schoenanthus L.)

STAPHISAGRIA, STAFISAGRIA s. stavesacre (Delphinium staphisagria L.)

STERNUER v.n. to sneeze (sternutare)

STERNUTATION s. sneezing ['sternutation'] (sternutatio)

STINCCIS, STINCI s. pl. tench (stincus)

STIPTIQUE a. styptic (stipticus)

STORAX CALAMITA / CALAMITE s. styrax, resin from Styrax officinalis / Liquidamber orientalis (storax calamite)

STRANGU(I)RIA s. strangury, difficulty in urination (stranguria)

STRIGNUM s. black nightshade (Solanum nigrum L.) (strignum)

STROPHICUS a. S. DOLOR a pain in the lower intestine (see 111)

SUBCITRIN a. yellowish (subcitrinus)

SUBFUMIGACION s. suffumigation, treatment with aromatic fumes (subfumigatio, suffumigium)

SUBLANC a. palish (subalbidus)

SUBPALE a. palish (subpallidus)

SU(B)STANCE s. solid matter (substantia)

SUBSTANCEL, SUSTANTEL a. substantial (substantialis)

SUCCITRIN a. yellowish (subcitrinus)
SUC(C)ER, SUCC(H)IER v.a. to suck (sugere)
SUCCUM s. juice
SUEEF adv. gently (leniter, suaviter)
SUER v.a. and n. to sweat (sudare, resudare)
SUFFOCATION s. choking, suffocation (suffocatio)
SUFFRE VIF s. sulphur vivum, virgin sulphur
SUMAC s. sumach (Rhus coriaria L.)
SUMEÇON s. tip, top (summitas)
SUPERFICÉ s. surface (superficies)
SUPERFLUEL a. superfluous
SUPERFLUITÉ s. excess, superfluity, waste product (superfluitas)
SUPERHABUNDANCE s. great abundance
SUPPOSITORIE, SUPPOSITOYRE, SUPPOSITURE, SUPPOSITOIRE, SUBPOSITOIRE s.
    suppository (suppositorium, stuellum)
SUSBLANC, SUZBLANC a. whitish (subalbidus)
SUSPICION, SOSPICION, SUSPECION s. suspicion ['suspeccion .i. a thow3t or myststyng of
    good to bad regnyng'] (suspicio)
SUSROGE a. reddish ['subrubicund'] (subrufus, subrubicundus, subrubeus)
SUSTANCE COLOQUINTIDE s. 'interior coloquintide' (q.v.)
SUSTENIR v.a. to sustain, nourish
SUZRUF a. reddish (subrufus)
TABORT s. drum (timpanum)
TAILLEURE s. cutting
TAINT p.p. discoloured, polluted (infectus)
TAMARIND(E, THAMARINDE s. tamarind (Tamarindus indica L.)
TAMARIT, TAMARIZ s. tamarisk (Tamarix gallica L.) (tamariscus)
TAN, TANO s. tan
TANT adv. NE TANT NE QUANT not at all
TANT I A QUE conj. loc.
TANT NE QUANT, NE TANT NE QUANT nothing at all
TANT SOLEMENT adv. only
TAPSIE BARBASTE s. mullein (Verbascum thapsus L.)
TARTARI s. tartar, wine lees
TEINT p.p. dipped (intinctus)
TEINT ind. pr. 3 of TEINDRE v.a. to infect, taint (inficere) TEINT, TIENS p.p. (infectus)
TEINT, TENT, p.p. tinged (with colour) (tinctus, intinctus)
TEMPRER v.a. to mix with a liquid v.n. to soak, steep TEMPRÉ p.p. mixed with water (lim-
    phatus, infusus)
TEMPRIER v.n. to soak, steep (temperare)
TENAILLES s. pl. forceps
TENDRONS s. pl. tender parts, costal pleura ['tenderhed'] (teneritas)
TENASMON s. constipation, unsuccessful need to evacuate bowels
TENDRUN, TENDRON s. shoot (of plant)
TENDU p.p. distended
TENSION s. tension (tensio)
TENTE s. tent, pledget, seton (stuellum, licinium)
TENVE a. thin (tenuis)
TENVETÉ s. thinness (tenuitas)
TEODERICON, THEODERICON s. a medicament AN117 (theodoricon)
TERDRE v.a. to wipe (tergere)
TERREBENTINE, TERBENTINA, TERBENTINE s. terpentine, terebinth, resin of Pistacia tere-
    binthus L.
TERRIEN a. (colour) of earth (terreus)
TEST s. eggshell (testa)
TEVE, TIEVE a. lukewarm (tepidus)
TEVETÉ s. luke-warmness (tepor)
THEODERICON ANACARDI, THEODORICUM ANACARDINUM s. a medicament AN118

THEODOR[IC]O[N] [EU]PERISTON s. a medicament AN117
THIMUM s. thyme (Thymus serpyllum L.)
TIEDE a. lukewarm (tepidus)
TIERÇAIN(E, TIERCEIN(E a. and s. tertian (fever), marked by paroxysms every other day
TIERCE s. HORE DE T. tierce
T(I)EULE s. tile (tegula)
TIMBRE s. drum (timpanum)
TIMPANISTE(S s. distension of the abdomen by gas or air in the intestine
TINNITUS s. buzzing in ears, tinnitus
TINUISSEMENT, TINISEMENT, TINNISSEMENT s. buzzing in ears, tinnitus (tinnitus)
TIRIACA s. theriac, medicine effective against poison
TIRIAQUE s. theriac, medicine effective against poison
TISICLE s. phthisis, wasting caused by lack of moisture (tisis)
TITILLATION, TITILACION s. tickling (titillatio)
TITIMALLE see TITIMALLUS
TITIMALLUS s. spurge (Euphorbia L. spp.) or houseleek (Sempervivum tectorum L.)
TIULE, TIEULE s. tile (tegula)
TOIE s. membrane of the eye (pannus)
TONEL s. cask (dolium)
TONISSEMENT s. buzzing in the ears, tinnitus (tinnitus)
TORCIONS s. pl. tormina (tortio)
TORDRE v.a. to twist (obtorquere) TORT p.p.
TORTRE s. turtle-dove (turtur)
TOSTER / TOSTIR v.n. toast (exurere, torrefacere)
TOUS(S)E, TOUSCE s. cough (tussis)
TOUSER, TO(U)SSIR v.n. to cough (tussire) TOUST ind. pr. 3
TRACHEA ARTERIA s. trachea (trachea arteria)
TRAIRE v.a. to draw
TRAITIÉ s. section, treatise (tractatus)
TRANSGLUTER, TRANSGLOTIR v.a. to swallow (transglutere)
TRENCHEMENT s. cutting, severing (incisio)
TRESOR s. wealth (pecunia)
TRESPASSEMENT s. passage (transitus)
TRIACLE s. theriac, an antidote to poison (tiriaca)
TRIANGULUS s. a type of cautery (cauterium triangulum)
TRIAQUE s. theriac
TRIASANDALI s. electuary made of three types of sandalwood AN116 (triasandali)
TRIBLER v.a. to grind, pound, crush (terere)
TRIBOILLER v.n. to gurgle
TRIFFE LA GRANT, T. LE G. s. soothing medical preparation AN114 (trifera magna)
TRI(F)FE SARRAZIN(E s. soothing medical preparation (Grk. trypheron) (trifera saracenica)
TROBLE a. murky, muddy (turbidus)
TROCISQUE s. trocisk
TROCLETEM a. see MIRRE (troclitem)
TROUBLER v.a. to disturb (perturbare) TROUBLÉ p.p. cloudy (turbulentus, turbidus)
TROVOIR v.a. to find
TUCIA s. natural zinc ore (tuscia)
TUEL s. tube, pipe (calamus, embotum)
TURBIT(H) s. turpeth (Ipomoea turpethum)
TYMUM s. thyme (Thymus serpyllum L.)
TYMPANITE(S) a. suffering from distension of the abdomen by gas or air in the intestine (timpa-
nites)
TYPE s. cold fever (tipus)
TYRIA s. type of leprosy
TYRIASIS s. type of leprosy
UEUS a. watery (aquosus) cf. EWEUS, EVEUS
ULCERATION s. ulcer, ulceration, scarred tissue (ulceratio, ulcera)
UNCE s. ounce (uncia)

UN(E)S a. some, several (quidam, quedam)
UNGUENTUM AUREUM s. a medicament (see below p. 328)
UNGUENTUM STEPHANONIS s. a medicament (unguentum Stephani, u. Stephanonis)
UNIVERSAL a. general, universal (universalis)
USIER v.a. to employ, use
UVA s. uvula (uvula)
UVE PASSE s. black grape (Vitis vinifera L.)
UWEL a. equal (equalis)
UWEL(L)EMENT adv. in equal measure (equaliter)
VEDVE s. widow (vidua)
VEINE, FEINE, VOINE s. vein (vena, vas)
VENE MESERAICE s. pl. mesaraic veins (vena mesaraica)
VENIMEUX s. poisonous (venenosus)
VENIN, VENIM s. poison (venenum)
VENTOSITÉ s. flatulence, morbid wind in body (ventositas)
VENTOUSE, VENTUSSE s. cupping glass (ventosa)
VENTRAIL s. intestines; belly, abdomen
VENTRAILLIE s. ventricle, cell (ventriculus)
VENTUSER, VENTOUSER v.a. to cup, bleed
VER s. spring (ver)
VER s. worm (vermis) V. FAUS (vermis sophisticus)
VERBENA s. vervain (Verbena officinalis L.)
VERDURE s. green colour
VERGE s. penis (virga)
VERGÉ a. streaked (with colour), striated (of urine) (virgatus)
VERMAIL a. red
VERMINE s. worm (reptilis)
VERT JUS s. verjuice
VERTIZ s. crown (of head) ['schod'] (vertex)
VESSIE s. bladder (vesica)
VEUE s. sight, vision (visus)
VIELER v.n. to play the fiddle
VIEILLE s. old woman (vetula)
VILE s. skin, lining (villus)
VILLOSITÉ s. roughness (villositas)
VIOLETTE s. violet (Viola L. spp.)
VISCOS, VISQUOUS, VISCOSEUS, VISCOUS a. viscous ['lymy'] (viscosus)
VISCOSITÉ s. viscosity (viscositas)
VISIBILE a. visible (visibilis)
VIT s. penis (priapus)
VIVIFICATIF a. restorative, life-giving ['lyfly'] (vivificans)
VOIDER v.n. to evacuate
VOIDESCE s. emptiness, void (vacuitas)
VOIRRE s. glass
VOIZ a. empty, void (vacuus)
VOMITE, VOMITU s. vomitory V. SCARPELLE (vomitus scarpelle) V. PATRIARCIE,
    VOMITU(S) PATRIARCHE (vomitus patriarche)
VOU s. vow
VONCHEMENT s. vomiting
VONCHEURE s. vomiting
VONCH(I)ER v.n. to vomit (vomire, evomire) n. vomiting
VU s. vow
XILOBALSAMUM s. fragrant wood of balsam (Commophora opobalsamum (Kunth) Engler)
YCTERICE, YTERICE see YCTERICIA
YCTERICIA s. jaundice
YDROPIQUE a. and n. (patient) suffering from dropsy
YDROPISIE s. dropsy
YERA RUFINI s. an electuary AN142

YGIA s. a medicament AN51
YLIACUS a. of the kidneys
YMAGINATION s. faculty of the imagination ['ymaginatif'] (imaginatio)
YPOSARCA s. type of dropsy, oedema
YRICII s. pl. ? sea holly (Eryngium maritimum) (hiricii que in mare inveniuntur)
YSMOM s. passage between the oesophagus and the trachea ['a litel folikel or litel skyn bytwen
    the weyn ysofagus and the tracheam'] (ismon)
YSOP s. hyssop (Hyssopus officinalis L.)
YSOPHAGUM s. oesophagus (ysophagus)
YVERNEL a. winter, wintry (hiemalis)
ZINZIBERIS s. ginger
ZUCARRUM s. sugar
ZUCRE s. sugar

APPENDIX

Medicamenta from the *Antidotarium Nicolai*[1]

(excluding compounds in dia-)

2. **ADRIANUM** dictum est quod ab Adriano imperatore romanorum compositum fuit. Valet proprie ad omne vitium capitis ex frigiditate et ad gravedinem oculorum et obscuritatem contra emigraneam. Datur cum vino calido ubi cocta sit salvia in sero in modum avellane. Detur etiam quartanariis cum decoctione gentiane vel pigami ante horam accessionis. Datur etiam accipitri lapidem habenti, sed si homini habenti lapidem, detur cum vino in quo cocta sit saxifragia vel milium solis. Decima pars confecta est libra .i. Recipe opii tebaici dragmas .iii., casie lignee, jusquiami amborum ana dragmas .ii. et grana .vi. et tertiam partem unius grani, siseleos, seminis apii ana dragmam .i. et scrupulum semis et grana .ii., folii, origani, draganti ana dragmam .i., opobalsami, petroselini, macis, storacis calamite, zinziberis, xilobalsami, ciperi, carpobalsami ana dragmam .i., musci grana .vi., seminis maratri, calami aromatici ana scrupulos .ii. et grana .ii., cinamomi, spice, croci, costi, reupontici, piretri, acori, dauci cretici, anisi ana dragmam semis et grana .vi., castorei dragmam .i. et semis, serapini, mirre, rose, cardamomi, amomi, rute agrestis, seminis ameos ana scrupulum .i., grana .iiii., casie fistule scrupulum .i. Alii addunt lilifagi dragmas .ii. Mellis quod sufficit.

132. **UNGUENTUM AGRIPPA**, quo Agrippa rex Judeorum utebatur, quod tante dignitatis erat quod nemini discipulorum tradere volebat. Valet ydropicis et omnibus tumoribus in quacunque parte corporis fuerint, et ad nervos indignatos. Urinam provocat. Inunctum super ventrem laxat et dolori renum ex frigida causa optime facit. Quarta pars est libre .v. Recipe brionie libras .ii., radicis ebuli, tribuli marini ana uncias .ii., radicis siccidis libram .i., squille uncias .vi., yreos uncias .iii., radicis filicis uncias .ii. Omnes radices ter vel quater bene abluantur et in pilo marmoreo terantur. Et in quatuor libris olei lentisci ponantur per duos dies, sed si per .vi. vel per .vii. dimittatur, plus valet, quia calorem et odorem sibi et efficaciam vendicat. Tertio vero, velut dictum est, ad ignem ponatur et tamdiu bulliat donec incipiat dimitti. Deinde ponatur in sacco et exprimando coletur. Et cum colatum fuerit, super ignem ponatur et cum bullire inceperit, ponantur uncie .v. cere albissime et liquefacta cera ab igne deponatur et cum frigidatum fuerit, collige et serva.

131. **UNGUENTUM ARAGON**. Aragon id est adiutorium. Valet ad dolorem ex frigiditate viri et mulieris tali modo inunctum. In testa ovi primum calefac ad ignem. Deinde superinungatur et postea testa calida superponatur loco patienti. Valet ad spasmum et tetanum et ad dolorem ilii et renum tali ordine ut supra diximus. Arteticis

---

1 I have used the Latin text in W.S. Van den Berg, *Eene middelnederlandsche Vertaling van het Antidotarium Nicolai* (Leiden, 1917), correcting errors, introducing more detailed punctuation, and expanding the symbols for quantities. The numbers of the receipts refer to Van den Berg's numbering of the Latin text. The receipts are arranged alphabetically according to the name they bear in the Anglo-Norman text (see Glossary)

et sciaticis multum prodest. Quartanariis si spina inungatur ante horam accessionis, ut dictum est, mirifice prodest. Quarta pars est libre .vi. Recipe roris marini, majorane, radicis jari, serpilli, rute, radicis siccidis ana dragmas .iii. et semis, foliorum lauri, salvie, savine ana uncias .iii., policarie majoris et minoris uncias .ix., brionie uncias .iii., laureole uncias .ix., nepite libram semis, masticis, olibani ana dragmas .vii., piretri, euforbii, zinziberis, piperis ana unciam .i., olei muscellini unciam semis, petrolei unciam .i., adipis ursini, olei laurini ana uncias .iii., butiri uncias .iiii., olei communis libras .v., cere libram .i. Herbarum radices hora supradicta colligantur, omnes herbe uno vel duobus diebus ut dictum est superius. Fortiter contusis ponantur in oleo per .vii. dies. Octavo autem die super ignem ponantur et coquantur donec herbe destruantur. Postea per saccum fortiter colentur et iterum super ignem ponantur. Et cum bullire inceperint, addantur oleum laurinum, butirum, adeps ursinus et cera, qua liquefacta adde petroleum et muscelinum, postea masticem et olibanum, zinziber, piper, piretrum et euforbium et tunc ab igne deponatur et recondatur.

4. **ATHANASIA** .i. immortalis proprie valet ad fluxum sanguinis mulieris. Datur cum succo plantaginis. Succus debet prius duci super lapidem molarem cum lapide emathitide tamdiu donec in sanguineum colorem vertatur. Et cum tali succo distemperata medicina detur et eadem bombice intincta et sepius in vulva missa sanguinem constringit. Hoc quidem facit emothoicis cum tali ordine distemperata et naribus attracta fluxum sanguinis narium sistit. Sexta pars confecta est libra .i. Recipe cinamomi, casie ana dragmas .iii. et grana .vi., croci orientalis, squinanti, storacis calamite, fu, sileris, jusquiami, apii, dauci, anisi, opii ana dragmam .i. et semis et grana .iii., spice, folii, castorei, mirre, lapidis emathitis, sanguinis draconis, coralli, rubei, mumie, costi, boli, simphiti, lempnias, asari, acori, corticis, mandragore, pulegii, baccarum lauri, meu, macropiperis, leucopiperis, petroselini ana dragmam .i., mellis quod sufficiat. Dosis eius est dragme .iii. Cum succo plantaginis propinata lientericis, dissintericis et ad diariam valet.

1. **AUREA ALEXANDRINA** dicta est ab auro, alexandrina ab Alexandro peritissimo philosopho a quo inventa est. Proprie valet ad omne capitis vitium ex frigiditate maxime et ad omnem reumaticam passionem que a capite ad oculos et aures et gingivas descendit et ad gravedinem omnium membrorum que fit de eodem humore. Datur eunti dormitum cum vino calido. XVIII pars confecta est libre .ii. Recipe asari, carpobalsami, jusquiami ana dragmas .ii. et semis, gariofilorum, opii, mirre, ciperi ana dragmas .ii., balsami, cinamomi, folii, zedoare, zinziberis, costi, coralli, casie lignee, euforbii, dragaganti, turis, meu, storacis calamite, saliunce, cardamomi, siselei, napei, saxifragie, aneti, anisi ana dragmam .i., ligni aloes, reubarbari, alipte, castorei, spice, galange, opoponacis, anacardi, masticis, sulfuris vivi, pionie, yringi, rose, thimi, acori, pulegii, aristologie longe, gentiane, corticis mandragore, camedreos, fu, baccarum lauri, amei, dauci, macropiperis, leucopiperis, xilobalsami, karvi, amomi, petrosellini, seminis levistici, rute, seminis sinoni ana dragmam .i. et semis, auri purificati, argenti meri, albarum margaritarum, blacte, bizantie, ossis de corde cervi ana scrupulum .i. et grana .xiiii., eboris limature, calami aromatici, piretri ana grana .viiii., mellis quod sufficit. Detur in modum avellane febricitantibus cum aqua calida, non febricitantibus cum vino calido.

9. **BENEDICTA** dicitur quoniam ab omnibus a quibus sumitur est benedicta. Detur habentibus infirmitates contra quas inventa fuit. Valet ad guttam arteticam, podagricis ex frigiditate, renes et vesicam purgat. Media pars confecta est libre .ii. Recipe turbit,

esule, zuchari ana dragmas .x., diagridii, hermodactili, rosarum ana dragmas .v., gariofilorum, spice, zinziberis, croci, saxifragie, macropiperis, amomi, cardamomi, petroselini, litospermatis, salis gemme, galange, macis, carvi, feniculi, sparagi, bruxi,
granorum solis ana dragmam .i., mel quod sufficit. Datur in sero cum vino calido ad
modum castanee.

8. **BLANCA** dicta est quoniam albos purgat humores .i. flegmaticos. Valet cephalargicis et oculorum doloribus et sanguinolentis et tumoribus et lippis. Optime facit
contra omnia que turbant fantasiam, rationem et memoriam. Utilis est tremulosis,
epilenticis et paraliticis. Nona pars confecta est libra .i. Recipe terbentine, opoponacis, galbani, ase, serapini, castorei, antimonii, sulfuris, bdelii, aspalti, armoniaci,
storacis liquide, carnis leonis, diagridii, euforbii, agarici, interioris colloquintide, el-
leborii nigri, polipodii, tapsie, piretri, squinanti, peucedani, asari, ciperi, pionie, betonice, camedreos, polii, amomi, levistici, seminis rute, sanguinis draconis ana
dragmam .i., cinamomi, gariofilorum, macis, cardamomi, anisi, maratri, balsami ana
scrupulum .i. et semis, ambre grana .v., mel quod sufficit. Datur cum vino in quo cocta
sit salvia aut herba paralisis in sero in modum castanee.

54. **KATARTICUM IMPERIALE** id est laxativum pro imperatoribus factum et pro
aliis delicatis hominibus. Ducit enim sine lesione. Hec precipue confert pinguibus
hominibus qui semper sunt constipati. Valet multum iliosis. Iuvat eos qui ex ventositate stomaci et intestinorum laborant. Medietas libra .i. Recipe diagridii, zuchari ana
dragmas .iiii. semis, cinamomi, nardi, saxifragie, polipodii ana dragmas .ii., mirobalanorum, citri, hermodactili, polipodii ana dragmas .ii., gariofilorum, zinziberis, celtice,
melanopiperis, macropiperis, cardamomi, amomi, ana dragmam .i. semis, mel quod
sufficit. Sumatur cum vino calido vel aqua calida mane vel sero.

40. **ELECTUARIUM DUCIS** dicitur quia abbas de curia illud composuit ad opus
ducis Rogerii filii Roberti Viscardi propter indigestionem et ventositatem stomaci et
intestinorum et ilii dolorem et vitium lapidis. Recipe anisi dragmas .ii. et grana .xv..
liquiricie, masticis ana scrupulos .ii. et grana .v., camedreos, zinziberis, cinamomi,
galange, maratri, karvi ana scrupulum .i., grana .xv., xilocasie, calamenti, dauci, piretri, piperis albi et longi, ciperi, squinanti, yreos, amomi, folii, asari ana scrupulum .i.,
spice, croci, gummi arabici, dragaganti, seminis aneti, calami aromatici, cubebe, gariofilorum, carpobalsami, juniperi, alexandri, sileris, pentafilon, seminis sparagi, citri,
acori radicis, ameos, reubarbari indi, urtice, reupontici, nucis miristice, ligni aloes,
basilici, milii solis, saxifrage, seminis citroli, melonis, cucumeris et cucurbite, scariole,
petrosellini, been albi et rubei, storacis calamite, cardamomi ana grana .xv., penido-
num unciam semis et scrupulos .ii. et semis, mel quod sufficit. Datur post prandium et
ad cenam cum vino calido. Si datur contra lapidis vitium, sumatur cum decoctione
milii solis vel scolopendrie.

48. **FILOANTROPOS** amicus hominis interpretatur. Proprie valet stranguiriosis,
nefreticis. Calculos in renibus habentibus et in vesica mirabiliter frangit et fractos
expellit. Valet etiam ad duritiem splenis et epatis. Dolori iliorum subvenit cum scrupulo .i. semis diagridii. XII pars libra .i. Recipe folii, squinanti, ciperi, asari, euforbii,
thimi, petrosellini macedonici, aneti, milii solis, lapidis lyncis ana scrupulos .ii. et
semis, cinamomi, calami aromatici, polipodii, fisalidi, melanopiperis, seminis levistici
et petrosellini et urtice, seminis citri, litospermatis, bardane, baccarum edere ana
scrupulos .ii., galange, nardi, zedoarie, betonice, fu, meu, sparagi, cardamomi, apii,

maratri, eruce, sinapis, orobi albi et rubei ana dragmam semis, gariofilorum, zinziberis, casie lignee, piretri, costi, spice celtice, mirobalanorum corticis, olibani, leucopiperis, carpobalsami, carvi, cimini, baccarum lauri, sileris ana dragmam .i. vel scrupulum .i., olei nardini, pulegii, sambucini, muscellini ana grana .xx., mel quod sufficit. Datur cum vino calido.

43. **ELECTUARIUM FRIGIDUM SECUNDUM COPHONEM** quod optime tercianarios et quotidianarios et erraticas febres purgando sanat. Et etiam habentibus stomacum colericum familiare est. Tertia pars confecta est libre quatuor. Recipe sandalorum alborum et rubeorum et spodii, dragaganti, gummi arabici, amili, rasure eboris, reubarbari, sene, rosarum, violarum, seminis fumiterre, berberis, sebesten, seminis portulace, maratri, anisi ana drammas tres, emblici unciam unam. Conficitur sic. Psillii uncie octo ponantur in sufficienti aqua ferventi in qua bullierit libra media polipodii quercini viridis, mundati et triti. Omnes herbe diuretice, violarum et prunorum [. . .] et tamdiu dimittantur donec bene congelentur. Deinde coletur fortiter per saccum. Ad meliorem vero mucilaginis constrictionem intromittatur in saccellum aliquantulum aque ferventissime et colature addantur scamonee uncie sex pulverizate, prius tamen cum aqua frigida inter manus fricate, et bene cum eadem mucilagine fricentur manibus. Deinde apponantur zuchari libre quatuor dissoluti prius cum sufficienti aqua decoctionis polipodii et ceterarum herbarum diureticarum. Et colati deinde super ignem positum bullire permittatur cumque ad medium decoctionis pervenerit, addantur uncie due tamarindorum et uncie due casie fistule dissolute prius in sufficienti aqua decoctionis prunorum et predictarum herbarum diureticarum et per caciam colate usque ad perfectam coctionem bullire permittatur. Signum autem decoctionis est: si super marmor positum et infrigidatum aliquantulum viscosum fuerit et digito adheserit, motione tamen baculi ab ipso decoctionis principio non cessante. Cumque coctum fuerit, ab igne deponatur et in mortario posito pulvis predictarum specierum super spargatur et cum pistello bene conterantur usque ad ipsius jus viscositatis et gummositatis remotionem. Deinde recondatur. Detur colatura casie fistule in sero vel media nocte.

141. **YERALOGODION MEMPHYTUM.** Yera id est sacra, logos id est sermo, memphytum id est impeditio. Curat enim impeditam locutionem ex quacunque causa. Simplex vel laxativum datum purgat melancoliam et flegma mirabiliter cum calida. Datur epilenticis cum calida sale et mulsa. Curat stomaticos et spumantes , caducos vertiginosos et qui linguam sibi mordent, cephalargicis, emigranicis et qui ita vexantur ex capitis commotionibus ut videantur quasi demonum habere. Singulis mensibus, ut diximus, data purgatione paraliticis tremulosis medetur. Pleureticis, epaticis, spleneticis subvenit, et menstrua educit, nefreticos, sciaticos et arteticos alleviat, lepras et hernias et varias maculas emendat. Decima pars est libra. Recipe coloquintide interioris, polipodii ana uncias .ii., euforbii, polii, coconidii ana dragmam .i. et semis et grana .vi., absinthii, mirre ana unciam .i. et grana .xii., centauree, agarici, armoniaci, timiamatis, folii, spice, squille, diagridii ana dragmam .i., aloes, thimi, cimarum rubearum, casie, camedrei, bdellii, prassii ana scrupulum .i. et grana .xiiii., cinamomi, opopanacis, castorei, aristologie longe, piperis albi et nigri et longi, croci, serapini, petrosellini ana dragmam semis, ellebori albi et nigri ana grana .vi., mel quod sufficit. Datur mane et sero cum calida in modum castanee.

143. **YERAPIGRA GALYENI.** Yera id est sacra, picra id est amara que facit ad diversas capitis passiones sive egritudines aurium, oculorum distemperantiam. Stoma-

cum quoque optime purgat. Causas epatis emendat, splenis duritiem et densitatem removet et extenuat, renibus et vesice proficit et matricis distemperantiam emundat. Decima pars est libra .i. Recipe cinnamomi, spice, croci, squinanti, asari, xilocassie, xilobalsami, carpobalsami, viole, absinthii, agarici, rosarum, turbit, coloquintide, masticis ana scrupulos .ii., aloes ad pondus omnium specierum .x. dragmas et scrupulos .ii., mel quod sufficit. Dosis eius dragme .iii. cum abstinentia mane cum calida. Si vero pilulas informes, da .xv. aut .xvii. cum sufficienti diagridio.

55. LITONTRIPON pertundens lapidem interpretatur. Hoc proprie lapidem frangit et expellit si in renibus vel vesica fuerit. Hac medicina utentes nec dolorem ilii nec lapides vitium incurrunt. Stranguiriam et dissuriam sine mora solvit. Octava pars est libre .ii. Recipe nardi, zinziberis, xilobalsami, acori, cinamomi, peuzedani, meu, melanopiperis, leucopiperis, macropiperis, saxifragie ana dragmas .ii. semis, opobalsami, gariofilorum, costi, reupontici, liquiricie, ciperi, draganti, alexandri, camedreos, seminis apii, sparagi, basiliconis, urtice, seminis citri ana dragmam .i. et grana .xv., folii, croci, squinanti, casie lignee, bdelii, masticis, seminis granorum solis,, petroselini, seminis sinoni, cardamomi, aneti, seminis euforbii, lapis lincis, olei nardini, muscelini ana scrupulum .i. minus grana .iiii., mel quod sufficit. Detur in sero cum vino calido.

130. UNGUENTUM MARCIATON magnum a Martiato peritissimo medico dicitur a quo fuit inventum quod facit ad dolorem et frigiditatem capitis et pectoris et stomaci. Et ad sclirosim splenis et epatis et ad ilii dolorem ad solem vel ad ignem inunctum statim subvenit. Paraliticis, sciaticis, nefreticis, podagricis prodest. Tumores reprimit et contra omnes dolores medetur potenter. Quarta pars est libre .viiii. Recipe cere albe libras .ii., olei libras .viii., roris marini, foliorum lauri ana dragmas .viii., rute uncias .vii., amarici uncias .vi., eleborii, savine, balsamite, lilifagi, ozimi, polii, calamenti, artemisie, enule, betonice, brance ursine, spergule, herbe venti, pimpinelle, agrimonie, absinthii, herbe paralisis, herbe sancte Marie, cimarum sambuci, crassule, millefolii, sempervive, camedrei, centauree, fragarie, quinquefolii, herba tetrait ana uncias .iiii. et semis, evisci, radiis cimini, mirte ana uncias .iiii., fenugreci unciam .i. et semis, butiri unciam .i. et dragmas .ii., urtice, violarum, papaveris nigri, mente sarasenice, et alie mente, politrici, lapaceoli, carduncelli, matris silve mature, herbe muscate, alleluia, lingue cervine, crispule, camphore, storacis, medulle cervine ana unciam et semis, adipis ursini, gallinacei, masticis ana unciam .i., thuris unciam semis, olei nardini dragmas .ii. Herbe colligantur in medietate mensis Maii. Uno die omnes herbe iste colligantur vel duobus, si potest ab hora tertia usque ad meridiem. Conficitur sic: herbas tritas diebus .vii. in optimo et odorifero vino infunde. Octavo vero die ad lentum ignem ponantur et cum vinum aliquantulum consumari addatur supradictum oleum. Et bulliant donec incipiant diminui. Deinde studiose colentur et projectis herbis iterum super ignem ponantur. Et cum inceperit bullire, pone storacem. Et cum modicum bullierit, pone butirum et assungiam aliquantulum tonsam et oleum nardinum, masticem, et olibanum et postea ceram. Et cum cera liquefacta fuerit, semper cum spatula agitando ab igne deponatur et cum coagulatum fuerit, in vase reserva.

58. MICLETA id est experta. Proprie valet ad emorroydas et ad ventris tortionem et rugitum, lienterie et dissinterie. Et optima est omni solutioni ventris. Medietas est libra .i. Recipe mirobalanorum citrinorum, indorum, kebulorum, mundatorum, assatorum ana dragmas .ii. semis, nasturcii dragmas .ii., bellericorum, emblicorum assatorum dragmas .ii., cimini, anisi, ameos, carvi ana dragmam .i. et semis. Infusa in aceto die ac nocte dimittantur et assata pulverizentur. Tunc adde spodium, balaustias, sumac, masticem, gummi arabici ana dragmam .i. et grana .xv. Fricentur omnia cum oleo rosarum et temperentur omnia mirtino syrupo. Dentur cum aqua pluviali mane, meridie et sero.

56. **METRIDATUM** id est mater omnium antidotorum sive a Metridato rege dictum faciens ad omnes passiones capitis virorum et mulierum si fuerint ex frigiditate. Maxime valet melancolicis et timidis, epilenticis, maniacis, fantasticis. Mirabiliter prodest cephalargicis, emigraneis, dolorem cilii patientibus et lacrimantibus oculis. Et ad omnia capitis vitia vel aurium subvenit. Dentium doloribus et palato et omnibus vitiis oris et maxillarum medetur si super locum dolentem ponatur. Et iterum ad modum emplastri ponatur in temporibus unde fit discursio, squinantiam solvit et apopleticis cum cerusa acceptum facit. Tussientibus et asmaticis, emoptoicis, peripleumonicis et omnibus doloribus qui intra corpus humanum fiunt succurit. Ciliacis, dissintericis et lientericis optimum est. Si detur cum decoctione balaustie, extensionem humerorum, thethanos sive spasmos patientes et paraliticos sine mora curat. Diafragmati ypocondriis subvenit, renibus et vesice opitulatur. Calculos frangit, menstrua provocat, omniaque vitia matricis excludit, sclirosim patientibus et podagricis singulis presidium est. Precipue datur contra venenum impositum sive bibitum, cum magna admiratione emendat et contra morsum rabidi canis vel alicuius reptilis si destemperatum fuerit. Et cum succo mente potetur vel supponatur, quotidianariis et quartanariis etiam ante horam accessionis datum mirifice prodest cum vino tepido. XXVII pars confecta libre .iii. Recipe storacis calamite dragmam .i. et scrupulum .i., gariofilorum, nardi, xilobalsami, orobi, lentici, draganti, masticis, galbani, gummi cedri, aspalti, castorei, olphei, bdellii, terre figuli, melliloti, laudani, opopanacis, armoniaci, apii, sulfuris vivi, liquoricie, nitri, ypoquistidos, acacie, rosarum, camedrei, ypericon, abrotani, pionie, ysopi, origani, elempnii, rami cedri et dampnicon, aristologie longe, epithimi, peucedani, centauree, roris marini, yringi, radicis balaustie, cimarum mirte, psidie, romei, squille, carpobalsami, git, anisi, jusquiami, cimini, feniculi, cardamomi. siselei, tesapii, amei, sinoni, levistici, seminis rute, seminis miconis, apii, dauci, seminis rape, macropiperis, ozimi, amomi ana dragmam .i., acori, illafeos, cassami, filis, zuccozarie, catariaci ana scrupulos .ii., balsami, cinamomi, croci, costi, squinanti, zinziberis, folii, terbentine, mirre, olibani, casie, agarici, spice celtice, reupontici, yrei, asari, diptami, prassii, interioris coloquintide, sticados, artemisie, calamenti, scordei, silfii, camapitheos, leucopiperis, melanopiperis, ozimi, seminis petroselini, seminis anagodam, malabatri, cardamomi, pentafilon ana scrupulum .i., dampnococci tertiam partem scrupuli .i. et grana .vii., vini vetustissimi unciam .i., mel quod sufficit. Datur in sero in modum avellane cum vino in quo cocta sit salvia.

57. **MUSEA ENEA.** Musa a peritissimo philosopho inventa, faciens ad omnes accessiones periodice febris .i. quotidiane, tertiane, quartane si ante horam accessionis in modum avellane cum vino calido detur, et acutarum angustias tollit. Tamen cum dederis, considera virtutes eorum qui patiuntur quia statim medelam sentiunt. Et etiam si cum tepida distemperetur, et ex ea in acutis et peracutis pulsus et tempora inungantur, et si sudorem provocat, erit signum evasionis si vero non mortis. Inflationem stomaci emendat, suspiriosis, ptisicis et his qui putredinem screant subvenit. Ydropicis, spleneticis et colicis subvenit. Lapidem in vesica frangit et his quibus penitus urina denegatur. Recipe piperis albi grana .xvii., thuris masculi, mirre, gentiane, jusquiami ana dragmas .vi., opii dragmas .iiii., croci dragmas .iiii., musci grana .vii., euforbii, aristologie longe dragmam .i. et scrupulum .i., mandragore dragmam .i. et scrupulum .i., mel quod sufficit. Detur ut superius in laude diximus.

69. **OPOPIRA MAGNA**. Opopira dicitur a succo et igne; opos enim grece, latine succus, pir id est ignis. Inde opopira id est ignitus succus. Proprie valet contra guttam que oculum et linguam et labium distemperat, ut recte sermonem non proferat aut non loquatur. Peculiariter curat paralisim oris et gutturis et manuum et pedum atque crurum. Et totius corporis optime medetur cum vino ubi cocta sit salvia et castoreum et costum in sero in modum avellane. Prodest tremulosis cum eadem decoctione bibitum. Contractioni nervorum subvenit. Colericis cum decoctione polipodii, epilenticis melancholicis et maniacis cum decoctione thuris masculi auxiliatur. Tussientibus in omnibus doloribus pectoris et stomaci cum decoctione calamenti et cimini, epaticis cum apozimate apii et eupatorii, spleneticis cum decoctione capparis et absintii, pleureticis cum apozimate ysopi et pulegii, yliosis cum decoctione yris et macedonici, calculosis cum apozimate saxifrage et ozimi, tipice febricitantibus cum decoctione pigami, nasturcii, piretri, prodest et multas corporis passiones facit. XV pars confecta libre .ii. Recipe opii thebaici dragmas .ii. et scrupulum .i. et grana .iiii., cinamomi, gariofilorum, nardi, galange, croci, costi, zedoarie, zinziberis, xilobalsami, reupontici, piretri, coralli albi et rubei, draganti, mirre, castorei, opoponacis, piperis nigri, albi et longi ana dragmas .ii. et grana .vi., rasure eboris, lilifagi, herbe paralisis ana dragmam .i. et grana .xiiii., balsami, musci, xiloaloes, squinanti, casiefistule, storacis calamite, masticis, confite rubee, galbani, serapini, asari, melliloti, aristologie rotunde, dragontee, assari, ellimpni, meu, peonie, raphani corticis, peucedani, acori, mandragore, betonice, gentiane, camedrei, pulegii, centauree majoris et minoris, celtice, absinthii, proserpinace, blactei, capillorum veneris, sponse solis, ypericon, vincetoxici, prassii, pigami, millefolii, cardamomi, calamenti, carpobalsami, anisi, seminis levistici, jusquiami, seminis lupini et pollinis orobi, alexandrini, baccarum lauri, maratri, sileris montani ana scrupulum .i. et grana .xviii., mel quod sufficit. Detur ut superius diximus.

72. **OXIMEL** sic fit. Recipe mellis despumati libram .i., aceti fortissimi libram .i. et semis in quo bulliant radices feniculi dragmas .ii., radices rafani unciam semis, radices apii, petroselini macedonici, sparagi, bruxi, saxifrage ana uncias .iiii., polipodii uncias .viii. Omnia ista bulliant in libras .ii. aceti. Deinde coletur et colatura supradicto melli addatur, in stagnato vase semper agitando cum spatula tamdiu lento igne bulliat donec ad consumptionem succi deveniat. Valet ut oxizaccara; digerit, dividit et flegma mirabiliter purgat. Datur in mane cum calida.

74. **PAULINUM ANTIDOTUM**. Paulinum id est magnum, antidotum id est contradatum, quia magnam virtutem et efficaciam habet. Datur proprie veteri et nove tussi que fit ex discursione reumatis a capite. Valet contra vitia pectoris ex frigiditate in sero cum vino calido. Sed si distemperatum accipere non poterit, fac inde pilulas .viiii. vel .xi. facto cum opio. Sed si confectum fuerit sine opio et laxativum facere volueris, da dragmas .ii. cum scrupulis .ii. scamonee in pilulis factis. Caput et stomachum ex flegmate et malicia purgat et oculorum gravedinem tollit. Quarta pars est libra .i. quia in unaquaque receptione ponunt libram .i. et semis mellis dispumati. Recipe aloes dragmas .xi. et grana .xv., croci, costi, anacardi, agarici, coralli, mirre, armoniaci, terbentine, galbani, serapini, opoponacis, confite rubee, storacis calamite, yrei ana dragmas .iiii. et semis, opii, olibani, masticis, bdelii, cozumbri ana dragmas .ii. et grana .xv., balsami, folii ana dragmam .i. et semis, melisse dragmas .ii. Conficiantur sic: galbanum, serapinum, armoniacum, opoponacum. Iste gumme aliquantulum terantur et in albo et odorifero vino sufficienter nocte una imponantur. Mane vero super ignem ponantur et bulliant. Postea adde mellis dispumati uncias .iiii. et dimittantur

bullire quousque incipiant inspissari. Tunc storax calamita, confita rubea et cozumbrum cum pistello calido optime trita ponantur in caldario semper agitando cum spatula donec liquefiant et postea addatur terbentina. Et si probare volueris utrum coctum sit, pone aliquantulum supra marmor et si statim ad modum mellis se coagulaverit, coctum est. Caldario mox in terra posito addatur mirra cum bdelio, deinde mastix et olibanum, postea costum, anacardum, agaricum, coralli, yreos, opium, folium, melissa. Omnia simul pistata et pulverisata in caldario mittantur. Et hoc totum supra marmor inunctum prius oleo laurino ponatur et cum pulvere aloes malaxetur. Simul crocum cum speciebus terunt et ad ultimum cum croco orientali magdaliones informentur. Detur in modum avellane cum vino calido.

79. **PILULE AUREE**. Pilule a rotonditate dicte, auree ab excellentia auri dicuntur. Sicut enim aurum inter cetera metalla preciosus habetur, sic pilule iste inter alias meliores approbantur. Proprie purgant caput, lumen oculorum acuunt, ventositatem stomaci et intestinorum expellunt et sine molestia purgant. Medietas est libre .ii. et uncie .ii. Recipe aloes, diagridii ana dragmas .v., rosarum, apii seminis ana dragmas .ii. et semis, anisi, seminis feniculi ana dragmas .ii. et semis, croci, coloquintide interioris, masticis ana dragmam .i. Informentur in modum ciceris cum aqua infusionis draganti. Dentur in sero .ix. vel .xi. cum mulsa aut cum vino.

80. **PILULE DIACASTOREE** a castoreo dicte sunt quod intrat. Paraliticis mirabiliter prosunt. Una vel tres distemperate cum aqua calida naribus iniciantur ita ut supinus ipse patiens iaceat iuxta ignem parvum, aliquantulum vertat se et ore aperto sinat flegma exire. Oculos mundificant et dentes lapsos confirmant, stranguiriam curant, dolorem cilii ex aliquo frigido reumate solvunt. Tertia pars est libra .i. et semis. Recipe castorei, apii, croci, zinziberis, piretri, euforbii, elacterii, mabatematicon, leucopiperis, nigelle, stafisagrie, epithimi, ellebori albi, spice ana dragmam .i. Confice cum succo bete et informa in modum ciceris.

81. **PILULE ARTETICE** valent contra arteticam et podagram. Recipe hermodactili, turbiti, agarici ana dragmas .iiii., casie lignee, gariofilorum, xilobalsami, carpobalsami, zinziberis, masticis, feniculi, anisi, saxifrage, semen sparagi, bruxi, rose, granorum solis, sal gemme ana dragmam semis, aloes ad pondus omnium. Conficitur cum succo feniculi.

84. **PILULE DE QUINQUE GENERIBUS MIRABOLANORUM**. Recipe mirabolanorum citrinorum, chebulorum, beliricorum, emblicorum, indorum, agarici, dyagridii, coloquintide, sene, anisi ana unciam semis, turbit, anisi, maratri, masticis, lapidis lazuli ana dragmas .ii. et semis et grana .vi., aloes unciam .i. Fiant pilule. Valent arteticis, podagricis, spleneticis et ad visum clarificandum. Coleram purgant adustam.

41. **[ELECTUARIUM] PLIRIS ARCOTICON**. Pliris est completa medicina, arcoticon principium interpretatur. Valet tristibus melanconicis et ad magnam stomaci debilitatem et cordis .i. sincopim; memoriam reparat, sensum acuit. Epilenticis, anheliticis, acatalecticis prodest et omnem debilitatem cerebri reparat. Octava pars libra .i. Recipe cinamomi, gariofilorum, ligni aloes, galange, spice, nucis muscate, zinziberis, spodii, squinanti, ciperi, rosarum, violarum ana dragmam .i. et grana .xv., folii, liquiricie, masticis, storacis, sansuci, balsamite, basiliconis, cardamomi, macropiperis et leucopiperis, mirtilli, corticis citri ana scrupulos .ii. et grana .v., gemmarum, been albi et rubei, coralli, serici combusti ana scrupulum .i. et grana .ii., musci grana .vii. et

semis, camphore grana .v., syrupi rosacei quod sufficit. Detur febricitantibus cum aqua mane et sero, non febricitantibus cum vino.

73. **POTIO SANCTI PAULI**. Dicitur potio a potando, sancti Pauli quia sanctus Paulus eam composuit. Hec eadem a romanis potio maior vocatur, quia Paulus magnus interpretatur. Datur proprie epilepticis, catalepticis, analepticis, stomaticis cum vino in quo coctum sit tus masculum vel pionia mixta. Hec eadem cum Esdra datur hyemali tempore et vernali quartanariis et sanat cum vino in quo cocta sit gentiana vel saliunca et castoreum ante horam accessionis. Medetur etiam arteriacis et paraliticis cum vino in quo cocta sit salvia vel castoreum. XV pars est libra .i. Recipe nitri dragmas .iii. et scrupulum .i., castorei, antimonii, sinoni, folii, dampnococci, sileris, apii, petroselini, maratri, dauci, stafisagrie ana dragmam .i. et scrupulum .i., calami aromatici, mirabolanorum, liquiricie, draganti, pionie, piretri ana scrupulos .iii., costi, coloquintide, agarici, masticis, aristologie longe et rotunde, rosarum, mabathematicon, asari, lilifagi, aaronis, diptami, basiliconis, brance ursine, balsamite, origani, pulegii, camedrei vel ysopi, saturegie, piperis albi et nigri et longi, seminis rute ana scrupulum .i. et grana .xviii., cardamomi, turis ana scrupulum .i. et grana .iiii., balsami, nardi, croci, squinanti, casie, mirre, opoponacis, sulfuris, mandragore, gentiane, braccei, euforbii, amomi, sanguinis merguli ana scrupulum .i., cinamomi, gariofilorum, zinziberis, anacardi, xilobalsami, reupontici, peucedani, carpobalsami, storacis calamite, serapini, asari, sanguinis draconis, coaguli leporis, coaguli agni et caprioli et vituli et fellis ursini, sanguinis anatis, petrolei ana scrupulum .i. minus grana .iiii., herbe paralisis dragmas .vii. et grana .iiii., mel quod sufficit. Datur capitalibus passionibus in sero ad modum avellane vel cum decoctionibus supradictis.

95. **REQUIES MAGNA** vel magna medicina. Requies dicitur eo quod requiem patientibus prestat et sompnum maxime typice febricitantibus, quotidianariis, tertianariis, quartanariis acutis et peracutis prestat. Sexta pars est libra .i. Recipe rosarum et violarum ana dragmas .iii., opii, jusquiami, miconis, papaveris albi, mandragore, scariole, lactuce, seminis portulace, psilii, nucis muscate, cinamomi et zuchari ana dragmam .i. et semis, sandali albi et rubei et citrini, spodii, draganti ana scrupulos .ii. et grana .v. Da patientibus acutam cum syrupo violato, patientibus interpolatam cum melle confectam dare possumus. Datur quartanariis cum vino calido, acutis et peracutis et tertianariis cum aqua calida vel syrupo. Requies est opiata quasi frigida. Precipue valet ad sompnum inducendum ad modum castanee data. Cum autem est data hominibus quasi sanis, tempestive debent multum comedere vel cenare et postea detur eunti dormitum. Quod si aliquis abhorret sumere, distemperatur cum succo rosarum vel syrupo violato et coletur et postea detur. Licet omnino non faciat effectum, nam multum valet etiam sic data. Item attendendum est quod ex speciebus huius medicine syrupus factus bonus est ad sompnum provocandum, scilicet ut species bulliant in aqua trite et colentur et apposito zucharo fiat syrupus. Item in acutis quibuslibet potest dari ad sompnum inducendum.

94. **RUBEA TROCISCATA** dicitur ab ipso colore, trociscata a trociscis, qui ibi ponuntur dicta. Valet tercianariis, quotidianariis ante horam accessionis data cum rodostomate ad modum avellane. Naribus et pulsibus de eadem inunctis sanitatem prestat. Reumati ex acri flegmate facto data cum tipsana subvenit. Octava pars est libra .i. Recipe liquiricie, cinamomi, papaveris albi ana dragmas .iii. et scrupulum .i. et grana .v., croci, jusquiami, rosarum, apii seminis ana dragmas .ii. et grana .xvi., nardi, violarum ana dragmam .i. et grana .viii., gariofilorum, storacis optime, opii thebaici

ana scrupulum semis, trocisci croci magnetis et ydiocri, mirre, anisi ana grana .xv. vel syrupi rosarum vel rodactilis, mel quod sufficit.

117. **THEODORITON EUPERISTON**. Theodoriton dicitur a deo datum, euperiston id est bene expertum interpretatur. Facit enim contra emigraneum dolorem et vertiginem capitis et contra fluxum flegmatis quod in faucibus et gutture decurrit. Unde fit homo quandoque sine voce. Valet etiam spleneticis sine febre. Colorem bonum facit si simplex detur. Sed si purgationem facere volueris, adhibeas scrupulos .ii. scamonee et fortius operabitur. XII pars libre .ii. Recipe aloes epatici dragmas .iii. et grana .iii. et tertiam partem unius grani, cinnamomi, camedrei, acori ana dragmas .iii., croci, casie lignee, reupontici ana dragmas .ii. et grana .xvi., agarici dragmas .ii. et semis, nardi, costi, masticis, asari, silfii, squille, asse, armoniaci, bdellii, electuarii indi, ypericon, epithimi, polipodii, brasice succi, piperis albi et longi ana dragmam .i. et semis, squinanti, zinziberis Smirne, mirabolanorum, coloquintide, serapini, opoponacis, castorei, absinthii, aristologie longe, petroselini, gentiane, amomi ana scrupulos .ii., diagridii, piperis nigri ana scrupulum .i., mel quod sufficit. Datur mane et sero cum vino calido dragmas .iii.

118. **THEODORITON ANACARDINUM** ab anacardis dicitur, qui ibi reperiuntur. Datum mirabiliter memoriam reparat, vertiginem capitis et maxime posteriori parte aufert, flegma quod ibi est purgat, causis matricis mirabiliter confert, si eam purgare volueris. Octava pars confecta est libre .ii. Recipe aloes epatici unciam .i., yrei, casie ana dragmas .vii., musci grana .xvii., zinziberis, anacardi, carpobalsami ana dragmas .iiii. et semis, folii, spice, mirabolanorum corticum, meu, epithimi ana dragmas .iii. et scrupulum semis, gariofilorum, reupontici, masticis, squinanti ana dragmam .i. et grana .iii., mel quod sufficit. Conficitur sic. Accipe corticis radicis feniculi bene triti et abluti libram .i. et pone in duabus libris aceti et stet ibi per .vii. dies. Et postea tere ipsas radices et in eodem aceto coque usque ad tertiam partem. Et cum omni diligentia cola per pannum et pone in duabus libris mellis dispumati et bulliat usque ad aceti consumptionem. Cum tali melle confice. Supradicte autem radices colligantur in Maio vel Julio, quia ante hoc tempus humide sunt et post hoc sicce sunt. Dosis est dragmam .i. vel .ii. Cum mulsa valet.

111. **TYRIACA MAGNA GALENI**. Tyriaca dicitur domina medicinarum, Galieni quia ab eo composita fuit. Facit contra gravissimas passiones totius humani corporis epilenticis, cathalenticis, apopleticis, cephalargicis, stomaticis, emigranicis. Prodest ad raucedinem vocis et constrictionem pectoris. Optima est arteticis, asmaticis, emoptoicis, yctericis, ydropicis, peripleumonicis, yliosis et vulnera in intestinis habentibus. Nefreticis, calculosis, colericis subvenit. Menstrua educit et fetum mortuum expellit. Lepros et variolas et frigorem periodicum et ceteras passiones inveteratas emendat. Precipue contra omnia venena et serpentum morsus et reptilium valet. Sed diversa est eius dosis pro quantitate et qualitate uniuscuiusque passionis que in fine scribitur. Omnem defectionem sensuum relevat. Cor, cerebrum, epar, stomacum confortat. Totum corpus incorruptum ducit et custodit. Octava pars libre .ii. Recipe trociscorum squilliticorum dragmas .ii. et scrupulos .ii., piperis longi dragmas .ii., trociscorum tyri et diacoralli ana dragmam .i. et scrupulum .i., xilobalsami scrupulum .i. et grana .vii., opii, agarici, yris, rose, scordei, seminis rape silvestris, cinamomi, opobalsami ana scrupulum .i. et grana .xiiii., reubarbari, cere, spice, costi, squinanti, zinziberis, cassie lignee, storacis calamite, mirre, terbentine, turis masculi, calamenti, diptami, sticados, pollii radicis, pentafilon, petrosilini, piperis albi ana scrupulum .i. et grana .vii., folii,

gummi arabice, acori, calcanti usti, serapini, terre sigillate seu boli, succi ypoquistidos, celtice, camedrei, gentiane, meu, carpobalsami, amomi, apii, maratri, carvi silvestris, siselei, nasturcii, seminis nasturcii, anisi, ypericon ana scrupulum .i., mumie, castorei, opoponacis, aspalti, galbani, centauree minoris, aristologie longe, dauci silvatici ana scrupulum .i., mellis dispumati quod sufficit. Que terende sunt tere et gummas in vino liquefactas cum pulvere et melle commisce sufficienti vel cum speciebus teras. Datur in modum avellane cum tepida apoplecticis, scotomaticis, cephalargicis, emigranicis, ad raucedinem vocis et constrictionem pectoris cum melle aut dragaganto ita ut in ore teneatur, asmaticis cum decoctione lilifagi, emoptoicis ex pectore et pulmonis vitio cum ptisana, ad veteratas passiones cum apozimate ysopi, yctericis cum decoctione assari, ydropicis cum oximelle vel oxizaccara, peripleumonicis cum jure vel decoctione marubii, iliosis cum apozimate apii, in intestinis vulnera habentibus cum decoctione sumach, nefreticis, calculosis et colericis cum apozimate granorum solis, apii silvatici vel domestici, arteticis cum jure vel pigami decoctione. Ad venena et menstrua educenda et fetus cum vino calido vel mulsa cum aqua ubi cocta sit menta vel ozimum et frigori periodico et cunctis passionibus cum tepida.

116. **TRIASANDALI** dicitur a tribus generibus sandalorum qui ibi intrant. Datur proprie contra calorem epatis et stomaci ptisicis et yctericis. Medietas est libre .ii. Recipe sandali albi et rubei et citrini, rose, zuchari ana solidos duos, reubarbari, spodii, succi liquiricie, seminis portulace ana solidum .i. et semis, amili, gummi arabici, draganti, seminis melonis, citri, cucumeris et cucurbite, seminis scariole ana solidum .i., camphore scrupulum .i. et semis. Alii quadruplicant pondus rosarum, syrupi rosacei quod sufficit. Datur mane et meridie in modum castanee cum frigida.

114. **TRIFERA MAGNA** dicitur quia magnam utilitatem et fructum mulieribus confert. Datur contra dolorem stomachi virorum et mulierum cum aqua in qua cocta sint semina feniculi, anisi et masticis. Datur contra vitium matricis ex frigiditate si distemperata bibatur cum vino in quo cocta sit artemisia. Provocat etiam menstrua si fiat cum artemisia bene trita et oleo muscelino commixta. Pessarium ex bombace factum si fuerit ex ea inunctum et in vulvam mulieris immissum menstrua provocat mulieri non concipienti. Si detur cum vino in quo cocta sit mandragora vel sambucus miro modo prodest pueris qui non possunt dormire et in nocte nimio garriunt. Distemperata cum lacte mulieris in modum ciceris et bibita prodest. Octava pars libra .i. Recipe opii dragmas .ii., cinamomi, gariofilorum, galange, spice, zedoarie, zinziberis, costi, storacis calamite, calami aromatici, ciperi, yris, peucedani, acori, mandragore, celtice, rose, piperis, anisi, apii, petroselini macedonici, dauci, jusquiami, feniculi, ozimi, cimini ana dragmam .i., mellis quod sufficit. Datur in modum castanee, ut supra diximus.

113. **TRIFERA SARACENICA**, id est juvenilis, juvenem hominem reddit. Saracenica quia a Saracenis inventa. Datur proprie yctericis, epaticis et patientibus dolorem capitis ex fumositate colere rubee. Datur contra duplicem tertianam. Et restaurat visum amissum ex calore et colorem perditum ad pristinum revocat. Datur mane cum tepida. Octava pars libra .i. Recipe zucchari uncias .iii., mirabolanorum citrinorum corticis, medulle cassie fistule et tamarindorum ana unciam .i. et semis, kebulorum mundatorum, manne ana dragmas .vi. et scrupulos .ii. et grana .v., indorum, violarum recentium si possunt inveniri ana unciam semis, anisi, maratri ana dragmas .ii. et grana .xv., masticis, macis ana dragmam .i. et grana .vii. et semis, bellirici, emblici ana unciam semis et grana .iiii. Conficitur sic. In duabus libris aque

ponantur uncie .iii. violarum recentium si poterunt inveniri, si non siccarum, et bulliant donec deveniat aqua ad purpureum colorem et viole sint remisse. Postea leviter expressum coletur. De colatura illa pars accipiatur et casie fistule et tamarindorum per caciam abluantur et colentur per eadem. In alia aqua libra .i. et uncias .viii. zuchari immitantur et super ignem ponantur et ad spissitudinem bulliat. Et cum inceperit inspissari, addatur colatura casie fistule et tamarindorum, postea manna. Cum volueris scire utrum sit coctum, ponatur gutta super marmor et si quasi mel colligitur, coctum erit. Tunc ab igne deponatur et cum infrigidatum erit, pulvis supradictarum specierum apponatur, semper cum spatula agitando donec incorporetur. Ad ultimum supradictum zuccharum bene pulverizatum mitte. Datur in modum castanee, si fit ex distemperantia caloris cum frigida, si fit ex abundantia frigidi humoris cum calida.

[–] **UNGUENTUM AUREUM** valet contra omnes guttas acutas frigidas, et maxime contra lapidem in renibus et hydropicis. Recipe radicis evisci, phu, meu, ana libras .ii., utriusque aristolochie, helenii, hyssopi, pulegii, artemisie, pentaphylli, rute, foliorum lauri, acori, herbe venti, roris marini, matrisilve, saxifragie, cyperi, chamedryos, asparagi, brusci, feniculi, anisi ana libram .i., apii, ireos, levistici, granorum solis, petroselini, sileris, amomi, cardamomi, anethi, baccarum lauri, juniperi, lapidis lyncis ana libram semis, basilice, seminis urtice, seminis citri, sinapis, euphorbii ana uncias .iiii., adipis ursini et vulpini, olei laurini, petrolei ana uncias .iii., schoenanthi, costi, pyrethri, thuris, masticis, myrrhe ana uncias .ii., muscelini olei unciam .i., et cere quod sufficit. Herbe colligantur in mense Maii et contrite mittantur in oleo vel vino albo, in quo sint viginti diebus. Postea addatur oleum, quod sufficit, et bulliant donec herbe incipiant diminui et colentur per saccum. Et ponantur ibidem cere libras .xii. Bulliant quousque cera sit bene commista. Deinde superponantur pinguedines bene dissolute et colate. Et permittantur parum bullire. Post superfundatur oleum laurinum et deposito ab igne superinducantur alia olea, tertio pulveres costi, pyrethri, schoenanthi etiam, quarto olibani, quinto mirre. Et hoc per intervallum fiat, postea cera, et deposito ab igne ponatur euforbium, ultimo vero ponatur petroleum.

128. **VOMITUS PATRIARCHE**. Recipe tapsie libram .i., croci affricani uncias .iiii., cinamomi, asari ana uncias .ii., catapucie uncias .ii., mel quod sufficit. Detur cum tepida ante accessionem.

142. **YERA RUFINI**. Yera ut diximus, Rufini ab auctore dicitur. Datur proprie scabiosis ex flegmate salso, elefantiosis, serpiginosis. Curat utramque morpheam cum tepida. Destruit antiquam cephalicam et emigraneam et monopagiam dolorem capitis vel stomaticis, epilenticis, catalenticis et eis qui ex fumo stomaci extenebrescunt ita ut subitaneum timorem viderent vel ex ventositate stomaci tinitum aurium patiuntur ut in furias vertantur deponitur cacocimia stomaci, epatis et splenis. Elefanticis et podagricis confert auxilium et menstrua educit. Sed si purgationem inde facere volueris, cum scrupulo .i. scamonee fiat. .XII. pars est libre .ii. Recipe aloes unciam .i., ellebori albi et nigri ana unciam semis, diagridii et colloquintide interioris ana dragmas .iii., nitri, euforbii, polipodii, salis armoniacis ana dragmas .ii. et grana .xv., piperis, camedrei, croci, agarici, masticis, epithimi ana dragmam .i. et semis, casie lignee, xilobalsami, opopanacis, git ana scrupulos .ii. et semis, mirre grana .xv., mellis quod sufficit. Datur in sero cum calida in modum castanee.

51. **HYGIA GRECA**. Hygia id est salvatrix, greca dicitur quia a grecis fuit inventa. Valet proprie ad reuma gingivarum et dolorem dentium fricata super eos, ore sepe

abluto cum aceto calido. Et sordidas nebulas ab oculis aufert. Sexta pars est libra .i. Recipe jusquiami seminis dragmas .ii. et scrupulos .ii., opii dragmas .ii. et scrupulum .i., costi dragmam .i. et grana .xv., storacis calamite, galbani, agarici, mirre, opoponacis, scordeon, origani ana dragmam .i. et grana .x., gentiane, pigami, sticados, prassii, cardamomi ana scrupulos .ii. et semis, balsami, nardi, croci, squinanti, thimiamatis, armoniaci, terbentine, casie lignee, mandragore, yringi radicis, rose, eupatorii, euforbii, melanopiperis, levistici, dauci, feniculi, trifolii seminis ana scrupulos .ii., mel quod sufficit. Datur cum vino calido in modum avellane.